A
CHECKLIST of
AMERICAN IMPRINTS
for
1822

Items 7727 - 11516

Compiled by

Richard H. Shoemaker

The Scarecrow Press, Inc.

Metuchen, N.J.   1967

Abbot, Abiel, 1770-1828
An address delivered before the Essex Agricultural Society at the agricultural exhibition in Danvers, October 17, 1821. By Rev. Abiel Abbott, of Andover. Andover, Pr. for the Society by Flagg and Gould, 1822. 14 p. DLC; ICJ; ICN; MB; MBAt; MHi; MH-AH; MNe; MPeHi; MTop; MWA; MnHi; NN; NjR; RPB.   7727

Abbott, C. C., comp.
The young convert's pocket companion... Boston, Pr. by James Loring, 1822. 63 p. 40 plates. MBNMHi; MWA; MeBat.
                              7728
Abbott, Charles, 1st baron Tenterden, 1762-1832
A treatise on the law relative to merchant ships and seamen: in four parts... 3d Amer. ed., improved ay[!] a digest of American decisions subsequent to Judge Story's notes. Exeter, N. H., G. Lamson, 1822. xxvii, [1], 668, xxviii p. CSfU; CSt; CtY; DLC; ICLaw; MB; MH-L; MWCL; MnHi; MoS; MsWJ; N-L; NNC; NjP; OCl; PHi; PP; PPB; PU-L; RPB; ViU; VtBrt.   7729

Abbott, James
The challenge accepted; or the doctrine of the decrees vindicated, in the spirit of Christian candor... Portsmouth, Ohio, Pr. by C. Hopkins, March 1822. 40 p. PPPrHi.   7730

Abbott, Warren
Address to the Danvers Auxiliary Society, for Suppressing Intemperance and other Vices, and Promoting Temperance and General Morality. April 30, 1822. Salem, Pr. by John D. Cushing and Brothers, 1822. 16 p. MB; MH; MSaE; MWA; MiD-B.   7731

Abstract of sacred history, being the first part of the Geneva Catechism. Printed for the Trustees of the Publishing Fund, by Hilliard and Metcalf, Cambridge. Sold by Cummings & Hilliard, Boston, and other agents of the Publishing Fund. 1822. 42 p. CBPac; MH; MWA.   7732

Account of John Boltwood: a boy bitten by a mad dog. To which is added; Memoir of Sophia Holmes. Hartford, G. Goodwin & Sons, 1822. 22 p. CtHi. 7733

Account of the ceremony and dedication of Washington Hall in New-London, by the brethren of Union Lodge, No. 31, in New-London on the 24th of June A. L. 5822. Also on oration... by Bro. Thomas Shaw Perkins Esq. New-London, Pr. by Bro. Samuel Green [1822] 7, 10 pp. CtHi.   7734

An account of the dreadful fire, which occurred at the orphan asylum... 24th of January, 1822. [Philadelphia, 1822.] 8 p. MWA; PHi; PPL.   7735

An account of the execution of Samuel Green, who suffered the sentence of the law, April 25,

1

1822, for the murder of Billy Williams, which crime was committed on the 8th November, 1821 in the State Prison Yard, both being fellow convicts... Boston, N. Coverly, 1822. 14 p. MWA; NCooHi.   7736

An account of the unparalleled sufferings of James Washburn, on board the ship Delphos, of Boston, John Knight, Commander, as taken from the trial before the Supreme Judicial Court, holding at Boston, Nov. 1821. Boston, pr. for the purchaser, 1822. 12 p. MBilHi; MH.   7737

Achates, pseud.   See Pinckney, Thomas.

The actor of all work.   See Colman, George, 1762-1836.

Adams, Daniel, 1773-1864
    The scholar's arithmetic; or federal accountant... Stereotype ed., rev. and corr., with additions.   Keene, N.H., Pr. by John Prentiss, 1822. 224 p. ICU; MWHi; NNC.   7738

Adams, John, 1750?-1814
    Flowers of ancient history; comprehending, on a new plan, the most remarkable and interesting events, as well as characters, of antiquity... Leesburg, Va., S. B.T. Caldwell, 1822. 300 p. DLC.   7739

Adams, John Quincy, pres. U.S., 1767-1848
    The duplicate letters, the fisheries and the Mississippi. Documents relating to transactions at the negotiation of Ghent. Washington, Pr. by Davis and Force, 1822. 256, [2] p., 1 l. A-Ar; ArU; C; CSmH; CSt; CU; CtW; CtY; CoFcS; DLC; IC; ICHi; ICN; ICU; IGK; IaHi; InU; KyBgW; KyU; LNH; LU; M; MB;

MBAt; MBL; MH; MHi; MS; MWA; MdBP; MdHi; MeHi; MiD-B; MiU; MnHi; MnU; MoSW; MoU; Ms; NB; NIC; NN; NNLI; NNU; NT; NbHi; NbU; NcD; Nh-Hi; NjP; OCHP; OMC; OO; P; PHi; PP; PPL; RNR; TNV; TxD-W; TxU; Vi; WHi; WaU.   7740

Additional facts, remarks, and arguments, illustrative of the advantage to the people of the United States, of a national circulating medium, by the author of Jomo and Justianian. Washington, Pr. by Edward DeKrafft, 1822. 22 p. DLC; MBAt.   7741

Address of the lay trustees to the congregation of St. Mary's Church on the subject of the approaching election.   Philadelphia, Robert Desilver, 1822. 25 p. DLC; PHi; PPAmP; PPL; PPPrHi.   7742

An address to every believer in America.   See Clark, Benjamin.

An address to the citizens of the United States, on the subject of ardent spirits.   No. 8. New-York, Mahlon Day, 1822. 12 p. MnU; NNG.   7743

Address to the citizens of the United States on the tendency of our system of intercourse with foreign nations.   See Carey, Mathew.

Address to the Right Rev. the Bishop of Pennsylvania.   See Carey, Mathew.

Address to the Senate and House of Representatives of the United States.   See Carey, Mathew.

[Adolphus, John Leycester] 1795-1862
    Letters to Richard Heber, esq. containing critical remarks on the

series of novels beginning with "Waverley," and an attempt to ascertain their author. Boston, Samuel H. Parker; Munroe & Francis, printers, 1822. 216 p. CtHT; ICMe; MB; MBAt; MBL; MCon; MH; MLy; MS; MMeT; MWA; MiD; NN; NNS; PPA; PPL; PWW; RPB; RNR.   7744

Advice to the young mother in the management of herself and infant. By a member of the Royal College of Surgeons. Philadelphia, H.C. Carey & I. Lea, 1822. 96 p. PPL.   7745

Aeschylus.
     Selections from tragedies of Aeschylus, Sophocles, and Euripides. Philadelphia, Bradford, 1822. 442 p. CU; CtHT; KyLx; MB; MMidb.   7746

Aesopus.
     Aesop's Fables... New York, Samuel Wood & Sons, 1822. 44 p. NN.   7747

African Methodist Episcopal Church
     Minutes of three conferences of the African Methodist preachers, held at Baltimore, Philadelphia, and New York, in April, May, and June, 1822. [Published for the conference, Philadelphia, J.H. Cunningham, printer] 1822. 30 p. WHi.   7748

African Society of Boston
     Grand & splendid bobolition of slavery and "Great anniversary fussible" by de Africum Shocietee of Bosson. [2d ed.] Boston, 1822. Broadside. MH.   7749

The African Union hymn book, designed as a companion for the pious, and friends of all denominations. 1st ed. Pub. by P. Spencer for the African Union Church, in the United States.

Wilmington, Pr. by R. Porter, 1822. 144 p. NNUT.   7750

The African widow. An interesting narrative. By a clergyman. Published by the Philadelphia Female Tract Society [Philadelphia, L.R. Bailey, 1822] 8 p. TxU.   7751

The Agricultural almanac for 1823. By John Sharp. Baltimore, Fielding Lucas, Jr.; John D. Toy, printer [1822] 18 ll. NNA; PYHi.   7752

---- Philadelphia, Solomon W. Conrad [1822] 24 ll. CtY; DLC; MWA; N; NN; PDoBHi; PHi; PPL.   7753

Agricultural Society of Albermarle
     Charlottesville, Dec. 1, 1822. Sir, The undersigned are a committee appointed by the Agricultural Society of Albermarle, (under certain resolutions of that body of the 7th of Oct. last and which are hereto subjoined) to solicit donations, from individuals... for the purpose of erecting a fund to support a professorship of Agriculture in the University of Virginia... [1822] 2 p. DLC.   7754

[Aikin, John]
     The farm-yard journal, also, The history of the marten. [By John Aikin and Mrs. Barbauld] New-Haven, Pub. by J. Babcock and Son, and S. Babcock and Co. Charleston, S.C. Sidney's Press [1822?] [31] p. CtHi; CtY.   7755

Aikin, Lucy, 1781-1864
     Juvenile correspondence, or letters, designed as examples of the epistolary style, for children of both sexes. From the 2d London ed. Boston, Pub. by Cummings and Hilliard. Hilliard & Metcalf, 1822. 191 p. IObB; MBAt; MH.   7756

---- Memoirs of the Court of King James the First. Boston, Wells and Lilly, 1822. 2 v. CoCsC; CtHT; CtW; IQ; IaK; InU; KyLoP; LNH; MB; MBL; MDeeP; MH-AH; MHi; MLanc; MLy; MMe; MNBedf; MNF; MWel; MdAs; MdBJ; MdHi; Me; NBP; NNS; NUt; NcU; NjP; OO; OT; PPA; PPL; PR; PU; RNR; ScC; ScU; ViAl; WHi.   7757

Ainsworth, Robert, 1660-1743
An abridgment of Ainsworth's Dictionary, English and Latin, designed for the use of schools. Philadelphia, U. Hunt & Son, 1822. 1028 p. Wv.   7758

Air, avec douze variations pour s'accoutumer à metre les deux mains ensemble. New York, Pub. for the editor by E. Riley [1822] 6 p. MWA.   7759

Akenside, Mark
The pleasures of the imagination. And other poems. New York, R. & W.A. Bartow & Co., Gray & Bunce, printers, 1822. 214 p. LNT-M; NjP; RJa; RPB.   7760
---- ---- New York, R. & W.A. Bartow & Co., and Richmond, W.A. Bartow & Co., 1822. Gray & Bunce, printers. 144 p.NCoxHi; RNR; ScCliTO.   7761

Alabama (State)
Acts passed at the third annual session of the General Assembly of the state of Alabama. Begun and held in the town of Cahawba, on the first Monday in November, one thousand eight hundred and twenty-one. Cahawba, Pr. and for sale at the Press-Office by Wm. B. Allen & Co., printers to the state. Jan. 1822. 120 p. A-SC; AB; AU; In-Sc; MH-L; NN; NNB; NNLI; PU-L; RPL; BrMus.   7762
---- Journal of the House of Rep-

resentatives of the state of Alabama. Begun and held at the town of Cahawba, on the first Monday in November, 1821. Being the third session of the General Assembly of said state. Cahawba, Pr. by William B. Allen & Co., 1822. 240 p. A-SC; BrMus.   7763

---- Journal of the Senate of the third annual session of the General Assembly of the state of Alabama. Begun and held in the capitol, in the town of Cahawba, on the first Monday of November, in the year of our Lord, one thousand eight hundred and twenty one. Cahawba, Pr. by William B. Allen & Co., state printers, 1822. 168 p. A-SC; BrMus.   7764
The Alabama almanack for 1823. By John Beasley. Huntsville, Boardman & Adams [1822] 12 ll. AU; DLC.   7765

Albany (City)
Report of the Chamberlain to the corporation of the City of Albany, October, 1821. Albany, Pr. by E. & E. Hosford, 1822. 34 p. NNS.   7766

Albany County Agricultural Society.
Albany County agricultural tracts, No. 1, for Oct., 1822. Albany, D. Steele & Son, Packard & Van Benthuysen, prs., 1822. 48 p. NN.   7767
---- A geological survey of the county of Albany... [Albany, 1822] 55 p. PPL.   7768

Alden, Abner
The reader. Containing... prose...verse. Being the third part of a Columbian exercise... 5th ed. Boston, James Loring, July, 1822. 228 p. CtHT-W; CtY; MB; MH; MHi; MLy;

MMedHi; MWHi; MiD-B. 7769

Alexander, Caleb, 1755-1828
A grammatical system of the
English language: comprehending
a plain and familiar scheme of
teaching young gentlemen and
ladies the art of speaking and
writing correctly. Rutland, Vt.,
William Fay, 1822. 96 p. MH;
VtMiS. 7770

---- ---- From the 10th ed.,
corr. by the author. Windsor,
Vt., Pr. by Simeon Ide, 1822.
84 p. NCaS; OCIW. 7771

Alexandria almanack for 1823.
By Joshua Sharp. Alexandria,
John A. Stewart [1822] 20 ll.
DLC. 7772

Alfred the Great, an historical
tragedy. See Magnus, Julian.

Aliquis, pseud. See Marks,
Richard.

Allegheny, Pa. Western University of Pennsylvania.
The system of education, the
code of discipline, and the pro-
fessorships, adopted by the trustees of the Western University of
Pennsylvania; together with the
addresses of the president of the
Board to the public, and the principal to the students. Pittsburgh,
J. B. Butler, printer, 1822. 30,
[2] p. CSmH; DLC; MB. 7773

Allen, Benjamin
Jesus Christ, and Him cruci-
fied: being a view of the Trinity,
the divinity of Christ, the atonement, and the character and in-
fluences of the Holy Spirit...
Philadelphia, James Crissy, 1822.
120 p. CtHT; GMM; ICU; MdBD;
NN; NjP; PHi; PLT; PPL;
PPLT; TNP; ViAlTh. 7774

Allen, Francis D.

The New-York selection of
sacred music; containing a great
variety of plain, repeating and
fugue tunes... New York, Gilley,
1822. 221 p. ICN. 7775

[----] Documents and facts, showing the fatal effects of interments
in populous cities. New-York,
Pub. by F. D. Allen; G. F. Hopkins, printer, 1822. 24 p. DLC;
ICJ; MB; MH; MWA; NBM;
NNMus; NNNAM. 7776

Allen, Heman, 1779-1852
Allen's exposition of the con-
troversy subsisting between Silas
Hathaway and himself. [Mont-
pelier? 1822?] 40 p. MB; MH-L;
NhD; VtHi; VtU; BrMus. 7777

---- Remarks of Mr. Allen,
Counsel upon the petition of Silas
Hathaway, praying for a new trial,
and drawn up by S. Prentiss, with
the opinion of Daniel Webster upon the validity of the Act of the
Vermont Legislature of 1821,
granting a new trial in the action
of Heman Allen vs. Hathaway and
Uziel Pierson. [Burlington?
Privately printed, 1822] 40 p.
DLC; MB; MH; NhD; BrMus.
7778
---- State of Vermont, Chittenden County, ss. Heman Allen
against Usal Pierson and Silas
Hathaway. [Montpelier? 1822?]
24 p. BrMus. 7779

---- Statement of the cause of
Heman Allen vs. Hathaway &
Pierson. [1822] 48 p. VtU.
7780
Allen, Joseph
A discourse, delivered at
Shrewsbury, on New Year's Day,
one thousand eight hundred and
twenty-two. Worcester, Pr. by
Manning & Trumbull, Jan. 1822.
15 p. DLC; MB; MH; MHi; MNF;
MWA; MiD-B; NjPT. 7781

Allen, Paul, 1775-1826
A history of the American
Revolution; comprehending all the
principal events both in the field
and in the cabinet. Baltimore,
Pr. for Franklin Betts; William
Wooddy Jr. , printer, 1822. 2 v.
CSmH; CtW; CtY; DLC; DSI;
GA; GAuY; GU; MeHi; MeLL;
MGref; MH; MiD; MiMarqN;
MiSH; MB; MLow; MNF; MiU-
C; PPL; BrMus.   7782

Allen, Stephen, 1767-1852
Letter of the Hon. Stephen
Allen, Mayor of the city of New-
York, to Joseph Bayley... in re-
lation to the cases of yellow fever,
at the quarantine ground in 1821,
and Dr. Bayley's report thereon.
Published by order of the Board
of health. [New York] Van Pelt
& Spear, 1822. 37 p. CtY; DLC;
MB; MBM; NN; NNNAM; NRU-
M.   7783

Allen, William
A sermon delivered in Farmington, June 26, 1822, before the
Maine Missionary Society, at their
fifteenth anniversary... Hallowell,
Pr. by Goodale, Glazier & Co. ,
1822. 40 p. MWA.   7784

Allen, William, 1784-1868
An American biographical and
historical dictionary... 2d ed.
Boston, Hyde & Co. 1822. 800 p.
DLC; M; MB; MeB; MiD; MnH;
Nh; NjP; RPJCB.   7785

Allerton, Isaac
The communion of all saints
demonstrated by Christian experience; the word of God; and historical facts. A sermon addressed particularly to the Baptist denomination. 2d ed. , enl.
Mount-Pleasant, N. Y. , R. W.
Knight, 1822. 48 p. CtY; NNUT;
NRAB; NcWfC; PPL; PPiW.
                            7786
[Allinson, David]

Annual, Law register of the
United States. Vols. 3d & 4th,
for 1821, 2. The editor informs
the publick, that two volumes of
this annual work will soon be
published... Burlington, N. J. ,
1822. 11 p. NjR.   7787

American Academy of Language
and Belles Lettres
Circular no. III; to the American members, and patrons of
the institution, from the corresponding secretary. New-York,
Pr. by Charles N. Baldwin, Jan.
1822. 40 p. CtHT-W; DLC;
MBAt; MWA; NCH; NN; OCHP;
PHi; PPAmP; PPL; TKL. 7788

American Academy of the Fine
Arts, New York.
Catalogue of paintings and engravings, exhibited by the American Academy of the Fine Arts...
1822. 8th exhibition. New York,
Pr. for the Academy, by Thomas
Longworth, 1822. 8 p. CSmH.
                            7789
American Asylum at Hartford for
the Education and Instruction of
the Deaf and Dumb.
Sixth report of the directors
of the American Asylum at Hartford, for the Education and Instruction of the Deaf and Dumb
exhibited to the asylum, May 11,
1822. Hartford, Hudson and Co. ,
printers, 1822. 32 p. CtHC;
CtHT; CtY; DLC; ICU; KHi; MB;
MdFred; MdHi; MeB; MiU; MoS;
OMC; PPL; TNP; WHi.   7790

American Bible Society
Sixth report of the American
Bible Society, presented May 9,
1822, with an appendix, containing extracts of correspondence,
etc. New York, Pr. for the Society, by Daniel Fanshaw, 1822.
244 p. CtHT-W; DLC; GDC; M;
MeBaT; MiD-B; NRAB; PLT;
PWCHi; VtU; WBeloC.   7791

American Board of Commissioners for Foreign Missions

Report of the American Board of Commissioners for Foreign Missions; compiled from documents laid before the board, at the thirteenth annual meeting, which was held at New Haven, Conn., Sept. 12, & 13, 1822. Boston, pr. for the board by Crocker and Brewster, 1822. 87 p. IAlS; ICP; MA; MH-AH; MeB; MeBat; MiKC; TxFS.   7792

---- To all who love Zion, the prudential committee of the American Board of Commissioners for Foreign Missions, address themselves in behalf of the Missionary Herald. [Boston, 1822] 12 p. DLC; WHi.   7793

American Colonization Society

Fifth annual report of the American Society for Colonizing the Free People of Colour of the United States. With an appendix. Washington City, Pr. by Davis & Force, 1822. 120 p. CU; CtHT-W; DLC; KHi; M; MA; MPeaI; MWA; MdHi; MeB; MiD; MsJS; PPL; RP; ScU; TxH.   7794

---- To the citizens of Boston... (Appeal for funds) July 3, 1822. Broadside. MHi.   7795

---- To the public. Address of the Board of Managers of the American Colonization Society. Washington, Columbian Star Office [1822] 16 p. DLC; MdBP.   7796

American cookery. See Simmons, Amelia.

American domestic cookery. See Rundell, Mrs. Maria Eliza (Ketelby).

American Education Society

Seventh report of the directors of the American Education Soci-

ety, October 2, 1822. Andover, Pr. by Flagg and Gould, 1822. 64 p. CtHT-W; CtW; DLC; ICP; MA; MNE; MBev-F; MeB; MeBat; MBev-F; MNE; NRAB; NjR; OCIW.   7797

---- Northwestern Branch

Second report of the directors, presented at the annual meeting, at Rutland, Feb. 5, 1822. Middlebury, Pr. by J.W. Copeland, 1822. 40 p. MBC.   7798

American farmers' almanack for 1823. By Charles F. Egelmann. Hagers-Town, John Gruber and Daniel May [1822] 18 ll. CLU; DLC; MWA; MdBE; NBuG; NN; NjR; PPL; PYHi; ViW; WHi.   7799

American ladies pocket book for 1823. Philadelphia, A. Small [1822] 90 ll. PHi.   7800

American museum, and repository of arts and sciences, as connected with domestic manufactures and national industry. [v. 1, pt. 1] Also, a list of all the patents granted by the United States up to the end of the year 1821. Washington, Pr. by S. Elliot [etc.] pub. by J. Milligan, Georgetown, D.C., 1822-[23] 60, 72, xxiv, 13, 16 p. DLC. 7801

The American primer, abridged; containing short and easy lessons for little children. Cincinnati, O. Farnsworth & Co., 1822. 23 p. MWA.   7802

American sketches. Farmer's fireside. A poem. Concord, N.H., Pr. by Hill and Moore, 1822. 20 p. CtY; DLC; MWA.   7803

---- ---- Concord, N.H., Pr. by Hill and Moore, 1822. 12 p. DLC; MH; Nh-Hi; TxU.   7804

American Society for Colonizing

the free people of Colour of the
United States. See American
Colonization Society.

American Society for Educating
Pious Youth for the Gospel Min-
istry. See American Education
Society.

American Society for Meliorating
the Conditions of the Jews
   Constitution and documents.
[New York, 1822] 16 p. CtY; M;
MNtcA.   7805

American Society for Promoting
the Civilization and General Improvement of the Indian Tribes
Within the United States.
   A new society for the benefit
of Indians, organized at the city
of Washington, February, 1822.
[Washington, 1822?] 15 p. CSt;
CSmH; CtY; ICN; WHi.   7806

[----] ---- [Washington, Davis &
Force, print. , 1822?] 12 p. CSt;
ICHi; MB; MdBP; MiU-C; ScC.
                                7807
Americanischer Stadt und Land
Calender auf 1823.   Philadelphia,
Conrad Zentler [1822] 18 ll.
CLU; CtY; DLC; MWA; N; NN;
NjP; P; PDoBHi; PHi; PPCS;
PPeSchw; PYHi.   7808

Der Amerikanisch-Teutsche Haus-
freund und Baltimore Calender
auf 1823.   Baltimore, Johann T.
Hanzsche [1822] 18 ll. MWA;
MdHi; PHi.   7809

Amherst College
   Catalogue of the officers and
students of the Collegiate institu-
tion, Amherst, Mass. Oct. 1822.
[Greenfield, Mass. , Denio &
Phelps, 1822] 11 p. MiU-C.
                                7810
Amicus, pseud.
   Observations on the principles
of correct education. By a friend
to youth. New York, Pr. for the

publisher, 1822. 12 p. DLC;
MdBP.   7811

Anderson, Isaac
   Inaugural discourse delivered
in the Church at Maryville, Ten.
in presence of the directors of
the Southern & Western Theological Seminary, on the 25th day
September, 1822. . . [Knoxville?
Heiskell & Brown? 1822] 39 p.
NjPT; TKL-Mc.   7812

Anderson, William
   System of surgical anatomy.
Part first.   Of the structure of
the groin, pelvis, and perineum,
as connected with inguinal and
femoral hernia. . . New York, pub.
by James V. Seaman; James and
John Harper, printers, 1822.
199 p. CSt; CSt-L; CtY; GU-M;
ICU-M; IEN-M; MBU-M; MH-M;
MdBJ; MdBM; MeB; NBM;
NNNAM; NhD; OC; OKentC;
OClM; PMA; PPAmP; PPC; PU;
PPiAM; ScCMeS; ViRA; VtU.
                                7813
Andover, Mass. Phillips Academy
   Catalogue of the trustees, in-
structors and students. . Aug. 20,
1822.   [Andover] Pr. by Flagg
and Gould [1822] 8 p. MH-AH.
                                7814
Andover Theological Seminary
   Catalogue of the professors
and students of the Theological
Seminary, Andover, Mass. Feb.
1822. [6] p. DLC; GDC; MeB.
                                7815
---- Exercises at the annual examination of the Theological Seminary, Andover, Sept. 25, 1822.
4 p. MH; MNtcA.   7816

---- An outline of the course of
study in the department of Christian theology, with references to
the principal books in the library,
pertaining to that department.
Andover, Flagg & Gould, 1822.
53 p. Ct; ICP; MAnP; MBC;
MH-AH; MHi; MWiW; MeB;

MeHi; NNUT; NjPT; OMC;
PPPrHi; RPB; VtMiM; VtU;
WBeloC. 7817

Andrews, Elisha
  Strictures on Rev. Mr.
Brooks's essay on the terms of
Communion. Worcester, pr. by
William Manning [1822] 43 p. M;
MDeeP; MWA; NRAB; Nh. 7818

Animadversions upon Mr. Allerton's sermon entitled The "Communion of all saints," (etc.) New
York, 1822. 15 p. NcWfC;
NjPT. 7819

The annual Connecticut register,
and United States calendar for
1823. New-London, Samuel
Green [1822] 80 ll. CtHi; CtLHi;
CtNwchO; CtY; InU; MB; MHi;
MNF; MWA; N; NNUT; Nh;
PPL. 7820

Annual, law register of the
United States. See Allinson,
David.

The annual visiter and citizen and
farmer's almanac for the year of
our Lord 1823. Wilmington, Del.,
J. Wilson, [1822] [7] p. (Un-
paged; incomplete.) DeHi. 7821

An answer to the greatest false-
hood ever told by a Providence
lawyer, alias 'Demens Egomet."
2d ed. [Providence] New-England,
Pr. for the benefit of the publick,
1822. 12 p. MB. 7822

Anti-persecutor, pseud.
  Deaf and dumb school [Phila-
delphia, 1822] bdsd. PPL. 7823

The Antipodean whirligig; or Universal songster. Containing a selection of the most approved
songs, national, sentimental,
anacreontic, &c. &c. Philadelphia, E. Buck, D. Dickinson,
printer, 1822. 70, [2] p. P. 7824

An appendix, to the Rev. Mr.
Clowes's pamphlet or Sweden-
borgianism displayed. Philadelphia, 1822. 32 p. MH; MW.
7825
An appeal from the denunciations
of the Rev. Dr. Mason. See
Sewall, Henry Devereux.

Appleton, Jesse, 1772-1819
  Lectures, delivered at Bow-
doin College, and occasional ser-
mons... Brunswick, Pr. by Joseph
Griffin, 1822. 421 p. CBPSR;
CtY; DLC; GDC; ICP; ICT; IEG;
IU; IaU; MB; MBAt; MBC;
MCET; MH; MH-AH; MLow;
MNtcA; MWiW; MeB; MeBaT;
MeHi; MeWaC; MiKL; MoSpD;
NBuG; NCaS; NN; NSyU; Nh-Hi;
NjP; NjPT; NjR; OMC; OO; PSt;
RPB; TxAuPT; VtB; BrMus.
7826
The Arabian nights entertain-
ments consisting of one thousand
and one stories told by the sultan-
ess of the Indies to divert the
sultan... Hartford, Bowles and
Francis, printers, 1822. 2 v.
CtEhad; MB; MH; RPB; TNP.
7827

Archdale, John, 1642?-1717
  A new description of that fer-
tile and pleasant province of Caro-
lina... London, Pr. in 1707.
Charleston, S.C., Repr. and
sold by A.E. Miller, 1822. 33 p.
CtW; DLC; ICN; MdBE; MdHi;
NIC; NN; NNS. 7828

Arden, the unfortunate stranger,
who was tried for the murder of
Miss Harriet Finch, but was ac-
quitted through the interposition
of a young lady whom he afterwards married, a true story...
New York, J. Broderick, 1822.
28 p. CtY; MH; NjR; RPB;
7829
Aristotle, pseud.
  Nützliches und sehr bewährt
befundenes Weiber-Büchlein...

Ephrata, Pa. , Gedruckt im Jahr
1822. 20 p. PPL.   7830

Arkansas (Territory)
Acts passed by the general
assembly of the Territory of Arkansas, at the session of October 1821. Little Rock, A. T. ,
Pr. by William E. Woodruff,
1822. 26 p. Ar-SC; ArU; DLC;
IU; Ia; MH-L; MdBB; Nv;
OCIW; OrSC; TxU; W.   7831

Arlincourt, Charles Victor
Prévôt, Vicomte d', 1789-1856.
The recluse; a translation of
"Le Solitaire" by M. Le Vicomte
D' Arlincourt. New York, Pr.
by William Grattan, for E.
Duyckinck [etc.] 1822. 209 p.
NjPT.   7832

---- The renegade. Tr. from
the French of M. le vicomte
d'Arlincourt... Philadelphia, H. C.
Carey & I. Lea; New York, H. C
Carey & co. , 1822. 2 v. in 1.
DLC; NRU; PU.   7833

---- El solitario o el misterioso
del monte, novela... Trad. al
ingles, y de este al espanol por
Eduardo Barry.   Filadelfia, En
la imprenta de H. C. Carey y I.
Lea, 1822. 199 p. PPL.   7834

---- The solitary; or, The mys-
terious man of the mountain. Tr.
from the French of Viscount
d'Arlincourt, by an American
lady... New York, H. Durell,
1822. 2 v. in 1. CtHT; DLC;
InID; MA; MH; MShr; PP;
VtMiM.   7835

Armstrong, John, 1784-1829
Practical illustrations of typhus
fever, of the common continued
fever, and of inflammatory diseases... 2d Amer. from the 3d
English ed. , with corr. and an
appendix.   Philadelphia, pub. by
James Webster.   William Brown,

printer, 1822. xvi, 434 p. ArU-
M; CSfCMS; CoCsE; CtY; ICJ;
ICU-R; IEN-M; IU-M; Ia;
KyLoJM; KyLxT; MB; MBM;
MH-M; MdBJ-W; MdBM; MeB;
MiDW-M; MoSU-M; MoSW-M;
NBM; NBatHL; NRAM; NbU-M;
OCGHM; PPC; PPiAM; PWbIM;
ScCMeS; TJaU; TNP; ViU;
ViRA; WMAM.   7836

Arnold, Samuel James, 1774-
1852
The devils bridge.   An opera,
in three acts.   Philadelphia, T.
H. Palmer, 1822. 55 p. CSmH;
CSt; CtY; MH; NjP; NjR; TxU.
                               7837
---- ... The shipwreck, a comic
opera... with prefatory remarks
... Boston, Wells and Lilly, New-
York, A. T. Goodrich & co. ,
1822. 47 p. CtY; DLC; MB; MH;
MeB; PPL; RPB.   7838

[----] The woodman's hut; a
melo-drame, in three acts. Boston, Wells and Lilly, 1822. 56 p.
MH; MWA; MeB; PPL; RPB.
                               7839
Arnold, Thomas
The American practical lunar-
ian, and seaman's guide... To
which are annexed, a compendium of marine law, and mercantile regulations and customs.
Philadelphia, R. Desilver, 1822.
844, 71 [5] p. CSmH; DLC; MH;
MdAN; MnU; PHi; PPAmP; PPF;
RP; ViFTBE.   7840

The art of conjuring made easy,
or An entertaining selection of
diverting tricks, deceptions and
experiments in sleight of hand
and legerdemain... New York, S.
King, 1822. 24 p. MH.   7841

Ashmun, Jehudi, 1794-1828
Memoir of the life and character of the Rev. Samuel Bacon,
A. M. ... Washington city, J. Gideon, jr. , printer, 1822. 288 p.

CSmH; CStcr; CtHT-W; CtW;
CtY; DLC; IC; ICN; KHi; KWiU;
M; MB; MH; MWA; MdBE;
MiD; NBLiHi; NNG; NT; NcDaD;
NcU; NjMD; NjP; OClWHi; ODW;
OSW; P; PHi; PLT; PP; PPL;
PU; RP; ScC; TNF; TxU; Vi;
ViAlTh; WHi; WNaE; BrMus.
7842
The assizes. Andover, Flagg &
Gould, printers, 1822. 8 p. MeB.
7843
Associate Reformed Church in
North America
Extracts from the minutes of
the Proceedings of the nineteenth
General Synod of the Associate-
Reformed Church in North Amer-
ica; held at Philadelphia, on
Wednesday, the 15th May, 1822
... Philadelphia, Pr. by Jacob
Frick & Co., 1822. [3], 20, [1]
p. DLC; KyDC; NcMHi; NjR;
PPAmP; PPL; PPiXT. 7844

Associate Reformed Synod of
New York
Extracts from the minutes of
the proceedings of the Associate
Reformed Synod of New York; met
at Newburgh, Sept. 13, 1822...
Schenectady, Pub. at the Cabinet
printing-house, Isaac Riggs, pr.,
1822. [3], 12 p. NcMHi. 7845

Association for the Relief of Re-
spectable Aged Indigent Females,
New York
The ninth annual report of the
Association for the Relief of Re-
spectable Aged Indigent Females,
established in New-York, Feb. 7,
1814. New-York, Pr. by Gray
and Bunce, 1822. 12 p. NNG.
7846
Association of the Confraternity
of the Rosary.
Established in Trinity Church,
Georgetown, D.C., 1822. By virtue of a permission to this effect,
obtained from his holiness Pius
7th, and sent by the Propaganda
to the Rev. Mr. Tessier, Vicar

General of the Archdiocese of
Baltimore. Permiss: Sup. Wash-
ington City, Pr. by Davis and
Force, 1822. 12 p. DLC; MdW.
7847
Astronomical calculations for
1823. By William Collom.
Natchez, Langdon and Baker;
Snodgrass & Whitney [1822] 12 ll.
Ms-Ar. 7848

Astronomical calendar; or farm-
ers' almanac for 1823. By
Joshua Sharp. Ithaca, A. P.
Searing & Co.; E. Mack; Spen-
cer & Stockton [1822] 18 ll. IHi;
InU; MB; MWA; N; NIC;
NRMA; OClWHi. 7849

An astronomical ephemeris, or
almanac for 1823. By Joel Sanford. Bridgeport, Lockwood &
Sterling [1822] 12 ll. CtHi; N.
7850
---- By Hosea Stafford. Bridgeport, Lockwood & Sterling [1822]
12 ll. CtLHi; CtY; N; NHi.
7851
Attwood, Thomas, 1765-1838
Humanity. A sacred song.
New York, E. Riley [1822?] 3 p.
NN. 7852

Austin, Arthur, pseud. See Wilson, John.

Austin, Samuel
An oration, pronounced at New-
port, Rhode-Island, July 4, 1822.
Newport, William Simons, 1822.
16 p. MH-AH; MWA; RNHi.
7853
Auxiliary Bible Society. Clinton
County
Constitution of the Auxiliary
Bible Society of the county of
Clinton. Wilmington, pr. by
George Denny [ca. 1822] Title
from The History of Clinton Coun-
ty, Chicago, 1882, p. 329.7854

Auxiliary Education Society of the
Young Men of Boston

Order of service, on Wednesday evening, January 23, 1822,
on the occasion of a sermon, before the Auxiliary Education Society of the Young Men of Boston.
Boston, Pr. by Joseph W. Ingraham [1822] 44 p. DLC; MWA;
MWo.   7855

Auxiliary New York Bible and
Common Prayer Book Society
   The sixth annual report of the
managers of the Auxiliary New-
York Bible and Common Prayer
Book Society. New-York, Pr. by
T. & J. Swords, 1822. 12 p.
InD.   7856

Avison, Charles, 1709-1770
   Sound the loud timbrel. Boston, Thomas Badger, Jr. [1822]
4 p. MWA; NN.   7857

Ayre, Joseph, 1781-1860
   Practical observations on the
nature and treatment of maras-
mus. And of those disorders al-
lied to it, which may be strictly
denominated bilious. Northampton, Mass., Pub. by Simeon Butler. J. Metcalf, printer, 1822.
219, [1] p. MB; PPL.   7858

B

Bacon, Ephraim
   Abstract of a journal of E.
Bacon, assistant agent of the
United States, to Africa: with an
appendix containing interesting ac-
counts of the effects of the gospel
among the native Africans. 2d ed.
Published for the benefit of Africa.
Philadelphia, Clark & Raser,
printers, 1822. 48 p. CtY; ICN;
InD; LNH; MBAt; MBC; MHi;
MWA; MdBE; NIC; NNMr; MiU;
PHi; WHi.   7859

[Bacon, Henry]
   To the electors of Montgomery
County. [Dayton? 1822?] 4 p.
OCIWHi.   7860

Bacon, Nathaniel
   Meditations for every day in
the year, collected from different
spiritual writers. Written first
in Latin... Georgetown, D. C.,
Pub. by Joseph Milligan, 1822,
J. C. Dunn, printer. 492 p.
DGU; MWA; MdBL; ScU.   7861

[Bailey, Jonathan]
   The sultana; or, A trip to
Turkey. A melo-drama, in three
acts, founded on Lord Byron's
Don Juan... New-York, C. N.
Baldwin, 1822. 34 p. DLC; ICJ;
ICU; MB; MH; MiU-C; PU.
                              7862
[----] ---- New York, N. B.
Holmes, 1822. 34 p. MB; MH;
PU; RPB.   7863

Bailey, Phinehas, 1787-1861
   An improved system of stenog-
raphy; containing analogous abbreviations...3d ed., enl. and
improved. Poultney, Vt., Pr. by
Smith and Shute, 1822. 44 p.
CSmH; DLC; NN; VtHi.   7864

Bailey, Robert, b. 1773
   The life and adventures of Ro-
bert Bailey, from his infancy up
to December, 1821. Richmond,
Pr. for the author, by J. & G.
Cochran, 1822. 348 p. CSmH;
CtY; DLC; IU; MdBP; MdHi; N;
NN; NcD; Nj; OC; P; PP; Vi;
ViHi; ViU; ViW; WHi.   7865

Bailey, Winthrop
   Sermons on the unity of God,
and on the character of Jesus
Christ. Springfield, A. G. Tan-
natt & Co., printers, 1822. 67,
[1] p. CBPac; DLC; ICMe; MB;
MBAU; MH; MHi; MNBedf;
MSHi; MWA; NjPT; RPB; WHi.
                              7866
Bailey's Washington almanac for
1823. Philadelphia, Lydia R.
Bailey [1822] 18 ll. MBAt; PHi.
                              7867
---- Philadelphia, Robert Di-

silver [1822] 18 ll. MWA; PP;
PPAmP; PPL. 7868

---- Philadelphia, Thomas Desilver [1822] 18 ll. ICHi; MWA;
NN. 7869

Baker, John
A description, by John Baker,
of the mode of spaying sows.
Boston, Pub. by Wells & Lilly,
1822. 63 p. MeB. 7870

[Baldwin, Loammi] 1780-1838
To the president and managers
of the Union Canal Company of
Pennsylvania [Lebanon, Pa. ,
1822] 8 p. MH-BA. 7871

Baldwin, Thomas
On the duty of parents to chil-
dren. A sermon, delivered in the
meeting-house of the Second Bap-
tist Church and Society in Boston
on the afternoon of Lord's-Day,
March 17, 1822. Boston, Pr. by
Lincoln & Edmands [1822] 28 p.
DLC; LNB; M; MB; MBC; MH-
AH; NNUT; NRAB. 7872

Ballou, Hosea, 1771-1852
The eleven sermons which
were preached by the Rev. Hosea
Ballou...during a visit to Philadelphia in the months of December and January, 1821-2...Phila-
delphia, Edwin T. Scott, 1822.
159 p. MMeT-Hi; NNS; OCM;
PLT; PPL; PU. 7873

---- Feast of knowledge, a lecture sermon, delivered in the
Second Universalist meeting house,
in Boston on the second Sabbath
in March, 1822. Boston, Henry
Bowen, 1822. 16 p. MMeT-Hi;
NNUT; WBeloC. 7874

---- The golden calf. A sermon,
delivered in the Second Universalist Meeting House, in Boston, on
the evening of the fourth Sabbath
in February, 1822. Boston, Henry

Bowen, 1822. 16 p. MMeT-Hi;
MWA; RPB. 7875

---- Jacob's ladder. A sermon
... Boston, Henry Bowen, 1822.
16 p. RPB; WBeloC. 7876

---- Notes on the parables of the
New Testament, scripturally il-
lustrated and argumentatively de-
fended. 3d ed. Hallowell, W. F.
Laine, Pr. by John Dorr, Wis-
casset, 1822. 298 p. MB; MBilHi;
MPiB; MeBaT; MeHi; MiGr;
NB; NNUT; NRU. 7877

---- St. Paul a Universalist; a
sermon, delivered in the Second
Universalist meeting house, in
Boston, on the afternoon of the
first Sabbath in September, 1822.
Boston, Henry Bowen, 1822. 15 p.
DLC; MH; MMeT-Hi; NCH; PPL;
WBeloC. 7878

---- A sermon, delivered at the
dedication of the Universalist
meeting-house in Cambridge-port,
on Wednesday, Dec. 18, 1822.
Boston, Henry Bowen, 1822. 16 p.
MB; MMeT-Hi; NN. 7879

---- A sermon, delivered in the
Universalist Meeting House in
Roxbury, on the evening of the
Third Sabbath in January, 1822.
Boston, Pr. by Henry Bowen,
1822. 20 p. DLC; ICN; NN.
7880

---- A sermon, on the nature
and tendency of the opposition to
the true doctrine of Jesus Christ
... Dedham [Mass.] Pr. by H. &
W. H. Mann [1822] 15 p. CSmH;
MBAt. 7881

Baltimore (City)
Ordinances of the Corporation
of the City of Baltimore; passed
at the extra sessions in 1821, and
at the January session, 1822. To
which is annexed, a list of the officers of the Corporation. Balti-

more, Pr. by W. Warner, 1822.
80 p. MdBB; MdBE; MdHi;
MdLR; MdBJ.   7882

---- Report of the Health committee and accompanying documents of the board of physicians
appointed to direct the vaccination of the city. Laid before the
city council of Baltimore, January session, 1822. Baltimore, Pr.
by J. Murphy, 1822. 15 p.
MdBB; MdBE.   7883

The Baltimore almanac, or,
Time piece for 1823. By John
Sharp. Baltimore, William War-
ner [1822] 18 11. NcD; PDoBHi.
                                7884
Baltimore Apprentice's Library Co.
  Catalogue of the Apprentice's
Library in Baltimore, to be
loaned gratis, to apprentices and
other young persons, with the
names of the donors... Baltimore,
Pr. by Thomas Murphy, March,
1822. 12 p. MdHi.   7885

---- Circular of the Apprentices'
Library Company of Baltimore.
Baltimore, T. Murphy, 1822. 8 p.
MdBE.   7886

Baltimore Unitarian Book Society
  Second annual report. Baltimore [1822] 16 p. MHi.   7887

Baltimore Vaccine Society for Ex-
terminating the Small Pox
  The constitution. Baltimore,
Edes, 1822. 12 p. MdBM.   7888

Bancroft, Aaron, 1755-1839
  Sermons on those doctrines of
the gospel, and on those constitu-
ent principles of the church,
which Christian professors have
made the subject of controversy.
Worcester [Mass.] Pr. by W.
Manning & son, 1822. 429, [1] p.
CBPac; CU; CtY; DLC; IAlS;
IC; ICHi; ICT; IEG; MB; MBAU;
MBAt; MBC; MBrZ; MDeeP; MH;

MMeT-Hi; MMh; MWA; MWH;
MWHi; MeB; MeBat; NCaS; NGH;
NIC; NNUT; NhPet; NjPT;
PPAmP; PPLT; RPB; TBriK.
                               7889
Bangor Bank, Bangor, Me.
  Report on the affairs of the
Bangor Bank. Boston, Pr. by
Russell & Gardner, 1822. 16 p.
DLC; IU; MWA; PHi.   7890

Bank of the United States, 1816-
1836
  Report on the condition of the
Bank of the United States, by the
committee of inspection and in-
vestigation ... 1822. Philadelphia,
Pr. by W. Fry, 1822. 88 p. Ct;
CtHT-W; CtY; DLC; DeGE; IU;
MB; MBAt; MH; MH-BA; MHi;
MWA; MdBJ; MdBP; MdHi;
MdToH; NIC; NIC-A; NNS;
OClFRB; OClWHi; OFH; PPAmP;
PPL; RPB; ScCC.   7891

Banks, Henry
  A review of political opinions,
published for the benefit of the
people of Kentucky. Frankfort,
Ky., Pr. by J.H. Holeman, 1822.
88 p. DLC; OC; OCHP; PHi;
PPL.   7892

The Baptist catechism, agreeable
to the confession of faith. Philadelphia, Sunday & Adult School
Union, 1822. 32 p. PPAmS.
                               7893
The Baptist catechism; or A
brief instruction in the principles
of the Christian religion... Boston,
Pr. and pub. by Lincoln & Edmands, No. 53 Cornhill, 1822.
34 p. MB; MBAt; MHaHi; MWA;
NN.   7894

Baptist Education Society
  Fifth annual meeting of the
Baptist Education Society, of the
State of New-York, held at Hamilton, the fifth day of June, in
the year of our Lord, one thousand eight hundred and twenty-

two. Morrisville, Pr. by John B. Johnson, 1822. 12 p. CSmH; MB; NRAB. 7895

Baptists. Alabama. Bigbee Association
Minutes of the Beckbee [sic] Baptist Association convened at Bassett's Creek Meeting-House, Clark [sic] County, Alabama, on Saturday before the Fourth Lord's Day, in September, 1822. [1822] 8 p. NRAB. 7896

---- ---- Cahawba Association
Minutes, of the Cahawba Baptist Association, began [sic] and held at Canaan Meeting House, in Jefferson County, on the Saturday preceding the Fourth Lord's Day in October 1822... Cahawba, Pr. by William B. Allen, 1822. 12 p. NRAB. 7897

---- Connecticut. Hartford Association
Minutes of the Hartford Baptist Association, held at Middletown, October second and third, 1822. Pr. at the office of The Christian Secretary, Hartford. 1822. 12 p. Ct; CtBB; NRAB. 7898

---- ---- New London Association
Minutes of the New-London Baptist Association, held at Waterford, New London County (Conn.) on the 15th and 16th of October, 1822. New London, Clapp & Francis, printers, 1822. 12 p. Ct; NRAB. 7899

---- ---- Stonington Union Association
Minutes of the Stonington Union Association, held at Groton, Conn. June 19th and 20th, 1822. Norwich, Pr. by Robinson & Dunham, 1822. 8 p. NRAB; RWe. 7900

---- Virginia. Columbia Association
Minutes of the Columbia Baptist Association, held by appointment, at Mount Pleasant, Fairfax County, Virginia, Aug. 23d, 24th, and 25th, 1822. Washington City, Pr. by Anderson and Meehan, at The Columbian Office, 1822. 16 p. ViRU. 7901

---- Georgia. Ebenezer Association.
Minutes of the Ebenezer Association, held at Mount Horeb, Pulaski County, from the seventh, to the tenth September, 1822. Milledgeville, Pr. by Grantland & Orme, 1822. 7 p. McArthur Baptist collection, Cordele, Ga. 7902

---- ---- Ocmulgee Association
Minutes of the Ocmulgee Association, held at Mount Gilead, Putnam County, from the 31st of August, to the 3d of September, 1822, inclusive. [Milledgeville? 1822?] 8 p. GU-De. 7903

---- ---- Savannah Baptist Convention
Minutes of the Savannah Baptist Convention, held at Blackswamp Church, S. C., Nov. 1822. [Savannah?] 1822. 11 p. Libbey. Savannah Imprints, item 227. 7904

---- Indiana. Blue River Association
Minutes of the Blue River Association. Held at Blue-River meeting house, Harrison county, Indiana, second Saturday in October, 1822. [Salem, Patrick & Wheelock, 1822] 4 p. InFrlC; NRAB; TxDaHi. 7905

---- ---- Salem Association.
Minutes of a Convention held at Salem Meeting House, in Gibson County, State of Indiana, commencing on the Saturday before the 4th Lord's day in October, A.D. 1822, and days following, by the ministers and messengers of the ten Baptist Churches a part

of which said Churches, were
striken off the Wabash District
Association. 7 p. NRAB.   7906

---- ---- Silver Creek Association
    Minutes of the Silver Creek
Association held at Middle Fork
meeting house, Jefferson County,
commencing 4th Saturday in August, 1822. [Madison, Lodge &
Arion, 1822] 4 p. In; NRAB.
                                 7907
---- ---- Wabash District Association
    Minutes of the Wabash Dis-
trict Association, convened at
Prairie Creek meeting house, in
Vigo county, Indiana, on the
fifth, sixth, & seventh days of
October, in the year of our Lord
one thousand eight hundred and
twenty-two. Pr. by E. Stout,
Vincennes, Ia. 1822. 6 p. In.
                                 7908
---- Maine. Bowdoinham Association
    Minutes of the Bowdoinham
Association, held at the meeting
house, in New Sharon, September
25 and 26, 1822: together with
their circular and corresponding
letters. Hallowell, S. K. Gilman,
printer, 1822. 8 p. MBC;
MNtcA; MWA; MeWC; NRAB.
                                 7909
---- ---- Cumberland Association
    Minutes of the Cumberland Bap-
tist Association, held at the Baptist Meeting-House in Bridgton,
October 2 and 3, 1822: together
with the circular and corresponding letters.   Portland, Pr. by
Todd and Smith, 1822. 20 p.
MH-AH; MNtcA; MWA; MeHi;
MeWC; NN; NRAB.   7910

---- ---- Eastern Maine Association
    Minutes of the Eastern Maine
Association, held at the meeting-
house in Addison, Wednesday and

Thursday, October 2d and 3d,
1822. Eastport, Pr. by Benjamin Folsom [1822] 16 p.
MNtcA; MeWC; NRAB.   7911

---- ---- Lincoln Association
    Minutes of the Lincoln Asso-
ciation, held at China, September 18 and 19, 1822. Hallowell,
Pr. by Goodale, Glazier and Co.
1822. 8 p. MWA; MeWC.
                                 7912
---- ---- York Association
    Minutes of the York Baptist
Association, held at the Baptist
meeting-house, in Buxton (Me.)
June 12th and 13th, 1822. Kennebunk, Pr. by James K. Remich, 1822. 8 p. MWA; MeHi;
MeWC.   7913

---- Maryland. Baltimore Association
    Minutes of the Baltimore Bap-
tist Association, held by appointment at Pleasant Valley, Washington County, Maryland, May
16th, 17th, and 18th, 1822.
Washington City, Pr. by Anderson and Meehan, at the Columbian Office, 1822. 8 p. NRAB.
                                 7914
---- Massachusetts. Boston Association
    Minutes of the Boston Baptist
Association, holden in the Second Baptist Meeting-House in
Boston, on Wednesday and Thursday, Sept. 18th & 19th, 1822.
Boston, Pr. by Lincoln & Edmands, [1822?] 19 p. CBB;
MH-AH; MiD-B.   7915

---- ---- Sturbridge Association
    Minutes of the Sturbridge Bap-
tist Association, held in the Baptist Meeting-House in Killingly
(Con.) August 28 and 29, 1822.
Worcester, Pr. by William Manning, Sept. 1822. 11 p. CBB;
MBC; MBNEH; NRAB.   7916

---- ---- Westfield Association

Minutes of the Westfield Baptist Association, held at the Baptist Meeting House, on Westfield Farms, Mass. Sept. 4th and 5th, 1822. [Pr. at the Office of the Christian Secretary, 1822] 8 p. M. 7917

---- ---- Worcester Association
Minutes of the Worcester Baptist Association, held in the Baptist Meeting-House in Bellingham, (Mass.) August 21 and 22, 1822. Worcester, Pr. by Wm. Manning, 1822. 12 p. MWA. 7918

---- Mississippi. Baptist Missionary Society
The fifth annual report of the executive board of the Mississippi Baptist Missionary Society, embracing a brief view of missions, &c. Natchez, Miss., Pr. by Andrew Marschalk, 1822. 27 p. MsU. 7919

---- New Hampshire. Dublin Association
Minutes of the Dublin Baptist Association, held at the Baptist Meeting-House in Winchendon, Mass. ... Keene (N.H.), John Prentiss, printer, 1822. 8 p. MWA. 7920

---- New Jersey. New Jersey Association
Minutes of the New-Jersey Baptist Association, held by appointment at Evesham, Sept. 4th and 5th, 1822. 8 p. NjR. 7921

---- New York. Black River Association
Minutes...1822. Sacket's Harbor, Pr. by M.M. Cole, 1822. 15 p. NRAB. 7922

---- ---- Chemung Association
Minutes of the Chemung Baptist Association, held at Canton Meeting House, Pa. Oct. 2d and 3d, 1822. Towanda, Pr. by

George Scott, 1822. 8 p. NRAB. 7923

---- ---- Franklin Association
Minutes of the Franklin Baptist Association, held in Maryland, Otsego County, on Wednesday, June 19, 1822. Together with their circular & corresponding letters. Cooperstown, Pr. by H. & E. Phinney, July 1822. 12 p. NRAB. 7924

---- ---- Genesee Association
Minutes of the Genesee Baptist Association, held at Ogden, on the 2d and 3d of October, 1822: with their circular and corresponding letter...[Rochester, E. Peck & Co., printers, 1822] 8 p. NRAB. 7925

---- ---- Holland Purchase Association
Minutes of the Holland Purchase Association, convened in the church at Eden, upon the 9th and 10th October, 1822; together with their circular and corresponding letter. Canandaigua, Pr. by John A. Stevens, 1822. 11 p. NRAB. 7926

---- ---- Madison Association.
Minutes of the Madison Baptist Association: held at Eaton Village, on the 11th and 12th days of September, 1822; together with their circular and corresponding letters. [Morrisville? N.Y., John B. Johnson and Son? 1822] 12 p. MB. 7927

---- ---- New York Association
Minutes of the New-York Baptist Association, held in the Baptist Meeting-House, in Plainfield, New Jersey, on the 29th and 30th days of May, 1822. 16 p. NRAB. 7928

---- ---- Ontario Association
Minutes of the Ontario Baptist association, holden at Pittsford,

September 25th, and 26th, 1822;
together with their circular and
corresponding letter. Canandaigua, Pr. by John A. Stevens,
1822. 12 p. NRAB.   7929

---- ---- St. Lawrence Associa-
tion
    Minutes... Potsdam, N.Y.,
Pr. by F.C. Powell, 1822.
NRAB.   7930

---- ---- Seneca Association
    Minutes... held with the Union
Church, Farmerville, September
4th and 5th, 1822. Together
with their circular and corre-
sponding letter. Ithaca, Pr. by
E. Mack, 1822. 11 p. MWA.
                            7931
---- ---- Union Association
    Minutes of the Union Baptist
Association, held with the First
Baptist Church in Fiskill, at the
Union Meeting-House, Beekman,
New York, on the first Wednes-
day & Thursday of September,
1822.   Norfolk, Conn., Pr. by
S.W. Benedict, 1822. 8 p.
NRAB.   7932

---- ---- Warwick Association
    Minutes of the Warwick Bap-
tized Association, held at First
Wantage, Sussex, New Jersey,
the 12th and 13th of June, 1822.
Goshen, Pr. by James A. Che-
vee, 1822. 16 p. NRAB.   7933

---- Ohio. Columbus Association
    Minutes of the Columbus Bap-
tist Association, held by appointment, at Bethel Church, Franklin County, Ohio, August 30,
31, Sept. 1, 1822. Delaware,
Ohio, Pr. at the Gazette office,
1822. 8 p. NRAB; OCIWHi. 7934

---- ---- East Fork of the Little
Miami Association
    Minutes of the East Fork of
the Little Miami Baptist Association, held at Clough Creek, Ham-

ilton County, Ohio, on the 31st
of August, and the two following days, 1822. [Cincinnati?
1822] 4 p. NRAB.   7935

---- ---- Grand River Association
    Minutes of the Grand River
Baptist Association convened at
Mentor, on the XI & XII September, 1822; together with their
circular and corresponding letters. Painesville, Pr. by E.D.
Howe, 1822. 8 p. NRAB. 7936

---- ---- Huron Association
    Minutes of the Huron Baptist
Association, convened at Black
River, Huron County, Ohio, October 2d and 3d, 1822. Cleaveland, Pr. by Z. Willes, 1822.
11 p. OCIWHi.   7937

---- ---- Mahoning Association
    Minutes of the Mahoning Bap-
tist Association, convened at the
Valley of Achor, Columbiana
County, Ohio, on Wednesday &
Thursday, the 28th and 29th of
August, 1822. Warren, Ohio,
Pr. by Hapgood & Quinby [1822]
10 p. OCIWHi.   7938

---- ---- Miami Association
    Minutes of the Miami Baptist
Association, held at Bethel Meet-
ing House, Warren County, Ohio,
on the 7th, 8th, and 9th days of
September 1822. [1822] 4 p.
OCIWHi.   7939

---- ---- Muskingum Association
    Minutes of the Muskingum Bap-
tist Association, held by appointment, at Hopewell Meeting-
House, Perry County, Ohio,
August 23, 24, 25, 1822. Zanesville, Pr. by Horatio J. Cox,
1822. 16 p. NRAB; OCIWHi.
                            7940
---- Pennsylvania. Philadelphia
Association
    Minutes of the Philadelphia

Baptist Association, held by appointment at Lower Merion on the 1st, 2nd and 3rd of October, 1822. Philadelphia, B. Redman, printer and bookseller, 1822. 16 p. PPN.   7941

---- Rhode Island. Warren Association

Minutes of the Warren Baptist Association, held at the Baptist Meeting House, in New-Bedford, on Tuesday and Wednesday, September 10 and 11, 1822. Providence, Pr. by Brown and Danforth [1822] 16 p. MB; NRAB; RHi.   7942

---- South Carolina. Charleston Association

Minutes of the Charleston Baptist Association, convened at the Ebenezer Church, Nov. 2, 1822. [Charleston, Pr. by Wm. Riley, 1822?] 16 p. NjR.   7943

---- Tennessee. Concord Association.

Minutes of the Baptists Concord Association, West Tennessee; held at West Station Camp Meeting-House, Sumner county, August 3d, 1822, and succeeding days. Nashville, Joseph Norvell, printer, 1822. 4 p. CSmH. 7944

---- ---- Flint River Association

[Minutes of the Flint River Association of Baptists convened at Union Church in Pulaski, State of Tennessee, on the Saturday before the 4th Sunday in September, 1822] [Huntsville? 1822?] (Not located. Ordered 600 copies printed ms. minutes, 1822)   7945

---- U. S. Board of Foreign Missions

The eighth annual report of the board of managers of the general convention of the Baptist denomination in the United States, for foreign missions... Washington City, Pr. for the convention by Anderson and Meehan, Columbian office, 1822. (377)-408 p. MNtcA.   7946

---- Vermont. Manchester Association

Minutes of the Manchester Baptist Association, holden at Rupert, September 1822, together with circular and corresponding letters. Salem, N.Y., Pr. at the Register Office, by B. Stiles, 1822. 7 p. NRAB.
                    7947
---- ---- Vermont Association

Minutes of the Vermont Baptist Association holden at the Baptist Meeting-House in Whiting on Wednesday and Thursday, October second and third, 1822. Poultney, Pr. by Smith and Shute, 1822. 15 [1] p. MtMiS; NRAB.   7948

---- ---- Vermont Central Association

Minutes of the Barre Association, held at Plainfield, Vt. September 11 & 12, 1822, with their circular and corresponding letters. Woodstock, Pr. by David Watson, 1822. 10 p. NRAB.
                    7949
---- ---- Windham County Association

Minutes of the Leyden Baptist Association, held at the 2d Baptist Meeting-House in Colrain, Ms., October 9th & 10th, 1822. Brattleboro, Pr. for the Association [1822] 12 p. MWA; NRAB.
                    7950
---- ---- Woodstock Association

Minutes of the Woodstock Baptist Association, holden at Newport, N.H., Sept. 25th and 26th, 1822; with their circular and corresponding letters, and the reports of the missionary and education boards for 1822. [1822]

(Caption title) 12 p. NRAB. 7951

---- Virginia. Dover Association
Minutes of the Baptist Dover
Association, held at Emmaus, in
New-Kent County, October 12th,
13th and 14th, 1822. Richmond,
Pr. by Shepherd & Pollard,
1822. 15 p. DLC; ViRU.   7952

---- ---- General Meeting of
Correspondence
Minutes of the Virginia Baptist General Meeting of Correspondence... Richmond, Shepherd & Pollard, printers, 1822.
6 p. ViRU.   7953

---- ---- Goshen Association
Minutes of the Goshen Baptist
Association, held by appointment
at Massaponax, Spotsylvania
County, Virginia, October 5th,
6th, & 7th, 1822. Pr. by James
D. Harrow, Fredericksburg, Va.
12 p. ViRU.   7954

---- ---- Ketocton Association
Minutes of the Ketocton Bap-
tist Association, held by appoint-
ment at Ebenezer Meeting House,
Loudon County, Virginia, August
14, 16, 17, and 18th, 1822.
Washington City, Pr. by Ander-
son and Meehan at the Columbian
Office, 1822. 16 p. DLC; ViRU.
                           7955
---- ---- Shiloh Association
Minutes of the Shiloh Baptist
Association, held at Gourdvine
Meeting-House, in Culpeper Coun-
ty, Virginia: commencing August
30th, 1822. Pr. by James D.
Harrow, Fredericksburg, Va.
12 p. ViRU.   7956

---- ---- Union Association
Minutes of the Union Baptist
Association, held at Valley
Church, Randolph County, Va.,
on the 23d, 24th and 25th of
Aug., 1822. Clarksbug[!] Va.,
Pr. by Alexander G. M'Rae,

1822. 8 p. NRAB.   7957

Barclay, Robert
A treatise on church govern-
ment. Philadelphia, Solomon W.
Conrad, 1822. 124 p. ICN; IP;
MB; MBC; MWA; MWHi; MiD-
B; MoWgT; NNFL; NcGu;
OClWHi; PPF; PHi; PHC;
PPAmP; PU; PSC-Hi; RP.
                           7958
Barlow, Joel
The hasty-pudding. A poem,
in three cantos. Canandaigua,
J.D. Bemis & co. [1822?] 23 p.
MWA.   7959

[Barnard, Sir John] 1685-1764
A present for an apprentice;
or A sure guide to gain both es-
teem and estate... Philadelphia,
Pub. by direction of the managers of the Apprentices' Library
of Philadelphia, 1822. 107 p.
IObB; MB; MdBL; P.   7960

Barry, Eduardo, 1809-1879
El espiritu del despotismo,
traducido del ingles y dedicado
al... Simon Bolivar... por Eduardo
Barry. Filadelfia, H.C. Carey,
y I. Lea, 1822. 223 p. C-S;
PHi.   7961

Barry, William Taylor
[Circular letter from a committee appointed by the Legislature of Kentucky to collect information and to arrange a plan for
carrying into effect in the best
manner possible, the benevolent
purposes of the state regarding
education.] March 13, 1822. 1 p.
DLC.   7962

---- Remarks of William T.
Barry, Esq. L.L.D. Lieutenant
Governor of Kentucky and Speaker
of the Senate, delivered in committee of the whole in opposition
to Mr. Flournoy's motion, to
strike out the first section of the
bill establishing the Bank of the

Commonwealth, at the session of 1820. Pr. at the Office of the Kentucky Gazette, 1822. 28 p. KyLo; KyLxT; NN.   7963

Bartlett, John
Sermon, preached in Winton-bury meeting-house, Windsor; on the occasion of the annual Thanksgiving, December 6th, A.D. 1821. Hartford, George Goodwin & sons, printers, 1822. 19 p. Ct; CtHi; CtY; MBC; NjPT; RBr.   7964

Bartlett, John Stephen
Physician's pocket synopsis; affording a concise view of the symptoms and treatment of the medical and surgical diseases incident to the human frame... Boston, Munroe and Francis, 1822. 396 p. CoCsE; CtY; InThR; MB; MBC; MBM; MH-M; MeB; NNNAM; Nh; OC; OClM; PPC; RPM.   7965

Bartlett, Montgomery Robert
The practical reader. In five books. New York, Pub. by the author and sold by Myers and Smith, booksellers, Myers & Smith, printers, 1822. 348 p. CSt; CtHT-W; DLC; MiD-B; NBuG; NCanHi; NjR; RPB. 7966

Bartlett, Robert
A discourse, delivered before the First Universalist Society in Warner, N.H., the third Sabbath in September 1822, upon the doctrine of election. Woodstock, Pr. by David Watson, 1822. 18 p. MMeT; Nh.   7967

Barton, Ira
An oration, delivered at Oxford, on the forty-sixth anniversary of American Independence. Cambridge, Hilliard and Metcalf, printers, 1822. 24 p. MB; MH; MHi; MWA; MWHi; MiD-B; RPB.   7968

Bason's country almanac for 1823. By Joshua Sharp. Charleston, S.C., W.P. Bason [1822] 18 ll. CtLHi; NcA-S.
                7969

---- ---- Charleston, S.C., W.P. Bason [1822] 22 ll. Issue with added signature. ViU.
                7970

Bates, Edward
Oration delivered before Missouri Lodge, No. 1, at St. Louis, on the anniversary of St. John the Evangelist: December 27, 1821. St. Louis, Pr. at the office of the St. Louis Register, 1822. 12 p. IaCrM; MB.   7971

Baury, Alfred Louis
The Christian minister's valedictory. A discourse, delivered on Sunday evening, Sept. 22, 1822, in Christ Church, Guilford, Vermont. Boston, Pr. by Joseph W. Ingraham, 1822. 16 p. MBD; MWA; MiD-B; RPB; VtU.   7972

Baxter, Richard, 1615-1691
A call to the unconverted to turn and live and accept of mercy while mercy may be had... Boston, T. Bedlington & C. Ewer, B. Field, printer, Dedham, 1822. 252 p. CSt; CtY; MAm; MB; MBC; MFHi; MHi; MWA; ScCoT; WWauHi.   7973

---- ---- 2d Canandaigua ed. To which is added, A discourse, concerning a death-bed repentance. By William Assheton, D.D. Canandaigua, James D. Bemis and co., 1822. 202 p. CSmH; NCH; NCanHi.   7974

---- Heaven lost. Extract from Baxter's Saint's rest. Andover, Flagg & Gould, printers, 1822. 16 p. MeB.   7975

---- The saints everlasting rest; or, A treatise of the blessed

state of the saints... Abridged by
Benjamin Fawcett. Boston, Pr.
by Jonathan Howe, for Samuel
West, Salem, 1822. 300 p. KM;
MB; MBC; MH; MTr; NN;
NNQ; OClW.   7976

---- ---- Abridged by Benjamin
Fawcett... Northampton, Mass.,
Pr. by J. Metcalf for Simeon
Butler, 1822. 309 p. MNF;
MWA.   7977

Bayard, Samuel
    Letters on the sacrament of
the Lord's Supper. Philadelphia,
William W. Woodward, 1822.
256 p. CtW; CtY; GDC; KWiU;
ICP; MBC; NN; NjP; P;
PPPrHi; ViRUT.   7978

Beach, Stephen
    What is truth? A sermon de-
livered before Mount Vernon
Lodge at Johnson, June 25, 1821.
On the festival of St. John the
Baptist. Burlington, Pub. by the
Lodge, 1822. 12 p. BrMus. 7979

Beasley, Frederick, 1777-1845
    A search of truth in the science
of the human mind, part first.
Philadelphia, S. Potter and co.,
1822. 561 p. CSmH; CtHT; CtY;
DLC; GDC; KyHbHi; MBAt;
MBC; MBM; MH; MLow; MdBd;
MdBJ; MdBL; MiU-C; MsOK;
NCH; NNG; NNUT; NjP; NjPT;
OrPD; PP; PPD; PPAmP;
PPC; PU; PPLT; PPL; PHi;
PPB; RPAt; ScC; TNDL; ViAl;
ViL; ViU; VtU.   7980

---- A sermon upon duelling:
delivered to the senior class in
the University of Pennsylvania,
on the Sunday before their Commencement, July 21st, 1822.
Philadelphia, Potter & Co., J.H.
Cunningham, printer, 1822. 25 p.
MiD-B; NGH; NjP; PHi; PPL;
PU.   7981

Beazley, Samuel, 1786-1851
    ...Is he jealous? An oper-
etta; in one act... the only edition existing which is faithfully
marked with the stage business,
and stage directions, as it is
performed at the Theatre Royal
English Opera. Boston, Wells
and Lilly, 1822. 38 p. CtY;
MH; MeB; NN; PPL.   7982

Beckes, Benjamin V.
    To the voters of Knox county
fellow citizens, I had fondly
hoped that no circumstance
would have rendered it necessary
for me to appear before you by
way of 'hand bill'... Very respectfully, B.V. Bekes. [1822]
In.   7983

Beddoes, Thomas
    The authentic history of Isaac
Jenkins, his wife, and their
three children; with an agreeable and happy sequel, shewing
the good effects of their worthy
friend Mr. Langford's admoni-
tions. Pr. for the trustees of
the publishing fund, by Hilliard
and Metcalf, Cambridge. Sold
by Cummings & Hilliard, Boston, and other agents of the
Publishing Fund. Feb. 1822. 40
p. DLC; ICMe; IEN-M; MB;
MBAt; MBNEH; MNF; MWA;
PHi; RPM.   7984

Bedlington and Ewer, firm,
Boston
    Catalogue of books, amounting,
at the retail prices, to over
100,000 dollars, which are now
offered for sale, in general at
fifty per cent discount, at the
literary rooms 48, Cornhill.
[Boston] S. Etheridge, printer,
1822. 64 p. DLC; ICN; M; MHi;
PU.   7985

Beers' almanack for 1823.
[1822] 18 ll. MWA; NHi. 7986

---- By Andrew Beers. Hartford, George Goodwin and Sons [1822] 12 ll. CtB; Ct; CtHi; CLU; CtLHi; CtHT-W; CtY; DLC; InU; MB; MWA; NN; N; WHi; WKenHi. 7987

---- ---- New-Haven, A. H. Maltby & Co. [1822] 12 ll. Ct; CtB; CtHi; CtLHi; CtY; DLC; InU; MH; MWA; NBuG; N. 7988

Beers' almanack or, New-York & Vermont calendar for 1823. [1822] NCooHi. 7989

Beers' calendar; or Hosford's New-York and Vermont almanack for 1823. By Andrew Beers. Albany, E. & E. Hosford [1822] 24 ll. CLU; DLC; InU; MWA; MnU; MiU-C; N; NN; NBuG; NCanHi. 7990

Beers' calender [sic]; or Hosford's New-York and Vermont almanack for 1823. By Andrew Beers. Albany, E. & E. Hosford [1822] 18 ll. MB; MWA; NHi; NN; NNSIHi; OClWHi. 7991

Beers' Carolinas and Georgia almanac for 1823. Charleston, S. Babcock & Co.; Ker Boyce and R. Missildine [1822] 25 ll. MiD-B; NBuHi; NN; ScU-S. 7992

Beers' Long-Island almanac for 1823. By Andrew Beers. Jamaica, Henry C. Sleight [1822] 24 ll. CtY; DLC; MWA; MiD-B; NBLiHi; NHi; NJQ; NN. 7993

Beethoven, Ludwig van, 1770-1827
O swiftly glides the bonny boat. A Scotch air. Baltimore, John Cole, [1822] 3 p. MB; MH; MWA; MdHi; NBuG; NN; PHi; PP-K. 7994

---- Beethoven's celebrated polacca. Arranged for the piano forte by P. K. Moran. New York, P. K. Moran [1822] 5 p. MH; NRU-Mus. 7995

Bell, John, 1763-1820
The anatomy and physiology of the human body... 4th Amer. from the 4th English ed. ... New York, Collins & co., 1822. 3 v. ArU-M; CSfCMS; CSt-L; CU; CtY; DLC; DNLM; ICJ; IEN-M; InU-M; KyLxT; LNoP; LNT-M; MB; MBM; MH-M; MdBJ; MdBL; MdBM; MdUM; MoS; NBuU-M; MoSU-M; NBM; NGH; NHem; NNC-M; NNNAM; NRAM; NbOC-M; PPC; RPB; RPM; ScCMeS; TU; ViRMC. 7996

Bellingham, Mass., Baptist Church
Articles of faith and covenant, adopted by the Baptist Church in Bellingham, September 28, 1821. Worcester, Pr. by William Manning & Son, Feb. 1822. 11 p. MBC; MWA; NjPT. 7997

Benedict, David, 1779-1874
The Pawtucket collection of conference hymns. 5th ed. Providence, Miller & Hutchens, 1822. 126 p. MWA; MNtcA. 7998

Benger, Elizabeth Ogilvy, 1778-1827
Memoirs of the life of Anne Boleyn, queen of Henry VIII. Philadelphia, Abraham Small, 1822. 401 p. CtHT-W; CtW; CtY; DeGE; ICMe; ICU; MB; MBL; MC; MH; MWA; MdBD; MoHi; NCH; NGH; NNS; NjMD; OClStM; PPA; PPL; RNR; RPAt; ScC; TxU; Vi. 7999

Bennett, James
Obligation of the Church to support its ministers. Substance of a sermon, preached at Sheffield, before the associated Churches and ministers, assembled there, April 25, 1821.

New-York, Pub. by N. Bangs
and T. Mason, for the Methodist
Episcopal Church, J. C. Totten,
printer, 1822. 27 p. CtY; DLC;
IEG; MH-AH; MWA; MsJS. 8000

[Bennett, William, English solic-
itor]
The cavalier; a romance, by
Lee Gibbons (pseud.) Philadel-
phia, A. Small, 1822. 2 v.
(Sometimes attributed to Thomas
Roscoe, jun.) MH; MnU;
PWWJS. 8001

Bennett & Walton's almanack for
1823. By Joshua Sharp. Philadelphia, Bennett & Walton [1822]
18 ll. DLC; InU; MWA; NHi;
NCH; PHi; WHi. 8002

Benson, Joseph, comp.
Hymns for children... New
York, N. Bangs & T. Mason,
1822. 160 p. NNUT. 8003

Berard, Claudius
Leçons françaises, a l'usage
des commençans et des cadets
de l'academic militaire des
Etats-unis à West Point, recueil-
lies par Claudius Berard... New
York, Berard, 1822. 236 p.
NWM. 8004

---- ---- Philadelphia, H. C.
Carey & I. Lea, 1822. 236 p.
NjP; OFH; OMC; PPF; PPL.
8005

Berkshire Medical Institution,
Pittsfield, Mass.
Catalogue of the officers and
students. [Pittsfield] 1822. bdsd.
MWiW. 8006

Berlin, Conn. Third Congregational Church
A brief summary of Christian
doctrine, and a form of Covenant,
adopted by the Third Church in
Berlin, October 4, 1822. And
publicly read on the admission of
members... Hartford, Pr. by

Goodsell and Wells, 1822. 12 p.
Ct; CtHi; CtY; DLC; MBAt;
MBD. 8007

Berrian, William
A sermon preached in St.
Paul's Church, Troy, October
17, 1822; for the relief of the
widows and orphans of clergy-
men of the Protestant Episcopal
Church in the State of New-York.
New-York, Pr. by T. and J.
Swords, 1822. 14 p. NIC; NNC;
NjR. 8008

Berridge, John
The Christian world un-
masked. To which is prefixed
the life of the author. Corr. and
abridged by Abner Morse...
Boston, Charles Ewer, W. Bel-
lamy, printer, 1822. 201 p.
ICP; MBNEH; MH-AH; MPiB;
MeB; MeBat; NN; NbOM;
NjMD; NjPT; OCIWHi. 8009

Berrien, John MacPherson
An oration delivered at the
Baptist Church in the City of
Savannah, on Friday, Feb. 22,
1822; at the request of the
Georgia Hussars... Savannah,
W. T. Williams, 1822. 24 p.
MBAt. 8010

Bible
The Columbian family and pul-
pit Bible... Together with a val-
uable appendix... 1st Amer. ed.
Boston, J. Teal, 1822. [1122] p.
DLC; IaGG; MB; MBC; MH-AH;
MHi; MWA; MiU; NN; PPL.
8011

---- The Hebrew Bible; from the
edition of Everardo van der
Hooght. New York, Samuel
Whiting, pr. by D. Fanshaw,
1822. 41 p. NCaS. 8012

---- The Holy Bible... Stereotyped
by D. & G. Bruce, New-York.
Albany, E. & E. Hosford, 1822.
837 p. LNH; NN. 8013

---- [The Holy Bible. Boston, pub. by S. Walker, 1822] 875, [1] p., 157, [1] p., 877-1222 p. CSmH; MB; PPL.   8014

---- The Holy Bible containing the Old and New Testaments, according to the authorized version; with explanatory notes, practical observations, and copious marginal references, by Thomas Scott... Stereotype ed. from the 5th London ed. Boston, S. T. Armstrong, and Crocker and Brewster (etc.) 1822-24. 6 v. CoMv; CtY; KW; NT. 8015

---- ---- Hartford, Pr. by Hudson and Co., 1822. DLC; NN.
8016
---- ---- Translated out of the original tongues and with the former translations diligently compared and revised. Stereotyped for the American Bible Society. By David G. Bruce. New York, Pr. by D. Fanshaw, 1822. 836 p. IaBo; MWA.   8017

---- The Holy Bible, containing the Old and New Testaments; together with the Apocrypha; translated out of the original tongues, and with the former translations diligently compared and revised; with Canne's marginal notes and references... New York, Daniel D. Smith (stereotyped by E. White), 1822. 4, 5, 5-570, 112, 571-770 p. IEG; MWA; NcMHi; OO; PP.   8018

---- ---- Stereotyped ed. New York, Pub. by E. White and E. Bliss, Abraham Paul, printer, 1822. 705, 215, 12 p. MHi; MTaHi.   8019

---- ---- 2d Stereotyped ed. New York, E. Bliss & E. White, 1822. 704, 216 p. CtHT-W; NNUT; PP.   8020

---- ---- (according to the present authorized English version) with notes... By the Rev. Joseph Benson... New York, Pub. by N. Bangs and T. Mason for the Methodist Episcopal church, 1822-24. 5 v. CtW; GHi; MiD; MsJMC; ODaB; TNL.   8021

---- ---- By the late Rev. John Brown... Embellished with a series of beautiful engravings... New York, T. Kinnersley, 1822. CtY; MMhHi; NR; NSchHi; NcWsM; PBa; PHi; PNazMHi; PPFHi; PU.   8022

---- ---- Together with the Apocrypha, to which are added an index. Philadelphia, H. C. Carey & Lea, 1822. 1030 p. MdU.   8023

---- ---- Stereotype ed. Stereo. by B. and J. Collins, New-York. Salem, Pr. by Cushing and Appleton, 1822. 790 p. MSaE.
8024
---- Das neue Testament unsers Herrn und Heilandes Jesu Christi, nach der Deutschen Uebersetzung D. Martin Luthers... Neunte Auflage. Germantaun, Gedruckt bey M. Billmeyer, 1822. 537 p. DLC; MH; MiU-C; P; PPL.   8025

---- New Testament of our Lord and Saviour Jesus Christ translated out of the original Greek. Amherst, Pr. by Luther Roby. Roby's stereo. ed. Stereo. by B. & J. Collins, New York. 1822. 381 p. Nh-Hi.   8026

---- The New Testament of our Lord and Saviour... Stereo. by J. Howe, New York. Boston, Pr. at Treadwell's power press, 1822. 288 p. PPL.   8027

---- ---- Brattleboro, Holbrook & Fessenden, 1822. 336 p.

VtMiS.   8028

---- ---- Stereo. ed. Cooperstown, Pr. by H. & E. Phinney,
1822. 324 p. CtY.   8029

---- ---- 17th ed. Hartford, Pr.
by Samuel G. Goodrich, 1822.
321 p. CtHi.   8030

---- ---- New York, pub. by E.
Bliss & E. White [A. Paul,
printer] 1822. 216 p. ICU; PAtM;
PU; RPB; TxH.   8031

---- ---- by the late Rev. John
Brown... New York, Pr. and pub.
by T. Kinnersley, 1822. 1210 p.
WaSpHi-M.   8032

---- ---- 2d Amer., from the
Cambridge stereo. ed., carefully rev. and corr. Utica, Pr.
by William Williams, 1822. 324
p. LNH; NN; PPL.   8033

---- The New Testament. Philadelphia, G.W. Mentz, 1822.
336 p. PPeSchw.   8034

---- ...Novum Testamentum
graecum ad exemplar. Cura P.
Wilson. Hartford, Apud Oliver-
um D. Cooke et filios, 1822.
369 p. CtHT; DLC; GAM-R;
GDC; ICLI; ICU; IEG; IaHol;
MAnP; MB; MBC; MBrid; MCE;
MHi; MMeT; MNan; MWA;
MdBJ; MiU-C; NCH; NjPT; NjR;
OO; RNHi; ScGaL ; TxAb; TxU;
WBeloC.   8035

---- ...Novum Testamentum
Graece ex recensione Jo. Jac.
Griesbachii. 2 vols. Vol. I.
Philadelphiae, cura et impensis
Abneri Kneeland, Typis W. Fry,
1822. MMeT; MdW; PPL.   8036

---- El Nuevo Testamento de
Nuestro señor Jesu Cristo...
Nueva York, Edición estereotipa,
por Elihu White, a costa de la

Sociedad Americana de la Bib-
lia, 1822. 376 p. MWA.   8037

---- The pronouncing Testament.
The New Testament... To which
is applied, in numerous words,
the orthoepy of the critical pronouncing dictionary... by John
Walker... To which is prefixed,
an explanatory key. By Israel
Alger... Boston, Lincoln & Edmands, 1822. 304 p. CBPac;
IaMp; MB; MWA; MWborHi;
PP.   8038

---- Psalms carefully suited to
the Christian worsihp [!] in the
United States of America...
Pittsburgh, Pub. by Cramer &
Spear, 1822. 348 p. OCIWHi;
PPiHi.   8039

---- ---- Pittsburgh, Patterson,
1822. 300 p. PPLT.   8040

---- The Psalms of David, imi-
tated in the language of the New
Testament, etc. Exeter, John
I. Williams, 1822. Tuttle.
                           8041
---- ---- A new ed. By Tim-
othy Dwight... At the request of
the General association of Con-
necticut. New York, Charles
Starr, 1822. 505 p. Ct; IEG;
MH; MNF; NPtc; PPL; WGrNM;
WKenHi.   8042

---- ---- Stereo. by B. and J.
Collins. Rochester, N.Y., E.
Peck & Co., 1822. 322, 282 p.
NN.   8043

---- The Psalms of David, in
metre... by John Brown... Green-
burg, David Maclean, 1821. 408
p. GDC.   8044

---- ---- Allowed by the authority of the General Assembly of
the Kirk of Scotland. Pittsburgh,
Eichbaum & Johnston, 1822. 267
p. Edie, no. 23.   8045

---- La Sainte Bible, qui conti-
ent le vieux et la nouveau testaments. Imprimée sur l'édition
de Paris de l'année 1805. Édition stereotype, revue et cor-
rigée. New York, American
Bible Society, par Daniel Fanshaw, 1822. 207 p. IaHumdt.
                                    8046

---- A scripture peace tract.
The song of angels at the Saviour's birth, illustrated by as
many texts of scripture as the
letters it contains. Boston, Pr.
by Jonathan Howe, 1822. 8 p.
DLC.   8047

Bible and Common Prayer Book
Society
    Consitution and officers of the
Bible and Common Prayer Book
Society of the central part of the
state of New York. Formed in
1820. Utica, Pr. by William
Williams. 1822. 8 p. NUt. 8048

Bible Society of Massachusetts
    Report of the Bible Society of
Massachusetts, prepared for the
anniversary of the society, May
2, 1822. Boston, Phelps &
Farnham, 1822. 8 p. CBPSR.
                                    8049
Bible Society of Philadelphia
    Fourteenth report... May 1,
1822. Philadelphia, Wm. Fry,
pr., 1822. 38 p. PPL.   8050

Bible Society of Virginia
    Ninth annual report of the Bible
Society of Virginia. Richmond,
Pr. for the Society at the Frank-
lin Office, 1822. 40 p. Vi. 8051

Bichat, Xavier, 1771-1802
    General anatomy, applied to
the physiology and medicine...
Trans. from the French. By
George Hayward...Boston, Rich-
ardson and Lord, 1822. 3 v.
CSt-L; CU-M; CtY; DLC; DNLM;
GEU-M; GU-M; ICJ; IEN-M; IU-
M; KyLoJM; MB; MBC; MBM;

MH-M; MMe; MdBJ-W; MdBM;
MdUM; MeB; MiDW-M; MoS;
MoSW-M; NBLiCM; NBMS; NIC;
NNU-M; Nh; NhD; OC; OClM;
OO; P; PP; PPC; PU; ScCM;
TJaU; TU-M; ViRMC; ViU;
VtU; WU-M; WaPS.   8052

Bickerstaffe, Isaac, d. 1812.
    The hypocrite. A comedy;
altered from Colley Cibber's
Non-juror...Boston, Wells and
Lilly, 1822. 95 p. CtHT-W; DLC;
MB; MH; MWA; PPL.   8053

---- ... Lionel and Clarissa, an
opera... Boston, Wells and Lilly,
1822. 94 p. CtY; DLC; MH; NN;
PPL; TJoT.   8054

---- ... Love in a village, a
comic opera; Boston, Wells and
Lilly; New York, A.T. Good-
rich & Co., 1822. 78 p. CtY;
DLC; MH; MeB; NN; PPL; PU.
                                    8055
---- ... The maid of the mill;
An opera...Boston, Wells and
Lilly; New York, A.T. Goodrich
& co., 1822. 89 p. CtY; MH;
MeB; PPL.   8056

Bickersteth, Edward, 1786-1850
    A Scripture help, designed to
assist in reading the Bible profit-
ably...1st Amer. ed. Trenton,
G. Sherman, 1822. 76 p. NjPT.
                                    8057
Biddle, James C.
    Statement by James C. Biddle
and William M. Meredith, of the
Phila. Bar. Philadelphia, 1822.
35 p. MH; MH-L; MiD-B; PHi;
PPAmP; PPM; PPB; P; PP;
PPL; PU.   8058

Biddle, Nicholas, 1786-1844
    Address delivered before the
Philadelphia Society for Promoting Agriculture, at its annual
meeting, on the fifteenth of January, 1822. Philadelphia, Clark &
Raser, 1822. 39 p. CtY; DLC;

DeGE; ICU; IaAS; M; MB;
MBAt; MBHo; MH; MHi;
MdBMAS; NbU; OA; PHi; P;
PPAmP; PPL; PPAN; PU;
NjR; NjP; ScC.   8059

Bigelow, Jacob, 1787-1879
A treatise on the materia
medica, intended as a sequel to
the Pharmacopoeia of the United
States... Boston, C. Ewer, 1822.
424 p. CSfCMS; CSt; CU-M;
DLC; DNLM; GU-M; ICJ; IU-
M; LNT-M; MB; MBHo; MBM;
MBP; MH-M; MdBM; MeB;
MiU; MsJS; NBMS; NIC;
NNNBG; NRAM; NRU-M; NbU-M;
NcD; NcU; Nh; NhD; NjR;
OCLloyd. OClM; PPC; PU;
PPiAm; RPB; RPM; ScCM;
TU-M; WMAM; WU; WaSK. 8060

Billerica, (Mass.) Town
A statement of expenses, of
the town of Billerica, from May
3, 1821, to May 3, 1822. Concord, Mass., Pr. by Asa Biglow, 1822. 16 p. MBilHi.   8061

Binney, Amos
Documents relative to the in-
vestigation, by order of the
Secretary of the Navy, of the of-
ficial conduct of Amos Binney,
United States Navy Agent at Bos-
ton, upon the charges made by
Lieutenant Joel Abbot and others.
Pub. by the accused. Boston,
Pr. by Phelps and Farnham,
1822. iv, 260 p. CSmH; CtY;
DLC; M; MB; MH; MWA; MdBJ;
MdBP; Me; MiD-B; NN; PHi;
ScU.   8062

---- Poetic essays to aid the de-
votion of pious people. Boston,
Lincoln & Edmands, 1822. 48 p.
MBNMHi; MH.   8063

Bird, Fitzgerald
An inaugural dissertation on
the Sanguinaria canadensis of
Linnaeus... New York, Pr. by H.

Sage, 1822. 74 p. CSt-L; DLC;
DNLM; MB; NNNAM; PPC.
                           8064
Bishop, Gary
Public controversy: or, Uni-
versalism weighed in the balance
and found wanting. Philadelphia,
Pr. for the author, 1822. 174 p.
MWA; PPPrHi.   8065

Bishop, Henry Rowley, 1786-
1855
The blind minstrel. Philadelphia, G. Willig [1822?] 3 p.
MWA; NN.   8066

---- Bright be thy dreams.
Duetto. Philadelphia, G. E.
Blake [1822] [2] p. MWA; NN.
                           8067
---- ---- Philadelphia, G. Wil-
lig [1822] [2] p. MWA; NN.
                           8068
---- Common sense and genius.
A popular French air. New
York, E. Riley [1822] 3 p. N.
                           8069
---- The crystal hunters. Swiss
air. A popular National Melody.
Philadelphia, G. E. Blake, [1822]
[2] p. MH; MWA; NN.   8070

---- ---- Philadelphia, G. Willig [1822] [2] p. MH.   8071

---- Go then -- 'tis vain. A
popular Sicilian melody. Philadelphia, G. E. Blake [1822] 1 l.
NN.   8072

---- ---- Philadelphia, Geo.
Willig [1822] 1 l. MdHi.   8073

---- Go youth beloved. A ballad. New York, Dubois & Stodart [1822] 3 p. DLC; NN; PP;
PPL; PU; RPB.   8074

---- A highland laddie heard of
war. Philadelphia, Geo. Willig
[1822] [2] p. MH; NN.   8075

---- Like the gloom of night retiring. Boston, G. Graupner [1822?] 4 p. DLC; MB; MH; MHi; MWA; NN; RPB.   8076

---- Oh! still remember me. Philadelphia, G. Willig [1822] p [1]-2. NN; PP-K; PPL.   8077

---- Oh! sweet was the scene. Boston, Edwin W. Jackson [1822?] 4 p. NN.   8078

---- The pilgrim of love. Pr. for B. Carr, Philadelphia [ca 1822] [2] p. DLC; MWA; NBuG; NN; PHi.   8079

---- Row gently here. A popular Venetian air. Philadelphia, G. E. Blake [1822] [2] p. DLC; MH; NBuG; NN; PP.   8080

---- ---- Philadelphia, G. Willig [1822] [2] p. CtY; DLC; MH; NN; PP; RPB.   8081

---- Say, what shall be our sport today? Sicilian air. Philadelphia, G. E. Blake [1822] [2] p. DLC; MWA; NN; ScU; RPB.   8082

---- ---- Philadelphia, G. Willig [1822] [2] p. DLC; NN.   8083

---- See, the dawn from heaven. Air. Philadelphia, G. E. Blake [1822] [2] p. DLC; PP.   8084

---- ---- Philadelphia, G. Willig [1822] [2] p. NN; PHi.   8085

---- To love thee night and day love! New York, E. Riley, [1822?] 3 p. DLC; NN; RPB.   8086

---- When love was a child. Swedish air. Philadelphia, G. E. Blake [1822] 1 l. NN.   8087

---- Who'll buy my love knots?" Portuguese air. Philadelphia, G. E. Blake. [1822] [2] p. MWA;

N; NN.   8088

---- The youth in his blooming array. Philadelphia, G. E. Blake [1822] 5 p. Wolfe 839.   8089

Bissett, Robert, 1759-1805 The history of the reign of George III... New ed., brought down to the death of the king... Philadelphia, Edward Parker, 1822. 3 v. fronts. ArBaA; CSmH; CtY; GAGT; IU; KyU; LMo; MA; MDeeP; MLaw; MNF; MSa; MdBJ; MiEaIC; MsJMC; NBuG; NRU; NcDaD; NcW; Nj; OClWHi; PHi; PPDrop; PPL; RBr; RNR; RP; ScCC; ScNC; TNJ; TxMinw; Vi; ViRU; VtBrt; WBeloC; WM; WyU.   8090

Black ey'd Susan, to which is added the much admired songs of Sainclaire's defeat, and The waterman. Baltimore, Pr. for the purchaser, 1822. 8 p. MdBP.   8091

Black Rock Harbor Company Documents, relating to the western termination of the Erie canal; with explanations and remarks. Pub. by direction of "The Black Rock Harbor Company." Black Rock, Pr. by L. G. Hoffman, 1822. 60 p. CSmH; DLC; N; NBu; NN.   8092

Blackstone, Sir William Commentaries on the laws of England... New York, Pub. by Evert Duyckinck, George Long, Collins & Co., Collins and Hannay, and Abraham Small, Philadelphia. George Long, printer. 1822. 4 v. IBloW; KyLoU-L; KyLxT; MA; MH-L; MdBD; MiDSH; NIC-L; NbOC-L; NbU; NcWfC; NjP; NjPT; OC; OMC; OO; PLL; PPAmP; PPF; PU; PW; RPL; ScNc; TU; TaU.   8093

Blagrove, Richard M.
The peasant's joy. Rondo.
A favorite new lesson. Charleston, J. Siegling [1822?] [2] p.
NN.   8094

Blair, David, pseud. See Phillips, Sir Richard.

Blair, Hugh, 1718-1800
An abridgment of lectures on rhetoric...rev. and corr. Brookfield, Pr. by E. Merriam & Co., 1822. 311 p. MB; MBrof; MChiA; NSherb; OHi.   8095

---- ---- Greatly improved by addition to each chapter of appropriate questions...2d ed. Concord, N.H., Pr. by Joseph Manahan, 1822. 304, ii p. MB; MH; MHollHi; MWHi; MoS; NRMA; NdVcT; Nh.   8096

---- ---- Greatly improved by the addition to each chapter of appropriate questions...3d ed. Concord, N.H., Hill and Moore, 1822. 304 p. CtW; IU; MB; MH; MNowdHi; MiU; OMC; TxU-T.
                                        8097
---- ---- Rev. and cor. To which are added, Questions adapted to the above work; for the use of schools and academies ... Exeter, John J. Williams, 1822. 258 p. MH; MHi; Nh; NhD; RPE; TxDaM.   8098

---- ---- Philadelphia, Hickman and Hazzard, 1822. 290 p. DLC; GHi; IaSIB; OPosm; P; PMA; TNP.   8099

---- ---- ---- Portland, Pub. by William Hyde, A. Shirley, printer, 1822. 296 p. MB; MH; MeB; ScCliJ; TxComT.   8100

---- ---- Rev. Worcester, Dorr and Howland, 1822. 311 p. MiU.   8101

---- Sermons...2d compl. Amer. ed. Philadelphia, Hickman & Hazzard, 1822. 2 v. CU; CoDelta; GA; GMM; IaDuU; MBBCH; MH; MNS; MRev; MiU; MsJMC; MsNF; NCoS; NbCrD; PLT; PPL; PReaAT; PU; Wv.
                                        8102
Blair, William W.
Opinion of Judge William W. Blair, delivered at the June term of the Montgomery Circuit Court, A.D. 1822; On a motion, made the preceding Fall term, to quash a Replevy bond. [Lexington? 1822] 20 p. ICU; KyLo; KyLxT; OCHP.   8103

Blake, Francis A.
Exposition of the causes which led to the late controversy between General William Lytle and James W. Gazlay, Esq., and to the criminal prosecution recently instituted against Gen. Lytle & Francis A. Blake. Cincinnati, Sept. 10th, 1822. 23 p. DLC; MnHi.   8104

---- ---- 2d ed. Cincinnati, Sept. 10th, 1822. 23, [1] p. MWA.   8105

Blake, John Lauris, 1788-1857
One thousand questions for the examination of scholars in Blairs rhetorick. Ed. 4. Concord, N.H., Pr. by George Hough, 1822. 53 p. MHi; Nh-Hi. 8106

[----] Questions adapted to Blair's Rhetoric abridged. 5th ed. Pub. by Cushing & Appleton. Salem, Pr. by J.D. Cushing & Bros., 1822. 45 p. InFtwL; MSaE; NN.   8107

---- Questions for the examination of scholars in "Conversations on natural philosophy." ...Concord [N.H.] Pr. by Hill and Moore, 1822. 60 p. CSmH; MH; NN; RP.   8108

Blake, Thomas H.
To the public. On yesterday
a hand-bill was circulated in
this town, signed by B.V.
Beckes...I have applied in vain
to Mr. Beckes to obtain honorable satisfaction for his unpro-
voked insults and aspersion of
my character...Vincennes, July
25, 1822. Bdsd. In.   8109

---- To the voters of the first
congressional district. Fellow-
citizens, I am informed that a
certificate has been shewn to
many of you, signed by G.W.
Johnston and B.V. Beckes, coun-
teracting a report that William
Prince, Esqr. was hostile to the
improvement of the navigation of
the river Wabash. July 22d,
1822. Bdsd. In.   8110

Blake's Evening companion. For
the flute, clarinet, violin or
flagelet. Book 8, vol. 2. Philadelphia, G.E. Blake [1822?] p.
30-58. PPL.   8111

Blane, Sir Gilbert, 1st bart,
1749-1834
Elements of medical logic, il-
lustrated by practical proofs and
examples...1st Amer. from 2d
London ed. Hartford, Hunting-
ton and Hopkins, 1822. 319 p.
(Verso: Goodsell & Wells,
printers). CSt-L; CtHi; DLC;
DNLM; ICACS; ICJ; MB; MBM;
MDeeP; MH; MdBJ; MdBJ-W;
MdBM; MdUM; MeB; MoSMed;
NBMS; NNF; NNMSCO; NNNAM;
Nh; OCGHM; OClM; OO; PPC;
PPL; RPM; TJaU; ViNoM; ViU;
VtU.   8112

Bledsoe, Jesse
An introductory lecture on the
study of the law, delivered in the
chapel of Transylvania University, on Monday, November 4,
1822. Lexington, Ky., Pr. by
Joseph Ficklin, 1822. 24 p.

CSmH; ICU; IU; NN; OCHP.
       8113
Blood, Caleb
A few historical facts, re-
corded for the benefit of youth;
or, A concise history of the
world, in matters of matrimony.
Pittsfield, Mass., Pr. by Phinehas Allen, 1822. 16 p. MPiB;
MWA.   8114

Blunt, Edmund M.
The American coast pilot...
with directions for sailing...To-
gether with a tide table. 10th ed.
New York, Pub. by Edmund M.
Blunt, for William Hooker. J.
Seymour, printer, 1822. 495 p.
DLC; DeWI; MAtt; MsU; NNA;
Nh-Hi; ScCleA.   8115

Blunt, Joseph, comp.
The merchant's and ship-
master's assistant...New-York,
pub. by Edmund M. Blunt, for
William Hooker, J. Seymour,
printer, 1822. 464 p. KyDC;
MBevHi; MH-L; MSaP; NN; NjP;
NjR; OCIWHi.   8116

Blunt's edition of the nautical almanac and astronomical ephemeris for 1824. New York,
1822. NN.   8117

Böhme, Jacob, 1575-1624
Ein systematischer Auszug
aus des Gottseligen und hocher-
leuchteten Deutschen Theosophi
Jacob Böhmens Sammtlichen
Schriften...Erste Auflage...
Ephrata, Gedruckt und zu haben
bey Joseph Bauman, 1822-24.
2 v. MiU-C; P; PHi; PPG;
PPeSchw; PPL; PU.   8118

Bolgolam, al Hafiz. pseud.
Story of the third old man,
which has hitherto been missing
from the first volume of the
Arabian nights entertainments...
Hartford, Huntington & Hopkins.
Goodsell & Wells, printers, 1822.

42 p. CSmH; CtHT; MNF; MNHi.
8119

Bolles, Lucius
    The importance of the scrip-
tures to a teacher of religion.
A discourse delivered in the
meeting house of the Second Bap-
tist Church in Boston, Sept. 18,
1822, before the Boston Baptist
Association.   Boston, Pr. by
Lincoln & Edmands, [1822] 24 p.
DLC; MB; MBAt; MH-AH;
NRAB; RPB.   8120

Bond, Henry, 1790-1859
    Practical and surgical anat-
omy.   Philadelphia, Nov. 1,
1822. 1 p. (Prospectus of Dr.
Bond's Anatomical Rooms.) PHi.
8121

Bonnycastle, John
    An introduction to algebra...
2d New York, from the 11th
London ed.   Rev. by James Ryan...New York, Evert Duyckinck
and George Long, 1822. 310,
[2] p. CU; CtHT-W; MH; MdW;
MeB; MoS; NMtv; NcU; NjP;
NjR; OClWHi; OU; OrSaW; PJA;
PPeSchw; PWc; SoCCit.   8122

The book of games; or, A history of juvenile sports practised
at the Kingston academy. New
York, George Long, 1822. 108 p.
DLC; MNBedf; P.   8123

The book of pictures.   Albany,
Pr. by G. J. Loomis & co. ,
1822. 16 p. DLC.   8124

Bosquejo ligerísimo de in revo-
lucíon de Méjico.   See Roca-
fuerte, Vincente.

Boston (City)
    Abstract of the bill of mortal-
ity, of the town of Boston. From
the 31st of December, 1820, to
January 1st, 1822, agreeably to
the record kept at the Health Office.   Pub. by order of the
Board of Health. Benj. Whitman,

Jr. Secretary. [Boston, 1822?]
bdsd. MB.   8125

---- At a legal meeting of the
Freeholders and other inhabitants of the Town of Boston,
holden on the 14th day of January, A. D. 1822, voted that the
Selectmen be requested to cause
to be published...a correct list
stating the amount of real and
personal estate on which the inhabitants of the town have been
valued, named, assessed and
taxed for the year 1821. Boston,
Pr. by True & Greene, 1822.
206 p. CtHT-W; CtY; DLC; ICN;
IaHA; MB; MBAt; MBB; MBC;
MBNEH; MH-AH; MLow;
MNBedf; MW; MiD; NBLiHi;
NSy; Nh; Nh-Hi; PHi; WHi.
8126

---- City ordinances. City of
Boston, December 10, 1822 [on
use of firearms and removal of
snow] [Boston, 1822] bdsd. MB.
8127

---- A full and authentic report
of the debates in Faneuil Hall,
Dec. 31, Jan. 1, & 2, 1821-2;
on changing the form of government of the town of Boston. Including the speeches of Messrs.
Clough, Emmons, &c. as furnished by themselves.   Boston,
Pub. by William Emmons, 1822.
44 p. MB.   8128

---- ---- Boston, Pub. by Wm.
Emmons, 1822. 48 p. DLC; M;
MH; PHi.   8129

---- In Common Council, Nov.
4, 1822, Ordered, that the Committee of Finance...be a Committee, to cause to be published
a report of the receipts and expenditures of the Town of Boston,
from the date of the ninth annual report to the first day of May,
1822...Sent up for concurrence.
Wm. Prescott, President. In the
Board of Aldermen, Nov. 11,

1822...Read and concurred, and the Mayor is joined. John Phillips, Mayor. [Boston, 1822] [12] p. MB.   8130

---- Notification. The freeholders' and other inhabitants of the town of Boston...are hereby notified to meet at Faneuil Hall, ...the 4th day of March...to give in their ballots on the following questions - viz. By order of the Selectmen, Thomas Clark, Town Clerk. Boston, February 26, 1822...Bdsd. M; MBAt; MH.   8131

---- Notification. The inhabitants of the city of Boston, qualified as the law directs, are hereby notified to assemble at Fanueil Hall, on Monday the sixteenth day of September... By order of the Mayor and Aldermen, S. F. M'Cleary, city clerk. City of Boston, September 9, 1822. Bdsd. MB.   8132

---- Official papers, printed for the Common Council of the city of Boston, comprising the Constitution of the United States, and the Constitution of Massachusetts with the amendments, City and Police acts; acts relating to the Board of Health, Overseers of the Poor, and Firewards. Together with an Act providing for an assessment of taxes. Boston, pr. by Russell & Gardner, 1822. 138 p. MB; MBAt; MBevH; MH; MHi; MH-L; OO; PHi; PPL.   8133

---- An order to regulate the stands of trucks, carts, sleds and other carriages, and for other purposes. Oct. 21, 1822. Boston, Russell & Gardner, printers [1822] Bdsd. MHi. 8134

---- Report, as amended by the inhabitants of the town of Boston, at a legal meeting, held on the 31st of December, and the two following days. [Boston, 1822] Bdsd. MBAt; WHi.   8135

---- Report on the charitable funds, under the superintendence of the Overseers of the Poor as trustees...Boston, Pr. by Phelps and Farnham, 1822. 20 p. MBAt.   8136

---- Rules and orderrs [!] of the Common Council...for the year 1822. Boston, Russell & Gardner, 1822. 15 p. MB; MH-L; MHi.   8137

---- A synopsis, of the several resolves, relating to a City Government, submitted to the people of Boston, on the 7th of January, 1822. [Boston? 1822?] Bdsd. MHi; WHi.   8138

---- City of Boston. Selectmen's room, March 13, 1822. Whereas it is provided, in the second section of an Act, entitled, "An Act establishing the City of Boston," as follows... [Listing of Wards 1-12, with no. of inhabitants and boundaries]... [Jonathan Howe, pr.] Bdsd. MB.
                                   8139
---- Tenth annual report of the Committee of Finance. August... 1822. [Boston, 1822] 14 p. MB; MWA.   8140

Boston Asylum for Indigent Boys
    Order of solemnities, at the Old South Church, on Friday, April 26, 1822, being the eighth anniversary of the institution of the Asylum for Indigent Boys... [Boston, 1822] Bdsd. MB. 8141

Boston Benevolent Society
    At a meeting, held March the 4th, 1822, and continued by adjournment, it was deemed expedient that a Society should be formed for social and charitable

purposes to be called The Boston
Benevolent Society... [Boston?
1822?] Bdsd. WHi.   8142

Boston Cadets march. New York,
A. & W. Geib [1822?] 1 l.
Wolfe 986A.   8143

Boston Commercial Gazette
    New Year's address of the
carrier, January 1, 1822. Boston, 1822. Bdsd. MBAt.   8144

The Boston directory; containing
names of the inhabitants; their
occupations, places of business
and dwelling houses; with lists
of the streets... Boston, Pub. by
John H. A. Frost and Charles
Stimpson, Jr. Pr. by John H. A.
Frost, 1822. 280 p. DLC; MB;
MBAt; MBNEH; MBrigStJ;
MLanc; MHi; MWA; NN.   8145

The Boston Handel and Haydn
Society collection of church music. See Mason, Lowell, comp.

Boston Light Infantry
    Constitution of the Boston
Light Infantry, established May
1798. rev. & ratified. 15th April.
1822. Boston 1822. 25 p.
MBVAFCC.   8146

Boston Museum
    A catalogue of the principal
articles contained in the Boston
Museum, consisting of upwards
of fifty wax figures... To be sold
at auction, Wednesday, Aug. 14,
1822. Boston, Newell & Allen,
printers, 1822. 8 p. MWA. 8147

Boston Recorder
    Two objects to be gained at
once [proposal of the proprietor
of the Boston Recorder for the
benefit of the American Education
Society and the improvement of
the Recorder]. [Boston, Nathaniel Willis? 1822] 14 p. WN.
                                8148

Boston Sea Fencibles
    Constitution and exercise of
the Boston Sea Fencibles; instituted 11 September, 1817. Boston, Pr. by Munroe and Francis,
1822. 60 p. MBAt; MBL. 8149

Boston Society for the Religious
and Moral Instruction of the Poor.
    Sixth annual report... pre-
sented at their anniversary, Nov.
6, 1822. Boston, Crocker &
Brewster, prs., 1822. 46 [2] p.
MWA.   8150

Boston. West Church
    Order of performance (An-
thems). Fast Day, April 4,
1822. Boston, True and Greene,
prs., 1822. Bdsd. MHi.   8151

[Boudinot, Elias] 1740-1821
    A memoir of the Rev. William
Tennent, minister of Freehold,
Monmouth County, N. J. First
published in the Evangelical Magazine, pr. in Philadelphia.
Springfield, pub. by G. W. Callen-
der; A. G. Tannatt & Co., print-
ers, 1822. 67 p. CSmH; MAnP;
MBNEH; MH; OClWHi; WHi.
                                8152
[----] Poor Sarah, an Indian wo-
man. Andover, Flagg & Gould,
printers, 1822. 8 p. MB; MeB.
                                8153
Bowdoin College, Brunswick,
Maine
    Catalogue of the officers and
students of Bowdoin College, and
the Medical School of Maine.
February, 1822. Brunswick, Pr.
by Joseph Griffin, 1822. 16 p.
CtY; DLC; M; MB; MH; MHi;
MKi; MWA; MeB; MeHi; Nh.
                                8154
---- Catalogue of the officers
and students of Bowdoin College,
Maine. October, 1822. Brunswick,
Joseph Griffin, 1822. 8 p. DLC;
MH; MeB.   8155

---- Catalogus senatus academ-

ici, et eorum, qui munera et
officia gesserunt, quique alicujus
gradus laurea donati sunt in Col-
legio Bowdoinensi... Brunsvici;
E Typis Griffin et Weld,
MDCCCXXII. 16 p. DLC; M;
MB; MH; MHi; MWA; MeB;
MeHi; MeLewB; NN; NNC-T;
PU; BrMus.   8156

---- Illustrissimo Albion-Keith
Parris, Armig. Gubernatori;
consiliariis et senatoribus, qui
literis reipublicae Mainensis
proprie praesunt; sociis curator-
ibusque Academiae Bowdoinensis
honorandis atque reverendis...
Excudebant Griffin et Weld. [1822]
4 p. MeB.   8157

---- Order of exercises for exhibition, May 7, 1822. Brunswick, Pr. by Joseph Griffin,
1822. 4 p. MeB.   8158

---- Order of exercises for exhibition, Dec. 3, 1822. Brunswick, Joseph Griffin, 1822. 3 p.
MeB.   8159

---- Athenaean Society.
[Catalogue of the library of
the Athenaean Society, Bowdoin
College. September, 1822] 12 p.
CtY.   8160

Bowen, Nathaniel, bp.
An address delivered before
the Charleston Protestant Epis-
copal Sunday School Society... by
Nathaniel Bowen... Charleston,
A. E Miller, 1822. 11 p. NNG;
ScC; TSewU.   8161

---- The duty of fulfilling all
righteousness; a sermon prepara-
tory to confirmation; to which
are annexed, an address, designed as well for such as are
not, as such as are preparing to
be confirmed... Charleston, A. E.
Miller, 1822. 60 p. NNG; PPL;
ScCC.   8162

Bowring, John
Specimens of the Russian po-
ets; with preliminary remarks
and biographical notices. Trans.
by John Bowring. Boston, Pub.
by Cummings and Hilliard, Hil-
liard & Metcalf, printers, 1822.
240 p. CSmH; CU; CtB; CtHT;
DLC; GDC; IU; IaDa; LNH; MB;
MBL; MCon; MH; MLei; MLy;
MNBedf; MSa; MWA; MWal;
MeB; MiOC; NAl; NICLA; NR;
NhPoA; NjP; OCad; PHC; PU;
PPL; ScC; TxU.   8163

Boyer, Abel, 1667-1729
Boyer's French Dictionary.
Boston, Pub. by William B.
Fowle, and Lincoln & Edmands.
Pr. by Lincoln & Edmands, 1822.
2 v. CU-M; IU; IaK; InVi; MB;
MDeeP; MNF; MWiW; MeU;
MoS; MoSpD; NHav; NcW;
TxH-C.   8164

Bracebridge Hall. See Irving,
Washington.

Bradford, Alden, 1765-1843
History of Massachusetts...
Boston, Richardson and Lord
[etc.] 1822-29. 3 v. AU; C;
CLU; CSmH; CU; Ct; CtHT-W;
CtSoP; CtY; DLC; FSa; I; ICN;
ICP; ICU; IEN; IU; IaCli; IaHA;
In; InCW; InU; KMK; LU; M;
MA; MAJ; MB; MBAt; MBB;
MBC; MBL; MBNEH; MC;
MCon; MDeeP; MH-L; MHa;
MHi; MMe; MMilt; MS; MSa;
MW; MWA; MWHi; MWey; MWo;
Md; MdBE; MdBJ; MdBP; MeB;
MeBa; MiD-B; MiU; MnHi;
MoSM; MsWJ; NBLiHi; NCH;
NIC; NN; NNS; NNUT; NRHi;
NSyU; NT; NWM; NbO; NcD;
NhD; NjP; NjPat; O; OC;
OClWHi; OMC; OO; P; PPA;
PPL; RP; RPJCB; Vi; VtNofN;
WM.   8165

[Bradford, Gamaliel]
The writer; a series of orig-

inal essays, moral and amusing.
By a gentleman of Massachu-
setts. Boston, Russell & Gard-
ner, printers, 1822. 131 p.
CtY; DLC; ICHi; MB; MBAt;
MS; MWA; NbU; OMC; PU;
ViL. 8166

Bradford Academy
Catalogue of the officers and
students...Haverhill, Mass.,
Burrill and Hersey [1822] Bdsd.
(Dated: July 1822) NN. 8167

Bradley, Charles
Sermons, preached in the
Parish Church of High Wycombe,
Bucks. 1st Amer., from 4th
London ed. Philadelphia, Wm.
W. Woodward, 1822. 603 p.
GHi; ICP; ICU; IEG; IaDuU;
InCW; KyLoP; MBC; MBat;
MsCliM; NBuDD; NjPT; OO; P;
PAtM; PLERC-Hi; PWW; NRAB;
RNR; TxBrdH. 8168

Bradley, Mrs. Eliza
An authentic narrative of the
ship-wreck and sufferings of
Mrs. Eliza Bradley...Boston,
Pr. for James Walden, 1822.
108 p. MdBE. 8169

[Bradley, William Henry]
Giuseppino, an occidental
story. Philadelphia, H.C. Carey
& I. Lea, 1822. 68 p. (Attri-
uted to Lord Byron.) ICN; MH;
RPB. 8170

Braham, John, 1777-1856
The anchor's weigh'd. Phila-
delphia, G.E. Blake [1822?] 3 p.
NN. 8171

---- Dulce domum. New York,
E. Riley, [1822?] 4 p. MWA;
NN. 8172

Brandywine Manufacturing Com-
pany
An act to incorporate the
Brandywine Manufacturing Com-

pany. [Wilmington, Del., R.
Porter, printer, 1822] 8 p.
DeGE; PHi; PPAmP. 8173

Brantz, Lewis
Meteorological observations
in the vicinity of Baltimore, during the year 1821. [Baltimore]
Pr. at the Office of the Federal Gazette by William Gwynn,
1822. [56] p. MdHi. 8174

Brashears, Noah
Poems on several occasions.
Washington city, Pr. by W. Duncan, 1822. 34 p. DLC; MtHi.
8175

Bray, John, 1782-1822
Peace and holy love. A
sacred song. Boston, E.W.
Jackson [1822?] 3 p. NN. 8176

Brief address to the Roman Catholic congregation. See Carey,
Mathew.

A brief exposition of the fanati-
cism, false doctrines, and absurdities of the people called
Shakers..Poughkeepsie, Pr. at
the Observer's office for the author, 1822. 24 p. ICN; MH;
MWiW; NGH; NNG; NNS; NP.
8177

A brief exposition of the views
of John L. Sullivan, esq. See
Colden, Cadwallader David.

A brief memoir of the late
Thomas Bateman, M.D. physi-
cian to the public dispensary,
Carey-street; and to the Fever
Institution...who died 9th April,
1821. 1st Amer. from the 5th
London ed. New York, Mahlon
Day, 1822. 34 p. InRchE; PHi;
PPL. 8178

Brief remarks addressed to a
Catholic layman, on his late
"Address to the Rt. Rev. Bishop
of Pennsylvania..." By a Protestant Episcopalian. Philadelphia,

Bernard Dornin, 1822. 18 p.
PPL.   8179

A brief review of the origin,
progress and administration of
the Bank of the U.S. to the present time... Ed. 2... by a friendly
monitor. [Philadelphia] Repub.
Sept. 20, 1822. 44 p. PPAmP.
                                  8180
A brief sketch of the last hours
of the Rev. Solomon Allen, who
died in the city of New-York,
January 19, 1821.   Philadelphia,
Pr. by S. Roberts, 1821. Repr.
at Pittsfield, by P. Allen, 1822.
48 p.   MWA.   8181

A brief topographical and statistical manual of the state of New
York.   See Goodenow, Sterling.

Bristed, John
    Thoughts on the Anglican and
American - anglo churches...
New York, J.P. Haven; Boston,
S.T. Armstrong [etc.] 1822.
500 p.   CU; CtHi; CtY; ICU;
IAlS; MB; MBAt; MBC; MBD;
NNS; NNUT; O; RBr; ScC;
ViAlTh; ViRUT.   8182

Brooke, Mrs. Frances (Moore)
1724-1789
    ...Rosina, a comic opera...
Boston, Wells and Lilly, New-
York, A.T. Goodrich & co.,
1822. 40 p. CtY; MH; MeB;
PPL; WM.   8183

Brooks, Charles, 1795-1872
    An essay on terms of com-
munion at the Lord's table.
Windsor, Pr. for the author by
Simeon Ide, 1822. 28 p. CBPSR;
Ct; MBC; MBev; MH; NhHi;
NjPT; VtU; BrMus.   8184

Brown, Goold, 1791-1857
    Child's first book; being a
new primer... New York, Mahlon
Day, 1822. 36 p. CtHT-W. 8185

Brown, James
    An American system of Eng-
lish grammar... Designed for the
use of schools.   New York, Pub.
by the author, sold by Myers &
Smith, 1822. 252 p. TNP. 8186

Brown, John, 1722-1787
    [A short catechism for young
children.   Lexington, T.T.
Skillman, 1822] 32 p. Title
from Smith Book Company list,
No. 73.   8187

---- A short catechism, containing the most of what is necessary to be known in order to admission to the Lord's table...
Pittsburgh, Pr. by John Andrews, 1822. 80 p. OCHP. 8188

---- A brief concordance to the
Holy Scriptures of the Old and
New Testaments... Rev. and
corrected.   Hallowell, Pr. and
pub. by Goodale, Glazier and
Co., 1822. 286 p. MMeT;
MiToC.   8189

Brown, Paul
    A disquisition on faith. Wash-
ington, Pr. for the author by
Andrew Way, 1822. 168 p.
NjPT.   8190

---- An inquiry concerning the
nature, end, and practicability
of a course of philosophical education;... Washington City, Pr.
for the author, by J. Gideon,
Jr., 1822. iv, 394 p. DGU; DLC;
MH-AH; MWA; NNU.   8191

Brown, Solyman
    The birth of Washington, a
poem; in two parts.   New-York,
Pr. by Daniel Fanshaw, 1822.
16 p. CSmH; MB.   8192

---- Constitution and by-laws,
of a classical and belles lettres
academy, to be opened, at No.
20, Wall-Street, on the first

Monday in May 1822, by Solyman Brown. New York, W.
Grattan, 1822. 12, 3 p. MH.
8193

Brown, Thomas
    The timber measurer's, mer-
chant's, and ship-master's assistant; consisting of tables to
expedite the measurement of all
kinds of sawed timber... New-
York, J. Seymour, 1822. 139 p.
MB.   8194

Brown, Thomas, 1778-1820
    Inquiry into the relation of
cause and effect. Andover, pub.
and for sale by Mark Newman,
Flagg & Gould printers, 1822.
255 p. CSansS; CoCsC; CtW;
CtY-D; DeWI; ICMe; ICP; IEG;
IU; IaHa; InCW; KWiU; LNB;
MAnP; MB; MBM; MBC; MCM;
MCon; MH-AH; MWiW; MdBD;
MeB; NBLiHi; NCH; NNNAM;
NR; NbOP; NcMHi; NjPT; O;
OCIW; OO; OSW; PCC; PPB;
PU; VtWinds; WBeloC.   8195

---- Lectures on the philosophy
of the human mind... Andover, M.
Newman, 1822. 3 v. CBPSR;
DLC; GAU; IEG; InCW; KyBC;
MA; MAnP; MB; MBC; MBM;
MBU-A; MBr; MCon; MH;
MLow; MWA; MWiW; MdUM;
MeB; MeBat; MeLewB; MeU;
MiAlbC; NCH; NbHC; NcD; NjP;
OAU; OO; P; RNR; TxGR; TxU.
8196

Brown University
    Catalogue of the officers and
students of Brown University.
Oct. , 1822. [Providence? 1822]
12 p. RHi; RPB.   8197

---- Commencement. Sept. 4,
1822. [Providence, Miller and
Hutchens, printers] 1822. 4 p.
RNHi.   8198

---- Exhibition in the chapel,
Wednesday, April 17th, 1822, by
a part of the junior class. Order

of exercise... [Providence] Miller & Hutchens, printers [1822]
bdsd. MB.   8199

---- Medical School
    Circular. Medical lectures
in Brown University. [Provi-
dence, 1822] 4 p. RPB.   8200

---- Philermenian Society
    Order of exercises at the
celebration... Sept. 3, 1822.
Providence, Miller & Hutchens,
[1822] [4] p. RPB.   8201

Brownell, Thomas Church, bp. ,
1779-1865
    A sermon, addressed to the
Legislature of the state of Con-
necticut, at the annual election,
in New-Haven, May 1st, 1822.
New-Haven, Pr. by A. H. Malt-
by and co. , 1822. 23 p. CtY.
8202
---- ---- New-Haven, Pub. by
order of the legislature, J.
Barber, printer, 1822. 16 p.
Ct; CtHi; CtHT; CtSoP; CtY;
DLC; M; MB; MH; MHi; MiD-
B; NIC; NNC; NNG; NjPT;
TChU; VtU.   8203

Bruce, John
    Juvenile anecdotes: or, Au-
thentic and interesting facts of
children and youth... Albany, Pr.
by E.W. Skinner & co. , 1822.
279 p. MeBat; NjR; VtU. 8204

Bruen, Matthias, 1793-1829
    A discourse, the substance of
which was delivered in Woodbridge, the day of public Thanksgiving and prayer... New York,
Pub. at the Literary rooms, cor.
of Broadway and Pine-Street.
Abraham Paul, printer, 1822.
48 p. CtHC; CtY; ICP; LNH;
MBD; MWA; MeLewB; NN; NNC;
NjPT; NjR; PHi; PPAmP;
PPPrHi; RPB.   8205

No entry.   8206

Buck, Charles
    The practical expositor; or
Scripture illustrated by facts.
1st ed.   Philadelphia, W.W.
Woodward, 1822. 386 p.
MBNEB.   8207

---- A treatise on religious experience; in which its nature,
evidences, and advantages, are
considered.   Boston, Lincoln &
Edmunds, 1822. 264 p. GMiW;
IObB; IEG; KyLoP; MDeeP;
MH-AH; MWA; OMC; OO.   8208

---- The works of the Rev.
Charles Buck...1st Amer. ed.
Philadelphia, W.W. Woodward,
1822. 6 v. CSansS; CtW; MB;
MBGCT; MLow; MeBaT; MoSpD;
NGH; NNUT; NhD; OSW; OWoC;
ScP; TxAuPT.   8209

---- The works of the Rev.
Charles Buck...1st Amer. ed.,
compl. Philadelphia, McCarty &
Davis, 1822. 6 v. GMM; ICP;
ICU; KyLoP; MH; MMeT; MeB;
MoWgT; PCC; PPLT; PLT;
PPPrHi; PU; WvW.   8210

Buckingham, Joseph Tinker,
1779-1861, comp.
    Miscellanies selected from the
public journals. Boston, Joseph
T. Buckingham, 1822-24. 2 v.
CtB; CtHT-W; DLC; IaU; MB;
MBAt; MH; MMeT; MNBedf;
MWA; MWiW; NBLiHi; PPL;
ScU; WHi.   8211

Bulger, Richard
    The Catholic doctrine of the
blessed Eucharist, commonly
called the Lord's Supper. In a
sermon, preached in the Court
House of Newton, Sussex County,
December 2, 1821, and now published at the request of the Catholics of that district.   New-York,
Pr. by Charles N. Baldwin,
1822. 36 p. DGU; MBtS; MdBS;
NNF; NjR.   8212

Bunyan, John
    The pilgrim's progress... A
new ed. divided into chapters,
with the life of the author...
New York, Pub. by William
Borradaile, Samuel Marks,
printer, 1822. 496 p. CoSsPM;
DLC; ICP; IaDmD; KyLoP; MA;
MB; MBC; MH; NHunt; NN;
OTU; PPLT; RPB; TxH. 8213

Burder, John
    Elementary discourses, or,
sermons addressed to children.
1st Amer. ed. Boston, Samuel
T. Armstrong and Crocker &
Brewster, New York, John P.
Haven, 1822. 212 p. MB; MdBD.
                                       8214

Burge, Caleb, 1782-1838
    An essay on the Scripture
doctrine of atonement...Hartford,
Peter B. Gleason, 1822. 294 p.
CBPSR; CU; CtHT-W; CtHi;
CtW;   CtY; ICU; IaSlB; KBB;
MA; MH-AH; MWA; MeBaHi;
NNUT; NSyU; NcCJ; OO; OSW;
PPLT; PWaybu; TxDeM; VtU.
                                       8215

Burges, Tristam, 1770-1853
    Address to the Rhode-Island
Society for the Encouragement of
Domestick Industry, delivered at
Pawtuxet, October 17, 1821.
Providence, Miller and Hutchens,
printers, Aug. 1822. 29 p.
CSmH; DLC; MBAt; MH; MWA;
PPAmP; PPL; RHi; RNHi; RP;
RPB.   8216

Burk, John Daly, d. 1808
    The history of Virginia, from
its first settlement to the commencement of the revolution.
Petersburg, Va. [Dickson & Pes-
cud, printers] 1822. 3 v. AB;
CtY; DLC; IaHA; MS; NcD; Vi;
ViU.   8217

Burnap, Uzziah Cicero, 1794-
1854
   The youth's ethereal director;
or, A concise and familiar explanation of the elements of astronomy...Middlebury [Vt.] Pr.
by J.W. Copeland, 1822. 95,
[1] p. DLC; GHi; MB; MH;
MnU; PU; TxU-T; VtHi;
VtMiM; VtMiS; VtU.   8218

Burnham, Daniel
   An address by Daniel Burnham on the culture of Indian
corn. Boston, Pub. by Wells &
Lilly, 1822. 31 p. MeB.   8219

Burns, Robert, 1759-1796
   The poetical works of Robert
Burns; with an account of his
life, and his correspondence with
Mr. Thomson.   Philadelphia,
M'Carty & Davis, 1822. 2 v.
CSmH; DLC; IaCrM; MB; PLFM.
                            8220
Burrall, Thomas D.
   Address, delivered before the
Ontario Agricultural Society, at
its fourth annual meeting, Oc-
tober 22, 1822...Canandaigua,
Pr. by J.D. Bemis & co., 1822.
23 p. DA; DLC; N; NCanHi.
                            8221
Burt, Adam
   The coronation; or Hypocrisy
exposed: also Sullivans Island;
Satirical poems; with notes.
Charleston, Pr. by Duke &
Browne, 1822. 70 p. ScCleA.
                            8222
Burt, Sylvester
   Importance of true charity. A
sermon, delivered at Cornwall,
Connecticut; at the exhibition of
the Foreign Mission School, May
15, 1822...Hartford, George
Goodwin & sons, printers, 1822.
16 p. CtHi; IEG; MBC; MH-AH;
NNUT; NjPT; WHi.   8223

Butler, Alban
   The lives of the fathers,
martyrs, and other principal

saints...1st Amer. ed. Philadelphia, Pub. by Bernard Dornin, 1822. 12 v. ArLSJ; CSfU;
DGU; GDC; MdBL; MdBS; MdW;
MiDSH; NcNbN; PPCHi.   8224

Butler, Frederick
   A complete history of the
United States of America, embracing the whole period from
the discovery of North America,
down to the year 1820...Eliza-
beth-town, N.J., M. Hale, 1822.
3 v. DLC; MdBP.   8225

---- Sketches of universal history, sacred and profane, from
the creation to the year 1818 of
the Christian era: in three parts.
4th ed., continued to 1822. Hartford, Oliver D. Cooke, 1822.
412 p. CtW; CtY; IEIsP; MB;
MeB; MiGr; MiU; MnHi; NGH;
NIC; NRU; NbO; NjMD;
OClWHi; PReaHi; RWoH; T;
VtMiS; WHi.   8226

Butler, Joseph, bp. of Durham,
1692-1752
   Analogy of religion, natural
and revealed...New Haven, A.H.
Maltby & Co., 1822. 299 p.
CoPu; CtHi; CtHT; ICU;
InWefU; MB; MWA; NSchk;
NbCrD; NjP; RPat; RPaw;
TWcW; TxBry; WaU.   8227

The butterfly's ball and the grass-
hopper's feast...New-York, Pub.
by Solomon King [1822] 24 p.
NN.   8228

Buttmann, Philipp Karl, 1764-
1829
   Greek grammar, tr. from the
German of Philip Buttmann, by
Edward Everett...Boston, O.
Everett, 1822. 292 p. CtHT-W;
CtY; DLC; GDC; ICP; IaDuU;
InU; KyDC; LNT; MB; MBAt;
MH; MHi; MWHi; MWiW; MdBS;
MnM; MoSU; MoSW; NN; NNC;
NSyU; NjP; OO; OOxM; PLFM;

PPiRPr; RPB; TxGR; TxU-T;
VtU; WHi.   8229

Byerly, Stephen
   Key to American tutor's assistant improved, in which solu-
tions are given of all questions
for exercise in various rules.
Philadelphia, M'Carty and Davis,
1822. 191 p. DAU; OO.   8230

---- Byerly's New American
spelling book.   Philadelphia, Pub.
by McCarty & Davis; [New York,
Stereotyped by J. Howe] 1822.
163 p.   PLFM.   8231

Byfield Female Seminary, Saugus,
Mass.
   Catalogue of the members of
the Female Seminary, under the
care of Mr. Emerson, com-
menced at Byfield and continued
at Saugus, near Boston.   [Boston,
Crocker and Brewster, printers,
1822?] 12 p. MShM.   8232

Byron, George Gordon Noël By-
ron, 6th baron, 1788-1824
   Cain, a mystery... New-York,
W. B. Gilley, 1822. 100 p. DLC;
MB; MH; NcD; PHi; PPWa.
                                  8233
---- La profezia di Dante. (Ital-
ian and English.) Tradotta in
terza rima da L. da Ponte. 2a
ed., Nuova-Jorca, B. e W. A.
Bartow, 1822. 100 p. CtY; NN.
                                  8234
---- Sardanapalus; a tragedy.
The two Foscari; a tragedy.
Cain; a mystery.   Boston, Wells
and Lilly, Munroe and Francis,
prs., 1822. 309 p. CtHT; CtY;
MBAt; MH; MWA; MeB; NIC;
PPL; RPB.   8235

---- ---- New-York, W. B. Gilley, 1822. 155 p. DLC; GHi;
LU; MB; MeB; PPWa.   8236

---- The Two Foscari, an historical tragedy.   New-York, W.

B. Gilley, 1822. 144 p. DLC;
GHi; LNH; LU; MB; MH;
MNBedf; MWA; MdBS; NIC;
NRivHi; PPA; PPWa.   8237

C

Cabinet of curiosities, natural,
artificial, and historical. See
Goodrich, Samuel Griswold.

Caldwell, James Stamford, 1786?
-1858
   A treatise of the law of arbi-
tration; with an appendix of
precedents... 1st Amer. ed.,
imp. by a copious digested index
of American decisions. Exeter
[N. H.] G. Lamson, 1822. 496 p.,
37, xxx p. DLC; ICLaw; Ia;
IaU-L; Ky; MB; MTaB; MWiW;
MeB; NNC-L; OClWHi; PU-L;
VtBrt; WaU.   8238

Caldwell, Joseph
   A compendious system of elementary geometry... Philadelphia,
Pr. by William Fry, for the author, 1822. 391 p. NcU; TNP.
                                  8239
Camoens, Luis de
   The Lusiad; or the discovery
of India; an epic poem translated from Camoens.   Philadelphia, Pub. by Samuel F. Bradford, William Brown, printer,
1822. 381 p. CtHT; IaBo; KyDC;
KyLo; KyLx; MWiW; PPL;
PPLT; PU; PPi; RPB.   8240

Campbell, Alexander, 1788-1866
   A debate on Christian baptism,
between Mr. John Walker, a
minister of the Secession, and
Alexander Campbell, held at
Mount-Pleasant, on the 19th and
20th of June, 1820... 2d ed. enl.
Pittsburgh, Eichbaum & Johnston,
1822. 292 p. DLC; IaDmD;
InIBU; KyLxCB; LNB; MB; MBC;
MH-AH; NRAB; OClWHi; PPi;
PPiU; PPins.   8241

---- Strictures on three letters respecting the debate at Mount Pleasant. Published in the Presbyterian magazine in 1821: signed Samuel Ralston. Pittsburgh, Eichbaum & Johnston, 1822. 76 p. NN; PPM.   8242

Campbell, Archibald
A voyage around the world, from 1806 to 1812; in which Japan, Kamschatka, the Aleutian Islands were visited...3d Amer. ed.   Charleston (S. C.) Pr. by Duke & Brown, 1822. 220 p. CSmH; CtHT; NcU; ScU.   8243

Campbell, George
To the public... Philadelphia, Apr. 1, 1822. bdsd. PPL.   8244

Campbell, John, 1766-1840
The two brothers; or the history of Alfred and Galba, supposed to be written by themselves.   For the use of young people.   Boston, Lincoln & Edmands, 1822. 108 p. MB; NN; WHi.   8245

Campbell, Thomas
The pleasures of hope, and other poems... New York, R. & W. A. Bartow, 1822. 216 p. CtHT; ICartC; IU; InCW; KyLo; MB; MBC; MdBS; NjR; ScAn.   8246

Candidatus, pseud.
A letter to Mr. George Withy, offering to his consideration, and to the society of Quakers, or Friends, some reflections on hearing the sermon preached by him in the City of Burlington, N. J. in Nov. last. Philadelphia, H. C. Carey & I. Lea, 1822. 12 p. MBAt; MH; NjR; PHC; PHi; RP; WHi.   8247

[Capen, Lemuel]
Tribute of affection to John Roulstone, Jr. a member of the freshman class in Harvard University; who died February 20, 1822. Aet. 17. Boston, Pr. by J. Cotton, jr. [1822?] 15 p. DLC; MBAt; MHi; MWA. 8248

Capers, John S.
Discourse delivered in the Baptist Church, Georgetown, S. C., on Thursday the 7th of November, commemorative of the late storm on the night of the 27th Sept. 1822. [Georgetown, S. C.] Winyaw Intelligencer Press [1822?] 27 p. WHi. 8249

Capers, William, bp.
A report before the bishops and South Carolina conference of the Methodist Episcopal church, at their annual meeting, held in Augusta, February 21, 1822. Georgetown [S. C.] Pr. at the Winyaw Intelligencer office, 1822. 31 p. CSmH.   8250

Carbery, Thomas
Doubts having been entertained with regard to the truth of some rumours in circulation, relative to the conduct of Captain Thomas Carbery, during the late war, the following statements of facts, have been obtained from eye-witnesses of known veracity ... [Statements from Benjamin Burns, Thos. Foyles and Th. Sangster] [Washington, 1822] 4 p. DLC.   8251

[Carey, Henry Charles]
A complete historical, chronological, and geographical American atlas, being a guide to the history of North and South America, and the West Indies... Philadelphia, H. C. Carey and I. Lea [T. H. Palmer, printer] 1822. 236 p. C-S; IC; LU; MB; MH; MWA; MdHi; MdBL; MiD-B; NBLiHi; NWM; OO; P; PHi; PPL; PPAmP; PU; RPAt; RNR; ViU; WHi.   8252

[Carey, Mathew] 1760-1839
Address to the citizens of the
United States on the tendency of
our system of intercourse with
foreign nations. No. 1. Philadelphia, H. C. Carey and I. Lea,
1822. 8 p. MBAt; MdBP; Nj;
PHi; PPAmP; PPL.   8253

[----] Address to the Right Rev.
the Bishop of Pennsylvania, the
Catholic clergy of Philadelphia,
and the congregation of St.
Mary's in this city. Philadelphia,
H. C. Carey & I. Lea, 1822.
31 p. DLC; GAM-R; MWA;
MdBL; NjPT; PHi; PPAmP;
PPL; ScC.   8254

[----] Address to the Senate and
House of Representatives of the
United States, on the subject of
the tariff. By a Pennsylvanian.
Philadelphia, 1822. 8 p. DLC;
MB; MWA; PPAmP.   8255

---- [Announcement of an new
edition of "Appeal to common
sense and common justice." Feb.
13, 1822] 1 p. DLC; MHi.   8256

---- [Announcement of the fourth
improved edition of "Facts and
observations on the past and
present situation, and future
prospects of the United States."
Nov. 28, 1822] 1 p. DLC.   8257

---- [Announcement of the publication of the fourth improved edition of "Prospect before us: or,
Facts and observations on the
past and present situation, and
future prospects of the United
States; with a sketch of the re-
strictive systems of the principal
nations of Christendom" Philadelphia, Dec. 13, 1822] 2 l. DLC;
PHi.   8258

---- An appeal to common
sense and common justice; or,
Irrefragable facts opposed to

plausible theories... Philadelphia,
H. C. Carey & I. Lea, Feb. 4,
1822. 92 p. DLC; ICU; InU;
MWA; PHi; PPL; Vi.   8259

---- ---- 2d ed. Philadelphia,
H. C. Carey & I. Lea, Mar. 7,
1822. 112 p. CtY; DLC; MBAt;
MH; MWA; MiU-C; P; PHC;
PPAmP; PU.   8260

---- ---- 3d ed. improved...
Philadelphia, H. C. Carey & I.
Lea, April 2, 1822. 112 p.
DLC; DeGE; ICJ; MBA; MHi;
MWA; PHi; TxU; PPL.   8261

[----] Brief address to the Roman Catholic congregation wor-
shipping at St. Mary's on the
approaching election for a board
of trustees. Philadelphia, 1822.
10 p. PHi; PPAmP.   8262

---- A catalogue of books... pub.
by Mathew Carey... [Philadel-
phia] Pr. by Wrigley & Berri-
man, 1822. 65 p. MWA.   8263

---- Catalogue of the library of
M. Carey... Philadelphia, Pr. by
Joseph R. A. Skerrett, 1822. 62
p. PPAmP; PPL.   8264

[----] A defense of direct taxes,
and of protective duties, for the
encouragement of manufactures
... Philadelphia, Pub. by U.
Hunt, D. Dickinson, printer,
1822. 43 p. MH-BA; MWA;
MiD-B; RPB.   8265

[----] .... A desultory examina-
tion of the reply of the Rev. W.
V. Harold to a Catholic layman's
rejoinder. By a Catholic layman.
Philadelphia, H. C. Carey & I.
Lea, 1822. 72 p. DGU; DLC;
MBAt; NIC; PHi; PPAmP; PPL;
WHi.   8266

[----] ---- 2d ed. Philadelphia,
H. C. Carey & I. Lea, 1822. 64 p.

CSfCW; DGU; MBAt; MHi; MWA; NjPT; P; PPL; PPPrHi.   8267

[----] Desultory facts, and observations, illustrative of the past and present situation and future prospects of the United States... Philadelphia, H. C. Carey and I. Lea, 1822. 40 p. CtY. MHi; MdBP; MiU; NBLiHi; PPAmP.   8268

---- Essays on political economy; or, The most certain means or promoting the wealth, power, resources, and happiness of nations: applied particularly to the United States. Philadelphia, H. C. Carey & I. Lea, 1822. 546, [10] p. CSmH; Ct; CtHT; CtY; DLC; DeGE; GDC; GU; ICJ; ICU; IU; InNd; LU; M; MB; MCM; MH; MWA; MWH; MdBJ; MdBP; MoSpD; NB; NN; NNS; NbU; Nh; OCMtSM; OO; PPA; PHi; PP; PPL; PPi; PU; RNR; TNP; TxShA; WHi.   8269

[----] Facts and observations; illustrative of the past and present situation, and future prospects of the U. S. : embracing a view of the causes of the late bankruptcies in Boston. Philadelphia, H. C. Carey & I. Lea, 1822. 54 p. DLC; MB; MBC; MH-BA.   8270

[----] ---- By a Pennsylvanian. 2d ed. greatly imp. Ed. 2 enl. Philadelphia, H. C. Carey & I. Lea, 1822. 54 p. DLC; MB; MBAt; MH; MiD-B; P; PPAmP.   8271

[----] ---- 3d ed. , imp. Philadelphia, H. C. Carey & I. Lea, 1822. 54 p. DLC; DeGE; IU; M; MB; MWA; MdBP; PHi; PPAmP; PPL.   8271a

[----] Messrs. Gales & Seaton [A letter] [Philadelphia, 1822?] 8 p. Signed Hamilton. MH-BA;

MWA; RPB.   8272

[----] The prospect before us: or, Facts and observations, illustrative of the past & present situation, and future prospects of the United States; embracing a view of the causes of the late bankruptcies in Boston. By a Pennsylvanian. 4th ed. , imp. Philadelphia, H. C. Carey & I. Lea, 1822. 62 p. DeGE; InU; MB; MH-BA; MWA; PHi; PPAmP; RPJCB; WHi.   8273

[----] Rejoinder to the reply of the Rev. Mr. Harold to the address of the Right Reverend, the Catholic bishop of Pennsylvania, the Catholic clergy of Philadelphia, and the congregation of St. Mary's, in which are detailed the inflammatory and violent proceedings of the Reverend Mr. H. in the year 1812 whereby discord and disunion were introduced into the congregation of St. Mary's. By "A Catholic layman." Philadelphia, H. C. Carey & I. Lea, 1822. 44 p. DGU; GAM-R; MBL; MWA; MdBS; PHi; PPAmP; PPL.   8274

[----] ---- Ed. 2. Philadelphia, H. C. Carey & I. Lea, 1822. 44 p. DGU; MBAt; MWA; NjPT; PPAmP; PPL; PPPrHi; ScC.   8275

[----] Review of three pamphlets lately published by the Rev. W. V. Harold...By a Catholic layman. Philadelphia, H. C. Carey & I. Lea, 1822. 40 p. DGU; DLC; MA; NIC; WHi.   8276

[----] ---- 2d ed. corr. and imp. Philadelphia, H. C. Carey & I. Lea, Chesnut St. , 1822. 40 p. DGU; MB; MBAt; MHi; MWA; NjPT; PHi; PPAmP; PPL; PPPrHi.   8277

[----] Hamilton, No. IV. To the

editors of the National Intelligencer. 4 p. DLC. (Oct. 12, 1822)
8278

[----] Hamilton - No. 5. To the editors of the National Intelligencer. 7 p. (Dated at end Philadelphia Oct. 29, 1822) DLC.
8279

Carll, M. M.
An address, delivered before the Academy of Teachers of Philadelphia, by M. M. Carll. To which is added, The constitution of the society. Pr. by order of the Academy. June 1, 1822. [Philadelphia] The Academy, 1822. 20 p. NjPT; P; PHi; PPPrHi.
8280

Carpenter, Benjamin
An introductory catechism, by Dr. Carpenter; and also a catechism of Scripture names, by Dr. Watts. Added prayers and hymns for children. Baltimore, Baltimore Unitarian Book Society, 1822. 36 p. MB.
8281

Carpenter, Lant
An introduction to the geography of the New Testament;... (Printed to accompany Paxton's 'Illustrations of the Holy Scriptures.') Philadelphia, 1822. J. Anderson, printer. 3 folded maps, 1 map, 48 p. MB; MH-AH; NN; NSchU; PPLT.
8282

Carr, Benjamin, 1768-1831
Musical bagatelles. Sixteen easy songs, to which are added three hymns, calculated for piano forte pupils. Philadelphia, B. Carr [1822?] 16 p. PP-K.
8283

---- Nature's holiday. Philadelphia, Pr. for B. Carr [1822?] 1 l. Wolfe 1629.
8284

---- The siege of Tripoli. An historical naval sonata for the piano forte. Op. 4. Baltimore, B. Carr [1822?] 11 p. Wolfe 1653B.
8285

Carré, John Thomas
A new and expeditious method for learning the French language, exemplified by an interlined translation of words, in English, of the first six books of the Adventures of Telemachus... Philadelphia, J. Maxwell, 1822. lxxxiv, 275 p. DLC; InGrD; MB; MH; OO; TNJ.
8286

Carson, Mrs. Ann (Baker)
The history of the celebrated Mrs. Ann Carson, widow of the late unfortunate Lieutenant Richard Smyth; with circumstantial account of her conspiracy against the late governor of Pennsylvania, Simon Snyder; and of her sufferings in the several prisons in that state. Written by herself... Philadelphia, the author, 1822. 315 p. MBAt; MH; MdBP; N; P; PHi; PP; PPL.
8287

Carter, Abiel
Questions, geographical, historical, doctrinal, and practical, upon the Gospel according to St. Matthew. Trenton, Pr. by Joseph Justice, 1822. 21 p. Nh.
8288

Cary, Alpheus
An address, delivered at the installation of officers, in Massachusetts Lodge, December 26, A. L. 5821. Boston, E. G. House, 1822. 17 p. NjPT; PPFM.
8289

The case of George W. Niven, esq. ... charged with mal-practices, and suspended by order of the Court of Common Pleas, of the City of New York... Reported by William Sampson, esq. ... New York, Van Pelt & Spear, printers, 1822. 95 p. DLC; MBAt; MH-L; MoU; N-L; NIC-L; NNMus; NTSC; PPB.
8290

The case of John I. Barr, vs.
Daniel Lee... New York, E. Conrad, 1822. 34 p. DLC. NBLiHi.
8291
[Castillo, J. G.]
Espiritu de los estatutos y
reglamento de la orden franc-
masonica, y diccanario de todos
los terminos y espresiones, que
estan en uso, para los trabajos
de los logias. Dado a luz en
castellano, por J. G. C. New
York, 5822 [1822] 83 p. MH.
8292
Catechismus, oder: Kurzer Un-
terricht Christlicher Lehre...
Zweyte auflage. Reading, Gedruckt ... bey Johann Ritter und
Comp. 1822. 104, [1] p. PLERC-
Hi; PLT; PReaHi; PPPrHi. 8293

Catholic Church
Roman Missal translated into
the English language for the use
of the laity, to which is prefixed
an historical explanation of the
vestments, ceremonies etc., appertaining to the Holy Sacrifice
of the Mass, New York, William
H. Creagh, B. Bolmore, printer,
1822. cxxxiii, 588, lxix p. GDC;
ICLoy; MNS; MdBP; MdBS;
MdW; MiDU; MoSU; PPL;
PPLT; ScC; ScU.   8294

---- Ordo divini officii recitandi,
et missae celebrandae... Pro
anno MDCCCXXIII... Ad usum...
Baltimorensis. Baltimore, 1822.
Parsons 745.   8295

A Catholic layman, pseud. See
Carey, Mathew.

Catholic of the olden time, pseud.
Strictures on strictures of
William Hogan upon the Rev.
William Harold's pamphlet. Phil-
adelphia, Dornin, 1822. 16 p.
DLC; PPAmP; PHi.   8296

Cato, pseud.
To the Citizens of the state of

Mississippi. [Natchez? 1822?]
Broadside. Ms-Ar.   8297

The Cayuga County agricultural
almanack for 1823. By Andrew
Beers. Auburn, U. F. Double-
day; Utica, W. Williams, print-
er [1822] 18 ll. DLC; NAuHi.
8298
Centlivre, Mrs. Susannah,
1667?-1723
...A bold stroke for a wife.
A comedy... Boston, Wells and
Lilly; New York, A. T. Good-
rich & Co. (etc.) 1822. 87 p.
CtB; CtHT-W; CtY; ICU; MH;
MeB.   8299

---- ...The busy body, a comedy... Boston, Wells and Lilly;
New York, A. T. Goodrich & co.,
1822. 108 p. CtB; CtY; PPL.
8300
---- ... The wonder: a comedy
...Boston, Wells and Lilly,
1822. 110 p. CtB; CtY; MnU;
NjP; PPL; PU.   8301

Cerneau, Joseph
Senda de las luces Masonicas.
New York, J. Kingsland & Co.,
1822. Eastman Estate, Roslyn,
N. Y.   8302

Chalmers, George
The life of Mary, queen of
Scots, drawn from the state
papers with six subsidiary mem-
oirs. Philadelphia, Pr. and pub.
by Abraham Small, 1822. 2 v.
CSmH; CtY; DeWI; GOgU; Ia;
LU; MB; MBAt; MBL; MDeeP;
MdHi; MeAu; MeB; MiD; MoSW;
NCH; NNS; NjP; OAU; OM; P;
PPA; PPL; RP; ScC; ViAl;
ViRVal.   8303

Chalmers, Thomas
The application of Christianity to the commercial and ordinary affairs of life... Lexington,
Ky., Thomas T. Skillman, 1822.
vi, 300 p. ICP; ICU; KyBgW;

KyDC; KyU; OClWHi; TxWB.
8304
---- The evidence and authority
of the Christian revelation.
Hartford, G. Goodwin & Sons,
1822. 197 p. Ct; KyDC; KyLoS;
LNL; LNT; MdW; MiU; NhD;
NjP; OCh; OMC.   8305

---- The works of Thomas
Chalmers...Hartford, George
Goodwin and Sons, 1822. 3 v.
Ct; CtB; CtHi; CtY; GDC;
GOgU; ICT; IU; IaGG; InCW;
IaMpl; KEmC; KyBC; KyDC;
LNB; LPL; MBC; MBev; MSa;
MdBL; MoFuWC; MsJMC; NCH;
NbLU; NcCJ; O; OMC; OO;
OWoC; PPLT; RNR.   8306

Champlin, G. B.
    A history of the twenty years
of Dr. G. B. Champlin's life; or,
A reproof of heedless youth...
Geneva, N.Y., Moses Eaton, Pr.
for the editor [by S. P. Hull]
1822. 171, [3] p. MBAt; N; NN.
8307
Chandler, A., firm, New York
    Specimen of ornamental type
and printing ornaments cast at A.
Chandler's foundry, in the rear
of No. 84 Maiden Lane, New
York, 1822. 21 l. NNC-Atf. 8308

Channing, William Ellery
    The duties of children. A
sermon, delivered on Lord's Day,
April 12, 1807, to the Religious
Society in Federal Street, Bos-
ton. 5th ed. Cambridge, pr. for
the trustees of the publishing
fund, by Hilliard and Metcalf;
sold by Cummings & Hilliard,
Boston, and other agents of the
Publishing Fund, 1822. 12 p.
ICN; MAnP; MBAU; MBC;
MDeeP; MH; MMhHi; MWA;
MiD-B; NCH; OClWHi; PPL.
8309
Chapin, Stephen, 1778-1845
    The Messiah's victory. A dis-
course, delivered at the installa-

tion of Casco Lodge, North-Yar-
mouth (Me.) June 24, 1822.
Portland, Pr. by Todd and
Smith, 1822. 26 p. CtW; ICU;
MB; MBAt; MBNEB; MNtcA;
MWA; MdCatS; MeLewB;
MePFM; MeWC; NRAB; NjPT;
ViU.   8310

---- A sermon, delivered at the
ordination of the Rev. Samuel
Cook, over the Baptist Church
and Society in Effingham, N.H.
Portland, Pr. by Todd and
Smith, 1822. 36 p. CSmH; ICU;
MB; MBC; MH-AH; MNtcA;
MeLewB; MeWC; NNUT; NRAB;
NjPT; RPB; ViRU; ViU.   8311

Chapone, Mrs. Hester (Mulso),
1727-1801
    Letters on the improvement of
the mind; addressed to a lady.
A father's legacy to his daughters. A mother's advice to her
absent daughters, with an additional letter, on the management
and education of infant children.
Boston, Pub. by Leonard C.
Bowles, Pr. by J.H.A. Frost,
1822. 328 p. AzPrHi; CtHT;
GDC; KyLoS; MB; MBAt; MBC;
MBedf; MNS; NFred; NOg;
NPalK; NhD; NjR; PP.   8312

Charges and specifications
against Brevet Major Samuel Miller of U.S. Marines by Lt. Col.
Archibald Henderson; together
with the opinion and decision of
the court. Washington, 1822.
43 p. MB; NcD; P; PPL. 8313

Charless' Missouri almanac for
1823. St. Louis, Edward Charless & Co. [1822] 18 ll. MoSHi.
8314
Charleston, S.C.
    An account of the late intend-
ed insurrection among a portion
of the blacks of this city. Pub.
by the authority of the corporation of Charleston. Charleston,

Pr. by A. E. Miller, 1822. 48 p.
CtY; DLC; GHi; GSHi; MB;
MBAt; MiU-C; NBLiHi; NN;
NNC; NcU; PHi; RP; ScC; ScCC.
8315

---- ---- ---- (2d ed.) Charleston, Pr. by A. E. Miller, 1822.
48 p. DLC; ICU; KHi; MdBJ;
NN; OO.   8316

---- ---- ---- (3d ed.) Charleston, Pr. by A. E. Miller, 4
Broad St., 1822. 48 p. CtY; MA;
NcD; ScHi.   8317

---- ... Negro plot. An account
of the late intended insurrection
among a portion of the blacks of
the city of Charleston, South
Carolina.   Pub. by the authority
of the corporation of Charleston.
Boston, J.W. Ingraham, 1822.
50 p. AB; DLC; GAU; ICN; M;
MB; MH; MHi; MWA; MdBJ;
NB; NcU; NjR; OCIWHi; OMC;
PBL; RPB; ScU; TxU; WaSp.
8318

Charleston Bethel Union
    First report of the Charleston
Bethel Union... at the Mariner's
Church, Monday evening, Dec.
9, 1822.   Charleston, S. C., Pr.
by Wm. Riley, 1822. 16 p.
NjPT.   8319

Charleston Protestant Episcopal
Sunday School Society.
    The third annual report of the
Board of Managers of the Charleston Protestant Episcopal Sunday
School Society, made at the anniversary of the society, on
Whitsun Tuesday, May 28th,
1822.   To which is annexed, a
list of the officers and members
of the society.   Charleston, Pr.
by A. E. Miller, 1822. 12 p.
NNG; TSewU.   8320

Charleston, S. C.   Second Independent or Congregational Church
    The constitution of the Second
Independent or Congregational

Church, in Charleston, South-
Carolina, incorporated 13th December, 1817.   Charleston,
S. C., Duke & Browne, 1822.
(iii), xii p. KyLoS.   8321

Charlie is my darling.   A popular Scotch song.   Philadelphia,
Geo. Willig [1822?] [2] p. DLC;
MB; N; NN; PPL.   8322

---- ---- New York, E. Riley,
[1822?] 3 p. MH; MWA; RPB.
8323
---- ---- New York, Dubois &
Stodart [1822?] 3 p. DLC; MWA;
NN; PP.   8324

---- ---- Boston, G. Graupner
[1822?] p. [1]-2. DLC; MB;
MHi; MWA; NN.   8325

Chase, Enoch
    The merchants tables, containing a new and enlarged table
of advance on British sterling;
with a variety of other calculations, equally useful and applicable to the business of importers and other dealers in British
and French goods.   Boston, J.
Loring, 1822. 120 l. DLC; MH;
NN.   8326

Chase, Irah, 1793-1864
    The sentence of our Lord on
anger; a discourse in the chapel
of the Columbian College, May
19, 1822.   Washington City,
Anderson and Meehan, 1822. 16
p. MH-AH; PCC; RPB.   8327

Chase, Philander, 1775-1852
    Baccalaurate address, delivered at the annual commencement of the Cincinnati College,
September 25, 1822, by the Rt.
Rev. Philander Chase, Bishop of
the Episcopal Church and president of the college.   Cincinnati,
Pr. by Thomas A. Wilson, 1822.
14 p. ICN; LNHT.   8328

Chase, Tallman
A solemn tragedy. Tune of the Batten Kill mourners. Lines composed on the death of Hiram Cornell, of White Creek, who was drowned while bathing, in Bennington River on the twenty ninth of June, one thousand eight hundred and twenty-two. 1 p. DLC.   8329

Chazotte, Peter Stephen
Facts and observations on the culture of vines, olives, capers, almonds, etc. in the southern states...Washington, 1822. 35 p. Smith Book Co. cat., 199. Oct. 1937, p. 11.   8330

Cherry, Andres, 1762-1812
The soldier's daughter, a comedy...Boston, Wells and Lilly and A.T. Goodrich & Co., New-York. 1822. 107 p. CtY; MB; MH; MWA; PPL.   8331

Chessman, Daniel, 1787-1839
A moral catechism adapted to the capacity of children. Hallowell, Pr. by Goodale, Glazier & Co. 1822. 24 p. MB.   8332

[Child, Mrs. Lydia Maria (Francis)] 1802-1880
The first settlers of New-England: or, Conquest of the Pequods, Narragansets and Pokanokets: as related by a mother to her children, and designed for the instruction of youth. Boston, Munroe and Francis; New York, C.S. Francis [1822?] 282 [1] p. CtY; DLC; MBAt.   8333

Children's amusements...New York, Pub. by Samuel Wood & Sons; Baltimore, Samuel S. Wood & Co., 1822. 30 p. CtY; DLC; RPB.   8334

The child's instructor, and moral primer; containing, besides the stops and principal characters used in punctuation, the figures and abbreviations, early lessons in prose; among which are some very pleasing and valuable pieces of sacred history, and the Ten Commandments; likewise a brief selection from Baldwin's Fables - History of the Elephant, Whale, Ant and Silk Worm, etc. etc. Ornamented with cuts... Portland, Pr. by A.W. Thayer. For sale by William Hyde, Portland; Ezekiel Goodale, Hallowell; Thomas Pickard, Belfast; Henry Little, Bucksport; Benjamin Tainter, Brewer, Benjamin Folsom, Eastport; John Andrews, Newburyport; Harrison Gray, and Co. Portsmouth; and Richardson and Lord, Boston, 1822. 72 p. CtHT-W; DLC.   8335

The child's instructor improved; consisting of easy lessons for children, on subjects which are familiar to them, in language adapted to their capacities. By a teacher of little children. 2d ed. Montpelier, E.P. Walton, 1822. 120 p. MH-AH.   8336

China Academy, China, Maine
Catalogue of the officers and students of China Academy, November, 1822. Hallowell, Goodale, Glazier and Co., printers, [1822] Bdsd. MWA.   8337

Chipman, Daniel, 1765-1850
An essay on the law of contracts, for the payment of specifick articles. Middlebury, Pub. by the author; pr. by J.W. Copeland, 1822. 224 p. CFrCL; CStcpU; CU-Law; DLC; IaU; ICLaw; IU; LN; MB; MBAt; MH-L; MiD-B; MnU; MSaEC; MWC; NN; NRAL; OCLloyd; OCoSC; OU; PPB; PU; TMeB; TU; VtBrt; VtMiS; WaU; WU; BrMus.   8338

The Christian almanack for 1823.

Boston, Lincoln & Edmands [1822] 21 ll. CLU; Ct; CtHT-W; CtY; DLC; ICHi (ntp); ICU; InU; MB; MBAt; MBC; MDedHi; MH; MHi; MNF; MProHi; MTaHi; MWA; MeHi; MiD-B; N; NB; NT; NUt; NHi; NN; NjR; OClWHi; OMC; RPB; VtHi; VtU; WHi.   8339

The Christian almanack, for the year of our Lord and Saviour Jesus Christ, 1823... Boston, Pub. by Lincoln & Edmands, No. 53 Cornhill, for the New-England Tract Society [1822] 48 p. ICMcHi; MBevHi; MPeHi; MSha; MShr; MeHi; NRAB; NbHM; NjR; WHi.   8340

The Christian almanack for 1823. Boston, Lincoln & Edmands; Rochester, Repub. by E. Peck & Co. [1822] 24 ll. MWA (23 ll); NRU.   8341

---- By Andrew Beers. Charleston, S. C. , Charleston Religious Tract Society; S. Babcock and Co. , New Haven, Sidney's Press [1822] 24 ll. GA; ScCC.   8342

The Christian and farmers' almanack for 1823. By Andrew Beers. Burlington, Vt. , E. and T. Mills [1822] 24 ll. CLU; MWA (two varieties); VtHi. 8343

---- Washington, Davis & Force; New-England Tract Society [1822] 24 ll. DLC; NCH; OClWHi.   8344

Christian character exemplified. See Merwin, Samuel.

The Christian register and almanack for 1823. By Benjamin Doe. Portsmouth, Robert Foster [1822] 16 ll. MWA; NhHi.   8345

---- ---- Portsmouth, Robert Foster [1822] 24 ll. MB.   8346

A Christmas at Brighton; or, Four times five. A colloquial, ventriloquial monopologue. With a comic song. As represented by Mr. Mathews. New York, E. M. Murden, 1822. 18 p. DLC; ICU; MA; MH; MWA; PU.
                                8347
Chronological compendium, or History in miniature, of the most noted revolutions, wars, discoveries, calamities and events, from the flood of Noah, to the present time. Embracing a period of 4170 years. Carefully selected from the works of Josephus, Goldsmith, Robinson, and other celebrated writers. Dedham, Mass. , by H. & W. H. Mann, 1822. Broadside. CSmH; MB.   8348

Church, John Hubbard
    The progress of divine truth. A discourse delivered at the eighth annual meeting of the New England Tract Society, in Boston, May 29, 1822. 32 p. ICU; MH-AH; MWA.   8349

Church, Rodney Smith
    A digested index of the reports of the Supreme Court, and the Court for the Correction of Errors, in the state of New York, In two volumes... New York, pub. by Gould & Banks and by Wm. Gould & Co. , Albany, 1822. 2 v. CU-Law; IaBo; LNB; MBS; MiDB; MsU; NcD; NhD; NjP; NjR; PU-L.   8350

Cicero, Marcus Tullius
    ...M. T. Cicero De oratore; or, His three dialogues upon the character and qualifications of an orator. Translated into English. With notes historical and explanatory and an introduction preface, by William Guthrie... 1st Amer. ed. Boston, R. P. & C. Williams, 1822. 296 p. MB; MH; MWA; OCl; OFH;

Cincinnati Gazette
A New-Year's lay; or, Retrospect of 1822, dedicated by the carrier, to the patrons of the Liberty Hall and Cincinnati Gazette. Cincinnati, January first, 1823. [Cincinnati, 1822] 11, [1] p. DLC.   8352

The Citizen's & farmer's almanac for 1823. By David Young. Morris-Town, Jacob Mann [1822] 18 11. DLC; MBC; MWA; NHi; NjHi; NjP; NjMo; NjR; PHi.   8353

Citizens & farmers' almanack for 1823. By Joshua Sharp. Philadelphia, Griggs & Dickinson [1822] 18 11. InU; MWA; N; PHi.   8354

City guards, Boston, Mass.
Constitution... names of members and government of the corps. Boston, Pr. by Phelps and Farnham, 1822. 20 p. M.
8355

[Clark, Benjamin]
An address, to every believer in America, in which are some important questions answered, in the words of Scripture, shewing the impropriety of Christians making captains and chiefs over them, and of learning war and shedding blood. Also, some errors in doctrine exposed. Buffalo, H. A. Salisbury, printer, 1822. 47 p. N.   8356

Clark, James
To the people of Kentucky. The following pages contain the opinion of Judge Clark on the constitutionality of the "Endorsement Law," and the proceedings of the General Assembly of Kentucky against the Judge, together with his defence. [Lexington, 1822] 20 p. ICU; KyLxT;

Clarke, C. C., pseud. See Philips, Sir Richard, 1767-1840.

Clarke, Daniel, 1796-1825
An oration delivered at Warren, (Me.) before St. George's, Amity, Orient and Union lodges of Free and Accepted Masons; on the festival of St. John the Baptist, June 24th, Anno Lucis 5822 - A. D. 1822. Wiscasset, Pr. by Bro. John Dorr, 1822. 24 p. DSC; IaCrM; MWA; PPFM.   8358

[Clarke, McDonald] 1798-1842
The elixir of moonshine; being a collection of prose and poetry, by the mad poet. A great proportion of which has never before been published... Gotham [New York] Pr. at the sentimental epicure's ordinary, a. m. 5822 [1822] 150 p. CSmH; DLC; ICU; MB; MH; MWA; NBuG; NN; OO; PU; RPB; WU.   8359

Clarke, Thomas H.
To the independent voters of Vigo county. Under the influence of many of you, I have given my name to the public as a candidate for the office of sheriff, at the election in August next... Terre Haute April 8, 1822. In.
8360

[Clayton, W. H.]
A collection of psalms and hymns, for social and private worship. 2d ed. Stereotyped by E. White, New York. New York, Abraham Paul, printer, 1822. 420 p. CSmH; MB; MHi; NIC; Nh; NjMD.   8361

A clear view of the state of the Roman Catholic succursal church styled St. Mary's, in Philadelphia; deduced from facts connected with the schism in that church. 15 p. (Finotti conjectures the author as Bishop England.) DGU. Parsons 771.   8362

Cleaveland, Nehemiah, 1796-1877
An address, delivered at Bowdoin College, before the Peucinian Society, at their annual meeting, September 3, 1821. Brunswick, Joseph Griffin, 1822. 30 p. CSmH; MB; MBAt; MBC; MH; MHi; MeAu; MeB; MeBaT; MeHi; MeP; MiU; MnHi; NNC-T; NNU; PPPrHi.   8363

Cleaveland, Parker, 1780-1858
An elementary treatise on mineralogy and geology, designed for the use of pupils...2d ed. Boston, Cummings and Hilliard, 1822. 2 v. in 1. C-S; CU; CtHT-W; CtY; DLC; ICU; IU; IaDaP; InGrD; LU; MA; MB; MBAt; MBP; MH; MSaP; MWA; MdBC; MdBJ; MdBMAS; MdBS; MdHi; MdU; MeBat; MnHi; NCH; NGH; NNE; NRU; NWM; NcD; NjP; O; OSW; OrP; P; PHatU; PPA; PPAmP; PPF; PPC; PPL; PPi; RNR; RP; RPB; TxU; ViU; WM; WU-G; WyU.   8364

Cleland, Thomas
Letters to Barton W. Stone, containing a vindication principally of the doctrines of the Trinity, the divinity and atonement of the Savior, against his recent attack in a second edition of his "Address." Lexington, Ky., Pr. for the author, by Thomas T. Skillman, 1822. 172 p. ICU; KyBgW; KyHi; KyLo; KyLoP; KyLx; KyLxT; PPPrHi; TxU.   8365

The clerk and magistrate's assistant; by a gentleman of the bar. Poughkeepsie, Pr. and pub. by Paraclete Potter, 1822. 260 p. NP; NPV; WBeloC.   8366

Clifton, Arthur, 1784-1832
Forget thee! no. Philadelphia, Geo. Willig [1822?] [2] p. MH;

MWA; NN; NRU-Mus; PPL; RPB.   8367

---- O Willie brew'd a peck o' maut. Baltimore, John Cole [1822] 1 l. DLC; MdHi; MH; MWA.   8368

Clinton, De Witt, 1769-1828
Account of the Salmo Otsego; or, The Otsego basse. New York, Pr. C. S. Van Winkle, 1822. 6 p. DLC; MB; MH; MdBD; NIC; NNM; NNNAM.   8369

[----] Letters on the natural history and internal resources of the state of New York. New-York, E. Bliss & E. White, 1822. 224 p. C; CSmH; CtW; CtY; DLC; GAuY; IC; ICF; ICJ; ICW; MB; MH; MHi; MLow; MS; MWA; MdBE; MiU-C; MiD-B; MnHi; MnU; NBLiHi; NBu; NCH; NCan; NCanHi; NGH; NIC; NN; NNE; NNQ; NNS; NNia; NPtc; NR; NSy; NjN; OCHP; OFH; PHC; PPA; PPL; RP; RNR.   8370

Clowes, John
A letter on the sacred doctrine of the divine Trinity, addressed to the editors of the Christian Observer. Trenton, J. Justice, 1822. 20 p. MH-AH; PHi; PPAmP; ScCC.   8371

Cobb, Lyman
A just standard for pronouncing the English language; containing the rudiments of the English language, arranged in catechetical order...Stereotyped by A. Chandler & Co. Pr. by E. Mack, A. P. Searing, & L. Howard, Ithaca, N.Y., 1822. v, 194 p. DLC; MWA.   8372

Cock Robin
The death & burial of cockrobin. Albany, Pr. by G. J. Loomis and co., 1822. 16 p. NNC.   8373

[Cocke, Charles]
To the freeholders of Albermarle. Esmont, Va., April, 1822. 15 p. ViU.   8374

Coffin, John Gorham
A discourse on medical education, and on the medical profession. Boston, Joseph W. Ingraham, 1822. 46 p. CtY; ICU; MB; MBAt; MBM; MH; MWA; MeB; MiD-B; NNNAM.   8375

Cohen, S. I.
Elements of Jewish faith. By Rabbi S. J. Cohen. Trans. from the Hebrew. Philadelphia, W. Fry, printer, A. M. 5582, 1822. 48 p. NjPT; PU.   8376

Colburn, Samuel W.
A sermon, delivered at the funeral, of Deacon Josiah Torrey, of Abington, who died, May 14, 1822, in the 68th year of his age. Boston, Crocker and Brewster, 1822. 16 p. MAbD; MB; MBC; MWA; MiD-B; RPB. 8377

Colburn, Warren, 1793-1833
Arithmetic; being a sequel to First lessons in arithmetic. Boston, Pub. by Cummings and Hilliard, Hilliard & Metcalf, printers, 1822. xii, 288 p. CtY; DAU; ICU; MB; MH; MMal; NNC; PAtM; PHi; TxDaM; VtMiS.   8378

---- First lessons in arithmetic on the plan of Pestalozzi. With some improvements. 2d ed. Boston, Cummings and Hilliard, 1822. xx, 195 p. CtHT-W; DLC; MB; MH; MHi; NNC; NcWsHi; PPL; RHi; WWauHi.   8379

Colby College, Waterville, Me.
Waterville College. Origin, progress, and present state of the college. [Portland, Pr. at the Argus Office, 1822] 8 p. MH; MeWC.   8380

[Colden, Cadwallader David]
1769-1834
A brief exposition of the views of John L. Sullivan, esq. who holds in virtue of an act of the legislature of Massachusetts, an exclusive right to the use of steam tow boats, on part of the water of that state for forty-two years, viz: from 1814 to 1856!!! in opposition to similar rights granted by the state of New-York, to Messrs. Livingston & Fulton. New-York, Pr. by Wm. A. Mercein, 1822. 28 p. DLC; MB; MH; MiD-B; MWiW-C; N; NN; NjR.   8381

Cole, John, 1774-1855
The Seraph; a new selection of Psalm tunes, hymns and anthems, from favorite and celebrated authors... Baltimore, Francis M. Wills; New York, W. Williams (etc.) [1822] 200 p. NNUT.   8382

---- The Seraph, part second: containing a selection of anthems, choruses, hymns &c.; adapted for the use of musical societies and choirs. Baltimore, John Cole, Fielding Lucas, Jr. and E. J. Coale [1822?] 147 (1) p. ICN; NL; NNUT   8383

---- When darkness brooded o'er the deep! A masonic ode. Baltimore, John Cole [1822?] 3 p. MdHi; NN.   8384

Cole, Samuel
La libreria Masonica y general Ahiman Rezon; conteniendo una delineacion de los verdaderos principias de Framasoneria, especulativa y operativa, religiosa y moral. Compilada de los escritos de los autores mas aprobados, con notas y observaciones casuales. Por Samuel Cole... Traducida al Español por Edu-

ardo Barry. Philadelphia: De la
Imprenta de H. C. Carey y I.
Lea. Año de 1822. 2 v. NOg;
PPFM; TxWFM.   8385

Colebrook (Conn.) Congregational Church.
Records of the Congregational
Church in Colebrook; containing,
their principles of church fellow-
ship and discipline - Confession of
faith - form of covenant - rules
of church practice - their constitution as a charitable society for
aiding the missionary cause...
Hartford, G. Goodwin & sons,
printers, 1822. 16 p. Ct; CtHi;
CtSoP; MBC; MWA; OO.   8386

Coles, George
The unpardonable sin; or,
Blasphemy against the Holy Ghost
...the substance of a sermon,
preached in the Methodist church,
Hudson, N.Y. ...July 21, 1822.
Hudson, Pub. by Norman Trus-
dell; Solomon Wilber, printer,
1822. 24 p. NNMHi.   8387

A collection of admired duetts for
two German flutes.   Philadelphia,
G. E. Blake [1822?]   p. 17-
28. NN.   8388

A collection of psalms and
hymns.   See Clayton, W. H.

College of Physicians and Surgeons of the Western District of
the State of New York.
Circular and catalogue of the
faculty and students of the College of Physicians & Surgeons of
the Western District of the State
of New York in Fairfield, (Herkimer county.) Albany, Pr. by
Websters and Skinners, 1822. 8 p.
MB; N.   8389

Colman, George, 1732-1794
...The clandestine marriage,
a comedy...Boston, Wells and
Lilly, New York, A. T. Goodrich

& Co., 1822. 129 p. CtB; CtY;
DeGE; MH; MeB.   8390

---- ... The jealous wife, a
comedy...Boston, Wells and
Lilly, 1822. 116 p. CtB; CtY;
DLC; LNH; MH; PPL; TxU.
                            8391
---- The manager in distress.
A prelude...New-York, Pub. by
E. M. Murden, Circulating li-
brary and dramatic repository
(Alexander Ming, jr., printer]
1822. 12 p. CSt.   8392
[Colman, Geo.] 1762-1836
The actor of all work; or, The
first and second floor. A farce.
In one act...New York, E. M. Mur-
den, 1822. 24 p. CSt; CtY; DLC;
MA; MWA; PU.   8393

---- Blue devils; in one act.
Philadelphia, T. H. Palmer, 1822.
28 p. MH.   8394

---- The law of Java: a play,
in three acts...New-York, Pub.
by William B. Gilley, J. Seymour, printer, 1822. 105 p. MB;
MH; MWA; PU; RPB.   8395

Colman, Henry, 1785-1849
An address delivered before
the Massachusetts Agricultural
Society at the Brighton Cattle
Show, October 17th, 1821...Bos-
ton, Wells and Lilly, Court St.,
1822. 17 p. CtY; DLC; MBHo;
MH; MHi; MeB.   8396

---- A discourse on pastoral
duty, addressed to the ministers
of the Bay Association at their
meeting in Hingham, August 21,
1822. Boston, Cummings and
Hilliard, 1822. 25 p. CtY; ICMe;
MBAU; MBAt; MBC; MDeeP;
MHi; MWA; NjPT; PPL; RPB;
VtMiM.   8397

[----] Review of the "Life of
Michael Martin, who was executed for highway robbery, Dec.

20, 1821, as given by himself''
... Boston, Wells & Lilly, 1822.
12 p. DLC; MBAt; MBNEH;
MHi; MWA; NjPT; PMA.   8398

Colombia (Républica, 1819-32.)
Constitucion de la Republica
de Colombia, impresa en la
villa del Rosario de cuocta, en
agosto de 1821, y reimpresa en
Filadelfia en 1822, para Roberto
Desilver, Librario, No. 110,
Calle de Walnut, Juan F. Hurtel,
Impresor, 1822. 84 p. LNT;
MiDSH; NbU; PPL.   8399

Colquhoun, John
Catechism for the instruction
and direction of young communi-
cants. Albany, Pr. by Websters
and Skinners, 1822. 96 p. MWA.
                                8400

Colton, Charles Caleb
Lacon; or, Many things in few
words addressed to those who
think. New York, E. Bliss &
E. White, 1822. 2 v. MB; ScC;
WBeloC.   8401

[Columbian, A.]
A series of numbers addressed
to the public, on the subject of
slaves and free people of colour;
first published in the South Carolina State Gazette in Sept., and
Oct. 1822. Columbia, State Gazette office, 1822. 22 p. ScC.
                                8402
...The Columbian tragedy...
[Boston, 1822] Bdsd. NN.   8403

Colvin, J. B.
Prospectus of a new work.
Presidents' speeches, &c...to be
edited for the publishers by J. B.
Colvin...Rockville, Md., June
1822. 1 p. DLC.   8404

Combe, George, 1788-1858
Essays on phrenology, or an
inquiry into the principles and
utility of the system of Drs. Gall
and Spurzheim, and into, the ob-

jections made against it...Phila-
delphia, Pr. for H. C. Carey
and I. Lea, 1822. 463 p. CtY;
DLC; DeWI; LNT; MB; MBM;
MH; MdBM; NBM; NN; NNS;
Nh; NjP; OC; P; PPC; PU;
ScC.   8405

Combe, William
The second tour of Dr. Syntax in search of consolation: a
poem. Philadelphia, H. C.
Carey and L. Lee, Chesnut St.
1822. William Fry, printer.
274 p. CSmH; MWA; MeB; NNS;
NPalK.   8406

The comic adventures of Old
Mother Hubbard and her dog...
Baltimore, Pub. by N. G. Max-
well, 1822. 16 l. MdHi.   8407

Comly, John
English grammar made easy
...12th ed. Philadelphia, Kim-
ber and Sharpless, pr. by J.
Ashmead & Co., 1822. 192 p.
CtHT-W.   8408

---- A new spelling book. Philadelphia, Kimber & Sharpless,
1822. 168 p. IHi.   8409

Commissioners of Maryland and
Virginia Appointed to Survey the
Potomac River
Message of the governor of
Maryland, communicating the report of the commissioners appointed to survey the river Potomac. Pub. by authority. Annapolis, Pr. by J. Hughes, 1822.
92 p. CtY; DLC; DNA; MB;
MBAt; Md; MdHi; ScU.   8410

The committees vindicated: an
examination of the Rev. Mr.
Barstew's ''Remarks on the pre-
liminary history of two dis-
courses, by Rev. Aaron Bancroft,
D.D.'' Pr. at Keene, N.H., 1822.
CtSoP; CtY; DLC; ICMe; MH-AH;
MH; MWA; NN; NhHi; NjPT; RPB;

BrMus.   8411

The Common almanac for 1823.
Watertown, N.Y. [1822] [Sabin
14995]   8412

A comparative view and exhibition of reasons, opposed to the
adoption of the new constitution,
of the state of New-York.   By an
old citizen.   New York, January
5, 1822. 20 p. (Handwritten signature of B. J. Romaine on p.
20) DLC; MB; MWA; NIC; NN;
NbU; NjR.   8413

A compendious trial of the Rev.
William Hogan, pastor of the Roman Catholic Church of St.
Mary's, on an indictment for an
assault and battery, on the person of Mary Connell.   By a lis-
tener.   Philadelphia, Pub. and
sold wholesale and retail, at no.
92, South Fifth St. [1822] 48 p.
PPL.   8414

A complete historical, chronological, and geographical American atlas.   See Carey, Henry
Charles.

Comstock, John Lee, 1789-1858
    Grammar of chemistry, on the
plan of the Rev. David Blair...
Adapted to the use of schools and
private students, by familiar illustrations and easy experiments,
requiring cheap and simple instruments...Hartford, Pub. by S.
G. Goodrich [Goodsell & Wells,
printers] 1822. 250 p. Ct; CtHi;
CtHT-W; CtY; DLC; ICU;
MDeeP; NN; NNC; OCG; TxU.
                              8415
Comstock, Joshua, b. 1790
    A short history of the life of
Joshua Comstock, together with
his sufferings, rise and conversion to Christianity. Written by
himself... Providence, Pr. for
the author by Brown and Danforth, 1822. 8 p. CSmH; MB;

PHi; RPB.   8416

Conduct of George M'Duffie, esq.
See Cumming, William.

Congregational Churches in Connecticut. General Association.
    Proceedings of the general as-
sociation of Connecticut, June,
1822. Hartford, Pr. by Peter
B. Gleason & Co., 1822. 42 p.
IEG; M; MBev; MiD-B; MoWgT;
NcMHi; PPL.   8417

Congregational Churches in Massachusetts
    Extracts from the minutes of
the general association of Massachusetts, assembled at Springfield, June 25, 1822. Boston,
Pr. by Crocker and Brewster,
1822. 20 p. MA; MBAt; MiD-B;
NjPT.   8418

Congregational Churches in New
Hampshire. General Association
    Extracts from the minutes of
the general association of New
Hampshire, assembled at Pem-
broke, Sept. 3, 1822. Dover, Pr.
by J. Mann for the Association,
1822. 16 p. CSmH; KWiU; MH;
NjPT.   8419

Congregational Churches in Vermont. General Convention
    Extracts from the minutes of
the General Convention of Congregational and Presbyterian
ministers in Vermont, at their
session at Norwich, S. P. September 1822. Woodstock, Pr. by
David Watson, 1822. 16 p. KWiU;
MiD-B; NcMHi; NjPT.   8420

---- Western District
    Articles of consocation,
adopted A.D. 1798, by the Congregational Churches in the Western Districts of Vermont and
parts adjacent; and amended by
the Churches, A.D. 1822. To
which is annexed a shorter con-

fession of faith, with scripture proofs, and a covenant for the use of the churches, in receiving members to their communion. Poultney, Pr. by Smith and Shute, 1822. 23 p. CtY; MNC; MWA; NjPT; Vt; VtU.   8421

Congregational Missionary Society of South Carolina

Twentieth report of the Congregational Missionary Society of South Carolina, 1822. Charleston, William Riley, printer, 1822. 16 p. MBC; MH; NjPT.   8422

Connecticut (Colony)

The code of 1650; being a compilation of the earliest laws & orders of the General court of Connecticut... Hartford, Silas Andrus, 1822. 120 p. Ar-SC; C; CO; CSmH; CSt; CU; CU-Law; Ct; CtHT; CtHT-W; CtMMHi; CtSoP; CtY; GMWa; I; ICLaw; ICLoy; ICN; IU; IaDaP; IaGG; IaU-L; InHi; InU; KyHi; LU-L; M; MB; MCET; MH-L; MW; MWA; MWCL; MnHi; NBLiHi; NHor; NIC; NN; NNCoCi; NNLI; NNUT; NRivHi; NcD; OCLaw; OCIW; OClWHi; OHi; OO; PP; PPL; PU; ScCC; ScCliP; ScY; WNaE; BrMus.   8423

Connecticut (State)

An act concerning the students of Yale College... Be it enacted by the Senate and House of Representatives in General Assembly convened, that no person, or persons shall give credit to any student of Yale College... without the consent... of his parent or guardian; or of such officer or officers of the college... as may be authorized... to act in such cases... [New Haven? 1822] bdsd. CtY.   8424

---- Act of incorporation of the Farmington Canal Company, with the reports of the Hon. Benja-

min Wright and Andrew A. Bartow, esq. and of the committee of the Legislature of Connecticut, on that subject. New-Haven, S. M. Dutton, printer, 1822. 13 p. CtHi; CtY; MH-BA.   8425

---- Adjutant General. General orders[regarding uniform dress] Norwich, July 30, 1822. Eben. Huntingon. Adj. Gen. 1 p. DLC.   8426

---- State of Connecticut. By His Excellency Oliver Wolcott, Governor and Commander in chief in and over the State of Connecticut. A proclamation... and do hereby appoint, Friday, the fifth day of April next, to be observed, throughout this state, as a Christian fast... in the year of our Lord, one thousand eight hundred and twenty-two...1 p. Bdsd. DLC.   8427

---- ---- ---- A proclamation ...'Resolved by this Assembly, that there may be contributions in the several religious societies and congregations in this state, on the first Sabbath in May, annually... Given under my hand at Litchfield, the twenty-sixth day of February, in the year of our Lord one thousand eight hundred and twenty-two...1 p. DLC.   8428

---- Governor's message. General Assembly, May session, A.D. 1822. 1 p. DLC.   8429

---- Public statute laws of the state of Connecticut. May session, 1822. Hartford, Charles Babcock, printer [1822] 37 p. CtHT-W; CtSoP; DLC; Ia; MB; MH; MdBB; Nb; OCLaw; W.
                                   8430

---- Report of a Committee of the Legislature, on the subject of a canal by the Ousatonic Valley. [New Haven, A.H. Maltby

& Co. , 1822] 15 p. CtY; N; NN.
                                    8431
---- Report of the Committee on
the claims of Connecticut against
the United States. [1822?] 8 p.
Ct.   8432

The Connecticut almanack for
1823. By Andrew Beers. New
Haven, A. H. Maltby & Co.
[1822] 12 ll. CRedl; CtHi; CtY.
                                    8433
The Connecticut emigrant. A
dialogue, between Henry--an intended emigrant.   Mary--his
wife...By a descendant of the
Connecticut pilgrims. Hartford,
Pr. for the purchasers, 1822.
12 p. Ct; CtHi; DLC; ICU; NN;
PU; RPB.   8434

Connecticut Missionary Society
    Twenty-third annual narrative
of missions...with an account of
books sent to the new settlements,
and a statement of the funds, for
the year 1821. Hartford, Pr. by
Peter B. Gleason & co. , 1822.
23 p. CtHC.   8435

Considerations on the practicability and importance of opening a
navigation. See Derby, Conn.

Constitutional law: comprising
the Declaration of Independence;
the articles of Confederation; the
Constitution of the United States;
and the constitutions of the sev-
eral states composing the Union.
Philadelphia, Pub. by Bennett &
Walton, 1822. 133 p. NNA; TNP.
                                    8436
Conversations on chemistry. See
Marcet, Mrs. Jane (Haldimand)

Converse, James, d. 1839
    A sermon delivered in Weath-
ersfield, Vt. , at the dedication
of the Meeting-House in that town,
October 23, 1822. Windsor, W.
Spooner [1822?] 20 p. ICN;
RPB.   8437

[Converse, S. pub.]
    Memoir of Jonathan Leavitt,
a member of the Junior class in
Yale College, who died May 10,
1821. By a sister: Just pub. and for
sale here. [New Haven, Pr. by S.
Converse, 1822] Bdsd. CtY.
                                    8438
Cooke, John
    The child's monitor: or, the
dying experience of Mary Jones,
with remarks. Hartford, George
Goodwin & sons, 1822. 16 p.
OCIWHi.   8439

Cooke,   Phinehas, 1781-1853
    A sermon preached in Ac-
worth, N. H. at the dedication of
the new meeting house in that
town, December 12, 1821. Bellows Falls, Pr. by Blake, Cutler and Co. , 1822. 24 p. CSmH;
CtHT; CtSoP; ICN; MB; MH;
MH-AH; MiD-B; MNe; MWA;
NhHi; RPB; Vt; BrMus.   8440

The cook's oracle.   See Kitch-
iner, William.

[Cooper, James Fenimore] 1789-
1851
    The spy; a tale of the neu-
tral ground...2d ed. New York,
Wiley and Halsted, Wm. Grattan,
printer, 1822. 2 v. GU; MWA;
NN; PPL; PU.   8441

[----] ---- by the author of
"Precaution." 3d ed. , New York,
Wiley and Halsted, 1822. 2 v.
MBAt; NIC; NN; NNS; NcAS.
                                    8442
Cooper, Samuel, 1780-1848
    A dictionary of practical sur-
gery...With notes and an appen-
dix, by William Anderson...
From the 4th London ed.   New
York, Pub. by Collins and Han-
nay, J. & J. Harper, printers,
1822. 2 v. CU; CU-M; CoCsC;
CtY; IU; MB; MdBM; NBMS;
NNNAM; NjMD; OAlM; PPC.
                                    8443

---- The first lines of the practice of surgery, designed as an introduction for students, and a concise book of reference for practitioners... From the 4th London ed. Corr. and enl. New York, James V. Seaman, James and John Harper, printers, 1822. 2 v. CSt-L; CU-M; CtY; MB; MBM; MdBJ-W; MdBM; MoSW-M; MsU; NBM; NBuU-M; NGH; NNC-M; NNNAM; NbU-M; OC; OCG; OCo; PPC; ScCMeS; WMAM; WU-M.   8444

[Coote, Charles] 1761-1835
   The history of modern Europe, from the treaty of Amiens in 1802, to the pacification of Paris, in 1815. In a series of letters from a nobleman to his son. Being a continuation of Russell's history. Keene, N.H., J. Prentiss, 1822. 430 p. CtHT; CtY; GHi; ICP; InRch; MBC; MDeeP; MHatf; MMhHi; MS; MeB; MoSpD; Nh; NhHi; OClW; OClWHi; OUrC; BrMus.   8445

Cornelius, Elias, 1794-1832
   The little Osage captive, an authentic narrative. Boston, S. T. Armstrong and Crocker & Brewster; New York, J.P. Haven, 1822. 108 p. CSmH; CtY; DLC; ICN; KHi; MBBC; MWA; MiU-C; OClWHi; RPB; BrMus.
                              8446
The coronation, or, The merry days of King Arthur. A burletta, in two acts... New-York, E. M. Murden, 1822. 17 p. DLC; NjP.
                              8447
---- ---- New-York, Pr. by J. W. Bell, 1822. 17 p. CSmH; DLC; NN.   8448

A correct statement and review of the trial of Joseph T. Buckingham, for an alleged libel on the Rev. John N. Maffit, before the Hon. Josiah Quincy, Judge of the Municipal Court, Dec. 16, 1822

...Boston, W.S. Spear, 1822. 16 p. DLC; MBAt; MH; MHi. MoU; NNLI; PP; RP; RPB.
                              8449
A correct view of the controversy between the Congregational Association of South Carolina and the Rev. L.D. Parks. In a letter to a friend. By a friend of truth. Charleston, Pr. for the author by C.C. Sebring, 1822. 24 p. NHi.   8450

The correspondence and documents relating to the proposals for five millions of five per cent, stock of the United States, created under the Act of Congress of the 3d of March, 1821. Philadelphia, Clark & Raser, 1822. 20 p. DLC; M; MBAt; MH-BA; MHi; MWA; MdBP; MiD-B; NbU; NjPT; PPAmP.   8451

Corri, Domenico, 1746-1825
   My ain kind deary, or The lee rigg. New York, E. Riley [1822?] DLC; NN; RPB. 8452

Cottin, Mme. Marie (Risteau) called Sophie
   Elizabeth; or, The exiles of Siberia; a tale founded upon facts. New-York, H.I. Megarey and W. B. Gilley; Wm. Grattan, printer, 1822. 164 p. CSmH; NjMD; NjN; RPB.   8453

Cotting, John Ruggles, 1783-1867
   An introduction to chemistry. With practical questions... Boston, C. Ewer, 1822. 420 p. ArCH; CtHT-W; CtY; DLC; ICU; IEN-M; IaHi; KU; MB; MBAt; MBC; MBP; MDeeP; MH; MiKC; MiU-C; NCH; NNC; NNNAM; NRU-W; NTRPI; NhD; NjHoS; PU; WKenHi.   8454

Cottom's new Virginia & North Carolina almanack for 1823. By Joseph Cave. Richmond, Peter Cottom [1822] 16 ll. ViW. 8455

---- ---- Richmond, Peter Cottom [1822] 18 ll. KyBgW; ViHi.
8456

Cowley, Mrs. Hannah (Parkhouse) 1743-1809
...The belle's stratagem, a comedy...Boston, Wells and Lilly, New-York, A. T. Goodrich & co., 1822. 109 p. CtY; MH; MeB; NN; PPL.   8457

Coxe, John Redman, 1773-1864
The American dispensatory... together with the operations of pharmacy; illustrated and explained, according to the principles of modern chemistry...5th ed. Philadelphia, H. C. Carey and I. Lea. Wm. Fry, printer, 1822. 816 p. DLC; GU-M; MB; MBM; MBP; MdBM; MdW; NBuU-M; NcD; OC; PPC; PU; ScSpW.   8458

Crafts, William
Oration, on the occasion of laying the corner stone of the lunatic asylum, at Columbia, S. C. July 1822. Charleston, E. A. Miller, printer, 1822. 24 p. MBAt; NcD.   8459

Cramer's magazine almanack for 1823. By Rev. John Taylor. Pittsburgh, Cramer and Spear [1822] 36 ll. CtY; InU; MWA; OC; OClWHi; OMC.   8460

Cramer's Pittsburgh almanack for 1823. By Rev. John Taylor. Pittsburgh, Cramer and Spear [1822] 18 ll. DLC; ICHi; InU; MWA; PPi; TKL; Wv-Ar; WvU.
8461

Crandell, Daniel
The Columbian spelling book: containing the elements of the English language...Stereotype ed. Cooperstown: stereotyped, pr. and sold by H. E. Phinney, 1822. 168 p. WGr.   8462

Crawford, Samuel

Proposals for publishing by subscription, in the City of Richmond, a semi-weekly and daily newspaper to be called The Virginia Times by Samuel Crawford. Dec. 12, 1822. 1 p. DLC. 8463

Creation versified. From Genesis, 1st and 2d. [Richmond, Ind. ? 1822] 7, [1] p. Byrd 119.
8464

[Creighton, James]
Correspondence [with William Woodville. Baltimore, 1822] 7 p. MdBJ-G.   8465

Cries of New-York. New-York, S. Wood & sons (etc., etc.) 1822. 45 p. CSmH; ICU; N; PPL.   8466

The crisis, by a Pennsylvanian. See Carey, Mathew.

Crisp, Stephen, 1628-1692.
The Christian experiences, gospel labours, and writings of that ancient servant of Christ, Stephen Crisp...Philadelphia, pub. by Benjamin and Thomas Kite...New York, Sold by S. Wood & Sons [J. R. A. Skerrett, printer] 1822. 412 p. DeWI; GB; ICU; IaOskW; InRchE; LNH; MA; MB; MH; MWA; MtBuS; NBF; NNUT; NcD; NcGu; NjR; OHi; OU; P; PHC; PHi; PPF; PReaHi; PSC-Hi; WU.   8467

---- A succinct view of the primitive apostolic church, and of the religious Society of Friends, in its rise and early progress, showing its unity and harmony, the necessity and salutary effects of church discipline, etc. Philadelphia, 1822. 16 p. InRchE; MH.   8468

Crockery's misfortunes, or Transmogrifications; a burletta, in one act. New-York, E. M. Murden, 1822. 18 p. MH; NN. 8469

Crooskeen laun. A favorite
Irish ballad. Philadelphia, G.
Willig [1822?] [2] p. MWA; NN;
PHi.   8470

Cropper, Benson & Co.
  Circular on the cultivation of
cotton. Liverpool, 9 Mo. 27,
1822... [Philadelphia? Pr. at the
office of The Aurora, 1822?] 16
p. PPAmP; PPL.   8471

Cross, Robert
  An oration delivered at Newburyport, on the forty-sixth anniversary of American independence, July 4, 1822. Newburyport,
[Mass.] Pub. by W. and J. Gilman [1822] 16 p. DLC; ICN;
MAtt; MBAt; MBC; MH; MNe;
MWA; MiD-B; NcU.   8472

[Croswell, Harry]
  A pastoral letter from the
rector of Trinity church, New-
Haven, to his parishioners, on
the subject of the religious instruction of children [New Haven,
1822] 8 p. NNG.   8473

Cruft & Elston, Terre Haute
  Furs. The subscribers will
pay twenty cents in cash, or
twenty-five cents in goods, for
any number of racoon skins, delivered at their store in Terre-
Haute. Cruft & Elston. Terre-
Haute, Oct. 16, 1822. Bdsd. In.
                                   8474

[Cubi y Soler, Mariano] ed.
  Extractos de los mas celebres
escritores y poetas españoles en
dos partes. Para el uso del
Colegio de Santa Maria. Baltimore: En la imprenta de J. Robinson y se baillara de venta en la
libraria de F. Lucas, mr., 1822.
2 v. in 1. MB; MH; MdBE;
MdBP; MdBS; PPL.   8475

---- A new Spanish grammar;
adapted to every class of learners.
By Mariano Cubi y Soler... Balti-

more, Pub. by Fielding Lucas,
Jun., No. 138 Market St., J.
Robinson, printer, 1822. 443 p.
CSmH; CtW; DGU; DLC; MdHi;
MH; MdBE.   8476

Cullen, William, 1710-1790
  First lines of the practice of
physic... 2d ed., rev. and enl.
Philadelphia, E. Parker, 1822.
2 v. CSfCMS; CtY; DLC; DNLM;
GEU-M; GU-M; ICJ; ICU-R;
IEN-M; Ia; KU-M; KyLxT;
LNOP; LU; MB; MBM; MH-M;
MdBJ; MdBM; MoKJM; MoSMed;
NBM; NCaS; NNMSCQ; NNNAM;
NcD; OCG; OCU-M; OClM; TNP;
TxU-M; ViNoM; ViU; WRacSL.
                                   8477

Cullom, Ed. N.
  To the independent voters of
Crawford & Clark counties. Fellow citizens, you have no doubt
heard before this, that I was a
candidate to represent you in the
senate of this state... Your friend
& humble servant, Ed. N. Cullom.
Palestine, July 1822. Bdsd. In.
                                   8478

Cumberland, Richard, 1732-1811
  ...The West Indian. A comedy...Boston, Wells and Lilly,
1822. 119 p. CtY; MH; MeB;
NN; PPL; TxU.   8479

---- The wheel of fortune, a
comedy...Boston, Wells and
Lilly, 1822. 98 p. MeB.   8480

Cumings, Samuel
  The western navigator: contain-
ing directions for the navigation of
the Ohio and Mississippi...Philadel-
phia, E. Littell, 1822. 232,[6] p.
CtHT-W; DLC; InHi; LNHT; MA;
MBAt; MH; MWA; MiU-C; MsJS;
NN; NjR; O; OClWHi; P.   8481

[Cumming, William]
  Conduct of George M'Duffie,
Esq., in relation to an intended
meeting between himself and Col.
William Cumming: with some il-

lustrative reference to a former
affair between the same parties.
Augusta, Pr. at the Chronicle
and Advertiser Office, 1822. 38 p.
GU-De; MB; MWA.   8482

Cummings, Abraham, 1755-1827
   The harmony of Christians,
the glory of God. A sermon, delivered at Sullivan (Me.) September, 1820. 2d ed. Hallowell, Pr.
by Goodale, Glazier and Co.,
1822. 16 p. DLC; MBC; MWA;
MeLewB; NjPT; RPB; BrMus.
                           8483
Cummings, Asa, 1791-1856
   A sermon, delivered Novem-
ber 7, 1821, at the ordination of
the Rev. John A. Douglass, to
the pastoral care of the Congre-
gational church in Waterford.
Portland, Pr. by Thayer, Tappan
& Stickney, 1822. 44 p. DLC;
MBC; MH; MNe; MeB; MeBaT;
MeHi; MeLewB; NBuG; NN;
NNUT; NRAB; NjPT; PPL; RPB.
                           8484
Cummings, Jacob Abbot
   First lessons in geography and
astronomy. 3d ed. Boston,
Cummings and Hilliard, 1822. 82
p. MH.   8485

---- An introduction to ancient
and modern geography, on the
plan of Goldsmith and Guy, comprising rules for projecting maps,
with an atlas. 9th ed. New York,
Collins & Co., 1822. 322 p. MH;
NBuT; OCo; PPeSchw.   8486

---- The pronouncing spelling
book...3d ed. Boston, Pub. by
Cummings and Hilliard, Treadwell's power press, 1822. 14 p.
MH; NNC.   8487

Curiosities for the ingenious: selected from the most authentic
treasures of nature, science and
art, biography, history, and general literature. Philadelphia, H.
C. Carey and I. Lea, 1822.

[192] p. CSmH; MBAt; MH;
MdBP; NN; OCl; ScSoh.   8488

Cushing, Caleb
   An oration, pronounced at the
request of the Washington Light
Infantry Company, in Newbury-
port, July 24, 1822, in com-
memoration of the company's
22d anniversary. Newburyport,
E.W. Allen, 1822. 14 p. MBAt;
MH; MHi; MNe; MWA; PHi.
                           8489
Cushman, Robert
   A sermon, describing the sin
and danger of self-love.
Preached at Plymouth, in New-
England, 1621. From an old edi-
tion. Stockbridge, Pr. by
Charles Webster, 1822. 40 p.
Ct; CtHT-W; CtY; DLC; ICN;
MBC; MHi; MPiB; MPlyP;
MWA; MiD-B; NN; NjPT;
PPPrHi; RPJCB; Vt.   8490

D

D. Heartt's North-Carolina almanac for 1823. By H.M. Cave.
Hillsborough, N.C., D. Heartt
[1822] 18 ll. DLC.   8491

Daboll, Nathan
   Schoolmaster's assistant...a
plain...system of arithmetic...
ed. by Green. New London, S.
Green, 1822. 240, [12] p.
CtHT-W.   8492

The dairyman's daughter. See
Richmond, Legh, 1772-1827.

Dalcho, Frederick
   An ahiman rezon, for the use
of the Grand lodge of ancient
Free-masons of South-Carolina,
and the lodge under register and
masonic jurisdiction thereof. 2d
ed. Charleston, S.C., Bro. C.
C. Sebring, 1822. 250 p. GDC;
NCH; NN; ScRhW; ScU.   8493

Dame Dearlove's ditties for the

nursery; To be either sung or said by nurse or baby. Baltimore, F. Lucas, Jr., 1822. 16 l. MdBE. 8494

Dana, Daniel, 1771-1859
North-Yarmouth, May 23, 1822. In consequence of letters missive from the Chapel Church in North-Yarmouth, under the care of Rev. Noah Cresey, and the First Church under the care of Rev. Asa Cummings, an ecclesiastical council convened at the house of Rev. Asa Cummings, May 22, 1822. 8 p. MWA. 8495

Dana, James Freeman, 1793-1827
Report on a disease afflicting neat cattle, in Burton, N.H. Read before the New-Hampshire Medical Society, June, 1822. Concord, Pr. by Hill and Moore, 1822. 8 p. MH-M; MHi; MWA; Nh; Nh-Hi; BrMus. 8496

Dana, Nathan
Prospectus, or Concise view of "A general abridgement and digest of American law." Salem, W. & S.B. Ives [1822] 13 p. DLC. 8497

Dana, Samuel, 1778-1864
A sermon delivered at the installation of the Rev. Daniel Dana, D.D. to the pastoral care of the West Presbyterian Church and congregation in Londonderry, January 16, 1822. Newburyport, Pr. by W. & J. Gilman [1822] 23 p. MA; MBC; MH; MiU-C; RPB. 8498

Danforth, Walter Raleigh
An oration delivered before the Providence Association of Mechanicks and Manufacturers, April 8, 1822, being the anniversary of the election of officers. [Providence] Miller and Hutchins, 1822. 24 p. CtY; MH-BA;

RPB. 8499

Daniell, Lewis
An appeal to his fellow-citizens. Charleston, Pr. by Duke & Browne, 1822. 57 p. MBAt. 8500

Dante Alighieri
The vision; or Hell, purgatory and paradise of Dante Alighieri. Translated by the Rev. Henry Francis Carey. Philadelphia, M'Carty & Davis, printers. Pub. by Samuel F. Bradford, for John Laval, Philadelphia; James Eastburn, New York; and Charles Ewer and Timothy Burlington, Boston, 1822. 2 vols. ICU; KyDC; KyLx; MB; MMidb; MWA; MdBL; MiOC; TxH. 8501

Darley, William Henry Westray, d 1858?
On a bright sunny morn. A ballad. Composed with an accompaniment for the piano forte. Philadelphia, G. Willig, 1822. 3 p. DLC; NN PPL. 8502

Darrow, Pierce
Cavalry tactics: comprising the modern mode of discipline and sword exercise, for the cavalry generally... Hartford, Oliver D. Cooke [Peter D. Gleason & Co., printers] 1822. 155 p. DLC; NWM; PMA; PWmp. 8503

---- National militia standard, embracing the discipline of infantry, light infantry, riflemen, light artillery, horse artillery, cavalry. Prepared in conformity to Gen. Scott's Regulations for the army established by Congress. Hartford, O.D. Cooke, 1822. 2 v. CtY; DLC; MBAt; MH. 8504

Dartmouth College
A catalogue of the officers and students of Dartmouth College, Hanover, New Hampshire, October, 1822. [Hanover? 1822]

13 p. MHi; MeB; Nh; OCHP.
8505

---- Catalogus Senatus Academici Collegii Dartmuthensi in Republica Neo Hantoniensi, Eorumque omnium, qui eodem munera et officia gesserunt... Portimuthi, Typis Tobiae Ham Miller, 1822. 35 p. DLC; M; MBNEH; MHi; MeB; MeBat; MeHi; MeLewB; NjPT.   8506

---- Laws of Dartmouth College, for the use of the students. Haverhill, N.H., Pr. by Sylvester T. Goss, 1822. 21 p. GDC; M.   8507

---- Society of Social Friends. Catalogue of the members of the Society of Social Friends, Dartmouth College, May, 1822. Haverhill, N.H., Pr. by Sylvester T. Goss, 1822. 31 p. DLC; Nh-Hi.   8508

[David] pseud.
Mount Carmel, February 1822. [New Haven, Conn., Patten, printer, 1822] 40 p. Signed: David, your friend. CSmH. 8509

Davies, Samuel, 1724-1761
A sermon on the sacred import of the word Christian. Portsmouth, N.H., Christian Herald, 1822. 12 p. NN.   8510

Davis & M'Carty's agricultural almanac for 1823. By John Ward. Wheeling, Va., Davis & M'Carty [1822] 18 ll. OCIWHi; PWW.
8511

Davis & M'Carty's magazine almanac for 1823. By John Ward. Wheeling, Va., Davis & M'Carty [1822] 30 ll. MnHi; NBuG. 8512

[Davison, Gideon Miner] 1791?-1869
The fashionable tour: or, A trip to the Springs, Niagara, Quebeck, and Boston, in the summer of 1821. Saratoga Springs, G.M. Davison, 1822. 165 p. 1st ed.   DLC; MBC; MiU-C; PPL.   8513

Davy, John, 1763-1824
Tho' you leave me. Baltimore, Carr [1822?] [2] p. MdHi.
8514

Dawn of day. The words written and music expressly arranged for these numbers.   Philadelphia, B. Carr [1822?] 1 l. Wolfe 2346.   8515

Day, Anthony
New York, 20th March, 1822. In answer to correspondents on the subject of hemp and flax, and the machine to dress the same in an unwretted (commonly called unrotted) state, I deem it advisable to send them all that I have written on the subject...[New-York, 1822] 15 p. DLC.   8516

Day's New-York miniature almanac for 1823.   New-York, M. Day [1822] 12 ll. MWA; NN; OCIWHi.   8517

Deaf and dumb, from the Columbian Observer, Apr. 20, 1822. [Philadelphia, 1822] bdsd. PPL.
8518

Deaf and dumb school.   See Antipersecutor, pseud.

Dean, Joseph C.
Truth vindicated, in a letter to a friend; shewing the nothingness of the soul in divine things in an uninspired state.   Poughkeepsie, Pr. for the author, 1822. 33 p. MNBedf.   8519

Deane, Samuel, 1733-1814
The New England farmer; or, Georgical dictionary...3d ed., cor., improved, greatly enl. Boston, Wells and Lilly, 1822. 532 p. CU; CtHT-W; DA; FWpR; ICJ; InLPU; M; MB; MBHo;

MH; MHi; MMe; MNBedf; MNe; MW; MWA; MWHi; Me; MiU; MnU; NB; NBLiHi; NNNBG; PP; PPL; PU; RNR; ViL; WHi; WU-A. 8520

The death bed of a free-thinker, exemplified in the last hours of the Hon. Francis Newport, son to the late Lord Newport. [Andover, Pr. for the New England tract society, by Flagg and Gould, 1822] 16 p. DLC; MTaHi. 8521

Dedham, Mass.-First Church

A brief summary of Christian doctrine and a form of covenant adopted by the First Church in Dedham, March 9, 1821, and publicly read on the admission of members. Dedham, B. Field, 1822. 23 p. MB; MBAt; MH; MHi; MMal; MWA; PHi. 8522

Defence of the Exposition of the Middling Interest, on the right of constituents to give instructions to their representatives and the obligation of these to obey them. Boston, July, 1822. 16 p. (Written as a supplement to the author's "Exposition of the Middling Interest.") ICU; LNH; M; MBAt; MH; MHi; MWA; NNC; OCLaw; PPL. 8523

A defense of direct taxes. See Carey, Mathew.

De Foe, Daniel, 1661-1731

The real Robinson Crusoe: or, History of Alexander Selkirk. New Haven, J. Babcock and Son, and S. Babcock and Co., Charleston, S. C., Sidney's press, 1822. 30 p. MWA. 8524

Deigendesch, Johannes

Nachrichters nützliches und aufrichtiges Pferd-Arzeneybuch... Harrisburg, Gedruckt bey Johann S. Wiestling, 1822. 213 [3] p.

MiU-C; OClWHi; P; PST; PU-V. 8525

Delano, Judah

Proposals, by Judah Delano, for publishing a directory for the City of Washington, showing the name, occupation, and residence of each head of a family, and person in business. To which will be added, a complete city register... Washington, July 1822. 1 p. DLC. 8526

---- The Washington directory, showing the name, occupation, and residence, of each head of a family and person in business; the names of the members of Congress, and where they board; together with other useful information. Washington, Pr. by W. Duncan, 1822. 148 p. DLC; DGU; DWP; MdBP; MeB; MiU-C; MiU; TJoT. 8527

Delaware (State)

Journal of the House of Representatives of the State of Delaware, commenced and held at Dover, on Tuesday the first day of January, in the year of our Lord one thousand eight hundred and twenty-two. Dover, Del., Augustus M. Schee, 1822. 255, 28 p. DeHi. 8528

---- Journal of the Senate of the state of Delaware, at the annual session, held at Dover, in the year of our Lord, one thousand eight hundred and twenty-two... Dover, Del., Augustus M. Schee, printer, 1822. 127, 23 p. DLC; DeHi; IU; MWA. 8529

---- Laws of the state of Delaware, passed at a session of the General assembly, begun and held at Dover, on Tuesday the first day of January, in the year of our Lord one thousand, eight hundred and twenty-two. Dover,

Augustus M. Schee, 1822. 125-248, 12 p. L; MdBB; Nb; Nj; O; T; W. 8530

The Delaware and Maryland almanac for 1823. Wilmington, J. Wilson [1822] 18 ll. DeHi; MWA; PHi. 8531

Deming, Calvin
An address, delivered before the Chittenden County Medical Society, at Burlington, Feb. 26, 1822. Burlington, Pr. by J. Spooner, 1822. 16 p. (Gilman, p. 72) 8532

Deming, Leonard, 1787-1853
The uncertainty of obtaining justice by the law; or, A history of 292 hens' eggs, to which is added a short account of the new method of hatching them without the use of animal heat. Middlebury [the author] 1822. 16 p. DLC; MBC; VtHi; VtMiS. 8533

Demme, Karl Rudolph, 1795-1863
Gesänge bey der Antrittspredigt unsers vielgebieten Lehrers ... Philadelphia, Conrad Zentler, 1822. 8 p. PHi; PPG; PPLT; PU. 8534

Denman, Thomas
Aphorisms on the application and use of the forceps and vectis; on preternatural labours; on labours attended with hemorrhage, and with convulsions. From the 7th London ed. Boston, Wells & Lilly, 1822. 95 p. DNLM; MB; MdBM; NBMS; NBuU-M; ViRMC. 8535

Dennant, J.
The Sabbath scholar. Andover, Pr. by Flagg & Gould, 1822. 12 p. MeB. 8536

Denniston, Alexander
The Christian's gain, a discourse, occasioned by the death of John S. Gano, formerly major general of the first division of Ohio militia; preached at Covington, Kentucky, on Lord's Day, January 20th, 1822... Cincinnati, Looker & Reynolds, printers [1822] 31 p. OCHP. 8537

Denny, Nathaniel P.
Address delivered before the Worcester Agricultural Society, September 25, 1822, being their anniversary cattle show and exhibition of manufactures, Worcester, W. Manning [1822] 24 p. MH; MWA; MWHI; MiD-B; NjPT; RPB. 8538

Derby, John Barton, 1793?-1867
An address (prefatory to the reading of the Declaration of Independence)... and an oration by Silas P. Holbrook, delivered before the inhabitants of Medford, July 4, 1822. Dedham, H. & W. H. Mann [1822] 20 p. CtSoP; MB; MBC; MH; MHi; MWA; PPL; RPB. 8539

Derby, Conn. Citizens
Considerations on the practicability and importance of opening a navigation to the interior of the state by the Housatonick River. [New Haven, A. H. Maltby & co., print., 1822] 12 p. CtY. 8540

Description of the Great Western Canal in a letter from a traveller-Saratoga-1822. Hill, William H., Press in Washington, Saratoga and Warren Counties, N. Y., 1930. Page 78. 8541

Description of the panorama of the Palace and gardens of Versailles. Painted by Mr. Vanderlyn. The original sketches of which were taken on the spot, by him in the Autumn of 1815. New York, Pr. by E. Conrad, 1822. 23 p. NKingS. 8542

A desultory examination of the reply of the Rev. W. V. Harold. See Carey, Mathew.

Desultory facts, and observations, illustrative of the past and present situation and future prospects of the United States.   See Carey, Mathew.

Dewey, Charles
Fellow citizens of the first congressional district.   The extraordinary malicious, and false attack, which has been made upon my political character, and I may say, upon my private reputation, has induced me, to lay before you, the following evidence.   Vincennes, 29th July, 1822.   Broadside.   In.   8543

---- To the electors of the first congressional district.   Fellow-citizens, duty again prompts me to make an appeal to your sense of justice, in defence of my character, as a candidate for your support, at the ensuing congressional election... July 18th, 1822.   Bdsd.   In.   8543a

---- To the voters of the first congressional district.   Fellow citizens, the period will shortly arrive, when your duty to your country will again call you to the polls... Vincennes, July 5, 1822. Bdsd.   In.   8543b

Dialogue between Calvin, Hopkins & Arminius.   New York, Pr. for the reader, 1822. 16 p. ICMe; MBC.   8543c

A dialogue between Steady and Candid, about going to church; altered from a religious tract published in England... and now re-published with further alterations and additions... New York, The Protestant Episcopal Tract Society, H. J. Swords, printer,

1822. 19 p. NNG; NjR.   8543d

Dibdin, Thomas, 1771-1841
The Pirate, a melodramatic romance, in three acts... Baltimore, Pr. and pub. by J. Robinson, 1822. 57 p. L; MB; MH; MWA; NN; NjP; PU; WGrNM.
8544
Dickinson College, Carlisle, Pa.
Statutes of Dickinson College, in Carlisle, Penns'a.   Enacted by the Board of trustees, February 15, 1822.   To which is annexed the rules for the government of the steward; an account of the expenses; and the rules of the grammar school.   Carlisle, Pr. by W. B. and J. Underwood [1822] 25 p. DLC; P.   8545

[Didier, Franklin James] 1794-1840
Franklin's letters to his kinfolk, written during the year 1818, '19 & '20, from Edinburgh, London, the Highlands of Scotland, and Ireland... Philadelphia, J. Maxwell, 1822. 2 v. CtB; DLC; MBBC; MWA; MdHi; NNS; PPA; PPL; ViAl.   8546

A digested index to the nineteen volumes of Mr. Vesey's reports of cases in the High Court of Chancery, with a table of the names of the cases.   By a barrister.   Philadelphia, H. C. Carey and I. Lea, [Pr. by J. R. A. Skerrett] 1822. 461 p. Ky; KyLxFL; KyLxT; MdUL; MiDU-L; NSsSC; NUtSC; Nm; P; PP; PScrLL; PWWL; ViU; WOshL; WvW-L.   8547

Dilworth, Thomas, d. 1780
Dilworth's book-keepers' assistant: shewing, in the plainest and easiest manner, the Italian method of stating debtor and creditor ... New York, J. C. Totten, 1822. 137 p. CtHT-W; DLC; MH; MiDT; MiU; NNC.   8548

Dilworth, Thomas, d. 1780
New guide to the English tongue in five parts. Wilmington, Porter, 1822. 108 p. DeWi; IU; MWA.   8549

Dimond, William
Aethiop; or, The child of the desert; a romantic play, in three acts. Philadelphia, Palmer, 1822. 75 p. CSmH; NCH; NN.   8550

---- The brother and sister. A petit opera, in two acts. New York, E. Murden, 1822. 36 p. LNH; MH; MWA; NCH; PU.   8551

Directory and stranger's guide for the City of Charleston...
Charleston, S.C., Pr. by Archibald E. Miller for James R. Schenck [1822] 51 p. ScC.   8552

The distrest mother.   See Racine, Jean Baptiste.

Dobell, John
A new selection of nearly eight hundred evangelical hymns, from more than 200 authors in England, Scotland, Ireland and America...Morris-Town, Pub. by P.A. Johnson, J. Mann, printer, 1822. IObB; InFtwL; MB; MdBB; NjMD; NjPT; OCoC; OO; PAle.   8553

Dobson, firm, booksellers, Philadelphia. (1822 T. Dobson & J. Dobson)
A catalogue of books, in the various departments of ancient and modern literature, being some of the most numerous of the stock of the late firm of Thomas Dobson & son; now offered to the trade on the most liberal terms by T. Dobson & J. Dobson... [Philadelphia] 1822. 19 p. DLC.   8554

The doctrine of Christian perfec-

tion an evincing proof that God is love.   By a friend of truth. 2d ed.   Portland, Pr. by Thayer, Tappan and Stickney, for the author. 1822. 31 p. MBNMHi; NjPT.   8555

Documents and facts, showing the fatal effects of interments in populous cities. See Allen, Francis D.

Documents shewing that Mecklenburg County, North-Carolina, declared her independence of Great-Britain, May 20, 1775. Copied from the Raleigh register. Raleigh, Pr. by J. Gales & son, 1822. 15 p. DLC; NcU; ViU; WHi.   8556

Doddridge, Philip, 1702-1751
Practical discourses on regeneration, in ten sermons, preached at Northampton...7th ed. Boston, Pub. by Charles Ewer & Timothy Bedlington, 1822. [Thomas Badger, Jr., printer] 1822. 264 p. GAGTh; ICT; KyLoP; MB; MH; MNe; MdBS; MeB; MeLewB; MoMM; NbOP; NcCJ; NhPet; PLT; PPLT; OCIW; OO; ScNC.   8557

---- The rise and progress of religion in the soul. Boston, Timothy Bedlington [Concord, N.H., Hill & Moore, printers] 1822. 294 p. CtHT; CtY; GDC; ILM; KBB; MB; MH; MWA; NcBe; PLT.   8558

Doddridge, Philip, 1702-1751
The rise and progress of religion in the soul. Providence, Joseph McIntire, 1822. 294 p. MeLewB; RNHi.   8559

Doe's Newtonian almanack, and agricultural and miscellaneous repertory for 1823.   By Benjamin Doe. Portsmouth, Harrison Gray & Co., Exeter, S.T. Moses, printer [1822] 12 ll.

NjR.   8560

Doe's Newtonian almanack, and
astronomical ephemeris for 1823.
By Benjamin Doe. Portsmouth,
Harrison Gray & Co., Exeter,
S. T. Moses, printer [1822] 24 ll.
DLC; InU; MWA; NhHi.   8561

Domestic Missionary Society
    Proceedings of a convention
of delegates for the formation of
a Domestic Missionary Society.
(Colophon:) J. Seymour, printer.
[New York, 1822] 16 p. NHi; NN.
                        8562
Domestic Missionary Society of
Connecticut.
    Sixth annual report of the di-
rectors of the Domestic Missionary Society of Connecticut for the
year ending June, 1822. New-
Haven, Pr. by Nathan Whiting.
1822. 11 p. CtHi.   8563

Donaldson, Peter
    Medical advice to European
emigrants, residing in the Continent of America. New York,
The author, 1822. 12 p. NN.
                        8564
---- The natural history of the
rise, progress and termination of
the epidemic inflammation, commonly called yellow malignant
fever, which prevailed in the city
of New-York, during the autumn
of 1822... New-York, The author,
1822. 36 p. DLC.   8565

Donnelly, Nicholas
    Synopsis of Latin grammar; or,
An easy introduction to the Latin
tongue... 1st Amer. ed. Philadelphia, Probasco, 1822. 19 p.
NNC.   8566

Douglas, James
    A statement of facts, relative
to the session of the Reformed
Presbyterian Church, New-York,
and the writer, James Douglas.
New-York, Pr. by E. Conrad,

1822. 23 p. MB.   8567

Dow, Lorenzo
    The stranger in Charleston!
or The trial and confession of
Lorenzo Dow... 2d ed. Boston,
Pr., Philadelphia, re-pr. for
the purchaser, 1822. 93[1] p.
DLC; NRivHi; PPL; RHi. 8568

Drake, Daniel, 1785- 1852
    A narrative of the rise and
fall of the Medical College of
Ohio, by Daniel Drake, M.D.,
late president of the institution.
Cincinnati, Ohio, Looker & Reyn-
olds, printers, 1822. 42 p. DLC;
DNLM; MH; MH-AH; MHi;
NNNAM; OCG; OCHP; OCIM;
OCIWHi.   8569

Drink to me only with thine eyes.
A glee. New York, E. Riley
[1822?] 1 l. MH; NN; NRU-
Mus; RPB.   8570

Drown, William, 1793-1874
    An appeal in favor of Sunday
schools; with directions for their
management... Cincinnati, Pr. at
Harrison's Press, 1822. 65, [1]
p. ICP; OCHP.   8571

Drury, Luke
    A geography for schools, upon
a plan entirely new... Providence,
Pr. by Miller and Hutchins, 1822.
42 p. maps. CtHT-W; CtY; DLC;
NBu; PU; RHi; RPB; WGr.
                        8572
The Dublin mail, or Intercepted
correspondence. To which is
added, a packet of poems. By
Thomas Moore. New York, H. I.
Megarey, 1822. 135 p. (Erro-
ously attributed to Thomas Moore
in this American reprint.)
GSTA; MB; MBAt; MH.   8573

Dudley, J. M.
    The soldiers' companion...
Amherst, N.H., Pr. by Elijah
Mansur, 1822. 75 p. MWA. 8574

Dunlap, Andrew, 1794-1835
An oration, delivered at the request of the Republicans of Boston, at Fanueil hall, on the fourth of July, 1822. Boston, Pr. at the office of the American statesman by True and Greene, 1822. 24 p. CtY; DLC; MB; MBAt; MBC; MBNEH; MH; MWA; MnU; NNC; PHi; RPB.
8575

Dunn, William
The farmer's daughter, an authentic narrative... Boston, S. T. Armstrong and Crocker & Brewster; New York, J. P. Haven, 1822. 108 p. MB.   8576

Du Ponceau, Peter Stephen
Notes and observations on Eliot's Indian grammar, addressed to John Pickering. Boston, John Eliot, Jun., 1822. 9 p. RPB.   8577

Duport, P. L.
Academician and professor of dancing, respectfully informs the citizens of Williamsburg and its vicinity... Norfolk, Va., Shields, Ashburn & Co., prs. [1822] bdsd. ViW.   8578

The Dutchess County farmer's almanack for 1823. By Andrew Beers. Poughkeepsie, P. Potter [1822] 18 ll. MWA; N; NHi; NP.   8579

Dwinel, John
Remarks, by John Dwinel, of cultivating a piece of land which was unusually productive. Boston, Pub. by Wells & Lilly, 1822. 3 p. MeB.   8580

Dyer, Mary (Marshall) See Marshall, Mary, b. 1780

Dyer, Samuel, 1785-1835.
(Selection of anthems) Dyer's second ed. of a selection of upwards of sixty favourite and approved anthems, set pieces, odes and choruses from the works of the most esteemed authors... Baltimore, Pr. for the author [c1822] 204, 24 p. CtW; ICN; MB.   8581

E

Early piety; or, memoirs of children... Hudson, Pub. by Wm. E. Norman. W. B. Stebbins, printer, 1822. 54 p. NN. 8582

Eastburn, James & co.
A catalogue of books, including two private libraries, now on sale, at the Literary rooms, at the prices affixed. New York, Pr. by Abraham Paul, 1822. 213 p. DLC; MH; MiU-C; OO.
8583

Eastman, Moses
A discourse delivered before the Hillsborough Agricultural Society, at Amherst, N. H. September 25, 1822. Amherst, Pr. by Richard Boylston, for the Society. 1822. 24 p. DLC; ICJ; MBAt; MBC; Nh; Nh-Hi; NjR; OCIWHi.   8584

Eastport, Maine. Female Benevolent Society
Constitution and subscribers' names of the Female Benevolent Society. Eastport, Benjamin Folsom, printer. 1822. 8 p. Williamson 3024.   8585

Eaton, Amos, 1776-1842
Chemical instructor: presenting a familiar method of teaching the chemical principles and operations of the most practical utility to farmers, mechanics, housekeepers... Albany, Websters and Skinners, 1822. 231 p. CtHT-W; CtY; DeGE; ICU; MH; MdBJ-W; N; NT; NTR.   8586

[----] Geological and agricultural survey of Rensselaer county,

in the state of New York, to which is annexed a geological profile, extending from Onondaga Salt Springs, across said county, to Williams College in Massachusetts... Albany, Pr. by E. & E. Hosford, 1822. 70 p. [pamphlet] CSmH; CtY; DLC; ICJ; ICU; MB; MBAt; MH; MHi; MPiB; MWA; MWiW; MdBJ; MoSHi; N; NBLiHi; NCH; NIC; NHi; NN; NNM; NNMuCN; NNNAM; NNNBG; NRom; NSyU; Nh-Hi; NjR; NjPT; PHi; PPL; ScC.   8587

---- Manual of botany, for the northern and middle states of America... 3d ed. , rev. and corr. Albany, Websters and Skinners, 1822. 536 p. CSt; CtHT; ICF; InNd; MB; MBAt; MH; MeU; MiD-B; N; NBM; NIC; NNC; NNMSCQ; NNNAM; NRU; NSyU; NTR; Nh; OCLloyd; OCIW; PPAN; PPL; RP; RPB; VtMiS; ViRU; WHi; WU.   8588

[----] To gentlemen residing in the vicinity of the Erie Canal. [Albany, N.Y. ? 1822] 10 p. (Signed at end: Amos Eaton. Troy (N.Y.) Dec. 13, 1822) MB.
                                          8589

Eberle, John, 1787-1838
   A treatise of the materia medica and therapeutics... Philadelphia, J. Webster, 1822 -23. 2 v. CtY; CSt-L; IEN-M; Ia; KyLxT; MBU-M; MdBM; MdUM; NBM; NNC-M; NNNAM; OCLloyd; P; PPC; PPHa; ViRMC.   8590

Eckartshausen, Karl von, 1752-1803
   Gott ist die reinste Liebe, oder Morgen- und Abend-opfer, in Gebeten, Betrachtungen und Gesangen. Ein gemeinschaftliches Gebet-Buch, bestehend in auszugen aus Witschels und Eckartshausen Gebatbuchern. Reading, Pa. , C. M'Williams & comp. , 1822. 300

p. DLC; MH; Mn; NNUT; P; PHi; PLT; PPLT; PPG; PPL; PPeSchw; PReaHi; PU.   8591

The economical hydrostatic Lift. See Kenworthy, William.

[Eddy, Thomas] 1758-1827
   [Facts and observations illustrative of the rise and progress of the present state of Society in New York. Philadelphia? 1822?] 10 p. MH.   8592

Eden, Robert Henley. See Henley, Robert Henley Eden, 2d baron.

Edgeworth, Maria, 1767-1849
   Frank, a sequel to Frank in Early lessons... Printed for the trustees of the publishing fund, by Hilliard and Metcalf, Cambridge. Sold by Cummings & Hilliard, Boston and other agents of the Publishing Fund. 1822. 2 v. MB; MH; PMA.   8593

---- Frank: a sequel to Frank in Early lessons... New York, W. B. Gilley, 1822. 2 v. DeGE; MH; ScCliTO.   8594

---- Tales of fashionable life. Six volumes in two. Philadelphia, and Trenton, Littell, etc. , 1822-23. 2 v. GS; IaU; MH; MWA; NNS.   8595

---- Works of Maria Edgeworth. Complete in thirteen volumes. Boston, Samuel H. Parker, Munroe and Francis, printers, 1822-25. 13 v. MeB.   8596

Edmund and Margaret; or sobriety and faithfulness rewarded. Printed for the Trustees of the Publishing Fund, by Hilliard and Metcalf, Cambridge. Sold by Cummings & Hilliard, Boston, and other agents of the Publishing Fund. March, 1822. 60 p. MB;

MH; MHi; MWA; NNC; PU;
RPB.   8597

Education in the city of New
York. [1822] 16 p. (On the 15th
of July, 1822, a meeting was
held in the room of the Philosophical Society, for the purpose
of devising means for the improvement of education in the
city of New York.) NjPT.   8598

Education Society of Nassau-Hall
    A short account of the forma-
tion and proceedings of the Education Society of Nassau Hall.
Pub. by order of the Society.
Trenton, Pr. by George Sherman, 1822. 13 p. DLC; PPPrHi.
                                8599
Edwards, John
    Account of the trial of John
Edwards of the city of New York;
who was prosecuted for collecting or promoting an assembly of
persons, under the pretence of
public worship in a public street,
on Sunday, June 16, 1822. With
a short account of his life, an
address to the mayor and corporation, and advice to the police
magistrates, etc. Written by
John Edwards. Except the trial,
which was taken down in short
hand. New-York, Pr. for the
author, 1822. 76 p. DLC; MH;
N-L; NjR.   8600

Edwards, Jonathan, 1703-1758
    Memoirs of the Rev. David
Brainerd; missionary to the In-
dians on the borders of New
York, New Jersey, and Pennsyl-
vania... New Haven, S. Converse,
1822. 507 p. A-Ar; CBB;
CBPSR; CLU; CSmH; CSt; CoD;
Ct; CtHi; CtHT-W; CtY; DLC;
DeWI; GDC; GEU; IaDuU; IaHA;
ICN; ICP; ICU; IEG; IU; InU;
KTW; KWiU; KyHi; LNH; MAnP;
MB; MBAt; MBC; MC; MNF;
MH-AH; MdBD; MdBE; MdBJ;
MdBP; MeB; MiD; MiU-C;

MnDu; MnHi; MoSHi; MoSpD;
NBLiHi; NNC; NNG; NNUT;
NPV; NSmB; NT; NUtHi;
NbCrD; NbL; NcAS; Nh; NjN;
NjR; NjT; OAU; OC; OCIWHi;
OMC; OO; OkHi; OkU; P; PHi;
PHC; PPAmP; PP; PU; PPL;
PPiU; PWW; RNR; ScC; TNV;
Tx; TxDaTS; ViAlTh; ViRut;
ViU; Vt; WBeloC; WHi; WM.
                                8601
Jonathan Edwards, 1745-1801
    The injustice and impolicy of the
slave trade and of the slavery of
Africans: illustrated in a sermon...
2d ed. Boston, Wells & Lilly, 1822.
40 p. CtSoP; CtY; DLC; IEG; ICT;
MA; MB; MBC; MNF; MWA;
MdHi; MiD-B; NCH; OCIWHi;
OO; PHi; PPPrHi; RPB; ViHaI.
                                8602
---- The theological questions of
President Edwards, Senior, and
Dr. Edwards, his son. Provi-
dence, Pr. by Miller and Hutch-
ins, 1822. 17 p. CBPSR; CSmH;
Ct; CtY; ICP; IEG; KWiU; MB;
MBAt; MBC; MWA; MabD;
MeBa; MeLewB; MiD-B; MoSpD;
NCH; NcU; OCIW; OO; PBA;
PPPrHi.   8603

Edwards, Justin, 1787-1853
    Christian communion. A ser-
mon, delivered June 12, 1822, at
the installation of the Rev. Thaddeus Pomeroy, as pastor of the
Congregational Church in Gorham.
Portland, Pr. by A. Shirley,
1822. 24 p. CtY; MBC; MNe;
MeHi; MeP; NjPT; PPPrHi;
VtMiM.   8604

Edwards, Ninian, 1775-1833
    Substance of the remarks of
Mr. Edwards, of Illinois in the
Senate of the United States, on
the resolution that "appropriations
of Territory for the purposes of
Education should be made to those
states in whose favour no such
appropriations have been made,
corresponding in just proportion

with those heretofore made to other states in the Union." Washington, E. DeKrafft, 1822. 36 p. CSmH; CtY; ICHi; KHesC; MMeT; MWA; MdBP; MeB; N; NIC; NjPT; PMA; PPAmP. 8605

Effects of drunkenness. See Weems, Mason L.

Egan, Pierce, 1772-1849
Sporting anecdotes, original and selected; including numerous characteristic portraits of persons in every walk of life... Philadelphia, H. C. Carey and I. Lea, 1822. 359 p. KyLx; MDeeP; MHa; MdBLC; MiU-C; PP; PPL. 8606

Egomet, Demons, pseud. See Williams, Thomas.

Eighth and ninth letters to Rev. Samuel Miller. See Sparks, Jared.

Einige Erklärungen der Methodistischen Lehrsätze. Reading, Pa., Gedruckt für de Verfasser, 1822. 38 p. PPL. 8607

The election. No. 1. New York. 1822. 15 p. DLC. 8608

Elegiac stanzas. See Pickering, Henry.

An elementary treatise on the application of trigonometry. See Farrar, John.

Elements of the grammar of the English language. New York, Pub. for the authors, William Bates, pr., 1822. 43 p. CtHT-W. 8609

[Eliot, Ephraim] 1761-1827
Historical notices of the New North Religious Society in the town of Boston, with anecdotes of the Reverend Andrew and John Eliot, &c. &c... Boston, Phelps and Farnham, 1822. 51 p. CtHT-W; CtSoP; CtY; DLC; ICME; ICN; M; MB; MBAt; MBNEH; MH; MHi; MWA; MiD-B; OO; PPL; WHi. 8610

Eliot, John, 1604-1690
A grammar of the Massachusetts Indian language. A new ed. As published in the Massachusetts historical collections. Boston, Pr. by Phelps and Farnham, 1822. 28, 3-66, lvi p. CSmH; CtY; DLC; MAbD; MBAt; MH; MdBP; MnS; NBLiHi; PPAmP; RPJCB. 8611

The elixir of moonshine. See Clarke, McDonald.

Ellingwood, John Wallace, 1782-1860
A sermon, delivered Feb. 20, 1822, at the ordination of the Rev. Charles Frost, to the pastoral care of the Congregational Church in Bethel, Me. Bath, Pr. by Joseph G. Torrey, 1822. 24 p. CSmH; CtSoP; CtY; IObB; M; MB; MBC; MBNEH; MH; MWA; MeB; MeBaT; MeHi; MeLewB; MiD-B; NN; NNUT; NjPT; OO; PPL; RPB; VtMiM. 8612

[Elliot, William]
The Washington guide: containing an account of the District of Columbia; its capture by the British, in 1814; abstract of the general laws of the corporation ...list of the officers of the corporation and arrival of stages and steamboats; judiciary; list of banks and directors, in Washington and Georgetown; diplomatic and consular agents residing in Washington; botany of the District of Columbia. Washington, Ŝa. A. Elliot, 1822. 138 p. DLC; MB; NGH; PPL. 8613

Eltinge, Wilhelmus
A discourse designed as an exposition and refutation of the reasons assigned in a pamphlet, by a number of ministers, elders, and deacons, for declaring themselves the True Reformed Dutch church, in the United States of America. Hackensack, N.J. , Pr. by John C. Spencer [1822?] 12 p. NjR; PPPrHi. 8614

Ely, Ezra Stiles
A synopsis of didactic theology. Philadelphia, J. Crissy [J. Crissy and G. Goodman, printers] 1822. 308 p. CBPSR; CtW; CtY; DLC; GDC; ICartC; ICMBI; ICP; IaHi; KWiU; KyLoP; MB; MBAt; MBC; MWA; MeBa; MeBaT; NCH; NNUT; NjMD; NjPT; NjR; OClW; OSW; PLT; PPPrHi; PPiW; RBr; RNR; RPB; TNP; ViRUT. 8615

Ely, Seth
Sacred music; containing a great variety of psalm and hymn tunes, selected principally, from the most eminent European authors, the greater part of which were never published in the patent notes. Cincinnati, Pr. by Morgan, Lodge and Co. , for the proprietors, 1822. 320 p. IEG; OC; OClWHi. 8616

Ely's pocket companion; comprising a selection of sentimental and humorous songs. Lexington, Ky. , Pr. by John Bradford, 1822. 47, [1] p. KyBgW. 8617

Emerson, Mrs.
Account of Mrs. Emerson, written by herself. Andover, Flagg & Gould, printers, 1822. 24 p. MeB. 8618

Emerson, Joseph, 1777-1833
The evangelical primer, containing a minor doctrinal catechism; and a minor historical catechism; to which is added the Westminster Assembly's shorter catechism...10th ed. Boston, Pr. for Samuel T. Armstrong by Crocker & Brewster, 1822. 72 p. CtHT-W; MNS. 8619

---- Female education. A discourse, delivered at the dedication of the Seminary Hall in Saugus, Jan. 15, 1822, to which is added, The Little reckoner, consisting principally of arithmetical questions for infant minds. Boston, S. T. Armstrong and Crocker & Brewster; New York, J. P. Haven, 1822. 40 p. CtHT-W; CtY; IU; MA; MB; MH; MReh; MWA; MiD-B; MiU; NIC; NjR; OO; WU. 8620

---- ---- Boston, Samuel T. Armstrong and Crocker & Brewster; New York, John P. Haven, 1822. 40, 3-4 p. DAU; DHEW; MiU-C; NNUT; Tx. 8621

---- Questions adapted to Whelpley's compend of history. 4th ed. Boston, Richardson & Lord, 1822. 48 p. MH. 8621a

Emmett, John Patten
An essay on the chemistry of animated matter,...New-York, Pr. by C. S. Van Winkle, 1822. 125 p. MdHi; NNC; NNM; PPC; PPF. 8622

Emmons, Nathaniel, 1745-1840
A sermon, preached at North Guilford September 5th, 1821, at the ordination of the Rev. Zolva Whitmore. New-Haven, A. H. Maltby & co. , 1822. 24 p. CBPSR; Ct; CtHi; CtSoP; CtY; MBC; MB; MH-AH; MWA; MeBat; NjPT; OC; RPB; 8623

Emmons, Richard
Battle of the Thames; being the seventeenth canto of an epic

poem, entitled The Fredoniad.
Lexington, Pr. at the Gazette
Office, 1822. 37 p. ICU.   8624

Endless amusements; A collection of nearly 400 entertaining
experiments in various branches
of science... to which is added
a complete system of pyrotechny
...Philadelphia, M. Carey &
Sons, 1822. 216 p. NcWsS. 8625

Engel, Johann Jakob, 1741-1802
   ...Auszüge aus Engel's
Philosop für die Welt...Middle-
bury, 1822. cover-title, 24 p.
CtY.   8626

The English practice.   See
Sedgwick, Henry Dwight, 1785-
1831.

Entick, John, 1703?-1773
   Tyronis thesaurus; or, Entick's new Latin-English dictionary, designed for the use of
grammar schools and private
education... A new ed., carefully
rev. and thoroughly augmented.
By William Crakelt. Baltimore,
E.J. Coale & Co., 1822. 586 p.
AzU; GDC; MB; MdBE; NCaS;
NN; NNC; ODW.   8627

Episcopalian, pseud.
   Summary of the persecution
of the Rev. Wm. Hogan from
Bishop Conwell & others with an
appeal to the consciences, judge-
ment, & feelings of every candid
person in his favour.   Philadelphia, 1822. 16 p. PPAmP; PPL.
                             8628
Epitome historiae Graecae.   See
Siret, Louis Pierre.

An epitome of polite literature
containing questions and answers
on astronomy, geography, chronology, philosophy, history, meta-
physicks, morality and religion.
For the use of schools and private families.   Philadelphia, 1822.

54 p. MB; MH. WEau.   8629

Erbauliches Gebät-buch und
Unterhaltungen mit Gott, zur
Beforderung der hauslichen Got-
tesverehrung, fur Christen von
allen Benennungen... Allentown,
gedruckt und zu haben bey H.
Ebner u comp. 1822. xiv, 202,
396 p. DLC; NN; PAtM; P;
PHi; PPG; PPL.   8630

Ernesti, Johann August
   Elements of interpretation;
trans. from the Latin... and ac-
companied by notes; with an ap-
pendix containing extracts from
Morus, Beck and Keil, by Moses
Stuart... Andover, Flagg and
Gould, 1822. 124 p. CU; GDC;
ICU; ILM; IU; InCW; KWiU;
MBC; MH; MdW; MeB; MeBaT;
NIC; NjMD; OO; RPB.   8631

Espinasse, Isaac
   A practical treatise on the
settling of evidence for trials at
nisi prius; and on the preparing
and arranging the necessary
proofs... Philadelphia, H. C.
Carey & I. Lea [Griggs & Dick-
inson, printers] 1822. 302 p.
CtW; ICLaw; IEN-L; ICP; In-
SC; LNT-L; MH-L; NRAL;
NUtSC; OCLaw; OMC; PU; PU-
L; Vi-L; VtBrt.   8632

---- A treatise on the law of ac-
tions on penal statutes in gener-
al. 1st Amer. from the last
London ed. Exeter, N.H., Pub.
by George Lamson, J.J. Williams,
printer, 1822. 188 p. CU; Ct;
ICLaw; IU; IaU-L; MH-L; MW;
NNCoCi; NNLI; NRAL; NhD; Nj;
OCLaw; OMC; PPB; PU-L;
TMeB; WU-L.   8633

Espiritu de los estatutos y reglamento de la orden franc-mason-
ica... See Castillo, J. G.

An essay on commonwealth's

Part 1. The evils of exclusive
and the benefits of inclusive
wealth.   Part 2. Extracts from
Robert Owen's "New view of society." Part 3. Melish's account
of the harmonist... New York,
The New-York Society for Promoting Communities, 1822. 64 p.
IObB; In; MH-BA; OC.   8634

Essays, mathematical and physical.   See Mansfield, Jared.

Essays on the observance of a
Sabbath.   See Leland, pseud.

Essays on various subjects of
taste, morals, and national policy.
See Tucker, George.

Essays tending to prove the
ruinous effects of the policy of
the United States.   See Carey,
Mathew.

Essex Agricultural Society
    The trustees' account of the
agricultural exhibition, at Danvers,
Oct. 16 and 17, 1821. Andover,
Pr. by Flagg & Gould, 1822.
53 p. MHi; MNe; MTop; MWA.
                                   8635
Essex Bank
    The subscribers hereby give
notice that the concerns of the
Essex Bank will be closed...
Salem, 1822. Bdsd. MSaE. 8636

Essex Circulating Library
    Catalogue of the Essex Circu-
lating Library kept by John M.
Ives at his book, stationary and
music store, Essex Street,
Salem, containing upwards of
three thousand volumes, and daily
increasing.   Salem, Pr. by John
D. Cushing and Brothers, 1822.
83 p. MSaE; MiD-B.   8637

Euclid.
    Euclid's elements of geometry,
the first six books, to which are
added, elements of plain and

spherical trigonometry, a system of conick sections, elements
of natural philosophy, as far as
it relates to astronomy; with
notes.   By the Rev. John Allen
.... Baltimore, Pub. by Cushing
and Jewett; J. Robinson, printer,
1822. 494 p. CtHT-W; DAU;
KyBC; KyU; MBAt; MH; Md;
MdBD; MdBE; MdHi; MdBL;
MeB; NN; NNC; NjP; OO; OU;
PU.   8638

Europe, or a general survey.
See Everett, Alexander Hill.

The Evangelical almanack; or
Religious monitor for 1823. By
Astro Theologus.   Albany, E. &
E. Hosford [1822] 18 ll. CtY;
MWA; N; NN; NT; OCIWHi
                                   8639

Evangelical Lutheran Church
    Extracts from the minutes of
the synod of the Evangelical Lutheran church, in the state of New-
York, &c.   Convened at Schoharie, August, 1822. New-York,
Pr. by E. Conrad, 1822. 16 p.
MB; NNG.   8640

---- Principles of the Christian
religion, in question and answers.
Designed for the instruction of
youth in Evangelical Churches.
Harrisburg, Pr. by John S.
Wiestling, 1822. 66 p. P; PMA.
                                   8641
Evangelical Lutheran Church in
the U.S. Joint synod of Ohio
and other states.
    Verrichtungen der Fünften Gen-
eral-Conferenz, der Deutsch.
Evangelisch Lutherischen Predi-
gern im Staat Ohio und den an-
grenzenden Staaten. Gehalten in
Grünsberg, Pennsylvanien, den
28sten September, 1822, und
denen darauf folgenden Tagen.
[Lancaster? 1822] 8 p. OCoC.
                                   8642
Evangelical Lutheran Synod of

Maryland.

Proceedings of the Evangelical Lutheran Synod of Maryland and Virginia, at Cumberland (Maryland) for the year 1822. Baltimore, Pr. by Frederick G. Schaeffer, 1822. 14 p. NNG. 8643

Evangelical Lutheran Synod of Pennsylvania

Verhandlungen der Deutsch Evangelisch Lutherischen Synode von Pennsylvanien, gehalten zu Germantaun, in der Trinitatis Woche. 1822. Reading, Gedruckt bey Johann Ritter und Comp. [1822] 27 p. PAtM. 8644

Evans, Edward

Address to his friends and the public in reply to the report of the committee and proceedings of New-Hampshire, in relation to him, June session, 1822. [Haverhill, N.H., Pr. by Sylvester T. Goss, 1822] 32 p. Nh-Hi. 8645

[Everett, Alexander Hill] 1792-1847

Europe: or a general survey of the present situation of the principal powers; with conjectures on their future prospects: By A citizen of the United States. Boston, Oliver Everett and Cummings and Hilliard, Hilliard & Metcalf, printers, 1822. 451 p. CL; CoFcS; CtHT; CtY; DLC; IEG; IU; In; KyLx; LN; LNH; M; MA; MB; MBAt; MBC; MBL; MH; MHi; MLow; MNBedf; MNF; MNe; MW; MWA; MdBP; MeB; Mi; MiD; MiU; MoSM; Ms; NBLiHi; NIC; NNC; NNUT; NT; NWM; NcU; Nh; Nh-Hi; NjR; P; PPA; PPL; ScC; ScU; TJaU; Vi; ViAl; VtB; WHi. 8646

Everett, Edward

[Review of] A pedestrian tour of two thousand and three hundred miles in North America... By P. Stansbury [Boston, 1822]

8 p. (Excerpt from the North American review. Oct. 1822. Vol. 15, no. 37. MC. 8647

[Everett, L. S.]

An examination of the substance of a discourse, on the unpardonable sin, &c. delivered by the Rev. George Coles. At the Methodist Church, Hudson (N.Y.) on Sunday evening, July 21, 1822. Hudson, Pr. by Ashbel Stoddard, 1822. 16 p. MBC. 8648

Ewell, James, 1773-1832

The medical companion, or Family physician treating of the diseases of the United States... 6th ed. rev. and enl. Baltimore, Pr. for the Proprietors, by B. Edes, 1822. 792 p. MdBE; MdBP; NcWfC; TU-M. 8649

An examination of the line of the Great Erie Canal, as adopted by the Commissioners from Schoharie Creek to its final destination at the tide waters of the Hudson River... Pr. for the Publisher, 1822. 32 p. DLC. 8650

An examination of the substance of a discourse, on the unpardonable sin. See Everett, L. S.

An excursion of the dog-cart; a poem by an imprisoned debtor. New York, W. Bonker, jr., 1822. 24 p. DLC; MB; MH; MWA. 8651

Execution of Samuel Clisby and Gilbert Close, Boston, March 8, 1822. Yesterday, pursuant to sentence, the awful penalty of the law was inflicted on Samuel Clisby and Gilbert Close who were convicted of highway robbery, at the last term of the Supreme Judicial Court. Broadsheet. MWeyHi. 8652

Religious tracts, V-2-No. 3. An

exhortation to the frequent reception to the Holy Sacrament of the Lord's supper... [Charleston] A. E. Miller, printer to the Society [1822] 6 p. RPB.   8653

An exposition of some of the evils arising from the auction system. See A New York merchant, pseud.

An exposition of the principles and views of the middling interest in the city of Boston. Boston, May, 1822. 8 p. Ct; CtY; DLC; M; MB; MBAt; MHi; MWA; NHi; PHi; PPAmP.   8654

Expositor and philanthropist.
    The carrier respectfully presents to his patrons, the compliments of the season, wishing them all the felicity that mortals can enjoy. Boston, 1822. Bdsd. MBAt.   8655

Extractos de los mas celebres escritores y poetas españoles en dos partes. See Cubi y Soler, Mariano.

F

Facts and observations, illustrative of the past. See Carey, Mathew.

Facts and observations, illustrative of the rise. See Eddy, Thomas.

Fair play on both sides. Mr. Wickliffe pleads the statute too!!! [Kentucky] August 5, 1822. 1 p. DLC.   8656

Fairfield, Sumner Lincoln, 1803-1844
    An address delivered before the Young Men's Missionary Society of Savannah. Jan. 2, 1822. Charleston, Pr. by C. C. Sebring, 1822. 19 p. GU-De.   8657

---- The siege of Constantinople. A poem. Charleston, S. C., W. Riley, 1822. 64 p. DLC; MH; RPB.   8658

Faith in Jesus Christ... Philadelphia, Benjamin & Thomas Kite, 1822. 12 p. NjR; PSC-Hi. 8659

Faithhorn, John
    Facts and observations on liver complaints, and bilious disorders in general... 2d Amer.ed. Philadelphia, Hickman & Hazzard, 1822. 158 p. CSfCMS; CtY; ICJ; ICU-M; IU-M; KyLoJM; MH; MNF; MWA; MdBM; MdUD; MoSU-M; MsU; NBM; NBuU-M; NIC-V; NNMSCQ; NNNAM; NSyHi; NhD; OC; PPAN; PPC; RPM; TNV; ViNoM.   8660

A false position exposed. New-York, Pr. for the publisher. 1822. 12 p. NNG; NjR; PPFYR.   8661

False stories corrected. New York, S. Wood & Sons, etc., etc., 1822. 41 p. MH; MnS; NN.   8661a

The family at Washington... See Watterson, George.

The farm-yard journal. See Aikin, John.

Farmer, Daniel Davis
    The life and confessions of Daniel Davis Farmer, who was executed at Amherst, N.H. on the 3d day of January, 1822, for the murder of the Widow Anna Ayer, at Goffstown, on the 4th of April 1821 to which is added his valedictory address and some of his correspondence during his imprisonment. Written by himself. Amherst, N.H., Pr. by Elisha Mansur, 1822. 32 p. DLC; MB; MWA; MoSM; Nh; Nh-Hi; PHi; PP.   8662

[Farmer, John] 1789-1838, comp.
The new military guide; containing extracts from the Constitution of the United States and of New-Hampshire; organization of the militia of New-Hampshire; duty of officers, non-commissioned officers and privates... Concord [N.H.] Pr. by Hill and Moore, 1822. 144 p. DLC; MB; MWA; NWM; Nh-Hi; OkFsAGM. 8663

The Farmer's almanack; and annual register for 1823. By Thomas Spofford. Andover, author; Exeter, Samuel T. Moses, printer [1822] 18 ll. DLC; MB; MBC; MHi; MWA; MiD-B; N; NCH; NN; NhHi; OClWHi. 8664

The Farmer's almanac for 1823. By Father Abraham; John Sharp. Baltimore, William Warner [1822] 18 ll. CtY; MWA. 8665

The Farmer's almanack, calculated on a new and improved plan, for...1823...Boston, Carter, Hendee and co. (etc.) 1822. CU. 8666

The Farmer's almanack for 1823. By Robert B. Thomas. Boston, Richardson & Lord [1822] 24 ll. AU; CLU; CU; CoD; Ct; CtHi; CtY; DLC; FTaSU; FWpR; GU; ICU; IHi; IU; InU; In; M; MB; MBAt; MBC; MBU; MHi; MH; MNF; MS; MTaHi; MWA; MWelC; MWiW-C; MeB; MeP; MnM; MiD-B; MiGr; MiU-C; MnU; MoS; NBuHi; NBLiHi; NBuG; NGcA; NHC; NIC; NHi; NJQ; NRMA; NN; NNU-H; Nh; NbHi; NbU; NcD; NhM; NhHi; NjHi; NjMoW; O; OClWHi; OMC; Or; OrCS; PHi; RP; RPA; RPB; RU; TxU; UPB; ViU; WHi. 8667

---- No. XXXI. By Robert B. Thomas. Boston, Pr. by J.H.A. Frost, for Richardson & Lord [1822] [48] p. ICMcHi; MBB; MBilHi; MHa; MNF; MPeHi; MWHi; MeHi; MdHi; MiGr; NbU; NjR; RWe; WHi. 8668

---- By Robert B. Thomas. Boston, J.H.A. Frost for West, Richardson & Lord [1822] MWA. 8669

---- By Andrew Beers. Burlington, Vt., E. and T. Mills [1822] 12 ll. CLU; CtY; MWA. 8670

---- Portland, Gazette and Argus Offices [1822] 24 ll. DLC; MB; MH; MWA; MeHi; MeP; MeB; MeWC; MiD-B; N; PHi. 8671

---- By James W. Palmer. Lexington, James W. Palmer; W.W. Worsley; W.G. Hunt [1822] 18 ll. CSmH; ICU; InHi; KyLo; KyLx; KyLoF; KyBgW; MoHi; NCH; OC; WHi. 8672

---- ---- ---- 24 ll. KyU. 8673

---- By John Ward. Philadelphia, M'Carty & Davis [1822] 18 ll. CLU; CtY; InU; MWA; NN; PHi. 8674

The Farmers' calendar, or Utica almanack for 1823. By Andrew Beers. Utica, William Williams [1822] 18 ll. DLC; ICHi; MWA (12 ll.) MnU; N; NBuG; NBuHi; NIC; NSyOHi; NUtHi; NUt; NHi (8 ll.) 8675

The Farmers' calendar, or Watertown almanack for 1823. By Andrew Beers. Utica, William Williams, for Adams, Lee & Co., Watertown [1822] 18 ll. MWA; NWattHi. 8676

The Farmer's diary, or Beers' Ontario almanack for 1823. By Loud and Wilmarth [1822] Canandaigua, J.D. Bemis & Co. [1822] 18 ll. MWA; N; NRU; NRMA. 8677

The Farmers' diary, or Ontario almanack for 1823. By Loud & Wilmarth. Canandaigua, J.D. Bemis & Co. [1822] 18 ll. CSmH; MWA; N; NN; NCooHi; NCanHi; NRMA.   8678

The Farmer's, mechanic's and gentleman's almanack for 1823. By Nathan Wild. Chesterfield, N.H., author [1822] 24 ll. MNF; MWA; NN (22 ll.) NhHi; OCIWHi.   8679

Farmington Canal Company
    The act of incorporation of the Farmington Canal Company, with the reports of the Hon. Benjamin Wright and Andrew A. Bartow, esq. and of the Committee of the Legislature of Connecticut on that subject. New Haven, S.M. Dutton, printer, 1822. 15 p. CtY.   8680

Farquhar, George, 1677?-1707
    ...The beaux stratagem, a comedy...Boston, Wells and Lilly, New York, A.T. Goodrich & Co. (etc., etc.) 1822. 106 p. CtY; MH; MPiB; MeB; PPL.   8681

---- ...The inconstant; or, The way to win him. A comedy... Boston, By Wells and Lilly, New York, A.T. Goodrich & co., 1822. 88 p. CtY; MH; MeB; PPL; PU; TxU.   8682

---- ... The recruiting officer, a comedy...Boston, Wells and Lilly, New-York, A.T. Goodrich & Co., (etc.) 1822. 102 p. CtY; MH; MeB; PPL; RPB.   8683

[Farrar, John] 1779-1853
    An elementary treatise on the application of trigonometry to orthographic and stereographic projection, dialling, mensuration of heights and distances, navigation, nautical astronomy, surveying and levelling...Cambridge

(Mass.) Hilliard & Metcalf, 1822. 153, [73] p. CSt; CtY; IHi; KMK; MA; MB; MH; MWiW; MdBD; MeB; MeBat; MiU; NIC; NNC; NWM; NjP; RPB; TNP; TxU-T; ViU.   8684

The fashionable letter center; or Art of polite correspondence and a new and easy English grammar. Rochester, N.Y., E. Peck & Company, 1822. 157 p. NBuHi.
                                  8685
The fashionable tour. See Davison, Gideon Miner.

Faucit, John Saville, 1783-1853
    The miller's maid; a melodrama in two acts. Founded on Bloomfield's poem of that name. Baltimore, J. Robinson, 1822. 40 p. IU; MH; NjP.   8686

The favorite of nature. See Kelty, Mary Ann.

Fay, Warren
    A sermon, delivered April 24, 1822 at the ordination of the Rev. Nathanael Cogswell, as colleague pastor of the Congregational Church and Society in Yarmouth, Mass. Boston, Crocker and Brewster, printers, 1822. 36 p. ICU; MB; MBNEH; MH-AH; NjPT.   8687

---- Sermon delivered January 1, 1822 at the ordination of Rev. Joseph Bennet, to the pastoral care of the Congregational Church of Woburn, Mass. Boston, Crocker and Brewster, 1822. 39 p. CtY; M; MB; MBNEH; MH; MWo; MiD-B; MnHi; NjPT; NjR; OCIWHi.   8688

Fayette election August, 1822. [Lexington, W.W. Worsley, 1822] 38 p. ICU; PPiU.   8689

Felbinger, Jeremias
    Christliches Hand-Buchlein...

von Jeremias Felbinger. Nechte und Orinungen des Hauses Gottes in Frag und Antwort... Lancaster, Gedruckt fur den Verleger, von Johann Bär, 1822. 128 p. DLC; MiU-C; P; PHi; PLFM; PPG; PPL.   8690

Felch, Cheever
An address delivered before Mount Carmel Lodge, at Lynn, June, 1821... Boston, Lincoln & Edmands [1822] 20 p. MB.   8691

Female Auxiliary Bible Society. Cincinnati
Sixth annual report of the Female Auxiliary Bible Society of Cincinnati, for the year ending on the last Thursday of July, 1822. [Cincinnati, 1822] 12 p. ICP.   8692

Female Bible Society of Philadelphia
Eighth report... Mar. 27, 1822. Philadelphia, Wm. Fry, printer, 1822. 20 p. PPL.   8693

Female Bible and Religious Tract Society of Kings County, L.I.
Reports of... from Oct. 2, 1817, to September 14, 1821; with a list of subscribers. Brooklyn, Alden Spooner, 1822. 23 p. NBLiHi.   8694

Female Missionary Society of the Western District
Sixth annual report of the trustees... Utica, Pr. by William Williams, 1822. 31, [2] p. NUtHi; BrMus.   8695

Female Society of Boston and Vicinity, for Promoting Christianity among the Jews
Constitution... together with the fifth and sixth annual reports. Boston, Munroe and Francis, 1822. 12 p. CtHT-W; DLC; MHi.
                    8696
Female Sunday School Society of

St. James Church, Lancaster, Pa.
First annual report of the Female Sunday School Society of St. James's Church, Lancaster (read at the annual meeting, May 27th, 1822). Together with the constitution of the Society, subscribers' names, &c. Lancaster, John Reynolds, pr., 1822. 19 p. MiD-B; P.   8697

Fessenden, Thomas Green, 1771-1837
An essay on the law of patents for new inventions. 2d ed. Boston, pub. by Charles Ewer, pr. by John Cotton, jr., 1822. 427 p. CU-Law; Ct; CtHT; ICLaw; Ia; IaU-L; LNT-L; MB; MBS; MH; MLowDC; MWCL; MWo; Md; MeU; MiU-C; NIC-L; NNLI; NRAL; NjR; OCl; OMC; PPAmP; PPB; PPT; PU-L; PPi; RPB; TMeB; ViU; DeGE.
                    8698
A few considerations in relation to the choice of president, written with a view to the approaching election, and respectfully offered to the citizens of the United States, by Atticus. 1822. 14 p. DLC.   8699

Field, Barnum
An oration, pronounced in commemoration of American Independence before the citizens of Dedham, and the military company for the day, composed of citizen volunteers, July 4, 1822. Dedham, Pr. by H. & W.H. Mann [1822] [3], 14-20 p. DLC; MH; MKi.   8700

Field, Barron, 1786-1846
An analysis of Blackstone's Commentaries on the laws of England, in a series of questions, to which the student is to frame his own answers... 1st Amer. from the 2d London ed. New York, S. Gould, 1822. 286 p.

CLSU; CU-Law; IBloW; MH-L;
NIC-L; NNLI; NhD; NjR; PPB.
8701
Field, Joseph
Clerical discipline, exemplified by the Franklin Association,
in the late measures, adopted by
them towards the author. Accompanied with illustrations and
remarks... Greenfield, Pr. by
Denio & Phelps, 1822. 23 p.
MBAU; MDeeP; MHi; MWA;
NjPT; WHi. 8702

Fielding, Henry, 1707-1754
The tragedy of tragedies, or,
The life and death of Tom Thumb
the great. Philadelphia, T. H.
Palmer, 1822. 36 p. MH; MiU-
C. 8703

Finley, Anthony
Catalogue of theological books,
for sale by A. Finley, Philadelphia, 1822. 20 p. OClWHi. 8704

---- The refuge. Philadelphia,
A. Finley, 1822. 333 p. GDC.
8705
The first settlers of New-England.
See Child, Mrs. Lydia Maria
(Francis)

Fishback, James
A defence of the Elkhorn Association; in sixteen letters, addressed to Elder Henry Toler,
pastor of the Grier's Creek Particular Baptist Church... Lexington, Ky., Pr. for the author by
Thomas T. Skillman, 1822. 185 p.
CSmH; ICU; KyLoF; KyLoS;
KyLx; KyLxT; NN; NRAB; ViRu.
8706
---- The substance of a discourse
in two parts; delivered in the
Meeting-House of the First Baptist Church in Lexington, Feb. 3,
1822... Lexington, Joseph Ficklin,
printer-Gazette Office, 1822. 22
p. KyLoF; KyLx; KyLxT; KyU.
8707
---- ---- (Part II) Lexington,

Ky., Pr. by Thomas T. Skillman, 1822. 23 p. KyLoF; KyLx;
KyLxT; KyU. 8708

Fisher, Abial, 1787-1862
Century sermons. Two dis-
courses, delivered at Bellingham
(Mass.) in the year 1822. The
first giving the civil and ecclesiastical history of the town, from
its incorporation, Nov. 27, 1719,
to Nov. 27, 1819; and the second, the memoirs of the three
ministers who died in the town,
during that period... Worcester,
Pr. by W. Manning, 1822. 28 p.
CtSoP; DLC; M; MBC; MBNEB;
MHi; MW; MiD-B; MnHi; NjPT;
RPB. 8709

Fisher, Elias
A sermon preached in Lem-
ster, N. H. at the dedication of
the new meeting-house in that
town, October 23, 1822. Bellows
Falls, Pr. by Blake, Cutler and
Co. [1822?] 16 p. MHi; Nh.
8710
Five letters of Atonement, in
which the opinions of Trinitarians and Unitarians are examined
with reference to their moral
tendency. By a Unitarian of Baltimore. Baltimore, Pub. by the
Baltimore Unitarian Book Society.
Sold by F. Lucas, Jr., and N. G.
Maxwell; John D. Toy, printer,
1822. 93 p. MA; MBAU. 8711

Flagg, Josiah Foster
The family dentist; containing
a brief description of the struc-
ture, formation, diseases, and
treatment of the human teeth...
Boston, J. W. Ingraham, 1822.
82 p. CU-M; ICU-R; IEN-D;
IU-M; MB; MBM; MBU-M; MH-
D; MHi; MWA; MdUD; MiU;
NBMS; NCH; NNC-M; NhD; OC;
OO; PPiU-D; WMMU-D. 8712

Fleetwood, John
Life of... Jesus Christ... to-

gether with the lives... of the holy evangelists, apostles and others... New York, T. Kinnersley, 1822. 31, 616 p. NPV. 8713

---- ---- Boston, S. Walker, 1822. 616 p. MWA.   8714

[Fletcher, Calvin]
   The Indiana justice, and farmer's scrivener: containing, the office and duty of justices of the peace, sheriffs, clerks, coroners, constables, township officers, jurymen and jailors... By a gentleman of the bar. Indianapolis, Smith & Bolton, 1822. 168, xl, 5 p. In; InHi; MiD-B.
                                8715

Fletcher, John, 1579-1625
   ... Rule a wife and have a wife; a comedy... Boston, Wells and Lilly, New York, A. T. Goodrich & co., 1822. 98 p. CtY; MH; MeB; PPL.   8716

Fletcher & Gardiner
   150 dollars reward.   The store of the subscribers was entered last night, and the following articles taken therefrom, viz... Fletcher & Gardiner. No. 130 Chestnut Street.   Philadelphia, August 9, 1822. [Philadelphia] T. S. Manning, printer [1822] 1 p. DLC.   8717

Flint, Jacob, 1767-1835
   Two discourses, containing the history of the church and society in Cohasset, delivered December 16, 1821; being the first Lord's day after the completion of a century from the gathering of the church in that place, and the ordination of the first pastor. With a geographical sketch of Cohasset.   Boston, Pr. by Munroe and Francis, 1822. 28 p. C; DLC; ICMe; ICN; ICU; IU; M; MBAt; MDeeP; MH; MMalHi; MWA; MeBat; MiD-B; MiU; OO; RPB; VtMiM.   8718

---- ---- Boston, Munroe & Francis, 1822. 37 p. CBPac; M; MBNEH; MWHi; MWeyHi; NBLiHi.   8719

Foote, Samuel
   The mayor of Garratt; a farce.   Boston, Wells and Lilly, etc., etc. 1822. 43 p. MH; MeB; NjR; PPL.   8720

For sale.   On the 8th of the sixth month (June) next... Mill site for sale, June 8, 1822, on Octorara Creek, in Caecil County, and state of Maryland... Wilmington, 5 mo. 6, 1822. Pr. by J. Wilson, Watchman office, 1822. Bdsd. DeHi.   8721

Foreign Missionary Society of Northampton.
   Annual report of the committee to the Foreign Missionary Society... Northampton, Mass., Pr. by Sylvester Judd, Jr., 1822. 16 p. MNF; MWA. 8722

The fortunes of Nigel.   See Scott, Sir Walter, bart.

Foster, John
   A discourse the substance of which was delivered at the annual general meeting of the Baptist Missionary Society in Bristol, (Eng.) September, 1818... Trenton, Pr. by George Sherman, 1822. 94 p. MB; NjR.   8723

A four fold cord, made up of the best gifts, the more excellent way -- marriage -- divorce -- and hospitality.   By a well wisher to fervent charity; a hater of putting away; and an advocate for kindness to strangers.   2d ed. on hospitality; with additions. Wilmington [Del.] Pr. by Robert Porter, 1822. 96 p. CSmH; IObB.   8724

Fowler, William Chauncey

Origin of the theological school of Yale College. [New Haven, 1822] 26 p. MH.   8725

Franklin, Benjamin, 1706-1790
Essays and letters, by Dr. B. Franklin. Vol. I, Part II. Commercial and political. New-York, Pub. by R. & W. Bartow and by W. A. Bartow & Co., Richmond (Vir.) Gray & Bunce, printers, 1822. Vol. 1, 213, (4) p. CtHT-W; CtY; MFran; MH; MWA; NRU; ViRUT.   8726

The Franklin almanack for 1823. By Dr. John Armstrong. Pittsburgh, Eichbaum & Johnston [1822] 18 ll. DLC; PPi; PPiU.
                                             8727
---- Richmond, Nathan Pollard [1822] 24 ll. DLC; MWA; Vi; ViW.   8728

The Franklin magazine almanack, for the year of our Lord 1823... Number V. Calculated by John Armstrong. Pittsburgh, Eichbaum & Johnston, sold by James Turnbull, Steubenville [1822] [72] p. MWA.   8729

The Franklin spelling book. Wilmington, Del., R. Porter; Baltimore, P. Lucas, jr. [etc.] 1822. 144 p. DHEW; MB.   8730

Franklin's letters to his kinfolk. See Didier, Franklin James.

Free-School Society of New York. See Public School Society of New York.

The Freeman's almanack, or, Complete farmer's calendar for 1823. Cincinnati, Oliver Farnsworth and Co. [1822] 28 ll. DLC; InRE; MWA; NN; O; OC; OCHP; OCIWHi; OHi.   8731

The Freeman's almanack, or Farmer's calendar for 1823.

By Samuel Burr. Cincinnati, Oliver Farnsworth & Co. [1822] 15 ll. DLC; ICN; IU; InHi; InU; MWA; OC; OCHP; OCIWHi.
                                             8732
Freemasons
[Resolutions of a meeting of the Masonic fraternity held in the Senate chamber of the United States, March 9, 1822, relative to the formation of a general Grand Lodge of the United States.] [1822?] 7 p. IaCrM.   8733

---- Alabama. Grand Lodge
Proceedings of the Grand Lodge of Alabama, at their first annual communication, held at the Masonic Hall, in the Town of Cahawba, in the year of our Lord 1821, and in the year of Masonry 5821. Cahawba, Pr. by William B. Allen & Co., 1822. 9, [1] p. AMFM; CSmH; IaCrM; MBFM.   8734

---- Bath, Maine. Solar Lodge.
The by-laws of Solar Lodge, at Bath, State of Maine. Adopted, Nov. 19 A.D. 1819. Bath, Pr. for Solar Lodge, J. G. Torrey, printer, 1822. 15 p. NNFM.   8735

---- Conn.   Grand Lodge.
Proceedings of the Grand Lodge of Connecticut, held at Mason's Hall, in the town of New Haven, May 8th, A. L. 5822- A. D. 1822. New Haven, Conn., Pr. by Joseph Barber, 1822. 18 p. NNFM.   8736

---- Easton, Pa. Lodge No. 152
The Mason's manual. Selected by a committee of Easton Lodge no. 152 and published with the approbation of the R. W. grandmaster of Pennsylvania. Easton, Pa., Pr. by H. and W. Hutter, 1822. 87 p. IaCrM; PPL; PPFM.   8737

---- District of Columbia. Grand Lodge

Constitution of the Grand Lodge of the District of Columbia, printed by order of the Grand Lodge. Washington City, Edward De Krafft, printer, 1822. 10 p. NNFM.   8738

---- Georgia. Grand Lodge

Proceedings of the R.W. Grand Lodge of the state of Georgia, at their annual communication, held at Milledgeville. On the first Saturday in December, A.L. 5821. Milledgeville, Pr. by Grantland & Orme, 1822. 22 p. NNFM.   8739

---- Hagerstown, Md. Mount Moriah Lodge.

Oration, sermon, &c. delivered at the ceremony of laying the foundation stone of the Masonic hall, in Hagerstown, June 24th, A.D. 1822, A.L. 5822. Hagers-town, Pr. by W. D. Bell, 1822. 32 p. DLC; MdBP.   8740

---- Indiana. Grand Lodge

Extract from the proceedings of the Grand Lodge of the most ancient and honorable fraternity of Free and Accepted Masons, of the state of Indiana; at its annual communication, held at Corydon, on the 1st Monday in October, A.L. 5822...Madison, Ia., Pr. by Carpenter & Douglass, 1822. 108 p. DSC; IaCrM; MBFM; NNFM.   8741

---- Kentucky. Grand Lodge

Grand Lodge of Kentucky, Friday, Aug. 30th, 5822. The Committee on Foreign Communications offered a report, which was...ordered to be recommitted to a select committee, with instructions to report against the proposition to establish a general Grand Lodge in the United

States. [Lexington? 1822] 8 p. CSmH.   8742

---- ---- ---- Proceedings of the Grand Lodge of Kentucky; begun and held at Masons' Hall in the town of Lexington, on the last Monday of August, being the twenty-sixth day of the month, A.L. 5822, A.D. 1822. Lexington, Joseph Ficklin, printer-- Gazette Office, 1822. 112 p. IaCrM; KyLxFM; MBFM; NNFM; PPFM.   8743

---- ---- ---- The select committee to whom was recommitted the report of the committee upon foreign communications, have agreeably to order had the same under consideration, and beg leave to report...[Lexington? 1822] 8 p. CSmH.   8744

---- ---- Royal Arch Masons. Grand Chapter

Proceedings of the Grand Royal Arch Chapter of Kentucky, at a Grand Convocation begun and held at Masons' Hall in the town of Frankfort, on the 3rd day of December, A.D. 1821, A.L. 5821, A.R. 2351. Lexington, Ken., Pr. by W.G. Hunt, 1822. 35 p. KyLxFM; MBFM; N; NNFM.   8745

---- Lancaster, Pa. Lodge No. 43

The proceedings of Lodge No. 43, Lancaster, and of the R.W. Grand Lodge of Pennsylvania, relative to certain differences between them, which occasioned the dissolution of Lodge No. 43. 1822. 29, 10 p. WHi.   8746

---- Lynchburg, Va. Marshall Lodge No. 39

By-laws of Marshall Lodge, No. 39, as amended and adopted Feb. 15th, A.D. 1822, A.L. 5822. Lynchburg, Pr. by G.

Maguire, 1822. 8 p. TxU.   8747

---- Maine. Grand Lodge
At a stated meeting of the
Grand Lodge of Maine, Portland,
July 11, A. D. 1822. The
amendment to the by-laws of the
Grand Lodge, recommended by a
committee at our last communi-
cation, was taken into consider-
ation and unanimously adopted
... Portland, July 13, 1822.
Broadside. DSC; MePFM. 8748

---- ---- ---- Grand Lodge of
the Most Ancient and Honorable
Fraternity of Free and Accepted
Masons, of the state of Maine.
Most worshipful Simon Greenleaf, esq. Grand Master. Portland, Pr. by Arthur Shirley,
1822. 10 p. CSmH; MHi;
NNFM.   8749

---- Massachusetts. Corinthian
Lodge
By-laws of Corinthian Lodge.
Concord, Mass. , Peters & Big-
low, printers, 1822. 14 p.
MWA.   8750

---- ---- Grand Lodge
Circular. Abstract from a
report of a committee, accepted
in Grand Lodge, June 12, 5822.
[1822] 1 p. DLC.   8751

---- ---- ---- Grand Lodge...
free and accepted masons of
Massachusetts... Boston, Pr. by
Joseph T. Buckingham, 1822.
10 p. NNFM.   8752

---- ---- Royal Arch Masons.
Grand Chapter
Grand Royal Arch Chapter of
Massachusetts. Boston, Nov.
1822. Boston, Pr. by comp.
E. G. House, 1822. 17 p. IaCrM;
NNFM.   8753

---- Missouri. Grand Lodge
Proceedings of the Grand
Lodge of Missouri, at its semi-
annual communication, held in
the town of St. Louis, April,
A. L. 5822. William Orr,
printer, 1822. 12 p. MBFM;
PPFM.   8754

---- ---- Grand Royal Arch
Chapter
By-laws of Missouri Royal
Arch Chapter, St. Louis, Apr.
10th, 1822. W. Orr, printer.
8 p. IaCrM.   8755

---- New Hampshire. Grand
Lodge
Journal of the proceedings of
the Grand Lodge of New-Hampshire, at their annual session
in Concord begun June 12 and
concluded June 13, 5822. Concord, Pr. by Hill and Moore,
1822. 18 p. DLC; MSa; MWA;
Nh-Hi.   8756

---- ---- Royal Arch Masons.
Grand Chapter
[Proceedings of the Royal
Arch Chapter of New-Hampshire,
at their annual meeting... Ports-
mouth... 5822] 1822. 6 p. (No
title page. Title by analogy
with 1823 Proceedings.) NNFM.
                           8757
---- New York. Grand Lodge
Constitution of the Grand
Lodge of the state of New-York.
[New York? 1822?] (2), 10 p.
MH.   8758

---- ---- ---- Proceedings of
the Grand Lodge of the most ancient and honorable fraternity of
free and accepted Masons, of
the state of New York, at its
quarterly communications and
meetings of emergency, held between the 24th of June, A. L.
5821, and the 24th of June 5822.
New York, Pr. by Bro. Edward
S. Bellamy, 5822. 58 p. IaCrM;
N; NNFM; PHi; PPFM.   8759

---- Ohio. Grand Lodge
Extract from the proceedings of the most worshipful Grand Lodge of the ancient and honorable fraternity of free and accepted Masons in the state of Ohio, at their annual communication, held at Columbus, on Monday, December 10, A.D. 1821-A.L. 5821, and by adjournments, until the twelfth of said month. Delaware, Pr. by Bros. Griswold & Howard, 1822. 30 p. CSmH; IaCrM. 8760

---- Pennsylvania. Grand Lodge
Grand Lodge of the most ancient and honourable fraternity of free and accepted Masons of Pennsylvania... in the city of Philadelphia, on Monday, the 2d of December, anno Domini 1822, anno Lucis 5822. 13 p. NNFM. 8761

---- Philadelphia. Columbia Lodge.
By-laws of Columbia Lodge No. 91. Philadelphia, Thomas S. Manning, printer, 1822. 20 p. PPFM. 8762

---- ---- Concordia Lodge
By-laws of Concordia Lodge, No. 67, as approved by the Grand Lodge, on the 2d day of April, 1821. Philadelphia, pr. 1822. 16, [8], 8 p. PPFM. 8763

---- ---- Solomon's Lodge, No. 114
By-laws of Solomon's Lodge, No. 114. Philadelphia, Pr. for the Lodge. D. Dickinson, printer, 1822. 12 p. PPFM. 8764

---- Rhode Island. Grand Lodge
The proceedings of the worshipful Grand Lodge of the state of Rhode-Island and Providence Plantations, at the annual meeting holden at St. John's Hall, in Newport, on Monday, 24th June, A.L. 5822. Providence, Pr. by Bro. John Miller, at the office of Miller and Hutchens, 5822 [1822] 8 p. NNFM. 8765

---- South Carolina. Grand Lodge
Abstract of the proceedings of the Grand Lodge of ancient Freemasons of South Carolina, from St. John the Evangelist's day, 5820, until St. John the Evangelist's day 5821, inclusive. Charleston, Pr. by A.E. Miller, 1822. 22 p. CSmH; NNFM. 8766

---- Tennessee. Grand Lodge
Proceedings of the Grand Lodge of the state of Tennessee, for the year 1822. Nashville, Pr. by Joseph Norvel [1822] 31, [1] p. IaCrM; MBFM; NNFM; T. 8767

---- ---- ---- Proceedings of the Grand Lodge of the State of Tennessee; held at Nashville, October 1, 2, 3, & 4, A.L. 5821. Nashville, Joseph Norvell, printer, 1822. 16 p. CSmH; IaCrM; MBFM; NNFM; PPFM. 8768

---- Vermont. Grand Lodge
Journals of the Grand Lodge of Vermont, at their annual communications holden at Montpelier, Oct. A.L. 5820 and 5821. Montpelier, Pr. by E.P. Walton, 1822. 51 p. DSC; MBFM; NNFM; VtBFM. 8769

---- Virginia. Grand Lodge
Proceedings of a Grand annual Communication of the Grand Lodge of Virginia, begun and held in the Masons' Hall, in the City of Richmond, the second Monday in December being the tenth day of the month, A.L. 5821, A.D. 1821. Richmond, Pr. by John Warrock, 1822. 46 p. MBFM. 8770

---- ---- Grand Royal Arch Chapter

Proceedings of the Grand Royal Arch Chapter of Virginia ...Richmond, December A.D. 1821. Richmond, Pr. by John Warrock, 1822. 15 p. NNFM.
8771

French, Jonathan, 1778-1856

A discourse delivered at Northampton, N.H., Nov. 18, 1821, being twenty years from the author's settlement in the Christian ministry in that place. Portsmouth, Pr. by T.H. Miller, 1822. 11 p. MBedfHi; MH.
8772

---- A sermon, preached at Concord, before His Excellency Samuel Bell, governor, the honourable Council, Senate, and House of Representatives, of the state of New-Hampshire, June 6, 1822. Being the anniversary election. Concord, Pr. by Hill and Moore, 1822. 26 p., 1 l. DLC; MB; MH-AH; MHi; MeBat; MiD-B; NhD; NjR; NjPT.
8773

Frick, William

The Baltimore waltz. Composed for the piano forte by William Frick. Baltimore, John Cole [1822] p [1]-2. NN.
8774

---- The breeze that wafts thee far away. A canzonet. Baltimore, John Cole [1822] 4 p. MdHi; NN; RPB.
8775

The friend of peace. See Worcester, Noah.

A friend to youth. See Amicus, pseud.

Friendly Botanic Society

A statement of the conduct of Elias Smith towards Dr. Samuel Thomson. [Boston, 1822?] 12 p. WU-M.
8776

The friendly instructor. See Harrison, Mrs. Elizabeth.

A friendly letter to a member of the Episcopal Church in Maryland. 1822. 8 p. DLC; MdBJ-G.
8777

Friends, Society of. Baltimore Yearly Meeting

Address of the sufferers of the Eastern District of the city of Baltimore, to the Yearly Meeting held in Baltimore, 10th month, 28th, 1822. 1822. 24 p. MdBE; MdToH; PHi; PPL; PSC-Hi.
8778

---- ---- Communication of the Society of Friends, for the Eastern district of Baltimore, to the General Assembly of Maryland...Annapolis, Pr. by J. Chandler [1822] 7 p. MdHi.
8779

---- ---- To the General Assembly of Maryland, the memorial of the representatives of the yearly meeting of the Religious Society of Friends...[1822?] 8 p. Signed: Thomas Ellicott, clerk, 1st mo. 19th, 1822. MiU-C.
8780

---- Indiana Yearly Meeting.

[Indiana yearly meeting held at Whitewater the 7th of tenth month, 1822. Richmond? 1822] In; InRchE; InU.
8781

---- London Yearly Meeting

The epistle from the yearly meeting, held in London, by adjournments, from the 22d of the fifth month, to the 31st of the same, inclusive, 1822, to the Quarterly and Monthly meetings of Friends, in Great Britain, Ireland and elsewhere. [Elijah Lacey, printer, Richmond, Ind.] 4 p. DLC.
8782

---- ---- The epistle from the Yearly Meeting held in London ...from the 23d of the fifth month, to the 31st of the same, inclusive, 1822...[Mt. Pleasant, O., 1822] 6 p. OCIWHi.   8783

---- New York Yearly Meeting of Women Friends
Minutes of... [New York] 1822. Broadside. PSC-Hi.   8784

---- Ohio Yearly Meeting.
A list of the meetings for worship and discipline, comprising the yearly meetings of Ohio and Indiana. Mt. Pleasant, Ohio, pr. by Elisha Bates, 1822. 12 p. Lindley.   8785

---- Philadelphia Yearly Meeting
A declaration of the Yearly Meeting of Friends, held in Philadelphia, respecting the proceedings of those meetings which have lately separated from the Society, and also showing the contrast between their doctrines and those held by Friends. New York, Pr. by Samuel Wood & Sons, 1822. 32 p. NcGU.   8786

---- ---- Extracts from the minutes of our Yearly Meeting, held in Philadelphia...from the 15th of the Fourth month to the 19th...1822. [Philadelphia, 1822] 3 p. NjR.   8787

---- ---- Memorials concerning deceased Friends, being a selection from the records of the Yearly Meeting for Pennsylvania, &c., from 1788 to 1819, inclusive; 2d ed.   Philadelphia, S.W. Conrad, 1822. 184 p. InRchE; MH; MtBuS; PPL; PSC-Hi.   8788

---- Providence Yearly Meeting.
Boarding School Committee
The religious education of the youth in our society, hath been from time to time, when assembled in this capacity a subject of much concern...[Provi-

dence, 1822] 3 p. DLC.   8789

Frith, Edward
Contented cottager. New York, E. Riley [1822] [2] p. DLC.   8790

Fuller, Allen
Grammatical exercises; being a plain and concise method of teaching English grammar. Plymouth, Mass., A. Danforth, printer, 1822. 108 p. DLC; MBAt; NNC; PPL.   8791

Fuller, Andrew, 1745-1815
The backslider; or, An enquiry into the nature, symtoms and effects of religious declension, with the means of recovery.   Providence, Brown and Danforth, 1822. 40 p. MB; MH; MHi; MNtcA; NRCR.   8792

---- Reasons for believing that the future punishment of the wicked, will be endless. [Andover, Pr. for the New England Tract Society by Flagg & Gould, 1822] 12 p. MeB.   8793

Fulton, Robert
The advantages of the proposed canal from Lake Erie, to Hudson's River, fully illustrated... [New York, 1822] 13 p. MBAt.
8794
Furman, Richard
The crown of life promised to the truly faithful.   A sermon, sacred to the memory of the Rev. Edmond Botsford, A. M. late pastor of the Baptist Church in Georgetown, S.C. Preached in substance at Georgetown, March 19, 1820...Charleston, Pr. by Wm. Riley, 1822. 36 p. MH-AH; ScGrvF; TxU.   8795

G

Gales's North-Carolina almanack for 1823.   By John Beasley.

Raleigh, J. Gales & Son [1822]
18 ll. MWA; Nc; NcD; NcU.
8796

Gallup, Joseph Adams, 1769-
1849
Pathological reflections on the
supertonic state of disease.
Read before the Vermont Medical Society, convened at Montpelier, October 10, 1822. Montpelier, Pr. by E. P. Walton,
1822. 26 p. CSmH; MBM;
NNNAM; OC; BrMus. 8797

[Galt, John] 1779-1839
The provost, by the author of
Annals of the parish; Ayrshire
legatees; and Sir Andrew Wylie.
New York, pub. by Evert Duyckinck, J. & J. Harper, printers,
1822. 228, [5] p. CtHT; CtY;
MB; MBAt; MBL; MFiT; MH;
MWA; NICLA; NNC; NjR; ViAl.
8798
[----] Sir Andrew Wylie, of that
ilk by the author of "Annals of
the parish" etc. New-York, Pr.
for the bookseller, W. Grattan,
printer, 1822. 2 v. CtY; MAnP;
MH; MNBedf; NcU; ViAl; VtU.
8799

Gamble, William
To the public. To be com-
pelled to lay before my fellow
citizens the following documents
in order to sustain the character
for moral uprightness...William
Gamble. [1822] Bdsd. In. 8800

Garden, Alexander, 1757-1829
Anecdotes of the Revolutionary
War in America, with sketches
of character of persons the most
distinguished, in the Southern
states, for civil and military
services...Charleston (S. C.),
Pr. for the author, by A. E. Mil-
ler, 1822. xi, 459 p. CO;
CtHT; CtW; CtSoP; DLC; FSaW;
GHi; GU-De; ICU; M; MB;
MBAt; MDeeP; MH; MHi;
MNBedf; MdBJ; MdBP; MdHi;
MiDU; MiToC; MiU-C; NN;

NNC; NNP; NNS; NcD; NcU; Nj;
OC; OCY; OM; P; PPL; PU;
ScC; ScU; T; Vi; WHi. 8801

Gardiner Lyceum, Gardiner, Me.
An address to the public
from the trustees of the Gardiner Lyceum. Hallowell, Pr.
by Goodale, Glazier and Co.,
1822. 8 p. DLC; MB; MBAt;
MH; MHi; MNtcA; MWA;
MeGard; MeHi; MeU; MiD-B;
NCH; NN; PHi; PPL. 8802

Garrick, David
Miss in her teens: a farce,
in two acts. As performed at
the Philadelphia Theatre. Philadelphia, Thomas H. Palmer,
1822. 34 p. MWA. 8803

Gay, Ebenezer
The old man's calendar. A
discourse on Joshua xiv. 10...
Salem, Repr. by John D. Cush-
ing and Brothers, 1822. 36 p.
CtSoP; CtHT-W; ICMe; ICU;
IObB; MB; MBAU; MBrZ;
MDeeP; MH; MNe; MSaE;
MTaHi; MiD-B; MiU-C; NCH;
NN; NjR; OO; PHi; VtU. 8804

Gay, John
The beggar's opera. Boston,
Wells and Lilly, 1822. 71 p.
MeB. 8805

Gebauer, François René, 1773-
1844
Sixty progressive lessons arr.
either for one or two clarinets
and composed for the use of beginners. Baltimore, J. Cole &
Son [1822?] Pl. no. 839. 39 p.
MdBP. 8806

Geburts- und Taufschein. Allentaun, Gedruckt und zu haben bey
H. Ebner und Comp. 1822. Private library of Alfred L. Shoemaker, Schnecksville, Pa. 8807

Geib, George, 1782-1842

God save America. A patriotic song. New York, Pub. by the Author [1822?] 4 p. DLC; NN.   8808

---- Major Ross's march. New York, Pub. by the Author [1822?] 4 p. DLC.   8809

Der Gemeinnützige Landwirthschafts calender auf 1823. Von Carl F. Egelmann. Lancaster, Pa., William Albrecht [1822] 18 ll. CLU; DLC; MWA; PHi; PLF; PLHi; PPL; PPeSchw; PYHi.   8810

General Bozzari's Greek march and quick step. Arranged for the piano forte. New York, Raymond Meetz [1822?] 3 p. PP.   8811

General Theological Seminary, New York. See New York.
General Theological Seminary of the Protestant Episcopal Church.

A general view of the manners, customs, and curiosities of nations. See Phillips, Sir Richard.

Geological and agricultural survey of Rensselaer county. See Eaton, Amos.

Georgia
    Acts of the General Assembly of the state of Georgia, passed at Milledgeville, at an annual session, in November and December, 1822. Milledgeville, Pr. by James Camak, state printer, 1822. 172 p. CSfLaw; DLC; G-Ar; GHi; GMBC; GMilrC; GU-De; In-SC; L; MdBB; Mi-L; Mo; NNLI; Nb; Nj; Nv; W; Wa-L.   8812

---- A digest of the laws of Georgia... Comp. by Oliver H. Prince. Milledgeville, Grantland & Orme, 1822. 669 p. A-SC; Ar-SC; C; CSt; CU-Law; Ct;

CtW; DLC; G-Ar; GAFL; GEU; GHi; GMBC; GMW; GMilv; GU-L; ICLaw; IU; Ia; IaU; MH-L; MWCL; MdBB; Mi-L; MnU; Mo; MoK; NIC; NN; NT; Nb; Nv; OCLaw; OCIW; Ok; Or; PPL; R; RPL; TMeB; W; WaU; Wa-L.   8813

---- Journal of the House of Representatives of the state of Georgia at an annual session of the general assembly begun and held at Milledgeville... Nov. and Dec., 1822. Milledgeville, Pr. by James Camak, 1822. 271 p. DLC; G-Ar.   8814

---- Journal of the Senate of the state of Georgia, at an annual session of the general assembly, begun and held at Milledgeville, the seat of government, in November and December, 1822. Milledgeville, Pr. by James Camak, state printer, 1822. 271 p. G-Ar; GMilv.   8815

---- Message from the Governor [John Clark] transmitting communications from the different banks in this state, made in pursuance of an act of the legislature. In Senate, Nov. 20, 1822... Milledgeville, 1822. 16 p. WHi.   8816

---- Report of the Select Committee of the House of Representatives of the state of Georgia, to whom was referred so much of the Governor's message to both branches of the general assembly of 1822, as relates to Col. Abner Hammond, Secretary of State. House of Representatives, December 12, 1822. Read, and ordered to be printed. Milledgeville, Pr. by James Camak, 1822. 106 p. G-Ar; GU-De; NcD.   8817

---- A statement of warrants drawn on the treasurer during

the political year 1822, or, be-
tween the first Monday in Novem-
ber, 1821, and the first Monday
in November, 1822. House of
Representatives, Nov. 7th...
Milledgeville, 1822. 24 p. WHi.
                                    8818
The Georgia and South-Carolina
almanack for 1823. By Robert
Grier. Augusta, William J.
Bunce [1822] 18 ll. MWA.   8819

---- ---- Milledgeville, Ga.,
Camak & Rines [1822] 24 ll.
DLC.   8820

Gerhart, Isaac
    Choral Harmonie. Enthal-
tend Kirchen-Melodien, die bei
allen Religious Verfassungen
gebräuchlick... Harrisburg,
Gedruckt bey John Wyeth, 1822.
132 p. ODW; P; PNortHi; PPL;
PPeSchew; PPPrHi; PU.   8821

The German alphabet. Philadelphia, G.E. Blake [1822?] 1 l.
NN.   8822

Germoglio. Rondo. Composed
for these numbers. Philadelphia, B. Carr [1822] [2] p. NN;
PP.   8823

Gibbon, Edward, 1737-1794
    The history of the decline and
fall of the Roman empire... 3d
Amer. ed. New-York, E. Duy-
ckinck (etc.) 1822. 6 v. CtW;
CtY; ICU; ILebM; MA; NPV;
OM; ScCh; TSewU.   8824

Gibbons, Lee, pseud. See Bennett, William, English solicitor.

Gibson, Robert
    A treatise on practical sur-
veying; which is demonstrated
from its first principles... 3d
ed. Revised, corrected and
adapted in the use of schools.
By John D. Craig. Baltimore,
Pub. by F. Lucas, Jun. and

Cushing and Jewett, J. Robinson,
printer, 1822. 326 p. CtY;
ICU; IObB; InFtWL; InLPU;
LNB; MdBE; MdBP; MoS;
NNC; NNE; NNY; NSyU.   8825

Gildon, John
    Japanese air. An easy les-
son for the piano forte. New
York, Geib & co., [1822] 3 p.
DLC; RPB.   8826

---- The jubilee rondo. Composed and arranged for the piano
forte. New York, Dubois &
Stodart [1822] [2] p. DLC; MWA;
N; NBuG; NN; NRU-Mus. 8827

---- Juliana. A favorite dance.
Arranged for the harp or piano
forte. Baltimore, John Cole,
[1822] 3 p. MdHi.   8828

---- Six duettos for juvenile per-
formers on the piano forte. New
York, Geib & co. [1822?] 13 p.
NN; RPB.   8829

[Giles, William Branch] 1762-
1830
    Letters addressed to the
people of the United States, by a
native of Virginia, on the subject of illegal and improper disbursements of the public money,
&c. Originally pub. in the Federal republican. Part 1st...
Baltimore, F.G. Schaeffer, 1822.
59 p. CU; DLC; ICN; M; MB;
MH; MWA; MdHi; MiU-C; NcD;
NbU; Nh; OCLaw; PHi; PPL;
ScU; Vi; ViU.   8830

[----] ---- Cincinnati, Pr. by
Morgan, Lodge and Co., 1822.
47 p. DLC; OCIWHi.   8831

[----] Public defaulters brought
to light, in a series of letters
addressed to the people of the
United States, by native of Virginia. New York, E. Bliss and
E. White, 1822. 54 p. Ct;

CtHC; DLC; ICN; MB; MBAt;
MH-BA; MWA; MdBJ; MiD-B;
MiU-C; NCH; NcD; Nh; NjR;
OCHP; PPAmP; PPL; RPB; Vi;
WHi.   8832

Gilfert, Charles, 1787-1829
    The cypress wreath. New
York, A. & W. Geib [1822?]
[2] p. Wolfe 3032B.   8833

---- Six waltzes. For the piano forte. New York, A. & W.
Geib [1822?] 7 p. NN.   8834

Gilles, Peter, jr.
    La bergère délaissée. Phila-
delphia, Pub. and sold by the
Author [1822] 5 p. MWA; NN;
PP-K.   8835

Gilles, Henri-Noel, 1778-1834
    Grand march. Performed at
the ceremony of completing the
battle monument in Baltimore on
the twelfth of September, 1822.
Baltimore, John Cole [1822?]
[2] p. Wolfe 3100.   8836

Gillies, John
    The history of ancient Greece,
its colonies and conquests...2d
Amer. from the last London ed.
Philadelphia, Pub. by James Y.
Humphreys, I. Ashmead & co.,
printers, 1822. 4 v. C-S; CtB;
CtHC; CtHT; GMWa; GU; I;
IRoC; IaU; InThE; KTW; KyLoP;
KyLoS; MA; MB; MMe; MNF;
MSh; Md; MdBP; MoS; MsJMC;
NIC; NcAS; NcHil; NjN; OHi;
OW; PFal; PPDrop; PV; TNP;
Vi; ViU; WBeloC; WDo.   8837

[Gilpin, Joshua] Vicar of Wrock-
wardine, Eng.
    A monument of parental af-
fection, to a dear and only son
...2d ed. Boston, Lincoln &
Edmands, 1822. 87, [1] p. MB;
MBedfHi; MScitHi.   8838

Gilpin, Thomas

A mathematical drawing chart.
[1822] bdsd. DLC.   8839

Giuseppino, an occidental story.
See Bradley, William Henry.

Gloucester Canal Corporation
    Act of incorporation and by-
laws of the Gloucester Canal
Corporation: instituted 1822.
Salem, Pr. by W. Palfray, Jun.,
1822. 15 p. MSaE.   8840

Gock, Carl
    Politische Ausicht und Fort-
setzung der Vertheidigung der
Freyen Kirche in Nord-Amerika.
Reading, Pr. auf Kosten des
Verfassers, 1822. 119 p. Seid-
ensticker p. 218.   8841

---- Die Vertheidigund der Frey-
en Kirche von Nord-Amerika.
In sechs Abschnitten abgefasst
von Carl Gock...Reading, (Pa.)
1822. 120 p. CtHT-W; DLC;
MHi; PHi; PNaz; PPG; PPL;
PPLT; PPeSchw; PReaHi. 8842

Göde, Christian August Gottleib,
1774-1812
    A foreigner's opinion of Eng-
land, Englishmen, Englishwomen,
English manners, English mor-
als... Boston, Wells and Lilly,
1822. 444 p. CtHC; CtY; DLC;
GU; MB; MBL; MBev; MH;
MLy; MNBedf; MNe; MWA; Me;
NCH; NIC; NNS; NNUT; NRU;
NcU; PBa; PPL; PU; RNR; RP;
ScU; ViAl; VtU; WHi.   8843

Goldsmith, J., pseud. See
Phillips, Sir Richard.

Goldsmith, Oliver, 1728-1774
    An abridgment of the History
of England. From the invasion
of Julius Caesar to the death of
George the Second. Baltimore,
Armstrong and Plaskitt, 1822.
322 p. DLC; IAGG; MdBE; NcU;
NbU; OrPD; PU; WvU.   8844

---- ---- Baltimore, Franklin Betts, 1822. 320 p. MdW.   8845

---- ---- Baltimore, Coale, 1822. 322 p. ICP.   8846

---- ---- Baltimore, Cushing & Jewett(!); Matchett, printer, 1822. 322 p. MdBE.   8847

---- The Grecian history, from the earliest state, to the death of Alexander the Great.   7th Amer. ed.   Philadelphia, A. Small, 1822. 2 v. in 1. CtW; MB; MH; MMarl; MdW; NNC; O; PMA.   8848

---- ---- 7th Amer. ed. Baltimore, Abner Neal, 1822. 2 v. in 1.   NcW; ScDuE.   8849

---- ---- 7th Amer. ed. Baltimore, Pub. by Cushing and Jewett, Matchett, printer, 1822. 2 v. in 1.   MH.   8850

---- ---- Baltimore, E. J. Coale & Co., publishers; Matchett, printer, 1822. 335 p. NcW. 8851

---- ... She stoops to conquer. A comedy... Boston, Wells and Lilly, 1822. 102 p. CtY; MH; PPL.   8852

---- Vicar of Wakefield, a tale. Albany, Pub. by Daniel Steele and Son, Packard and Van Benthuysen, printers, 1822. 224 p. CtHT-W; MWborHi; N.   8853

The good boy's soliloquy, containing his parents' instructions, relative to his disposition and manners.   New York, Samuel Wood & sons, 1822. 30 p. MiD-B.   8854

[Goodenow, Sterling]
    A brief topographical and statistical manual of the state of New-York... 2d ed. enl. and imp.

New-York, Pub. by E. Bliss and E. White, Pr. by D. Fanshaw, 1822. 72 p. Ct; CtHT-W; CtY; DLC; MB; MBC; MH; MdBP; MiD-B; NBu; NIC; NN; NNC; NNG; NRU; NbU; OClWHi; PPAmP; PPL; PHi; RPB; ViL; WHi.   8855

Goodrich, Charles Augustus, 1790-1862
    A history of the United States of America... With engravings. Boston, Richardson, Lord & Holbrook, 1822.   379 p. RPB.   8856
---- ---- 35th ed.   Boston, Richardson, Lord & Holbrook; New York, Roe Lockwood (etc.) [1822] 296 p. CtY; IHi; MDovC. MHi; MWbor; NNC; NPV; PAtM; PIndt; REd; RNHi; TxD-T.   8857

---- ---- Hartford, S.G. Goodrich.   Sold by Howe & Spalding, New-Haven, E. & H. Clark, printers, Middletown (Conn.), 1822. vi, 344 p. CtHi; MMhHi.   8858

Goodrich, Jeremiah
    Murray's English Reader or pieces in prose and poetry... with a few preliminary observations on the principles of good reading and are divided, defined and pronounced according to the Principles of John Walker. Boston, J. Reed, 1822. (Stereotyped by J. Reed) 304 p. ILM; NPStA.   8859

[Goodrich, Samuel Griswold] 1793-1860, ed.
    Cabinet of curiosities, natural, artificial, and historical, selected from the most authentic records, ancient and modern... Hartford [E. & H. Clark, printers, Middletown, Conn.] 1822. 2 v. in 1. CtHT; CtHi; CtW; CtY; InCW; MA; MB; MDeeP; MWA (v. 2); MiDSH; MoS; NCoxHi;

NIl; NNC; NNS; NcAS; PFal;
ScCliJ; ScCMu.   8860

Goodwin, John
    Public sale. On...the...day
of October, 1822, at the residence of the subscriber, in
Honey Creek Prairie, Vigo county, Ind. the subscriber will sell
the following property...John
Goodwin. September 26, 1822.
Bdsd. In.   8861

Gordon, Alexander
    The design and use of the
book of Psalms in the New Testa-
ment Church, illustrated and
proved. Philadelphia, Hogan,
1822. 144 p. PPPrHi; ScDuE.
                                  8862
[Gore, Christopher] 1758-1827
    Remarks on the censures of
the government of the United
States, contained in the ninth
chapter of a book entitled:
"Europe; or a general survey"...
by a citizen of the United States
[A.H. Everett] Boston, Wells
& Lilly, 1822. 20 p. ICN; ICU;
M; MB; MBAt; MH; MHi;
MWA; MnU; MiD-B; MiU-C;
WHi.   8863

Gossler, J.C.
    Lebensgeschichte Napoleon
Bonaparte's des ersten Kaisers
der Franzosen, mit besonderer
Rücksicht auf dessen zehn-
jährige Regierung, Verbannung
und Tod...Reading, Gedruckt bei
Carl A. Bruckman, auf Kosten
des Verfassers...1822. 443,
[1] p. P; PAtM; PHi; PNortHi;
PPL; PReaHi.   8864

Gott gewidwete Dank-Empfindung-
en bey der Ecksteinlegung der
zu erbunenden Reformirten
Salems-Kirche nahe bey Hagerstaun, auf den 27sten May, 1822.
Hagerstaun, J. Gruber und D.
May, prs. [1822] 8 p. PPL.
                                  8865

Godd ist die reinste Liebe   See
Eckartshausen, Karl von, 1752-
1803.

Gould, Nathaniel Duren
    Penmanship; or, The beau-
ties of writing, exemplified in
a variety of specimens. Boston,
1822. 6 p. 3 plates. CoD; MH;
MHi.   8866

The Grace of God manifested in
the experience of Eliza Nares,
one of the children of a Sunday
school in Manchester. Who died
November 9th, 1817, aged 15
years. Hartford, George Goodwin & Sons, 1822. 34 p. CtHi;
MH.   8867

Graham Hamilton. See Lamb,
Lady Caroline (Ponsonby).

A grammar of natural and experimental philosophy. See
Phillips, Sir Richard.

Grand sport. At the new tavern
in South Salem...Grand sporting
match...turkeys, geese, ducks
and chickens exposed to sharp-
shooters...Eben Thrasher to
continue his sports...Salem,
Dec. 6, 1822. Bdsd. MSaE.
                                  8868
Granger, Frederick, 1770-1830
    The star of Bethlehem. A
sacred song. Boston, Pub. for
the Author by G. Graupner
[1822?] 4 p. DLC; MH; MHi;
MWA; N; NBuG; NN; PP-K;
RPB.   8869

Granium gazette. From the
Cave. 1st of the month Nisan,
A.L. 5822. 4 p. DLC.   8870

Gray, John Chipman, 1793-1881
    An oration, pronounced on the
Fourth of July, 1822, at the request of the inhabitants of the
city of Boston, in commemoration of the anniversary of nation-

al independence. Boston,
Charles Callender, 1822. 20 p.
CtSoP; CtY; DLC; KHi; M;
MBB; MBC; MBNEH; MBAt;
MH; MHi; MWA; MiU-C; NCH;
NNS; PHi; RPB.   8871

Gray, Thomas
    A sermon, on the religious
opinions of the present day, de-
livered in two parts, morning
and afternoon, on Lord's Day,
Sept. 23, 1821, to the Church
and Congregation of Jamaica
Plain, Roxbury. 2d ed. Boston,
Repr. by R.M. Peck, 1822. 48
p. CBPac; ICMe; MA; MBAU;
MBAt; MBC; MBD; MDeeP; MH;
MHi; MWA; MeBat; MeHi; MiD-
B; OCIWHi; WHi.   8872

Gray, William
    Both sides of the question.
Containing four publications of
the Rev. William Gray...relative
to some statements made by Wilson Thompson...in a public discourse on the subject of Baptism...Lebanon, O., Pr. for the
publisher by William A. Camron,
1822. 72 p. OOxM.   8873

Great Britain
    Anno tertio Georgii IV regis.
An act to regulate the trade between His Majesty's possessions
in America and the West Indies
and other places in America and
the West Indies passed 24th June,
1822. [New York, Geo. F. Hopkins, 1822] 24 p. MdHi;
PPAmP.   8874

---- Reports of cases adjudged
in the Court of King's Bench:
with some special cases in the
Court of Chancery, Common
Pleas, and Exchequer, alphabeti-
cally digested under proper
heads...from the 6th London ed.
Philadelphia, H.C. Carey & I.
Lea; and H.C. Carey & Co.,
New York, 1822. 3 v. CoSC;

CoU; Ct; DLC; F-SC; In-SC;
MBU-L; MH-L; MTa-B; Md;
MdUL; Mi-L; MiDU-L; MoKB;
MS; NcD; NUtSC; OCIW;
PPiAL; PU-L; TChU; WaU.
                          8875

---- Reports of cases argued
and determined in the English
courts of common law. Edited
by Thomas Sergeant and John C.
Lowber, Esqrs. of the Philadel-
phia Bar. Philadelphia, H.C.
Carey & I. Lea, 1822-76. 118 v.
C-L; Ct; CtW; In-SC; InU;
KyU-L; MBS; MdU-L; MiDU-L;
NUtSC; Nj; OCIW; OO; PPB;
U; ViU.   8876

---- Reports of cases, argued
and determined in the high court
of chancery during the time of
Lord Chancellor Eldon from the
commencement of the sittings
before Hilary term, 1818, to the
end of the sittings after Michael-
mas term, 1819. By Clement
Tudway Swanston...1st Amer.,
from 1st London ed., with notes
and references to Amer. cases,
by Henry W. Warner...New
York, Pub. by S. Gould & co.,
1822-28. 3 v. C; C-L; CtW;
ICLaw; MTaB; Md; MoKB; Nj;
OCIW; PP; PPB; PU-L; Tx-
SC; WaU.   8877

---- Reports of cases argued and
determined in the high courts of
chancery, in the time of Lord
Chancellor Eldon, 1812-1814...
1st Amer. from 2d London ed.
Compiled by Francis Vesey and
John Beames, with notes and
references to American cases
by Edward D. Ingraham, esq.,
editor. Philadelphia, H.C.
Carey and I. Lea, 1822. 3 v. in
2. CLSU; CSt; Co-SC; CoU;
CtW; IaDaGL; In-SC; MTaB;
MdUL; Mi-L; MiD-B; MiDU-L;
MnU; MsU; NIC-L; NNC-L;
NPSC; NScSC; NUtSC; NcD;
NcS; Nj; NjP; Nm; OCLaw;

OCIW; P; PP; PPB; PU-L;
TChU; TU; U; ViU; VtBrt;
WOshL; WaU; WvW-L.   8878

Great national object. See La-
cock, Abner.

The greatest sermon that ever
was preached. See Williams,
Thomas.

Green, Dr.
   Questions and counsel. Andover, Pr. by Flagg & Gould,
1822. 20 p. MeB.   8879

Green, Aaron
   A sermon delivered in Mal-
den, November 25th, 1821, the
Lord's day after the interment
of Capt. Jonathan Barrett, who
died November 18th AET 46.
Boston, Pr. by Ezra Lincoln,
1822. 16 p. DLC; MH; MMal;
Nh-Hi; RPB.   8880

Green, Ashbel, 1762-1848
   Discourses, delivered in the
College of New Jersey; ad-
dressed chiefly to candidates for
the first degree in the arts...
Philadelphia, E. Littell; New-
York, R. N. Henry (etc.) 1822.
xi, 419 p. CSansS; CtHT;
CtMW; CtY; DHEW; DLC; ICN;
ICP; ICU; MB; MBAt; MBC;
MH; MnHi; MdBE; MiD; NCH;
NNC; NNUT; Nj; NjN; NjP;
NjR; NjT; O; OC; OO; PMA;
PPL; PPPrHi; PU; PU-S;
PWW; RPB; WHi.   8881

---- Doing good in imitation of
Christ. A discourse delivered
in the College of New Jersey...
Sept. 22, 1822... Philadelphia,
& Trenton, E. Little, Pr. by
Clark & Raser, 1822. 27 p.
CSansS; MH; NjP; PHi; PLT;
PPPrHi.   8882

Green, John C.
   The doctrine of the Trinity

proved and established; or, The
doctrines and errors of the Unitarians exposed and refuted; in
a sermon, preached at Brucetown,
Va. April 21st, 1822. Winchester, Va., Pr. by S. H. Ravis
[sic] 1822. 48 p. MB; PPL.
                         8883
Green, Jones
   To the legislature of Virginia. The memorial of Jones
Green of Fredericksburg, Robert
C. Nicholas of Richmond, Archibald Taylor of the Borough of
Norfolk, Ethelred Lundy of
Greensville, Charles Pope of
Goochland, James O. Christian
of New-Kent, Robert Douthat of
Charles City, on behalf of them-
selves and others: respectfully
represents... 1822? Broadside.
Vi.   8884

Green, Samuel
   Life of Samuel Green, executed at Boston, April 25, 1822,
for the murder of Billy Williams, a fellow convict with
Green, in the state prison. Written by himself... Boston, David
Felt, 1822. 47 p. DLC; MB;
MBAt; NNLI.   8885

Greene, Charles
   An address, delivered at Li-
mington, before Adoniram Lodge
of Free and Accepted Masons,
on the festival of St. John the
Baptist, June 24, A. L. 5822.
Portland, A. Shirley, printer,
1822. 16 p. PPFM.   8886

Greenleaf, Benjamin, 1786-1864
   A concise system of grammatical punctuation, selected
from various authors, for the
use of students. 2d ed. with
improvements. Haverhill, Burrill and Hersey, printers, 1822.
16 p. MH; NN; NjR; RPB.
                         8887
Greenleaf, Jeremiah, 1791-1864
   Grammar simplified; or, An

ocular analysis of the English
language. 4th ed. corr. , enl.
and imp. by the author. New
York, Charles Starr, stereotyped by E. White; J. Fanshaw,
printer, 1822. 50 p. MS;
NAlbi; NHem; NPV; NRU; NjR.
8888

Greenville & Company
John Anderson, my Jo John.
[Dayton, 1822] Bdsd. OCIWHi.
8889

Gregory, G.
A new and completed dictionary of arts and sciences... New
York, Collins and co. , 1822.
3 v. MnSH; NR; NSyU.   8890

Gregory, Olinthus Gilbert
Letters to a friend, on the
evidences, doctrines and duties
of the Christian religion. From
the 4th London ed. , rev. and
slightly abridged... New York,
American Tract Society [1822]
480 p. CLSU; GDC; IaDmD;
IaMpI; IaPeC; KSalW; KU; MH-
AH; NCH; NNUT; OCIW; OO;
PPT; PPiW; RPB.   8891

Grenville, A. S.
Introduction to English grammar. To which are added exercises in parsing. Commencing
according to the natural arrangement of the several parts of
speech... Boston, Edgar W.
Davies, 1822. 63 p. CtHT-W;
MB; MBAt; MH; MMedHi; NNC.
8892

[----] Original poetic effusions.
Moral, religious, and sentimen-
tal. From the pen of A. S. G.
Boston, E.W. Davies, 1822.
206 p. CtY; DLC; MB; MH;
NNC; NHuntHi; PU; RPB. 8893

Griffin, Edward Dorr, 1770-1837
An address delivered to the
class of graduates of Williams
College, at the commencement,
Sept. 4, 1822... Pittsfield, Phine-
has Allen, 1822. 12 p. Ct; M;

MH; MHi; MPiB; MWiW; N;
NN; PLT; PPPrHi; ViRUT.
8894

Griffin, John
Memoirs of Captain James
Wilson, containing an account of
his enterprises and sufferings in
India... 1st Amer. ed. Boston,
Samuel T. Armstrong, and
Crocker and Brewster, 1822.
219 p. CLU; CtHT; CtY; DeWI;
DLC; GDC; ICP; IaHoL; MB;
MBC; MH; MLow; MPiB; MSaP;
MShM; MW; MWA; MWH;
MiD-B; NCH; NNMr; NNPrM;
Nh; OAU; ODaV; OSW; PPiW;
ScNC; ViRUT; WHi.   8895

Griffith, William
Annual law register of the
United States. By William Griffith, counsellor at law... Burlington, David Allinson [D. Allinson, printer] 1822. Vol. 3 &
4.   C; Ct; DLC; IaUL; LNBA;
LU; MBAt; MH; MdBB; MiL;
MnU; N; Nj; NjN; NjR; OrSC;
PPA; PPB; PPL; PU-L; WaU.
8896

Griggs, Joseph
To the qualified voters of the
first congressional district. ...
I, the undersigned... of Gibson
county, Indiana... have... re-
flected upon all the knowledge I
have regarding the said Dewey
and his conduct during the last
war... 22d of July, A.D. 1822.
Joseph Griggs. Bdsd. In. 8897

Grimshaw, William, 1782-1852
An exposition of the situation,
character, and interests of the
American republic... Philadelphia,
1822. 31 p. DLC; ICN; MHi;
PPL.   8898

---- History of the United States,
from their first settlement as
colonies, to the cession of Florida... 3d ed. Philadelphia, Pr.
for the author, by Lydia R.
Bailey, 1822. 308 p. CtY; DLC;

GMWa; InLW; MB; MH; MWA;
NNC; NjPT; OCl; P; PWW;
ViL.   8899

Griscom, J.
   Geographical questions... New
York, Samuel Wood & Sons,
1822. 124 p. CtHT-W.   8900

Gross, Thomas
   A sermon delivered at Lisle,
County of Broome, state of New
York, Lord's Day, January 3,
1819... Norwich, N. Y., Pr.
Providence, R. I., repr. by Jones
and Wheeler, 1822. 19 p. MA;
MMeT; RPB.   8901

Groton, Mass.-Work House
   Bye laws of the Groton Work
House. Approved May 6, 1822.
Concord, Mass., 1822. 8 p.
MH.   8902

Grotz, Christopher
   The art of making fireworks,
detonating balls, &c. New York,
S. King, 1822. 26 p. MH. 8903

Gruger, Eberhard Ludwig
   Eberhard Ludwin Gruvers
Grundforschende Fragen, welche
denen neuen Taufern in Mitgen-
steinischen, Insonderheit zu
Beantworten vorgelegt waren...
Lancaster, Gedruckt fur den
Verleger, von Johann Bar. 1822.
40 p. DLC; P; PHi; PPG.
                             8904

Guernsey, Countess of, pseud.
   Death-bed confessions of the
late Countess of Guernsey, to
Lady Hamilton... 1st Amer. from
the 1st London ed. Philadelphia,
pub. by James E. Moore; J.
Harding, printer, 1822. 104 p.
MB; MdToH; NNS; PPL.   8905

Guilford, Nathan, b. 1786.
   Letter addressed to the chairman of the board of school commissioners, by N. Guilford, one
of the commissioners. Colum-

bus, pr. at the office of the
Columbus Gazette, by P. H.
Olmsted, 1822. 7 p. O; OCLaw.
                             8906

Gummere, John, 1784-1845
   An elementary treatise on
astronomy. In two parts...
Philadelphia, Pub. by Kimber &
Sharpless; J. Crissy and G.
Goodman, printers, 1822. ix,
357 p. 98 tab., 6 fold. charts.
CSfA; CtY; ILM; IU; MB;
MBAt; MH; MeB; MiDSH; MiU;
NNC; NjMD; NjP; NjR; OCX;
OO; P; PHC; PPAmP; PPL;
PU; PSC-Hi; ScC; TNDL; TNL;
TNJ; ViFbE.   8907

---- Mathematical tables: differ-
ence of latitude and departure:
logarithms, from 1 to 10,000;
and artificial sines, tangents,
and secants. Stereotype ed.,
carefully rev. and cor. Philadelphia, Kimber & Sharpless,
1822. 152 p. 8 fold. pl. DLC;
IaDuU; NIC; NjR; OMC; PP.
                             8908
Gummere, Samuel R., 1789-
1866
   Definitions and elementary observations in astronomy; also,
problems on the globes... Philadelphia, Kimber and Sharpless,
1822. 138 p. CtW; DLC; MB.
                             8909
Guy Mannering. See Scott, Sir
Walter, bart.

Gwinn, John
   A narrative of facts [relative
to Dr. G. McClellan] [Philadel-
phia] 1822. 11 p. DNLM; MdBJ;
PPAmP; PPL.   8910

H

H., J.
   Letter to a deist in Baltimore, on his address to Unitarian ministers. By a resident of
Frederick. Frederick, Md., Pr.
for the publisher, Samuel Barnes,

pr., 1822. 14,[1] p. NjPT. 8911

---- Letter to a deist in Baltimore; shewing the futility of his arguments against the Scriptures, in his address to the Unitarian ministers. By a resident of Frederick City. Frederick (Md.) Pr. for the publisher G. W. Sharp, printer, 1822. 16 p. DLC. 8912

Hachenberg, Caspar Frederick
Elements of Greek grammar, taken chiefly from the grammar of Caspar Frederick Hachenberg. 3d ed. Hartford, Pr. for the proprietor; and sold by Huntington & Hopkins; Roberts & Burr, printers, 1822. [4], 224 p. CoU; CtHT-W; CtW; CtY; DLC; GDC; ICP; ICU; IGK; KyLoS; MB; MBC; MByDA; MiD-B; MH; NNC; NcRSH; NCH; OMC; OWoC; RPB; TBriK; ViU. 8913

Hackley, Richard S.
Titles, and legal opinions thereon, of lands, in East Florida, belonging to Richard S. Hackley, Esq. Brooklyn, Pr. by G. L. Birch, 1822. 122 p. MH-L; PPAmP; WHi. 8914

The Hagerstown town and country almanack for 1823. Hagerstown, Md., J. Gruber and D. May [1822] Drake 2495. 8915

Haight, Samuel S.
A reply to Col. Troup's defence of the agency of the Pulteney estate against the charge of exerting its influence in the state elections. [Geneva? N.Y.] Pr. for the author, 1822. 31 p. MB. 8916

[Haight, Sarah (Rogers)]
A medley of joy and grief... By a lady of New-York... New-York, pub. by W.B. Gilley,

Gray & Bunce, printers, 1822. 298 p. DLC; MB; MH; MsSC; NN; NNC; NjR; PU; RPB; RJa. 8917

[Haines, Charles Glidden]
A letter to the Hon. Micah Sterling, member of Congress from the state of New-York, on the expediency of adopting a uniform system of bankruptcy in the United States. New York, E. Conrad, 1822. 52 p. ICU; MB; MH; MHi; MWA; MiD-B; Nh; NjPT; PPL; RPB. 8918

Hall, Lorenzo T.
The American directory and traveller's companion... Boston, Pr. by True & Greene, 1822. 36 p. DLC; ScC. 8919

Hall, Nathan H.
A reply to the Right Rev. Bishop David's Vindication of the Catholic doctrine concerning the use and veneration of images... Lexington, Pr. for the author by Thomas T. Skillman, 1822. 111 p. ICU; KyU; OCHP; PPPrHi. 8920

Haller, Karl Ludwig von, 1768-1854
A letter of the celebrated Charles Lewis de Haller, member of the Sovereign council of Berne, to his family, informing them of his conversion to the Catholic, apostolical, and Roman church. Washington city, Pr. by W. Duncan, 1822. 33 p. DGU; DLC; IC; MdBS; MdBL; MdW. 8921

Hamilton, James
Eulogium, on Col. Wm. A Trimble, delivered... Feb. 2d, 1822... Carlisle, Phillips, 1822. 15 p. PPPrHi. 8922

Hamilton, pseud. See Carey, Mathew.

Hamilton College

Catalogue of the officers & students of Hamilton College, December 2, 1822. Utica, Pr. by Merrell and Gray, 1822. [15] p. N; NCH.   8923

Hammond, Anthony, 1758-1838

A practical treatise on parties to actions and proceedings civil and criminal... 1st Amer. from the last English ed. Exeter, N.H., Pub. by G. Lamson, J.J. Williams, printer, 1822. 352 p. C; DLC; IaU-L; In-SC; MH-L; MNan; MWCL; NNC-L; NNLI; NRAL; NhD; OCLaw; RPL; TU; TJaU; W.   8924

---- A digest of reports in equity... 1st Amer. ed. Brook-field (Mass.), Pr. for E. Hammond, 1822. xx, 860 p. C; DLC; ICLaw; IaMp; M; MWCL; NNLI; NhD; ViU; VtBrt.   8925

---- A digest of reports in equity... 1st Amer. ed. New York, Stephen Gould, 1822. xx, 860 p. CtHT; MH-L; MnU; NUtSC; PP; PPiAL; ViU; WvW-L.   8926

Hampden Sydney College, Hampden-Sydney, Va.

Catalogue of the officers and students of Hampden Sydney College, December, 1822. Richmond, Pollard, 1822. 15 p. PPPrHi.   8927

---- [Circular. Text begins:] Those, who are appointed... [Text p. 2 begins:] For the summer... [Richmond? 1822] [2] p. ViU.   8928

The hand of Providence manifested in a faithful narrative of real facts... New York, pub. by W. B. Gilley; C.N. Baldwin, printer, 1822. 144 p. IObB; MA.   8929

Handel, Georg Friedrich, 1685-1759

Holy holy, Lord. Philadelphia, G. Willig [1822?] p [1]-2. DLC; NN; RPB.   8930

---- Lord remember David. Philadelphia, G. Willig [1822?] [2] p. CtY; MH; NBuG; NN; PP; RPB.   8931

---- Handel's water music. For the piano forte. New York, Geib & co. [1822?] [2] p. MWA; NBuG; NHi; NN; RPB.   8932

Handel and Haydn Society, Boston.

A select oratorio in two parts, performed on the evening of the 10th of December, at Boylston Hall... Boston, T. Badger, Jr., 1822. 8 p. MB.   8933

---- A select oratorio in two parts, performed on the evening of the 12th of November, at Boylston Hall... Boston, Pr. by Thomas Badger, jr., 1822. 8 p. MBAt.   8934

Happiness: a tale for the grave and the gay... Boston, S.T. Armstrong and Crocker and Brewster; New York, John P. Haven, 1822. 2 v. CtY; LU; MB; MBAt; MBL; NcU; WBeloC; WHi.   8935

---- Vol. 1. Philadelphia, H.C. Carey & I. Lea, 1822. 240 p. PHi.   8936

The Happy novice. Philadelphia, B. Carr [1822?] [2] p. NN.   8937

The happy waterman. Ed. 3. [Andover] Pr. for the New England Tract Society by Flagg and Gould, 1822] 8 p. MPeHi. 8938

The happy waterman; or,

Honesty the best policy: an interesting history for children and youth. Salem, N.Y., Pr. by H. Dodd and Co., 1822. 24 p. N.   8939

Hardcastle's annual Masonic calendar; and pocket magazine [for 1823] New-York, J. Hardcastle [1822] 36 ll. NHi; NNFM.   8940

Hardie, James, 1750?-1826?
An account of the yellow fever, which occurred in the city of New-York, in the year 1822... New-York, Pr. by Samuel Marks, 1822. 120 p. CtY; DGU; DLC; ICJ; ICU; LNH; M; MB; MBM; MH; MnU; NBM; NBuG; NNA; NNNAM; NRU-M; P; PPC; WHi; WaSp.   8941

Hardin, Robert
A discourse delivered at Maryville, Ten. September 25, 1822, at the inauguration of the Rev. Isaac Anderson, A.M. as Professor of didactic and polemic theology in the Southern and Western Theological Seminary. Knoxville Register Office, Pr. by Heiskell & Brown, 1822. 17 p. NjPT; TKL-Mc.   8942

Hare, Robert, 1781-1858
Minutes of the course of chemical instruction in the medical department of the University of Pennsylvania... Philadelphia, William Brown, printer, 1822-3. 3 pts in 1. DNLM; MoSU-M; NcU; NjHoS; PPAmP; PCC; PPF; PPL; PU; WU.   8943

The Harp of love. New York, E. Riley, [1822?] [3] p. DLC; MH; PP.   8944

The harp of the beech woods. See Turner, Juliana Frances.

Harold, William Vincent

Brief remarks, addressed to a Catholic layman, on his late "Address to the Right Rev. the Bishop of Pennsylvania, the Catholic clergy of Philadelphia, and the congregation of St. Mary's in this city." By a Protestant Episcopalian... Philadelphia, Bernard Dornin, 1822. 18 p. DGU; DLC; NNUT; PPAmP; PPL-R.   8945

---- Remarks on the Catholic layman's Desultory examination. Philadelphia, B. Dornin, 1822. 33 p. DGU; DLC; MBAt; MdBS; MdW; PPAmP; PHi.
                                8946
---- A reply to a Catholic layman on his late "Address to the Rt. Rev. the Bishop of Pennsylvania, the Catholic clergy of Philadelphia and the congregation of St. Mary's in this city." Philadelphia, Bernard Dornin, 1822. 64 p. DGU; DLC; GAM-R; ICU; MBAt; MdBL; MiDSH; NIC; NN; PHi; PPAmP; PPPrHi.   8947

---- A reply to the Catholic layman's rejoinder. By William Vincent Harold, Pastor in St. Mary's. Philadelphia, Pr. by Bernard Dornin, 1822. 28 p. DLC; DCU; MBAt; MdBL; MdBP; NN; PPAmP; PPM; ScU.
                                8948
---- ---- Philadelphia, Pub. by the Catholic Layman, 1822. 18 p. DGU; MBAt; MdW; ScU.
                                8949
Harris, Thaddeus Mason, 1768-1842
A discourse delivered at Marblehead June 24, 1822, before the officers, members, and brethren of Philanthropic Lodge, immediately after the dedication of their new Masonic Hall, and in presence of Essex, Mount Carmel, and Jordan Lodges. Cambridge, Pr. by Hilliard and

Metcalf, 1822. 24 p. DLC; MB;
MBAt; MBNEH; MH; MMhHi;
NjPT; PPFM.   8950

---- A discourse delivered be-
fore the African society in Bos-
ton, 15th of July, 1822, on the
anniversary celebration of the
abolition of the slave trade.
Boston, Pr. by Phelps and
Farnham, 1822. 27 p. CtY;
DLC; MBAU; MBAt; MB; MWA;
MBC; MH; MHi; MdBJ; NN;
NcD; NjPT; OCIWHi; RPB;
TNF.   8951

[----] Song, for the celebration
of the 4th of July, 1822, at
Dorchester. [Dorchester?
Mass., 1822?] Bdsd. MB. 8952

[Harrison, Mrs. Elizabeth]
The friendly instructor: or,
A companion for young masters
and misses. By a lady. Boston, Lincoln and Edmands,
1822. 70 p. MH; MHi.   8953

Harrowar, David
A defence of the Trinitarian
system in twenty-four sermons;
in which the leading controversi-
al points between Trinitarians
and anti-Trinitarians, are stated
and discussed. Utica, Pr. by
William Williams, 1822. 336,
[6] p. CSansS; CtHC; DLC;
GAGTh; ICP; IEG; MiD-B;
NCH; NFred; NN; NR; NRC-R;
NSyU; NUt; OCX; OO; OWoC;
TBriK; VtU; WWooV.   8954

Hart, Joseph, 1712?-1768
Hymns, composed on various
subjects. 4th ed., rev. and
corr. Brunswick (Me.) Griffin
and Weld, 1822. 228 p. CSmH;
MeHi; NBuG; NjPT; RPB. 8955

Hartford, Conn. First Church
of Christ
A brief summary of Chris-
tian doctrine and a form of cove-

nant, adopted by The First
Church in Hartford July 29th,
1822, and publicly read on the
admission of members. Hartford, Pr. by Hudson and Co.,
1822. 18 p. Ct; CtHi; CtSoP;
CtY; MiD-B.   8956

Hartford County, Conn. Missionary Society
The Hartford County Missionary Society present the following
address to the people of the
county. [Hartford, 1822] 22 p.
CtSoP; CtY.   8957

Harvard University
Catalogue of the officers and
students of the University in
Cambridge. October, 1822.
Cambridge, University Press-
Hilliard and Metcalf, 1822, 16 p.
MBevHi; MiD-B; NjR.   8958

---- ...The course of instruction for undergraduates for the
last year is continued, with the
variations which have been, or
may be announced...[Cambridge,
1822] 1 l. CtY.   8959

---- Illustrissimo Johanni
Brooks, Armig, LL.D. Guber-
natori; honoratissimo Gulielmo
Phillips, Armigero, Vice-Guber-
natori...Exercitationes hasce
juvenes in artibus initati. Die
August XXVIII Anno Salutis
MDCCCXXII...Typis Academicis
Excudevat Hillard et Metcalf.
3 p. DLC.   8960

---- Senior sophisters. 1822.
[Cambridge? Mass., 1822]
Bdsd. MB.   8961

---- A statement of the course
of instruction, terms of admission, expenses. Catalogue of
the officers and students of the
University in 1822. Cambridge,
Pr. by University Press-Hilliard
& Metcalf, 1822-23. 30, 17 p.

MBC.   8962

---- Porcellian Club
Catalogue of the honorary
and immediate members of the
Porcellian Club, of Harvard Uni-
versity, Cambridge, Mass. In-
stituted 1791. Boston, Pr. by
Wells and Lilly, Aug. 1822. 22 p.
MBAt; MHi; MWA.   8963

Harwood, Edward, 1707-1787
A revised copy of The dying
Christian. A celebrated ode.
Philadelphia, Pr. for B. Carr
[1822?] 3 p. Wolfe 3456.   8964

Hastings, Thomas, 1784-1872
Appendix to Musica sacra:
consisting of anthems and miscellaneous pieces, original and
selected.   Arranged for the organ or piano forte... Albany,
Steele, 1822. 54 p. ICN;
NNUT; NRU-Mus.   8965

---- Dissertation on musical
taste; or, General principles of
taste applied to the art of music.
Albany, Pr. by Websters and
Skinners, 1822. 228 p. CtHC;
CtHT-W; CtY; DLC; ICN; ICU;
MA; MB; MBC; MWA; MdBL;
MdBP; MiU; MoSU; N; NBuG;
NIC; NN; NNUT; NR; NcU;
NjPat; OO; OU; OWoC; PPL;
PU; TxU; VtNofN; VtU;
WBeloC; WU.   8966

---- Flute melodies... Utica,
N. Y., William Williams, 1822.
48 p. CtHT-W; DLC; MH;
NRU-Mus; ViU.   8967

---- Musica sacra; or, Springfield and Utica collections
united; consisting of psalm and
hymn tunes, anthems and
chants; arranged for two, three
or four voices... 3d rev. ed.
Utica, William Williams, 1822.
277, [3] p. CSt; CtHT-W;
CtSoP; CtY; DLC; ICN; IU;

MWA; NNUT; NUt; OCIWHi;
OO; OT; TxU.   8968

---- A new collection of flute
melodies; consisting of airs,
marches, cotillions, duets,
songs, waltzes, &c. ... Utica,
William Williams, 1822. 47 p.
NCooHi.   8969

Hawes, Joel
'What hath God wrought!" A
sermon, delivered in Hartford,
on the last Sabbath of the year.
Hartford, Hudson, 1822. 20 p.
OCIW.   8970

Hawes, William, 1785-1846
We're noddin at out house at
hame.   The popular ballad. New
York, Dubois & Stodart [1822?]
3 p. MB; MH; MWA; N; NBuG;
PP.   8971

Hawley, William, d. 1845
A letter to the Rt. Rev.
James Kemp, Bishop of the
Protestant Episcopal Church in
the diocese of Maryland; and an
address to the congregation of
St. John's church in the city of
Washington... Sunday, Dec. 9,
1821. Washington City, Davis
& Force, 1822. 8 p. CBPac;
CtY; DLC; MBAt; MBC; MH;
MHi; MdHi; NjPT; PMA;
PPAmP; PPL; ScU.   8972

---- Letter to the Right Rev.
James Kemp, D.D., in defence
of the clergy of the District of
Columbia, against certain charges
preferred against them in his
late pastoral letter... Washington, Pr. by W. Duncan, 1822.
31 p. DLC; MH; MdBD; MdHi;
NNG; NjPT; OCHP; PPL.   8973

Hawley, Zerah, 1781-1856
A journal of a tour through
Connecticut, Massachusetts,
New-York, the north part of
Pennsylvania and Ohio, including

a year's residence in that part of
the state of Ohio, styled New
Connecticut, or Western Re-
serve... New-Haven, Pr. by S.
Converse, 1822. 158 p. Ct;
CtHi; CtSoP; CtY; DLC; MB;
ICN; MiU-C; N; NBLiHi; NN;
OCIWHi; OHi; PPi; RPat; WHi.
8974

Hawney, William
   Hawney's Complete measurer;
or, The whole art of measuring
...5th ed. Baltimore, F. Lucas,
Jr., 1822. 312 p. MdHi.   8975

Hay, George, Bp.
   The sincere Christian in-
structed in the faith of Christ
from the written word.   1st
Amer. ed.   Philadelphia, Ber-
nard Dornin, Wm. Fry, printer,
1822. 2 v. DGU; IaDuMtC;
ICLay; MBBC; MdBL;
MWA; MdW; MiDSH;
PPCHi; PWmp.   8976

Hay, James D.
   "Thy cheek has borrowed
from the rose." Song. With an
accompaniment for the piano
forte.   Boston, Pub. for the
Author, by G. Graupner [1822?]
p [1]-2.   MH; NRU-Mus.   8977

Haydn, Franz Joseph, 1732-1809
   Selections from the oratorio
of The creation.   Philadelphia,
G. Willig [1822]   37 p.
MB; MiU-C; NN.   8978

---- The words of The creation
of the world, a sacred oratorio
by Joseph Haydn.   As performed
by the Musical Fund Society of
Philadelphia, at the Washington
Hall, June 10, 1822. With notes,
critical and explanatory, a memoir of Haydn, &c.   Philadelphia,
Musical Fund Society., T.H.
Palmer, Pr., 1822. 12, 16 p. P;
PHi; PPAmP; PPL.   8979

---- To sigh yet feel no pain.

Boston, E.W. Jackson [1822?]
p [1]-2.   MB; MWA; NN; RPB.
8980
---- ---- New York, E. Riley
[1822?] [2] p. NRU-Mus.   8981

---- With verdure clad.   From
Haydn's oratorio of The creation.   Philadelphia, G. Willig
[1822] p 3-8.   DLC; MB; MH;
MWA; NN; PP-K; RPB.   8982

No entry.   8983

Haynes, Lemuel, 1753-1833
   Universal salvation...A ser-
mon delivered at Rutland, West
Parish [Vt.] in the year 1805.
Providence, Repr. in 1822. 12 p.
CtY; DLC; MB; NN.   8984

Hazard, Ebenezer
   Historical collections; consisting of state papers, and other authentic documents; intended
as materials for an history of
the United States of America.
Philadelphia, Pr. by T. Dobson,
for the author, 1822. 2 v.
NNHuC.   8985

Hazen, Jasper
   The primary instructor and
improved spelling book.   Woodstock [Vt.] D. Watson, 1822.
156 p. DLC; MH; NhD; VtHi.
8986
---- ---- 2d ed. Windsor, Pr.
by Simeon Ide, 1822. 84 p. MH.
8987
The heart of man, either a
temple of God, or a habitation
of Satan represented in ten em-
blematical figures...Trans. from
the 5th German Augsburg ed.
Reading, Pa., H.B. Sage, 1822.

48 p. IU; MH; NSchU; PHi;
PPL.   8988

The heavenly pilot.   Andover,
Flagg & Gould, printers, 1822.
12 p. MeB.   8989

Hedding, Elijah
    The supreme deity of Christ
proved, the substance of a ser-
mon, delivered in Bath, Me.
July 4, 1822, before the New
England Conference ...of the
Methodist Episcopal Church.
Boston, Lincoln & Edmands,
1822.   32 p. DLC; IEG; IObB;
MBAt; MBC; MBNMHi; MWA;
MeHi; NNMHi; PPPrHi.   8990

Heidelbergh catechism...as
taught in Reformed Churches
and schools in the United States
of America, and Europe. Philadelphia, George W. Mentz, 1822.
88 p. MoWgT; PLT.   8991

Hemenway, Moses
    The manufacturer's, farmer's
and mechanic's guide; being a
compilation of the most valuable
receipts, for manufacturers,
agriculturists, and mechanics.
Pittsburgh, Pr. for the compiler,
1822. 175, [4] p. OClWHi.   8992

Henderson's almanack for 1823.
By John Beasley.   Raleigh, N. C.,
Thomas Henderson [1822] 18 ll.
MWA; NcD; NcU; TKL.   8993

Hendree, John
    John Hendree's Proofs against
the many falsehoods propagated
by one Abel P. Upshur: together with an exposure of the
man, & his pamphlet, entitled
"A. P. Upshur of Richmond, to
the Citizens of Phila." Richmond, Va., Pr. by Shepherd &
Pollard, 1822. 118 p. MWA;
PPC.   8994

---- Refutation of calumnies

propagated by Abel P. Upshur
of Richmond... By John Hendree
...Richmond (Va.) 1822. 23 p.
MWA; NcD; PPL.   8995

Henkel, Charles
    Eine Predigt über die Kinder-
zucht, welche gehalten wurde,
in Columbus, Ohio, im Jahr un-
sers Herrn 1821.   Neu-Market,
S. Henkel, 1822. 20 p. DLC;
MWA; NcD; PHi; PPL; TKL-
Mc; Vi; ViHarHi; ViNmT; ViU;
ViW.   8996

Henley, Robert Henley Eden, 2d
baron, 1789-1841
    A treatise on the law of in-
junctions. By the Hon. Robert
Henley Eden...1st Amer. ed.,
with notes and references to
American decisions.   Albany,
W. Gould and co.; New York,
Gould and Banks, 1822. 336 p.
ArU; CU; DLC; IaU; LNT-L;
MBS; MH-L; MiD-B; MsWJ;
NNIA; NPSC; NcD; Nj; OCLaw;
PU-L; TMeB; ViU; W; WaU;
WyU.   8997

Henry, Robert
    Eulogy on Jonathan Maxcy,
late president of the S. C. College, pronounced in the chapel
of the institution...Dec. 6, 1820.
Columbia, S. C., State Gazette
office, 1822. 14 p. ScU. 8998

Henry, William, 1774-1836.
    The elements of experimental
chemistry, ...2d Amer. from
the 8th London ed. (with a sup-
plement containing the new mat-
ter of the 9th)...Philadelphia, R.
Desilver, 1822-23.   3 v. CtW;
CtY; DLC; DNLM; GEU; ICJ;
IEN-M; IU; IaBo; KyLxT;
KWiF; MB; MBM; MH; MdBM;
MiU; NNCoCi; NWM; NcU;
OClW; OClWHi; OSW; PPC;
ScCC; ViNoM; ViU; WaPS.
                             8999
Henshaw, John Prentiss Kewley,

1792-1852
Address to the trustees of St. Peter's School, to the congregation of St. Peter's Church and to the public. [Baltimore, 1822] 6 p. RPB.   9000

---- Charity to poor children, enforced in a sermon, delivered on Sunday, the third of November, 1822, for the benefit of St. Peter's Free School, Baltimore ... Baltimore, Pr. by J. Robinson, 1822. 22, [1] p. MdBD; MdBJ-G; NjPT; PPL; TJaU.
                                9001
[----] A selection of hymns, for the use of social religious meetings... Philadelphia, S. Potter & Co., 1822. 212 [4] p. DLC; NNUT.   9002

Hentz, Nicholas Marcellus, 1797-1856
A manual of French phrases, and French conversations: adapted to Wanostrocht's grammar... Boston, Pub. by Richardson and Lord; J.H.A. Frost, printer, 1822. 154 p. CtHT-W; CtMMHi; CtW; MB; MBAt; MH; MWHi; MeHi; NIC; NNC. 9003

Herkimer (N.Y.) Bible Society
The fifth annual report of the Herkimer Bible Society, and a sermon on the divinity of the Bible, delivered 12th February, 1822, by Rev. John B. Spinner. Herkimer [N.Y.] Pr. by Edward P. Seymour, 1822. 18 p. N; NjR.   9004

Hervey, James, 1714-1758
Meditations & contemplations ... New York, Holmes & Samo, 1822. 434 p. Ct; CtW; LJI; InID; KyHe; MB; MPiB; NNUT; NPV; OO; OrPD; PSC; ScP.
                                9005
Das Herz des Menschen, ein Tempel Gottes oder eine Wekstätte Satans. In zehn Figuren sinn-

bildlich dargestellt... Nach der fünften verbesserten Augsburger Auflage, 1815. Reading, Heinrich B. Sage, 1822. 48 p. MH; PHi; PPL.   9006

Hewett, Daniel
The traveller's guide through the United States, and brief geographical view of the world. New York, pub. for the author, at No. 73 Vesey street, March, 1822. 30 p. CtHT-W; MH-AH; NNA; NNS; PPL.   9007

Hibernicus, pseud. See Clinton, DeWitt, 1769-1828.

Highmore, Anthony, 1758-1829
A treatise on the law of idiocy and lunacy...1st Amer. from the last London ed. Exeter, N.H., George Lamson, 1822. 194 p. DLC; ICJ; ICLaw; IaU-L; MB; MBS; MsWJ; NN; NNLI; NRAL; Nj; NjR; OCLaw; VtBrt.   9008

Hill, Benjamin Munro, b. 1793
A sermon, preached June 24th, 1822, at North-Mansfield, Conn. before Trinity chapter, Uriel, Eastern-stand and Worren lodges. Hartford, Bowles and Francis, pr., 1822. 16 p. MH.   9009

Hillard, Isaac
A wonderful and horrible thing is committed in the land. Hamilton, O., Repr. at the Volunteer office by J.L. Murray, 1822. 118 p. CSmH; DLC; ICN; OCIWHi; OOxM; T.   9010

[Hillhouse, William] 1757-1833
The three witnesses. New Haven, Gray & Hewit, printers, 1822. 35 p. CtY.   9011

Historical notices of the New North Religious Society. See Eliot, Ephraim.

The history of beasts & birds,
for the amusement and instruction of children... Portsmouth,
N. H. , Herald press, 1822. [16]
p.   DLC.   9012

The history of George Desmond,
founded on facts which occurred
in the East Indies... Boston, S.
T. Armstrong and Crocker &
Brewster, 1822. 209 p. NN.
                               9013
The history of Jacob; a scrip-
ture narrative, in verse.   New-
York, Pub. by Samuel Wood and
sons; and Samuel S. Wood &
Co. , Baltimore, 1822. 31 p.
CtMMH; DLC; MiGr.   9014

History of John Robins, the
sailor.   Hartford, George Goodwin & sons, 1822. 16 p. CtHi.
                               9015
The history of modern Europe,
from the treaty of Amiens. See
Coote, Charles.

The history of modern Europe,
with an account of the decline
and fall of the Roman Empire.
See   Russel, William.

History of the Bible.   Lansingburgh, Wm. Disturnell [G. J.
Loomis & Co. , printers] 1822.
255 p. NbHM.   9016

History of the trial of Truman
Dixon... held at Malone, April 2,
1822... Malone, N Y. , Pr. at
the Telegraph Office, 1822. 34 p.
MA.   9017

History of the United States of
America.   See   Prentiss,
Charles.

Hitchcock, Henry, compiler.
   The Alabama justice of the
peace, containing all the duties,
powers and authorities of that
office... William B. Allen and
Ginn & Curtiss, 1822. [2], 494,

[1] p. A-Ar; AB; AMob; AMonA;
AU; CSmH; ICN; MH-L; NN;
TxU.   9018

Hoadly, Benjamin, 1706-1757
   ... The suspicious husband, a
comedy... Boston, Wells and
Lilly, New-York, A. T. Goodrich & co. , 1822. 110 p. CtY;
MH; MeB; NN; PPL; RPB.
                               9019
---- ---- Philadelphia, T. [Pal-
mer? 1822?] 76 p. (Imperfect:
title page mutilated, part of imprint lacking.) MH.   9020

Hobart, John Henry, bp.
   An introductory address, on
occasion of the opening of the
General Theological Seminary of
the Protestant Episcopal Church
in the United States of America.
New-York, Pr. by T. and J.
Swords, 1822. 40 p. A-Ar;
CtHT; InID; MB; MBC; MHi;
MWA; MiD-B; NBLiHi; NCH;
NGH; NIC; NN; NNC; NNG;
NNS; NNUT; NcU; NjR; PHi;
PPAmP; PPL; TChU.   9021

---- An introductory lecture to
a course of religious instructions
for young persons... New York,
T. & J. Swords, 1822. 8 p.
NNG; NNS.   9022

Der Hoch-Deutsche American-
ische Calender auf 1823. Von
Carl Friedrich Egelmann. Ger-
mantaun, Pa. , M. Billmeyer
[1822] 18 ll. CLU; CtY; DLC;
DeWint; InU; MH; MWA; NHi;
NN; PAtM; PHi; PYHi; PLF;
PPL; PDoBHi; PPAmP;
PPeSchw; WHi.   9023

Hoch-deutsches Lutherisches A
B C und Namen-Buchlein... 3.
Ausgabe.   Reading, Johann Rit-
ter und Comp. , 1822. 32 p. NN;
PPL.   9024

Hodge, Charles

A dissertation on the impor-
tance of Biblical literature...
Trenton, Pr. by George Sher-
man, 1822. 51 p. CSansS; ICP;
MH-AH; NNG; NjP; NjR; PLT;
PPPrHi.   9025

Hofland, Mrs. Barbara (Hoole)
  Tales of the manor. New
York, E. Bliss & E. White,
1822. 2 v. CtHC; CtY; MBAt;
MBL; TVP.   9026

Hogan, William
  An answer, to a paragraph
contained in the United States
Catholic miscellany, edited by
the Bishop of Charleston, under
the title-Philadelphia. Philadelphia, 1822. 39 p. DLC; KyLoP;
PHi; PPAmP; PPPrHi.   9027

---- A pastoral charge, and a
specimen of classical latinity, or
The Latin commonwealth, vw.
William Pastor. [Signed] Guliel-
mus Hogan. Pastor Ecclesiae
Sanctae Mariae. Philadelphia,
13th Februarii A.D. 1822. 3 p.
DLC.   9028

---- Reply to sundry letters of
...Dr. England to the Bishop of
Philadelphia... Philadelphia, E. F.
Crozot, 1822. 56 p. DLC; PHi;
ScCC.   9029

---- Strictures on a pamphlet
written by William Vincent Har-
old entitled Reply to a Catholic
layman. Philadelphia, Robert
Desilver, 1822. 28 p. DLC;
DGU; MdW; NIC; NNUT;
PPAmP; PPM; PPL; PPPrHi;
PHi.   9030

Holcombe, Henry
  Primitive theology, in a se-
ries of lectures. Philadelphia,
Pr. for the author by J. H. Cun-
ningham, 1822. 300 p. IObB;
MdBD; NRAB; PCC; PPL;
RNR; ViU.   9031

---- ---- Philadelphia, Pr. for
the author, by J. H. Cunningham, 1822. xii, 307 p. GHi;
GU.   9032

---- A reply to objections
against his performance on Primitive theology... Philadelphia, Pr.
for the author, 1822. 24 p.
MeB.   9033

Holcroft, Thomas, 1745-1809.
  ... Deaf and dumb, an histor-
ical drama... Boston, Wells and
Lilly; New-York, A. T. Good-
rich & Co., 1822. 93 p. CtHT-
W; CtY; DeGE; MB; MH; MeB;
PPL.   9034

---- ... The road to ruin, a
comedy... Boston, Wells and
Lilly, New York, A. T. Good-
rich & Co., (etc.) 1822. 124 p.
CtHT-W; CtY; MH; MeB; PPL;
WM.   9035

Holder, Joseph William, 1765-
1832
  La petite sonate pour le piano
forte. New York, Dubois &
Stodart [1822] 5 p. DLC. 9036

[Holland, Edwin Clifford]
  A refutation of the calumnies
circulated against the southern
and western states, respecting
the institution and existence of
slavery among them... By a
South-Carolinian. Charleston,
Pr. by A. E. Miller, 1822. 86 p.
DLC; ICN; MBAt; MH; MdBJ;
NBLiHi; NN; NcU; PHi; PPAmP;
RP; ScC; ScU; Vi; Wv.   9037

Holley, Orville Luther, 1791-
1861
  An address delivered at the
request of the Mount-Moriah
Lodge at Palmyra, 24 June,
A. L. 5822, it being the anniver-
sary of St. John the Baptist.
Palmyra, N. Y., Pr. by T. C.
Strong, 5822 [1822] 13 p.

MH.   9038

---- An oration on the perman-
ency of republican institutions
delivered at Lyons, July 4,
1822. Lyons, N.Y., H.T. Day,
1822. 25 p. NCH.   9039

Holman, David
   A discourse delivered at Ux-
bridge, Mass., before Solomon's
Temple Lodge, in conjunction
with several others, on the festival of St. John the Baptist, June
24, A.L. 5822. Providence,
Miller and Hutchens, 1822. 16,
iii, [1] p. CBPSR; MWA; RPB;
BrMus.   9040

Holmes, Abiel
   A sermon delivered at the fu-
neral of the Rev. David Osgood,
D.D. pastor of the Church in
Medford, who died 12 December,
1822, in the 76th year of his
age, and 48th of his ministry.
Cambridge, Pr. by Hilliard and
Metcalf, 1822. 24 p. CtHC;
CtSoP; DLC; ICMe; M; MB;
MB-FA; MBC; MBNEH; MH-AH;
MHi; MWA; MiD-B; MiU-C;
NNG; NNUT; Nh-Hi; OCHP;
PHi; VtMiM.   9041

[Holmes, Isaac Edward]
   Recreations of George Taletell, F.Y.C. (pseud.) Charleston, Duke & Browne, printers,
1822. 74 p. CtY; DLC; MH;
PHi; PPAmP; ScCC; ScU.   9042

Holst, Matthias von, 1767-1854
   Cottage rondo. Charleston,
J. Siegling [1822?] 4 p. NN;
ScU.   9043

Holyoke, Edward Augustus
   Literature and science of the
United States. Memorial by Ed-
ward A Holyoke, and others to
Congress. From the Salem Ga-
zette, January 18, 1822. Bdsd.
MSaE.   9044

Homerus.
   Homeri Iliadis. Libri novem
priores librique XVIII, et XXII.
Ex Recensione C. G. Heyne...
Catskill, Veneunt apud N. Elli-
ott. Andoveriae, E. Prelo
Codmoniano, Flagg et Gould
Typographis. MDCCCXXII. 352 p.
CtY; IC; MH; N; NCH; NCaS;
NCoxHi; NOssMF; NPV; PMA.
                               9045

---- The Iliad of Homer; trans-
lated by Alexander Pope. Two
volumes in one. Philadelphia,
I. Ashmead & Co., printers for
Samuel F. Bradford, 1822. 2 v.
CtHT; CtY; KAStB; MNBedf;
P; PP; PU; TNJ.   9046

---- The Odyssey of Homer,
translated from the Greek by
Alexander Pope, esq. New
York, Myers & Smith, 1822. 2
v. CSansS; CStclU; CtHT; CtY;
IJI; MH; MiToC; MoSMa; NjP;
OCHP; ScCMu.   9047

---- ---- Philadelphia, I. Ashmead & Co., printers. Published by Samuel F. Bradford,
for John Laval, Philadelphia;
James Eastburn, New York; and
Charles Ewer & Timothy Bedlington, Boston, 1822. 502 p.
CtHT; KyLx; MMidb; P; PP;
PU.   9048

The honest thieves. See Howard,
Sir Robert.

Honour to the brave...It is an
act of justice to our worthy candidate for mayor, Captain Car-
berry, to narrate to our fellow
citizens a few of the distinguished
acts of his military career...
[Washington, 1822] 1 p. DLC.
                               9049

Hook, James, 1746-1827
   The garland of love. With
variations for the piano forte.
New York, P.K. Moran [1822?]
10 p. MWA.   9050

---- Morning. From the hours of love. Come, come my fair. New York, E. Riley [1822?] 3 p. NBuG; NN.   9051

---- The wedding day. A favorite song. New York, E. Riley [1822?] [2] p. NN.   9052

[Hook, James] 1772?-1828
    Pen Owen [a novel]... New York, Collins & co. (etc.) 1822. 2 v. CtHT; CtY; DLC; GHi; IU; MBAt; MBL; NCH; NcU; ViAl.   9053

Hooper, Robert
    Lexicon-medicum; or, Medical dictionary, containing an explanation of the terms in anatomy, physiology, etc. ... From the 4th London ed. New York, pub. by E. Bliss and E. White, J. and J. Harper, printers, 1822. viii, 953 p. DLC; NBMS; NBuU-M; OClM; PPC.   9054

---- ---- From the 4th London ed. New York, pub. by E. Duyckinck, Collins & Co., Collins & Hanney, and Samuel Wood & Sons, J. & J. Harper, printers, 1822. viii, 953, [5] p. CoDelta; IU-M; MMilt; MoSMed; NhD.   9055

[Hopkins, George F.]
    Observations on electricity, looming, and sounds. By Hortensius. New York, Pr. by George F. Hopkins, 1822. 24 p. CtHT-W; DLC; MB; NjR.   9056

Hopkins, Samuel Miles, 1772-1837
    Speech... upon... Taxing bank stock. Albany, 1822.   15 p. Sabin 32962.   9057

Horace of Cincinnati, pseud. See Pierce, Thomas, 1786-1850.

Horn, Charles E., 1786-1849

Deep in a hollow glen! New York, A. & W. Geib [1822] 6 p. N; NN.   9058

---- The rose of love! Boston, S. Wood [1822?] p [1]-2. DLC; MH; RPB.   9059

Hornblower, Joseph C.
    An address, delivered before the Newark Female Auxiliary Bible Society, at their annual meeting. Newark, N.J., John Tuttle, 1822. 8 p. CSmH; NjP; NjPT; PPPrHi.   9060

Horne, George, bp.
    A commentary on the book of Psalms... Philadelphia, pub. and sold by Alexander Towar... James Anderson, printer, 1822. 632 p. CtHC; CtY; DLC; ICP; IGK; IaDmD; InCW; KSalW; KyLoS; L; MA; MB-W; MBC; MH; MH-AH; MHi; MMaL; MdW; MeAu; MsJPED; NN; NbOP; NjPT; OkU; PPDrop; PPP; PPiW; ViRVal; VtU.
                                    9061
---- The doctrine of the Trinity, stated, and defended, in a sermon by Bishop Horne, and in extracts from the American edition of Mant and D'Oyl's family Bible, edited by Bishop Hobart... New York, T. & J. Swords, 1822. 26 p. DLC; MWA; MdHi; NjR; PPL.   9062

Horrid murder and suicide being an authentic account of a most tragical event, which took place in the upper part of South Carolina, on Sunday, July 21, 1822. Mrs. Brock, having a fit of insanity, first drowned one of her children in the well, and then hung herself... Boston, Pr. for Nathaniel Coverly, 1822. 24 p. MBNEH.   9063

Hortense, Queen of Holland, 1783-1837

The knight errant. Philadelphia, Pr. for B. Carr [1822?]
1 l. MH.   9064

---- ---- Philadelphia, G. E. Blake [1822?] 11 p. DLC.   9065

Hortensius, pseud. See Hopkins, George F.

Hosack, David
Observations on cruritis, or phlegmasia dolens... New York, Pr. by C. S. Van Winkle, printer to the University. 1822. 7 p. DNLM; NBM; NNNAM; NNU-M.
                            9066
---- Observations on ergot; communicated in a letter to James Hamilton, M. D. , F. R. S. E. New York, Pr. by C. S. Van Winkle, 1822. 7 p. DNLM; MH-M; NBM; NNNAM; NjP.   9067

---- Observations on the use of emetics in constipation of the bowels. Communicated in a letter to John B. Beck. New York, C. S. Van Winkle, 1822. 8 p. DLC; MH-M; NBMS; NNNAM; NNU-M.   9068

Housatonic Canal Company
Proposals for the stock of the Ousatonic Canal Company. [New Haven, A. H. Maltby & co. , print. , 1822?] 16 p. CtY. 9069

[Howard, Sir Robert] 1626-1698
... The honest thieves, a farce: by T. Knight... Boston, Wells and Lilly; New-York, A. T. Goodrich & co. , 1822. 51 p. DLC; MH; MWA; NN; PPL.   9070

Howard Benevolent Society, Boston
Howard Benevolent Society. Organized in Boston, June 1, 1812. Incorporated February 16, 1818... Boston, Pr. by Henry Bowen, 1822. 23 p. MWA. 9071

[Howe, John]
Hymn, for the installation of the officers of St. Paul's Royal Arch Chapter, February 1st, 1822. [Boston, 1822?] Bdsd. (In ink, recto: by John Howe.) WHi.   9072

Howe's Genuine almanac for 1823. By J. M. Howe. Enfield, Mass. , [1822] 12 ll. CSmH; CtHi; CLU; DLC; M; MHi; N; MWA; WHi.   9073

[Hughs, Mrs. Mary (Robson)]
Village dialogues. By the author of 'William's Return," "The Twin Brothers" "Henry Goodwin," &c. Philadelphia, Pr. for the "Tract and Book Society of the Evangelical Lutheran Church of St. John. " Joseph Rakestraw, printer, 1822. 76 p. IObB; PPLT; ScCMu.   9074

Hull, Justus
First fruit and lump, root and branch; being a comment on Romans XI. 16, 17 in a letter to Mr. Henry Hull. Poughkeepsie, Pr. by P. Potter, 1822. 16 p. NCasti.   9075

Humphreys, Charles
A compendium of the common law in force in Kentucky, to which is prefixed a brief summary of the laws of the United States. Lexington, Ky. , Pr. by William Gibbes Hunt, 1822. xi, 594 p. CU; DLC; ICLaw; Ia; KyHi; KyLo; KyRE; KyU; KyU-L; MWCL; MdBB; MnU; NIC-L; NNF; Nb; NcD; OC; OCLaw; TxH; TxU; Wa-L; WaU.   9076

Huneker, John
Christmas hymn. Composed & arranged as a duett for the organ or piano forte. Philadelphia, Pub. by the Author, [1822?] [2] p. NN.   9077

The Hungarian waltz. Philadelphia, Pr. for B. Carr [1822] 1 l.
PP.   9078

Huntington, David, 1788-1858
An intolerant spirit, hostile to
the interests of society, A ser-
mon delivered before His Excel-
lency John Brooks, esq. gover-
nor... Boston, B. Russell, 1822.
20 p. CBPac; CSmH; Ct; CtHC;
CtHT-W; DLC; ICMe; ICN; MA;
MB; MBAt; MBB; MBC;
MBNEH; MDeeP; MH; MHi;
MNBedf; MW; MWA; MWH;
MWHi; MWo; MeBat; MiD-B;
MnHi; NIC; NN; NNC; NjPT;
OClWHi; PHi; RPB; VtMiM.
                                   9079

Hupfield, Charles F., 1787-1864
Thema original, with variations for the piano forte. Philadelphia, G.E. Blake [1822?] 9 p.
PP-K.   9080

Hurlbut, Martin Luther
Address delivered before the
members of the New-England
Society, in Charleston, South
Carolina, at their anniversary
meeting, December 22d, 1821.
Charleston, A.E. Miller, 1822.
16 p. MBAt; MH; MHi.   9081

Hutchings' almanac for 1823. By
David Young. New-York, S.
Marks [1822] 18 ll. MWA; NHi;
NN; WHi.   9082

---- ---- New-York, Daniel D.
Smith [1822] 18 ll. CtHi; DLC;
NRMA.   9083

Hutchings' (Revived) almanac for
1823. By David Young. New-
York, Samuel Marks [1822] 18 ll.
DLC; MWA; NBLiHi; NBuHi;
NN; NjR.   9084

Hutchins' Revived. Astronomical calculations, or Almanac for
1823. By William Collom. New-
York, G. Long [1822] 18 ll.

ViHi.   9085

---- ---- By William Collom.
Poughkeepsie, Isaac T. Doughty
[1822] 18 ll. N.   9086

Hutton, Charles
A course of mathematics, for
the use of academies...3d Amer.
ed. New York, Pr. by Samuel
Campbell & sons, 1822. 2 v.
CLSU; CSmH; CSt; CtHC;
CtHT-W; CtMMHi; DLC; GDC;
MB; MiDSH; MiKC; MiU; NWM;
P; PAnL; PHarD; PU; RPB;
ScCoB; TU.   9087

Hutton, W.
Book of nature laid open, in
a popular survey of the phenom-
ena and constitution of the uni-
verse...1st Amer. from the 3d
London ed. Georgetown, D.C.,
Joseph Milligan, Pr. by Wm.
Cooper, Jun., 1822. 281 p.
InStmaS; MdBL.   9088

Hyde, Alvan
A sermon, delivered at Lee,
Massachusetts, May 15, 1822...
Hartford, G. Goodwin & Sons,
1822. 16 p. CtY; MB; NjPT;
RPB.   9089

[Hyer, William G.]
Rosa, a melo-drama, in three
acts. New York, E. Murden,
1822. 44 p. DLC; ICU; MH;
MWA; PU; RPB.   9090

Hymn, for the installation of the
officers. See Howe, John.

Hymns for children. Philadelphia, Conrad Zentler, 1822.
128 p. IEG; PNazMhi.   9091

I

Ide, Jacob, 1785-1880
A sermon, preached Sept. 12,
1821, at the ordination of the
Rev. George Fisher, as pastor

of the First Congregational
Church in Harvard. Concord,
Mass. , Peters & Biglow, 1822.
31 p. Ct; MBAt; MBC; MLanc;
NjPT; RPB; VtMiM.   9092

Imitatio Christi
   The imitation of Christ... by
Thomas a Kempis. Tr. from
the Latin by John Payne. With
an introductory essay, by Thomas Chalmers... New York, Collins and Brother [1822] 307 p.
InEv; KBB; MWH; NBuG;
PWmpDS.   9093

---- ---- New-Haven, Pub. by
William Storer, Gray & Hewit,
printers, 1822. 210 p. ArClC;
CtHi; CtY; CtY-D; ICP; ICU;
IaDaM; MA; MBC; MDeeP;
MWA; MoSpD; NN; OClW; OFH;
OHi; OMC; REd; RP; VtB;
VtMiS.   9094

Important information! The national colours and coat of arms
of the United States fully explained, in such a manner as is
highly interesting to every true
American. New York, Pr. by
Van Pelt and Spear, 1822. 12 p.
DLC; WHi.   9095

Inchbald, Mrs. Elizabeth (Simpson)
   Every one has his fault; a
comedy in five acts. Philadelphia, T.H. Palmer, 1822. 76 p.
MH.   9096

---- The mourning ring; a simple
story. New York, F. & R.
Lockwood, 1822. 310 p. MBAt;
MBL; MH; NN.   9097

Index to Robinson Crusoe. Albany, Pr. by G.J. Loomis &
Co. , 1822. 19 p. MeHi.   9098

---- Albany, G.J. Loomis &
Co. , 1822. 16 p. MiPh.   9099

Indian Council, Tonawanda, 1822
   Proceedings of the Great Indian Council, held at Tonawanta
[sic] August 8, 1822. At a
meeting of Indians assembled,
in a General Council, held in
the Indian Village of Tonawanda,
on the 8th day of August, 1822,
composed of the Seneca, Onondaga, Cayuga... nations to the number of two thousand six hundred
and eight... [Batavia? 1822]
Bdsd. (Title from a photostatic
reproduction in the New York
Public Library, made from a
copy offered for sale by the Cad-
mus Book Shop, May, 1928.)
                           9100
Indiana
   Journal of the House of Representatives, of the state of Indiana; being the sixth session of
the general assembly, begun and
held at Corydon, in said state,
on Monday the nineteenth day of
November 1821. New Albany,
Ind. , Pr. by Patrick & Wheelock, 1821-22. 422 p. In; InU.
                           9101
---- Journal of the House of
Representatives, of the state of
Indiana; being the seventh session of the general assembly,
begun and held at Corydon, in
said state, on Monday, the 2d
day of December, 1822. Corydon, Ind. , Pr. by Carpenter &
Douglass, 1822. 325 p. In.
                           9102
---- Journal of the Senate of the
state of Indiana; being the sixth
session of the general assembly,
begun and held at Corydon, in
said state, on Monday the nineteenth day of November, 1821.
New Albany, Ind. , Pr. by Patrick & Wheelock, 1821-22. 296
p. In.   9103

---- Journal of the Senate of the
state of Indiana, being the seventh session of the general assembly, begun and held at Cory-

don, in the county of Harrison, on Monday, the second day of December, in the year of our Lord eighteen hundred and twenty two. Corydon, Ind., Pr. by Carpenter & Douglass, 1822. 288 p. In.   9104

---- Laws of the state of Indiana, passed and published at the sixth session of the general assembly, held at Corydon, on the nineteenth of November, in the year one thousand eight hundred and twenty-one. By authority. New Albany, Patrick and Wheelock, state printers, 1821-22. 177, [1] xiii p. In; InHi; InU; In-SC; N.   9105

---- The militia law of the state of Indiana, passed at the session of 1821-22. New Albany, Pr. by Patrick and Wheelock, 1822. 76, [8] p. In; InHi.   9106

The Indiana justice, and farmer's scrivener. See Fletcher, Calvin.

Indigent Widows and Single Women's Society
    The fifth annual report, for the year 1821, of the managers of the Indigent Widows and Single Women's Society; with a list of the officers and managers, and of the contributors since the last annual report. Philadelphia, Pr. by order of the Society. Lydia R. Bailey, printer, 1822. 8 p. P; PPL.   9107

The infant's friend, or, A selection of lessons, for children. New-Haven, Pub. by J. Babcock & Son, and S. Babcock & Co. Charleston, S.C. Sidney's Press, 1822. 31 p. CtHi.   9108

Ingersoll, Charles M.
    Conversations on English grammar; explaining the principles and rules of the language ... 2d ed. New-York, Pub. by Wiley & Halsted, 1822. 296 p. CtHT-W; CtW; MA; MH; NNC; RPB; TXU-T.   9109

---- ---- 3d ed. Philadelphia, H.C. Carey & I. Lea, William Brown, printer, 1822. xix, 296 p. CSmH; MH; MTaHi; PPL; TxAuSE.   9110

---- Conversations on etymology and syntax... Philadelphia, Bennett and Walton, 1822. 172 p. DLC; MWHi; MiU.   9111

Ingraham, Edward Duncan
    A sketch of the insolvent laws of Pennsylvania; containing extracts of the acts now in force ... Philadelphia, P.H. Nicklin, 1822. xx, 167 p. MH-L; NNC-L; PPB; PPL; PPWa; PU-L.   9112

An inquiry into the fundamental principles of the Roman Catholics, in five letters, addressed to a Roman Catholic. By a Protestant... Washington city, the author, 1822. 18 p. DLC; MBAt; NjPT; WHi.   9113

Instances of early piety, designed for the instruction of children. Philadelphia, J.R.A. Skerrett, printer, 1822. 12 p. PPeSchw.   9114

Instructive alphabet. 40 illus., with poem. The negro complaint. New York, Samuel N. Wood, 1822. Burnham Antique Book Store, Cat. 53, April 1936, No. 1354.   9115

Introduction to the science of government, written for the youth of the United States. [New York?] 1822. 60 p. NN.   9116

Irvine, Baptis
    Commerce of southern America; its importance to us, with

some remarks on a canal at
Darien... Philadelphia, Pr. for
T. T. H. , 1822. 59 p. PPAmP;
PPL.   9117

Irving, Christopher
   Catechism of astronomy. 1st
Amer. ed. imp. & enl. New
York, Pr. by J. Oram, F. & R.
Lockwood, 1822. 99 p. MAm;
NN; PP.   9118

---- A catechism of classical
biography. 1st Amer. ed. , rev.
and imp. New-York, F. and
R. Lockwood, 1822. 88 p.
InCW; MH; MWA.   9119

----A catechism of Grecian antiquities... 1st Amer. ed. rev.
& imp. New York, T. & R.
Lockwood, 1822. 109 p. InU;
MBAt; MH; NN.   9120

---- Catechism of Jewish antiquities. 1st Amer. ed. New
York, F. & R. Lockwood, 1822.
80 p. IEG; MB; MWA; NN;
NcMHi; VtMiM.   9121

---- A catechism of mythology;
being a compendious history of
the heathen gods, goddesses and
heroes. 1st Amer. ed. , rev.
and imp. New-York, F. and R.
Lockwood, 1822. 88 p. MH.
                             9122
---- Catechism of practical
chemistry. 1st Amer. ed. imp.
& enl. New York, Pr. by J.
Oram, pub. by F. & R. Lockwood, 1822. 85 p. DLC; MB;
MAm; NN; NjP; PPL.   9123

---- A catechism of Roman antiquities... 1st Amer. ed. rev.
New York, F. & R. Lockwood,
1822. 106 p. NN; OAU.   9124

---- A catechism of universal
history. 1st Amer. ed. , rev.
& imp. New-York, F. and R.
Lockwood, 1822. 103 p. MH. 9125

---- A catechism on botany:
by C. Irving. New York, F. &
R. Lockwood, J. Oram, printer,
1822. 85 p. MAm; NCanHi;
NN; PP.   9126

---- Catechisms in a series of
numbers; adapted to the use of
schools in the United States. 1st
Amer. ed. imp. and enl. New
York, F. & R. Lockwood, 1822.
245 p. CtHT-W; MdBL; NcWsS
                             9127
---- Catechisms on practical
chemistry, astronomy, botany
[etc.] in a series of numbers...
1st Amer. ed. New York, F. &
R. Lockwood, 1822. v. p.
PPL.   9128

[Irving, Washington] 1783-1859
   Bracebridge Hall; or, The
humourists... New York, Pr. by
C. S. Van Winkle, 1822. 2 v.
CSmH; CtHT; CtW; CtY; DLC;
DeWI; GHi; ICU; InLW; MA;
MB; MBL; MH; MWA; MWiW;
MdBP; MeWebr; MiNi; MnU;
NN; NOx; NcGw; NcU; OCir;
PPL; PU; RBr; RPB; ScDuE;
ScSoh; ViAl; ViL.   9129

[----] The sketch book of Geof-
frey Crayon, Gent. (pseud.)...
New York, Pr. by C. S. Van
Winkle, 1822. 7 pts. KAStB;
KyDC; IUC; MWA; MdHi;
NBuU; ScCMu.   9130

J

Jachin y Boaz. See S. , R.

Jackman, Isaac, fl. 1795
   All the world's a stage. A
farce. In two acts. Philadelphia, Thomas H. Palmer, 1822.
40 p. MB.   9131

---- ---- Washington, Pr. by
Davis and Force, 1822. 40 p.
DLC.   9132

Jacobs, Samuel
  Valuable sale of furniture by
auction. On Saturday the 28th
of September, at the residence
of Samuel Jacobs, in Vincennes
...Vincennes, Sept. 1822. Bdsd.
In.   9133

James, Benjamin, 1768-1825
  A digest of the laws of South
Carolina...Columbia, Pr. at the
Telescope press, 1822. 710 p.,
1 l.   MdBJ; MdBB; MsJMC;
MnU; NcD; PPL; ScCleA;
ScCliP.   9134

James, Edwin, 1797-1861, comp.
  Account of an expedition from
Pittsburgh to the Rocky Mts. in
1819-20 under orders of Hon. J.
C. Calhoun, sec'y of War, in
command of Maj. S.H. Long.
Philadelphia, H.C. Carey & I.
Lea, 1822-23. 2 v. C; CU;
CoD; CoHi; CoGrS; CtHT-W;
CtW; DLC; DNLM; ICHi; ICN;
IEN-M; IP; IU; IaDaP; LN;
LNH; MB; MB; MFm; MH;
MWC; MdHi; MoHi; MiU-C;
MoKU; MoSM; NNA; NNC; NT;
NbHi; NbU; NjPT; OCIWHi; OO;
OkU; RP; RPA; RPJCB; Tx;
Vi; WHi.   9135

Jamieson, Alexander
  A grammar of logic and in-
tellectual philosophy, on didactic
principles...1st Amer. from the
last London ed. New Haven,
A.H. Maltby and co., 1822. 304
p. CU; CtHC; CtHT; CtY; GU;
ICP; KyDC; MBAt; MBC; MH;
MMel; MWiW; NIC; NNC; ODaV;
OrSaW; PU; ScDuE; TxFwTCU;
TxMinw; VtStjAc.   9136

Jamieson, R.
  Now by my troth. An orig-
inal Scotch song. Philadelphia,
G. Willig [1822] [2] p. MWA;
PHi; PP.   9137

Janeway, James

  Token for children...New
Haven, Pub. by A.H. Maltby &
Co., 1822. 150 p. CtHi; CtSoP;
CtY.   9138

Janke, John N., d. 1862?
  Two Bohemian waltzes. Philadelphia, J. L. Frederick [1822?]
2 p. NN.   9139

Jarvis, Samuel Farmer, 1786-
1851
  The conversation of our Sav-
iour with Nicodemus illustrated.
A sermon, preached in St. Paul's
Church, Dedham, Wednesday,
June 20, 1821, before the annual
convention of the Protestant Epis-
copal church, in the state of
Massachusetts. Boston, Joseph
W. Ingraham, 1822. 76 p.
CtHT; CtY; DLC; IObB; InID;
LNB; MA; MB; MBAt; MBC;
MBD; MWA; MdBD; MdCatS;
MdHi; MiD-B; NN; NNG; NcU;
NjPT; NjR; PHi; PPL; RPB;
ScC; VtU; WHi.   9140

---- Method of daily prayer for
the use of children and young
persons previous to confirmation. Boston, Joseph W. Ingraham, 1822. 36 p. MBAt. 9141

---- A sermon, preached before
the Auxiliary Education Society
of the Young Men of Boston,
January 23, 1822, on the occasion of their third anniversary
...To which are added the
treasurer's report for the year
1821, and the constitution of the
Society, together with a list of
officers and members. Boston,
Pr. by Joseph W. Ingraham,
1822. 24 p. DLC; IaGG; MB;
MBAt; MH; MHi; MWA; MWo;
MeBaT; MiD-B; NN; NNG;
NNUT; NjPT.   9142

Jay, William
  Prayers for the use of families; or, The domestic minis-

ter's assistant... 2d Amer. from
the 3d London ed. [Salem] Sold
by Henry Whipple; also sold by
C. Whipple, Newburyport; Burrill and Hersey, printers, 1822.
287 p. CBPSR; CtSoP; MBAt;
MBC; MH; MSaE; PLERC-Hi;
ScCMu; ViRU.   9143

Jefferson, Thomas, pres., U. S.,
1743-1826
    A manual of parliamentary
practice, composed originally for
the use of the Senate of the
United States... Washington,
Gales & Seaton, 1822. 224 p.
DLC; ICMcHi; MiU-C; PPL;
ViAl.   9144

Jefferson Benevolent Institution
of Pennsylvania
    Charter, as amended. Phila-
delphia, Pr. for the Institution
[by R. Wright] 1822. 30 p. PHi.
                               9145
Jenkins, Charles
    A bereaved husband's grief.
A sermon, preached in Greenfield, on Sunday July xxviii,
MDCCCXXII. Occasioned by the
death of Mrs. Ruth B. Jenkins
... Greenfield, Denio & Phelps,
1822. 24 p. MWA; NNG; NjPT;
OCIWHi; RPB.   9146

Jenks, Benjamin
    Prayers and offices of devo-
tion for families and for particular persons upon most occasions.
Philadelphia, M'Carty & Davis,
1822. 323 p. CtHC; MDeeP;
MH; PLT; RPB.   9147

Jenks, Samuel Haynes, 1789-1863
    An address, pronounced at
Nantucket, before the Urbanity
Lodge of Free and Accepted Ma-
sons; Oct. 3, A. L. 5822... Nan-
tucket [Mass.] Pr. by Joseph C.
Melcher, 1822. 21 p. MB. 9148

Jennings, Obadiah, 1778-1832
    A sermon, delivered in the

Second Presbyterian Church, in
the city of Pittsburgh, on the occasion of the organization of the
mission family lately sent by the
Board of trust of the Western
Missionary society to the Otto-
way tribe of Indians... Steubenville, O., Pr. by James Wilson,
1822. 23 p. CSmH; DLC;
PPPrHi; PPiXT.   9149

Jewett, Paul
    The New England farrier...
2d ed., enl. Exeter, N. H.,
Pr. by John Williams, 1822. 105
[3] p. MWA; Nh.   9150

Job printing on the vertical
press, neatly executed. Philadelphia, seventh month 31, 1822.
1 p. PHi.   9151

Jocelyn or Joscelin, fl. 1200.
    The life and acts of Saint Pat-
rick... now first translated from
the original Latin of Jocelin...
By J. C. O'Haloran, Esq. Philadelphia, Pr. for the publisher,
by Atkinson Alexander, 1822.
304 p. RPB.   9152

Johnson, Alfred, 1766-1837
    [The divinity of Christ consist-
ent with the unity of God. The
substance of a sermon held at
Knox, and published at the request of the hearers. With additional proofs and authorities.
Belfast, Me., Pr. by Fellowes
and Simpson, 1822.] 40 p. MBC;
MNe; MeHi; MeWC; NNUT;
NjPT; PPPrHi.   9153

Johnson, Francis, 1792-1844
    Captain James Page's kent
bugle military slow march.
[1822?] [2] p. Wolfe 4645. 9154

---- 'If sleeping now fair maid
of love.' A favorite serenade.
Philadelphia, G. Willig [1822?]
[2] p. NN.   9155

Johnson, Joseph
Address, to the Literary and Philosophical Society of South Carolina...May 8, 1822. Charleston, J. Hoff, pr. 1822. 11 p. MHi; ScC. 9156

Johnson, Richard M.
Senate of the United States, January 14, 1822. Speech of Col. Richard M. Johnson, of Kentucky on his proposition so to amend the Constitution of the United States as to give to the Senate appelate jurisdiction over the decisions of the Supreme Court in cases involving state sovereignty. [J. Ficklin, printer, Gazette Press] 40 p. Pierson; Coleman. 9157

---- Speech of Col. Richard M. Johnson of Kentucky, before the U.S. Senate, on his proposition so to amend the constitution of the United States as to give to the Senate appellate jurisdiction over the discisions of the Supreme court in cases involving state sovereignty. January 14, 1822. 28 p. KyBgW; KyLxT. 9158

Johnson, Samuel
Johnson's dictionary of the English language in miniature, to which are added an alphabetical account of the heathen dieties... by Joseph Hamilton. New York, G. Long, 1822. 295 p. AW; CtY; MnHi. 9159

---- The history of Rasselas... Philadelphia, Pub. by John J. Yardley, D. Dickinson, printer, 1822. 189 p. DGU; MdHi; NNS; NjP; PPL. 9160

---- The Rambler. Philadelphia, Abraham Small, 1822. 3 v. MB. 9161

Johnson, William, 1771-1834
Sketches of the life and correspondence of Nathanael Greene, Major General of the armies of the United States, in the war of the revolution. Compiled chiefly from original materials. Charleston (S. C.) Pr. for the author, by A. E. Miller, 1822. 2 v. C; CL; CtSoP; CtW; DLC; GAuY; GHi; GMiW; GSDe; GU-De; IC; ICHi; IHi; IU; IaU; In; KyLo; M; MB; MBL; MH; MS; MSo; MWal; MWiW-C; Md; MdBE; MdBJ; MdBP; MdHi; MiD-B; MiU-C; MnHi; MoSM; MsWJ; NBLiHi; NN; NNP; NNS; NT; NcAS; NcD; NcU; Nj; O; OCl; OCY; OMC; OkU; P; PHi; PPA; PPAmP; PPL; PU; RNR; RPB; Sc; ScC; ScCC; ScU; TN; TxHuT; TxU; Vi; ViU; WHi. 9162

Johnson's almanac for 1823. By Joshua Sharp. Philadelphia, Richards Johnson [1822] 18 ll. MWA. 9163

Johnson's Pennsylvania and New Jersey almanack for 1823. By Joshua Sharp. Philadelphia, Richards Johnson [1822] 20 ll. CtY; DLC; MWA; NBuHi; PHi. 9164

Johnston, Job
An oration in vindication of Free-Masonry; delivered at Newberry, South Carolina, St. John's day, June 24, 5822. Philadelphia, Pr. by J. Maxwell, 1822. 23 p. NNFM; PPFM. 9165

Jones, Amanda, fl. 1820.
Rules and directions for cutting men's clothes, by the square rule...Improved ed. Middlebury, Pr. by J.W. Copeland, 1822. 23 p. DLC; ICJ; MWA; NN; OHi; Vt; VtHi; VtMiS. 9166

Jones, Richard
Too late for dinner. A farce. In two acts. New-York, pub. by E. Murden, at the Museum Circulating Library. April, 1822. 53 p. MH; MWA. 9167

---- ---- Philadelphia, Thomas
H. Palmer, 1822. 53 p. MH;
MiU-C; NN; RPB.   9168

Jones, W.
   Opinion of Mr. Jones, on the
eligibility of Mr. Way, for the
mayoralty. June 2, 1822. 3 p.
DLC.   9169

[Jones, William] 1760-1831
   Reflections upon the perils
and difficulties of the winter
navigation of the Delaware.
Means by which these may be
meliorated... Philadelphia, pub.
by order of the Chamber of
Commerce, 1822. 15 p. DLC;
DeGE; MBAt; MWA; NN; NjPT;
P; PHi; PPAmP; PPL; ScC.
                              9170

Josse, Augustin Luis
   A grammar of the Spanish
language, with practical exer-
cises. 1st Amer. from the last
Paris ed. Rev., imp. and
adapted to the English language
by F. Sales... Boston, pub. by
William B. Fowle, Crocker &
Brewster, printers, 1822. 2 pts.
C-S; InFw; MB; MBBC; MH;
MW; MWHi; NIC; NN; NNC;
NNG; NNH; PU.   9171

The journal almanac for the state
of Georgia for the year of our
Lord 1823... By Robert Grier,
Milledgeville, Camak & Hines,
[1822] 48 p. GMWa; MiD-B.
                              9172
A journal of a march. See La-
trobe, John Hazlehurst Boneval.

Judah, Samuel Benjamin Herbert,
1799?-1876
   Odofriede; the outcast; a dra-
matic poem. New York, Wiley
and Halsted, 1822. 89 p. CSmH;
CtW; CtY; DLC; ICU; MB;
MH; MWA; MiU-C; NIC; NjR;
PMA; PPAmP; PU; RPB. 9173

---- The Rose of Arragon; or,

The vigil of St. Mark: a melo-
drama, in two acts. New-York,
S. King, 1822. 38 p. CtY; DLC;
MB; MH; MWA; PU; RPB.
                              9174
---- ---- 2d ed. New-York, S.
King, 1822. 38 p. DLC; ICU;
MB; MH; NN; NNC; PPDrop;
RPB.   9175

Judson, Roswell
   A letter to the Rev. Abner
Kneeland... containing a refuta-
tion of his alluring... inference
of the popular doctrine of uni-
versal salvation from the attri-
bute of universal benevolence in
Deity. Bridgeport, Lockwood &
Sterling, 1822. 34 p. CSmH;
NjPT.   9176

---- ---- 2d ed., rev., corr.,
and extended. Bridgeport, Pr.
by Lockwood & Sterling, 1822.
37 p. CSmH; CtHi; CtHC; CtY;
MBC; MH-AH; MWA; NN;
NNUT; NjPT.   9177

Juvenile poems, or, The alphabet in verse. Designed for the
entertainment of all good boys
and girls. New-Haven, Pub. by
J. Babcock and Son and S. Babcock and Co. Charleston, S.C.,
Sidney's press. 1822. 28 p.
CtHi.   9178

K

Karr, Henry, 1784-1842
   Fantaisie, avec sept variations. Philadelphia, G.E. Blake,
[1822?] 13 p. RPB.   9179

Kean, Laurence
   A sermon on the freeness of
divine grace... Preached in the
Methodist Church, John Street,
on Sunday August 18, 1822. New-
York, Pr. for W.H. Creagh.
Myers & Smith, printers, 1822.
40 p. IObB; MB; MWA. 9180

Keating, William H.
    Account of the jeffersonite, a
new mineral discovered at the
Franklin Iron Works, near Sparta,
N. J. by L. Vanuxem and W. H.
Keating.   Philadelphia, J. Hard-
ing, 1822. 12 p. NGeno; NNC;
PPAmP; ScU.   9181

Keenan, Charles
    The Baltimore directory for
1822 & '23.   Together with the
eastern and western precincts,
never before included; a correct
account of removals, new firms,
and other useful information.
Baltimore, Pr. by R. J. Matchett,
1822. 27 p. DLC; MdBB; MdBL;
MdBP; MdBE; MdHi.   9182

Kelly, Michael, 1762-1826
    Flora McDonald. A ballad.
New York, E. Riley [1822?] 3 p.
NHi.   9183

---- The grand march in Pizar-
ro, &c. New York, P. K. Mor-
an [1822?] p [1]-2. Wolfe 4845.
                               9184
---- Love & time. Boston, G.
Graupner. [1822?] 3 p. DLC;
MB; MH; MHi; MWA; NN;
NRU-Mus; RPB.   9185

---- ---- New York, Dubois &
Stodart [1822?] [2] p. NN; PP;
PPL.   9186

---- The ray that beams forever.
New York, E. Riley [1822] 5 p.
DLC; MWA; ViW.   9187

[Kelty, Mary Ann] 1789-1873
    The favorite of nature. A
tale... Boston, Wells and Lilly,
1822. 2 v. CtY; GU; MWalp;
NjR.   9188

Kemp, James, bp.
    A charge delivered to the
clergy of the Protestant Episcopal Church in the Diocese of
Maryland, at a convention held

in the City of Washington, on the
fifth day of June, 1822. Washington, Pr. by Davis and Force,
1822. 16 p. DLC; MdBD; MdHi.
                               9189
---- Pastoral letter addressed
to the members of the Protestant Episcopal Church in the
Diocese of Maryland.   Baltimore, Pr. by J. Robinson,
1822. 28 p. DLC; MH; MdBD;
MdBP; MdHi; NNG.   9190

Kendrick, Nathaniel
    A sermon in Madison, at the
interment of Mrs. Pamelia Nelson, consort of S. Nelson of
Cortland Village, Cortland County, N. Y. July 13, 1822. Pr. by
W. W. Phelps, Cortland Village,
1822. 10 p. Tuttle.   9191

Kennedy, Lionel H.
    An official report of the tri-
als of sundry Negroes, charged
with an attempt to raise an in-
surrection in the state of South-
Carolina... Charleston, Pr. by
James R. Schenck, 1822. 188,
4 p. InMuB; LNH; MB; MBC;
MH; MiU-C; MoS; NBLiHi; NN;
PP; PPAmP; ScBe; ScC; ScCC;
ScCliP; TSewU.   9192

Kennett, Basil, 1674-1715
    Romae antiquae notitia; or,
The antiquities of Rome. To
which are prefixed two essays,
concerning the Roman learning
and the Roman education... 1st
Amer. ed.   Philadelphia, Hick-
man & Hazzard, 1822. 356 p.
ill. CL; CtHT; CtY; DG; IU;
IaCrM; IaGG; KyBC; LNL; MA;
MAA; MAnP; MB; MCan; MH;
MLow; MNBedf; MNe; MWA;
MTop; MdBS; MoSM; NBu;
NCH; NGH; NNC; NNebg; NNUT;
NOg; OCIW; PFal; PP; PU;
PPAmP; PPL; PPaP; RNR;
RPA; RP; TSew-U; USlStM;
ViR; ViRVal; ViU; WU.   9193

Kenney, James
    John Buzzby: or, A day's
pleasure... New York, E. M.
Murden, 1822. 63 p. CSmH;
DLC; MB; MH; N; NN.   9194

Kenney, James, 1780-1849
    Turn out! A musical farce.
In two acts. Philadelphia, T. H.
Palmer, 1822. 44 p. MB; MH;
RPB; TxU.   9195

Kentucky (State)
    A digest of the statute of Ken-
tucky: being a collection of all
the Acts of the General Assembly of a public and permanent nature, from the commencement of the Government to May
session 1822. Also the English
and Virginia statutes, yet in
force; together with several acts
of Congress. With references
to Reports of Judicial decisions
in the Court of Appeals of Kentucky and Supreme Court of the
U. S. in 2 vols. By William Littell and Jacob Swigert. Published under the patronage of
the Legislature.   I. Frankfort, Pr. by Kendall & Russel,
printers for the state, 1822.
2 v. DLC; NNLI.   9196

Kentucky Bible Society
    Sixth annual report of the
board of managers of the Kentucky Bible Society, (Auxiliary
to the American Bible Society.)
Read before the Society, at Lexington, April 11, 1822. Lexington, Pr. for the Society, by
Thomas T. Skillman, 1822. 16 p.
KyLxT.   9197

[Kenworthy, William]
    ... The economical hydrostatic
lift. [Baltimore, 1822] 12 p.
("From the American farmer,"
being a reprint from v. 4, no.
10, 31st May, 1822.) DLC. 9198

Key adapted to the questions for

Grimshaw's History of the
United States. Philadelphia, Pr.
for the author, by Lydia R.
Bailey, 1822. 73 p. CtHT-W;
MB.   9199

A key to the shorter catechism
... New York, J. Leavitt, 1822.
216 p. GDC.   9200

Killingly Auxiliary Bible Society
    Constitution of the Killingly
Auxiliary Bible Society; with a
list of the board of directors &
an address to the people in Killingly & vicinity. Brooklyn,
Conn. , H. Webb, 2d, 1822. 8 p.
Ct.   9201

Kimball, David T.
    A sermon, preached at Need-
ham, December 12, 1821, at
the installation of the Rev. Wm.
Ritchie, as pastor of the First
Church and Society in that town.
Dedham, Pr. by H. & W. H.
Mann, 1822. 38 p. MA; MB-FA;
MBC; MBNEH; MH; MHi; MNe;
MWA; MeHi; N; NjPT; PHi;
RPB; VtMiM; WHi.   9202

Kimber, Emmor
    The Church of Christ, and
way of salvation universal.
Philadelphia, E. Littel, for the
author, 1822. 24 p. PHi; PSC-
Hi.   9203

---- A letter to a Friend in
New York, in answer to a late
anonymous publication, entitled
A false position exposed. Philadelphia, E. Littell, for the author, 1822. 22 p. DeGE; PHC;
PPL; PSC-Hi.   9204

King, Matthew Peter, 1733-1823
    Eve's lamentation. Boston,
E. W. Jackson, [1822?] p [1]-2
MWA; NBuG; NN; RPB.   9205

---- Father thy word is past.
Philadelphia, G. Willig [1822?]

3 p. MWA; NN; PP; RPB. 9206

King, Solomon
King's choice selection of
Scottish songs, consisting of
funny, droll, comical, serious,
jovial, tragical, whimsical,
laughable, sentimental, quizzical,
pathetical, curious, and humer-
ous songs. New York, S. King,
1822. 38 p. DLC; MH. 9207

---- King's Scotch song book,
containing a choice selection of
comic, sentimental, and humourous Scottish songs. Vol. 1. New-
York, S. King, 1822. 191 p.
MH; WHi. 9208

---- ---- Selected from the
works of Burns, and other celebrated authors. New-York, S.
King, 1822. 192 p. CtHT-W;
CtY; MH. 9209

Kingsbury, Jedidah
A new, improved dictionary
for children, or Definition book
for the use of schools. Boston,
Munroe & Francis, 1822. 299 p.
CtHT-W; CtY; MB; MH; PU;
RPB. 9210

Kingsley, James Luce, 1778-
1852
An eulogy on Alexander Met-
calf Fisher, A. M. Professor of
Mathematics and natural philos-
ophy, in Yale College, who per-
ished in the wreck of the Albion,
April 22nd, 1822. Delivered in
the College Chapel. June 26,
1822. New Haven, Pr. at the
Journal Office, 1822. 23 p.
CSmH; CoCsC; CtHC; CtHi;
CtHT; CtY; DLC; IC; M; MA;
MAnP; MB; MBAt; MBC; MH;
MHi; MW; MWA; MeBat; MiD-
B; NjPT; NjR; OO; OWoC;
PHi; PPL; RPB. 9211

[Kinne, William]
A short system of practical

arithmetic...Ed. 4. Hallowell,
Me., Goodale, Glazier & Co.,
[1822] 240 p. NNC; Karpinski
p. 171. 9212

[Kitchiner, William]
The cook's oracle; containing
receipts for plain cookery, etc.
The result of actual experiments
instituted in the kitchen of a
physician. From the last London ed. which is almost entirely
re-written. With an appendix
by the American publishers.
Boston, Munroe and Francis,
1822. 380 p. DNLM; MB; MBM;
MBevHi; MH; MLaw; MMe;
MNBedf; MSa; MWA; NN; NcAS.
9213

Kite's town and country almanac for 1823. By William Collom. Philadelphia, Benjamin
and Thomas Kite [1822] 18 ll.
InU; MB; MWA; N; NbHi; PHi.
9214

Kliene Spruch-Bibel mit kurzen
Ermunterungen fur auf merkerk-
same Kinder. Baltimore, Johann T. Hansche, 1822. 32 p.
PHi; PYHi. 9215

Klinck's Albany directory, for
the year 1822, containing an
alphabetical list of residents
within the city, and a variety of
other interesting matter. Albany,
Pr. by E. & E. Hosford, 1822.
79 p. MBNEH; N. 9216

Knight, Thomas, d. 1820. The
honest thieves. See Howard,
Sir Robert, 1626-1698.

Koczwara, František, d. 1791
The battle of Prague. For
two performers on one piano
forte. New York, A. & W.
Geib [1822?] 15 p. MH. 9217

Koecker, L.
An essay on the devastation
of the gums and the alveolar
processes. [Philadelphia, H. C.

Carey & I. Lea, Chesnut Street,
William Fry, printer, 1822] 15 p.
IEN-D; MB; MBM; NNNAM.
                                    9218
Kollock, Henry, 1778-1819
    Sermons on various subjects,
with a memoir of the life of the
author. Savannah, S. C. & I.
Schenk, 1822. 4 v. CtHC; CtW;
CSansS; CtY; GDC; GEU; GHi;
GMM; GU-De; ICU; IEC; IU;
InCW; KyDC; MA; MWA; MiD-
B; MiU; MtHi; NCaS; NGH; NN;
NNG; NP; NcAS; NcD; NcMHi;
NcU; NjPT; OWoC; PPiW;
PPPrHi; RPB; TNY.   9219

Kollock, Shepard K.
    The duty of Christians to pray
for ministers: A sermon,
preached at the installation of
the Rev. Samuel L. Graham.
Raleigh, Pr. by J. Gales & Son,
1822. 35 p. ICMe; NN; NjR;
PHi; RPB; ScCC.   9220

Kotzebue, August Friedrich
Ferdinand von
    Stranger, a play tr. from the
German by Benj. Thompson...
Boston, Wells & Lilly, 1822.
94 p. MeB; PPL; PU.   9221

Kozeluch, Leopold, 1752-1818
    A favourite duett for two per-
formers on one piano forte.
Boston, E.W. Jackson [1822?]
15 p. NN.   9222

L

The L... family at Washington.
See Watterson, George.

Lacey, William Brittainham,
1781-1866
    The utility of apprentices' li-
braries: a sermon, delivered
in St. Peter's Church in the city
of Albany, 22d February 1822.
Albany, Websters and Skinners,
1822. 16 p. DLC; IObB; MB;
MWA; N; NjPT; NjR; PHi;

PPPrHi; RPB.   9223

[Lacock, Abner] 1770-1837
    Great national object. Pro-
posed connection of the eastern
& western waters, by a communication through the Potomac
country. [Washington, 1822]
38 p. DLC; N; OCIWHi; PPL.
                                    9224
The ladies' and gentlemen's
diary and almanack for 1823.
By Asa Houghton. Bellows Falls,
Vt. , Bill Blake & Co. [1822]
24 ll. Drake 13617.   9225

Lafont, Charles Philippe, 1781-
1839
    Sweet is the tear. Philadel-
phia, G. Willig [1822] [2] p.
NN; PPL.   9226

Laicus, pseud.
    Remarks on religious associa-
tion. By Laicus. Boston, Pr.
by J. G. Bolles, at the Watchman Office [1822] 16 p. MH;
MWA.   9227

The laity's directory to the
Church service, for the year of
our Lord, MDCCCXXII. A table
of moveable Feasts. Revised
and corrected by the Rev. John
Power, of St. Peter's Church.
New York, Published by William
H. Creagh. B. Bolmore, print-
er, 1822. 138 p. DLC; MBrigStJ;
MdBL; MdW; MiDSH; MiNazC;
NGH; NPStA.   9228

[Lamb, Lady Caroline (Ponsonby)] 1785-1828
    Graham Hamilton... Philadel-
phia, H. C. Carey and I. Lea,
1822. 2 v. in 1. DLC; DeWI;
PHi; RPB.   9229

Lancaster, John
    The life of Darcy, Lady Max-
well, of Pollock; late of Edinburgh: compiled from her volum-
inous diary and correspondence,

and from other authentic documents... 1st Amer. from 1st London ed. New York, Pub. and sold by N. Bangs and T. Mason, No. 5 Chatham Square for the Methodist Episcopal Church, and to be had of the Methodist preachers throughout the United States. Meyers and Smith, printers, 1822. 2 v. ArBaA; ArCH; CtW; CtY-D; DLC; IEG; IU; KBB; MoSpD; NNMHi; NNUT; OCIWHi; PPiRPr.   9230

Laneham, Robert
Laneham's letter describing the magnificent pageants presented before Queen Elizabeth, at Kenilworth Castle: in 1575... Philadelphia, Hickman and Hazzard, 1822. CSf; DLC; DeGE; MBAt; MdBJ; LNH; MH; NNC; NcU; Nh; PHi; PPL; RPA; RPB; RNR.   9231

Latham, Allen
A roll of the officers in the Virginia line, of the Revolutionary Army, who have received land bounty, in the states of Ohio and Kentucky... [Chillicothe, Ohio, Feb. 15, 1822] 20 p. MiU-C; NcD; OCHP; OCIWHi.
                        9232
Latour, Jean Tatton, b. 1766
Overture for the piano forte. New York, A. & W. Geib [1822?] 4 p. MWA; PP; PP-K.
                        9233
[Latrobe, John Hazlehurst Boneval] 1803-1891
A journal of a march, performed by the corps of cadets of the United States military academy, in the year eighteen hundred and twenty-one. Newburgh [N.Y.] Pr. by W.M. Gazlay, 1822. 40 p. DLC; MdBP; NN.
                        9234
Latta, John Ewing, 1772?-1824
A sermon, delivered October 16, 1822, before the Bible Society of Delaware, at Newark. Wilmington, Robert Porter, 1822. 16 p. ICP; MH-AH; PPPrHi; ScCC.   9235

The lavender girl. Baltimore, John Cole [1822] 1 l. MdHi; NN; NRU-Mus; ViW.   9236

Law, William
A practical treatise upon Christian perfection... 1st Amer. ed. Portsmouth, Pub. by Charles Morgridge; R. Foster, printer, 1822. 348 p. CSmH; CBCDS; CtHC; CtSoP; CtW; ICP; InRchE; MB; MBAt; MBC; MBrZ; MDeeP; MH; MNBedf; MPiB; MW; MWar; MWo; MdBD; MeBat; MoFuWC; NNG; NNMHi; Nh; Nh-Hi; NhP; OCIWHi; OO; RPB; RJa. 9237

The law of the Legislature of the state of New York, entitled "An act to provide for the indigent deaf and dumb within this state."... New York, 1822. 16 p. DLC; MWA.   9238

Law papers and documents relating to the management of the Old, or Fulton ferry. Brooklyn, 1822. 80 p. MH-BA; NB; NBLiHi; NNC; NSmB; PPL.
                        9239
Lawrence, James Vallentine O'Brien, 1791-1823
Experiments on the power of the veins and the lymphatics. Philadelphia, 1822. 48 p. DLC.
                        9240
Leavitt, Miss
Memoir of Jonathan Leavitt, a member of the junior class in Yale College, who died at New-Haven the 10th of May, 1821, aged eighteen years... By a sister. New Haven, Pr. by S. Converse, 1822. 283 p. CtHi; CtY; DLC; ICU; MA; MB; MFiHi; MGref.   9241

Leavitt's genuine, improved New-
England farmer's almanack, and
scholar's diary for 1823. By
Dudley Leavitt. Concord, Hill
and Moore [1822] 12 ll. MHi;
MWA; NhHi. 9242

---- ---- Concord, Hill and
Moore [1822] 24 ll. CLU; CoCC;
DLC; InU; MH; MBC; MWA;
MdBJ; MiD-B; N; NN; NHi;
NBLiHi; Nh; NjR; WHi. 9243

Lechler, John
Bekäntniss, oder die letzten
Lebens-Stunden von John Lechler,
...[Lancaster, Pa.? 1822] bdsd.
PPL. 9244

---- Das lezte Bekenntniss von
John Lechler, Welcher fur die
Ermordung seiner Frau, Mary
Lechler, vor Gericht gezogen,
uberwiesen und verurtheilt wurde,
am 25 sten October, 1822...
Lancaster, S.C. Stambaugh
[1822] 16 p. P; PHi; PPG; PSt.
9245

Lechmere Point Library Association.
By-laws of the Lechmere-
Point Library Association. Instituted May 22, 1822. Cambridge,
Pr. by Hilliard and Metcalf,
1822. 8 p. MH. 9246

Lee, Nathaniel, 1653?-1692
...Alexander the Great, a
tragedy...Boston, Wells and
Lilly, 1822. 76 p. CtY; DLC;
MH; PPL. 9247

Legaré, John Berwick
An oration, delivered in St.
Michael's Church, Charleston,
South-Carolina, on the fourth of
July 1822; before the '76 Associa-
tion. Charleston, Pr. by A.E.
Miller, 1822. 28 p. DLC; NN;
ScC. 9248

Leggett, William, 1802-1839
Poems by William Leggett.

Edwardsville, Pr. by and for
the author, 1822. 46 p. RPB.
9249
Lehigh Coal and Navigation Co.
An act to improve the navigation of the River Lehigh and an
act to incorporate the Lehigh
Coal and Navigation company together with the bye-laws. Philadelphia, Atkinson & Alexander,
printers, 1822. 37 p. IU; MB;
MH-BA; PHi; PPL. 9250

Leigh, Benjamin Watkins, 1781-
1849
Speech of Mr. Leigh, Com-
missioner from Virginia; on the
subject of the military land
claims--Delivered before the
Legislature of Kentucky on the
17th of May 1822. 33 p. ViW.
9251
Leland, pseud.
Essays on the observance of
a Sabbath...Philadelphia, Pr. by
Joseph Rakestraw, 1822. 48 p.
PPL. 9252

Lemoine, Henry, 1786-1854
New cotillions for the piano
forte. New York, A. & W. Geib.
[1822?] 1 p 1, p 2-8. NN. 9253

Lempriere, John, 1765?-1824
A classical dictionary...3d
Amer. ed. Philadelphia, Pub. by
James Crissy, J. Maxwell,
printer, 1822. xxix, [850] p.
CBPSR; CSansS; CStelU; CtHT;
CtY; DLC; ICHi; ICU; InNd;
KyLx; MH; MNBedf; MWA;
MdAN; MeLewB; MiU; MoFloSS;
NCaS; NN; NPStA; NSyHi; NbYC;
NcRSh; OAkU; OClWHi; ODaAl;
PPAmP; RP; TxDaM; VtHig.
9254
Letter from a gentleman in Bos-
ton to a Unitarian clergyman of
that city. Ed. 4. Boston, T.R.
Marvin, printer, 1822. 20 p.
MTemNHi. 9255

Letter to a deist. See H., J.

Letter to a member of Congress. See Lewis, Zechariah.

A letter to Mr. George Withey. See Candidatus, pseud.

A letter to the Hon. Micah Sterling. See Haines, Charles Glidden.

A letter to the Rev. William Vincent Harold, of the order of Dominican friars, on reading his late reply to a "Catholic layman". By an admirer of Fenelon... Philadelphia, Robert Desilver, March 30, 1822, T. Town, printer.   32 p. DGU; DLC; MdW; NIC; PPAmP; PPL; PPPrHi.   9256

A letter to the Roman Catholics of Philadelphia, and the United States of America. By a friend to the civil and religious liberties of man. 1822. T. Town, printer. 60 p. DGU; DLC; InNd; MdBL; MdW; PPAmP; PPL.
9257
Letters addressed to the people of the United States. See Giles, William Branch.

Letters from Paris, on the causes and consequences of the French Revolution. See Somerville, William Clarke.

Letters on practical subjects. See Sprague, William Buell.

Letters on the natural history and internal resources of the state of New York. See Clinton, De Witt.

Letters to C. C. Biddle, Wm. McIlvaine, Mary Corvgille, and John Bacon. See Seixas, David G.

Letters to Richard Heber, Esq. See Adolphus, John Leycester.

Letters to the Roman Catholics of Philadelphia, and the United States of America. By a friend to the civil and religious liberties of man. Philadelphia, pub. by Robert Desilver, T. Town, printer, 1822. 61-82 p. DGU; DLC; MWH; MdW; NIC; PPL; PPPrHi.   9258

Levington, William
    An address delivered before the Female Benezet Philanthropic Society, of Albany, January 1, 1822, it being the anniversary of the abolition of African slave trade. Albany, Pr. by Packard & Van Benthuysen, 1822. 12 p. N.   9259

Lewes, Alonzo
    Lessons in English grammar. Designed to render the study of the English language simple and familiar to young learners. Boston, Pr. by Lincoln & Edmands, 1822. 50 p. MBAt; MH; NNC.   9260

Lewis, Matthew Gregory, 1775-1818
    Ambrosio, or the Monk; a romance...3 vols. in 2. Vol. I. New York, W. Boradaile, 1822. 244 p. MB; MMhHi; PPL.
9261
---- ...The castle spectre, a dramatic romance...Boston, Wells and Lilly, New York, A. T. Goodrich & co., 1822. 97 p. CtY; MH; MWA; MeB; NN; PPL.   9262

---- ...Rugantino; or, The bravo of Venice...Boston, Wells and Lilly; New York, A.T. Goodrich & co., 1822. 51 p. CtY; DLC; LNH; MH; MeB; NN; PPL.   9263

[Lewis, Zechariah]
    Letter to a member of Congress, in relation to Indian civil-

ization. By the domestic secretary of the United Foreign Missionary Society. New-York, D. Fanshaw, 1822. 15 p. DLC; MB; MWA; MiD-B; NbU.   9264

Lexington Female Academy
   Catalogue of the instructers [sic] visiters [sic] and pupils of the Lexington Female Academy ... Lexington, Ky., July 2, 1822. Bdsd. MH.   9265

L'Homond, Charles F.
   Epitome historiae sacrae... Editio nova, ... Novi-Eboraci: Typis et Impensis Georgii Long, 1822. 156 p. CtHT-W; NN; PPeSchw.   9266

The life of Eleanor Moreland, in a letter to her niece. Pr. for the Trustees of the Publishing Fund, by Hilliard and Metcalf. Cambridge, sold by Cummings and Hilliard; Boston, and by other agents of the Publishing Fund, Jan. 1822. 64 p. DLC; MB; MBAt; MBNEH; MHi; MeBat; WGrNM.   9267

Life of T. H. Bowden Lambrith (native of Boston), one of the largest men in the World. [1822] Sabin 38743.   9268

The life of Tom Thumb. Ornamented with cuts. Boston, N. Coverly, 1822. 16 p. NN.   9269

The life of William Kelly, or The converted drunkard. Philadelphia, Sunday and Adult School Union [1822?] 12 p. DLC. 9270

Lights and shadows of Scottish life. See Wilson, John.

Lillie, Charles
   The British perfumer: being a collection of choice receipts and observations made during an extensive practice of thirty years, by which any lady or gentleman may prepare their own articles of the best quality, whether of perfumery, snuffs, or colours... Now first edited by John Mackenzie, Second edition. London, J. Sauter, New-York, W. Seaman, 1822. xxvi, 372 p. ICJ.   9271

Lillo, George
   Geo. Barnwell, or The London merchant; a tragedy, in five acts. New-York, A. King, 1822. 52 p. MH; PPL; RPB.
                                  9272

Lincoln, Barnabas
   Narrative of the capture, sufferings and escape of Capt. Barnabas Lincoln and his crew, who were taken by a piratical schooner, December, 1821, off Key Largo... Boston, Pr. by Ezra Lincoln, 1822. 40 p. DLC; MB; MBAU; MBAt; MH; MHi; MSaP; Vt.   9273

Lincoln, E.
   Scripture questions; or, Catechetical exercises designed for children in Sabbath schools and families... Ed. 4. Boston, Lincoln & Edmands, 1822. CtHC.
                                  9274

Lindsay, George
   Essays on the human mind, as connected with a future state of existence, and the revelations of Providence. No. 1. New York, Pr. by J. Seymour, 1822. 69 p. DLC.   9275

Lindsey, John
   A discourse, delivered before the Honourable Legislature of Vermont, on the anniversary election, October 10, 1822. Montpelier, Vt., Pr. by E. P. Walton, 1822. 27 p. DLC; MB; MBC; MH-AH; NBM; NN; NjPT; OCHP; Vt; VtBrt; VtMiM; VtMiS; VtU.   9276

Lisher, George B.
The sin against the Holy
Ghost illustrated in a discourse
delivered on the evening of the
7th February, at the capitol in
the city of Albany. Albany, Pr.
by J.W. Clark, 1822. 16 p.
MB; MMeT-Hi; MeBat.   9277

---- The will of God... Cooperstown [N.Y.] Pr. by Crandal &
Nash, 1822. 16 p. CSmH.   9278

Little, J.H.
Little Bo Peep. New York,
E. Riley [1822?] 1 l. CtY; DLC;
MH; MWA; NHi; NN.   9279

Little, Robert
Religious liberty and Unitari-
anism vindicated; a sermon
preached in... the House of Rep-
resentatives... Apr. 28, 1822.
Washington, Pishey Thompson;
F. Lucas, Baltimore; A. Small,
Philadelphia. A. Way, Jr.,
printer, 1822. 22 p. MB; MH;
NjPT.   9280

Living manners; or, The true
secret of happiness. A tale.
Philadelphia, Anthony Finley,
1822. 108 p. MBAt; PPL.   9281

Livingston, Edward, 1764-1836
Rapport fait a l'Assemblée
Générale de l'État de la Louisi-
ane, sur le projet d'un code
penal, pour le dit État. Nou-
velle-Orleans: De l'imprimerie
de Benjamin Levy & co., 1822.
170 pp. L-M; LNP; NN; PPL.
                             9282
---- Report made to the Gener-
al Assembly of the state of
Louisiana, on the plan of a penal
code for the said state. New-
Orleans, Pr. by B. Levy & co.,
1822. 159 p. DLC; IU; LNH; LU-
L; M; MB; MBAt; MBC; MHi;
MWA; MdHi; MiD-B; MnU;
MoSM; NBLiHi; NN; NNC-L;
NNLi; Nb; NjP; OCLaw; OU; P;

PPL; TxU-L.   9283

Locke, John, 1632-1704
An abridgement of Mr. Locke's
essay concerning human under-
standing. .. from the Edinburgh
ed. Boston, Cummings and Hil-
liard and B. Perkins, Hanover,
N.H., [Treadwell's Power
Press] 1822. 271 p. CtW; CtY;
MB; MPalY; MSaT; MeLewB;
NLag; NNUT; OCIW; OO; PPL.
                             9284
[Lockhart, John Gibson] 1794-
1854
Some passages in the life of
Mr. Adam Blair. Minister of
the gospel at Cross Meikle.
Boston, Wells and Lilly, 1822.
251 p. KPea; MA; MB; MBAt;
MBC; MBL; MCot; MH; MPeHi;
MiU; RPA; VtU.   9285

Logan, a family history. See
Neal, John.

The Lollards: a tale, founded
on the persecutions which marked
the early part of the fifteenth
century... New York, Pr. by
James & John Harper, for the
bookseller, 1822. 2 v. GHi;
MHa; NGH.   9286

Long, Stephen Harriman, 1784-
1864
Maps and plates for expedi-
tions to the Rocky Mts. Philadelphia, Carey & Lea, 1822.
2 maps, 7 plates. DeWI; MWA;
OMC.   9287

Longden, Henry, 1754-1812
Life of Mr. Henry Longden
(late of Sheffield) compiled from
his own memoirs... 2d Amer. ed.
from the 2d English ed. Baltimore, Armstrong & Plaskitt,
1822. 177 p. MdBaHi; MoS;
NcD; NjMd.   9288

Longworth's American almanac,
New-York, register, and city

directory for the forty-seventh
year of American independence...
New York, Thomas Longworth,
William Grattan, printer, June
25, 1822. [14], 496 p. DLC;
MWA; NHi; NN; NNMus; NNS;
PPL. 9289

Lord, Henry
A sermon, delivered before
the Hampshire Missionary Socie-
ty, at their annual meeting
Northampton, Aug. 22, 1822.
Northampton, Pr. by Sylvester
Judd, Jr., 1822. 38 p. MNF;
NNG. 9290

Lord, Joseph
The militiaman's pocket companion, with a method to form
company, and an explanation of
the exercise of the same...2d
ed. much enl. and improved.
Hudson, N.Y., W.E. Norman,
1822. 155 p. MH; MWA; N;
NCooHi; NUtHi. 9291

Lord, Nathan, 1793-1870
A sermon, delivered at the
ordination of the Rev. Robert
Page, jr., to the pastoral care
of the Congregational church in
Bradford, N.H., May 22, 1822.
Amherst, Pr. by Richard Boyls-
ton, 1822. 23 p. CSmH; DLC;
MBC; MH-AH; Nh; Nh-Hi; RPB.
9292

Loring, Nathaniel Hall
An address, delivered at the
request of the Republican Committee of arrangements, on the
anniversary of independence,
fourth July, A.D. 1822. Charlestown, Mass. Boston, Pr. at the
office of the American Statesman by True and Greene, 1822.
24 p. CtSoP; DLC; MBAt; MHi;
RPB. 9293

The lottery ticket: an American
tale. Cambridge, Pr. for the
trustees of the Publishing Fund,
by Hilliard and Metcalf, 1822.

51 p. DLC; MBAt; MBC; MH;
MHi; MNF; MPlyA; MWA;
MeBat; NN; Nh-Hi; PPL. 9294

Louisiana (State)
Acts passed at the second
session of the 5th Legislature of
the state of Louisiana...Monday
[Jan. 7, 1822] New Orleans,
Pr. by J.C. de St. Romes,
1822. 130 p. IU; LNHT; LU.
9295
---- Journal de la chambre des
representans durant la seconde
session de la cinquième legislature de l'état de la Louisiane...
Nouvelle Orleans, Imprime par
J.C. de St. Romes, 1822. 90 p.
LU. 9296

----Journal du senat durant la
seconde session de la cinquième
legislature de l'état de la Louisiane...Nouvelle Orleans, Im-
primé par J.C. de St. Romes,
1822. 69 p. LU. 9297

---- Journal of the House of
Representatives during the second session of the fifth Legislature of the State of Louisiana...
New-Orleans, Pr. by J.C. De
St. Romes, state printer, 1822.
88 p. DLC; LNH. 9298

---- Journal of the Senate during
the second session of the fifth
legislature of the state of Louisiana...New Orleans, Pr. by J.C.
de St. Romes, 1822. 68 p.
LNHT; LU. 9299

The Louisiana almanac for 1823.
By M. Nash. New-Orleans, B.
Levy & Co. [1822] 24 ll. NbO.
9300

Lowber, John C.
A digest of the ordinances of
the corporation of the city of
Philadelphia, and of the act of
assembly relating thereto. Philadelphia, Robert Desilver, 1822.
301 p. AB; Ct; DLC; MB;

MH; MdBJ; NIC; PP; PPAmP;
PPB; PHi; PPL; PPT.   9301

Lownsdale, James
The noted horse Hailstorm...
Will stand this season in Gibson
county...James Lownsdale, Feb.
1822. Brdsd. In.   9302

Low's almanack and mechanic's
and farmer's calendar for 1823.
By Nathanael Low. Boston,
Munroe & Francis [1822] 18 ll.
DLC; ICN; ICU; InU; MB; MBC;
MDedHi; MH; MHi; MWA; MWO;
MeHi; N; NRMA; VtHi; WHi.
                          9303

Lucas, Fielding, publisher
Plan of the city of Baltimore,
compiled from actual survey
made under the direction of the
commissioners appointed by the
Legislature of Maryland and by
Lewis Brantz, Esqr. under the
authority of the Mayor and City
Council of Baltimore. Engraved
by B.T. Welch & Co., Baltimore,
F. Lucas, Jr., 1822. MdBE;
NjP; PHi.   9304

Ludington, Horace
To the independent voters of
Vigo county. Under the influence of many of the people of
this county, I introduce the following for public satisfaction...
[1822] Bdsd. In.   9305

Ludlow, Charles
A correspondence between
Charles Ludlow and the United
States Navy Department, in the
year 1813. Republished at the
request of his friends. [New
York,] 1822. 8 p. CSmH.   9306

Lummus, Aaron
The life and adventures of Dr.
Caleb; who migrated from Egypt,
and afterward practised physics
in the land of Canaan and elsewhere. An allegory; designed
principally to amuse and edify

young people. Boston, Pr. for
the author by Lincoln & Edmands, 1822. 230 p. DLC; MA;
MB; MBM; MBNMHi; MLy;
MNan; RPB.   9307

Luther, Martin, 1483-1546
Der Kleine Catechismus des
seligen D. Martin Luthers,
nebst den gewöhnlichen Morgen-
Tisch- und Abend-Gebeten...
Canton (Ohio), Gedruckt bey
Jacob Sala, 1822. 130 p.
OClWHi; PPL.   9308

Lynch, W.R.
The world described, in easy
verse...For the use of young
persons...1st Amer. ed. with
additional notes. New-York, S.
Wood and Sons, [etc.] 1822.
215 p. ICU; MB; MH; PPL.
                         9309

M

M., A.
Niagara. A poem. By A.M.
New York, J. Seymour, printer,
1822. 24 p. NBu; NNia. 9310

McCall, John C.
The troubadour, and other po-
ems. Philadelphia, H.C. Carey
& I. Lea, 1822. 64 p. MdBP;
NNS; PPL; ViRVU.   9311

M'Carty & Davis Pennsylvania
almanac for 1823. By John
Ward. Philadelphia, M'Carty &
Davis [1822] 18 ll. MWA. 9312

M'Chesney, John I.
An English grammar, com-
pendiously compiled for the use
of schools. Philadelphia, Pub.
by the author, J. Bicking,
printer, 1822. 108 p. MH;
NNC; WU.   9313

M'Chord, James
Sermons on important subjects,
selected from the manuscripts of

the late Rev'd James M'Chord.
Lexington, K., Pr. by Thomas
T. Skillman, For the benefit of
the children of the author, 1822.
357 p. CSmH; ICU; KyBgW;
KyLo; KyLx; KyLxT; KyRE.
9314

McClellan, George, 1796-1847
A statement of facts. Phila-
delphia, July 18, 1822. 24 p.
DLC; MB; MBM; NNNAM; PHi;
PPL; PPAmP; PPPrHi. 9315

M'Dowell, John, 1780-1863
Questions on the Bible for the
use of schools. Elizabethtown,
N.J., Mervin Hale; stereotyped
by A. Chandler & co., 1822.
152 p. MH; NjP; NjR. 9316

---- ---- 6th ed. Newark, N.J.
Benj. Olds, 1822. 152 p. CSmH;
CtSoP. 9316a

McDuffie, George, 1790-1851
Speech of the Hon. George
McDuffie, on the bill in addition
to the Act to reduce and fix the
military peace establishment.
Delivered in the House of Representatives of the United States
on the 16th April, 1822. Charleston, S.C., John Hoff, 1822. 19 p.
ScC; ScU. 9316b

Macgillivray, W.A.M.
The travels and researches
of Alexander von Humboldt...
New York, Pr. and pub. by J.
& J. Harper, 1822. 367, 4 p.
PPF. 9316c

M'Henry, James, 1785-1845
The pleasures of friendship,
a poem in two parts; to which
are added a few original Irish
melodies. Pittsburgh, Eichbaum
& Johnston (prs.) 1822. 72 p.
CSmH; DLC; NBuG; PHi; PPM;
PPi; PPiHi; PPins; RPB. 9316d

---- ---- Pittsburgh, The author, 1822. 70 p. DLC. 9316e

McHenry, John, d. 1860
The ejectment law of Maryland, embracing within a nar-
row compass, all the decisions
of the Courts of Law of Maryland, deemed worthy of notice,
relating to the title and location
of land. Frederick-Town, Pr.
at the Herald Press, by John P.
Thomson, for the Author, 1822.
264 p. DLC; Md; MdBB; MdBE;
MdBP; MdUL; MH-L; PPB.
9316f

McIntosh, Nathan
The Scriptures an allegory,
both Old and New Testaments
...Marietta, O., Pr. by R.
Prentiss, 1822. 48 p. CSmH;
OMC. 9317

Mack, Alexander
Kurze und einfältige Vorstel-
lung der aussern, aber doch
eiligen Recht und ordnungen des
Hauses Gottes... Lancaster,
Gedruckt fur den Verleger, von
Johann Bär, 1822. 99 p. DLC;
P; PHi. 9318

M'Kay, Samuel M.
An address delivered before
the Berkshire Association for
the Promotion of Agriculture and
Manufactures at Pittsfield October 3, 1822... Pittsfield, Pr.
by Phinehas Allen, 1822. 34 p.
M; MB; MH; MPiB. 9319

M'Kenney, Thomas L.
Prospectus of the Washington
Republican and Congressional
Examiner. (August, 1822) Bdsd.
MHi. 9320

McLean Asylum for the Insane,
Belmont, Mass.
Rules and regulations for the
government of the Asylum for
the Insane, adopted December 1,
1822, additional to those adopted
July 5, 1821... Boston, Pr. by
Russell and Gardner, 1822. 10
p. DLC; MHi. 9321

Macready, William Charles
The village lawyer; a farce,
in two acts. Philadelphia, T. H.
Palmer, 1822. 22 p. MH.   9322

McVickar, John, 1787-1868
A domestic narrative of the
life of Samuel Bard, M. D.,
LL. D., late president of the
College of Physicians and sur-
geons of the University of the
state of New York... New York,
The literary rooms [Columbia
College] A. Paul, printer, 1822.
244 p. DLC; DNLM; IC; ICJ;
ICN; MB; MBD; MH; MdBE;
MdBM; MdBS; MWA; MoSW-M;
N; NN; NBLiHi; NBM; NIC;
NNC; NNMus; NNS; PPL;
PPPH; PU; RNR; TxGR; ViRA;
WHi.   9323

Mad. de Nouville's waltz. Philadelphia, G. Willig [1822?] 1 l.
MWA; NN; PP; RPB.   9324

---- Philadelphia, G. Willig
[ca 1822] 1 l. MWA; NN.   9325

Maddock, Henry, d. 1824.
A treatise on the principles
and practice of the High court of
chancery... 2d Amer. from the
2d London ed., rev. and enl.
by the author. Hartford, O.D.
Cooke & sons, 1822. 2 v. CoU;
CtW; KyU-L; LNT-L; MH;
MiD-B; MnU; MsU; NNIA; NNU;
NNebgL; OMans; PP; PPB; PU-
L; ICLaw; TxSaWi; TxU-L;
ViU.   9326

Maffit, John Newland, 1794-1850
Epitome of Mr. Maffit's discourse (on Prov. xxix. 1), taken
down verbally. [Concord?
1822] BrMus.   9327

Magendi, François, 1783-1855
A summary of physiology.
Tr. from the French, by John
Revere... Baltimore, E. J. Coale
& Co., 1822. John D. Toy,

printer. 430 p. CSt-L; DLC;
ICJ; IU-M; MdUM; MdHi; MiD-
M; MWiW; MH-M; MeB; MB;
MdBE; NBMS; NcU; Nh;
NNNAM; OC; PBa; PPL;
ScCMeS.   9328

[Magnus, Julian?]
Alfred the Great; an histori-
cal tragedy, in five acts. By a
young gentleman of this city.
New-York, E. Murden, May,
1822. 107 p. CLU; DLC; ICU;
MB; MH; MWA; NCH; NRU;
RPB.   9329

The magpie. See Pocock,
Isaac.

Maine.
[An act for the relief of poor
debtors. Thayer, Tappan and
Stickney, printers to the state,
1822] 16 p. (Imprint from colophon. Dated on p. 16: January
24, 1822) MeHi.   9330

---- [An act, in addition to an
act, entitled, "An Act, ascertaining what shall constitute the
legal settlement and for providing for the relief and support,
employment and removal of the
poor." No imprint] 3 p. (Dated
on p. 3: January 23, 1822)
MeHi.   9331

---- [An act to establish a
Court of Common Pleas for the
state. Thayer, Tappan and
Stickney, printers to the state,
1822] 8 p. (Imprint from colo-
phon. Dated on p. 8: January
23, 1821 [i. e. 1822]) MeHi.
        9332
---- By Albion K. Parris,
Governor of the state of Maine:
a proclamation, for a day of
public humiliation and prayer...
Given at the council chamber in
Portland, the sixteenth day of
February, in the year of our
Lord, one thousand, eight hun-

dred and twenty-two...Thayer, Tappan and Stickney, printers [1822] Bdsd. MeHi.   9333

---- By Albion K. Parris, Governor of the state of Maine: a proclamation, for a day of public thanksgiving and praise... Given at the council chamber, in Portland, the tenth day of October, in the year of our Lord, one thousand, eight hundred and twenty-two...Abijah W. Thayer, printer [1822] Bdsd. MeHi. 9334

---- Laws of the state of Maine; to which are prefixed the constitution of the United States and of said state, with an appendix. Hallowell, Pr. and published by Goodale, Glazier and Co., 1822. 682 p. CtY-L; C; DLC; ICLaw; IU; Ia; MeU; MeWC; Mi-L; NcD; OCLaw; OrPML; BrMus.
                                9335
---- Laws of the state of Maine; to which are prefixed the constitution of the United States and of said state, in two volumes. With an appendix. Vol. II. Hallowell, Pub. by Calvin Spaulding; Goodale, Glazier and Co., printers, 1822.   682 p. M; MWA; MeBa; NN.   9336

---- Laws of the state of Maine, to which are prefixed the constitution of the United States and of said state, with an appendix. Portland, Pub. by William Hyde; Goodale, Glazier and Co., printers, 1822. 682 p. DJ; M; MWA; MiU-L.   9337

---- [Message of the Governor of the state of Maine, to both branches of the Legislature, January 5, 1822.] 8 p. MeHi.
                                9338
---- Private acts of the state of Maine, passed by the Legislature, at its session, January, 1822. Portland, Abijah W. Thayer,

printer to the state, 1822. [115]-220 p. C; CSfLaw; CtY-L; DJ; DLC; IaU-L; In-SC; M; MH-L; MWA; MWCL; Me-LR; MeU; MeWebr; Mi-L; Mo; Nb; TxU-L; W; BrMus.   9339

---- Public acts of the state of Maine, passed by the Legislature, at its session, held in January, 1822. Portland, Thayer, Tappan and Stickney, printers to the state, 1822. [873]-913 p. CSfLaw; CtY-L; DJ; DLC; IaHi; In-SC; L; M; MH-L; MHi; Me-LR; MeU; Mi-L; MiU-L; Mo; NN; NNLI; Nb; T; TxU-L; W.   9340

---- Public laws of the state of Maine. January, 1822. With an appendix. [Hallowell, Goodale, Glazier and Co., 1822] 30; 22 p. Cover title. At head of title: No. 1...Vol. 2. Goodale, Glazier and Co's. edition. DLC; MiU-L.   9341

---- Regimental orders. Third regiment, first brigade, fourth division. Bowdoin, July 20th, 1822. 1 p. DLC.   9342

---- Regulae generales. At York, April term, 1822. Hallowell, Pr. by Goodale, Glazier and Co., 1822. 17 p. Williamson 6044.   9343

---- Reports of cases argued and determined in the Supreme Judicial Court of the state of Maine. By Simon Greenleaf, Counsellor at Law. Vol. 1. containing the cases of the years 1820 and 1821. Hallowell, Pr. by Goodale, Glazier and Co., 1822. viii, 436 p. AzU-L; CHanKL; CSfBar; CSfU; CSjoSCL; CStoSL; Ct; DBA; DJ; DLC; F-SC; FDeS; ICLaw; ICU; IU; KyU-L; L; LNHT; M; MH-L; MTaB; MWCL; MdBB;

MdU-L; Me-LR; MeBa; MeWC;
Mi-L; Mn; Ms; N-L; NN;
NNLI; NNU; NNia; Nb; NbU-L;
Nc-SC; Nd-L; NdU-L; Nj;
OCLaw; OClW; ODal; Ok; Or-
SC; OrPML; PPB; PPiAL; RPL;
Sc-SC; T-SC; TMeB; TxDaCiA;
TxHHarL; TxU-L; U; Vi-L;
ViU-L; W; WaSpSCL; WaU;
BrMus.   9344

---- Resolves of the Legislature
of the state of Maine, passed at
its session, which commenced
on the second day of January,
and ended on the ninth day of
February, one thousand eight
hundred and twenty-two. Portland, Thayer, Tappan and Stickney, printers to the state, 1822.
[103]-186 p. CSfLaw; CtY-L;
DJ; DLC; In-SC; M; MH-L;
MWA; Me-LR; MeHi; MeU;
MeWebr; Mi-L; MiU-L; NNLI;
Nb; RPL; TxU-L; W.   9345

---- Rules and orders to be observed in the House of Representatives, of the state of Maine,
during the continuance of the
second Legislature. Portland,
Pr. by Thomas Todd, 1822. 24 p.
MeHi; MeWC.   9346

---- Adjutant General's Office.
Portland, June 1, 1822. Sir,
The officers of the militia being
required by the 13th section of
the militia law to wear an "uniform dress"... Broadside. CtY.
                                9347

---- Cumberland S.S. ... To the
assessors of the town of West-
brook in said county, greetings.
...this second day of April,
A.D. 1822. Wm. T. Vaughan,
clerk. Bdsd. MeWebr.   9348

---- [Treasurer's report. No
imprint] 8 p. (Dated on p. [1]:
January 9th, 1822) MeHi.   9349

Maine Charity School, Bangor,
Maine.
Catalogue of the officers,
graduates and students... November, 1822. Hallowell, Me.,
Goodale, Glazier and co., printers, [1822] Bdsd. M.   9350

The Maine farmers' almanac for
1823. By Daniel Robinson.
Hallowell, Me., Goodale Glazier
& Co. [1822] 24 ll. CLU; DLC;
MB; MBAt; MWA; MeB; MeBa;
MeHi; N.   9351

Maine Missionary Society
[Report] 15th, 1821/22- Hallowell, Pr. by Goodale, Glazier
and Co., [etc.] 1822. M. 9352

The Maine register, and United
States' calendar for 1823. By
William B. Sewall. Portland,
A. Shirley and Todd & Smith
[1822] 90 ll. ICN; InU; MHi;
MWA; Me; MeBa; MeP; MeU;
Nh.   9353

Malcolm, Howard
Hymns for conference meetings, and private devotion selected from Watt's psalms and
hymns, and Rippon's supplemental selection. Hudson, Pr.
by J.W. Dutcher, 1822. 136 p.
DLC; IAlS; NRAB.   9354

Manesca, John
Historiettes nouvelles. Nou-
velle-York, G. Grattan, 1822.
62 p. MH; PU.   9355

The maniac: a poem descrip-
tive of all persons now in the
madhouse of this city with other
original poems on various subjects by the author. Charleston,
Pr. for the author by C.C. Sebring, 1822. 36 p. MH.   9356

Mann, Herman
Remarks, accompanying the
reading of the Declaration of

American independence, Dedham,
July 4, 1822. Dedham, H. & W.
H. Mann [1822] 20 p. MH; PHi;
RPB.   9357

[Mansfield, Jared] 1759-1830
  Essays, mathematical and
physical: containing new theories and illustrations of some
very important and difficult subjects of the sciences. New-
Haven, Pr. by William W. Morse,
[1822?] 274 p. KyLxT.   9358

[Marcet, Mrs. Jane (Haldimand)]
1769-1858
  Conversations on chemistry;
in which the elements of the sci-
ence are familiary explained and
illustrated by experiments... 8th
Amer. from 6th London ed.,
rev., corr. and enl. Hartford,
Oliver D. Cooke [P. B. Goodsell,
printer] 1822. 383 p. CSmH;
CtHT-W; CtW; CtY; DLC; DSG;
GDC; MAm; MB; MA; MBevHi;
MH; MQ; MnU; NBatHL; NNC-
P; NNN; NRU; NSyU; NcD; NjP;
P; PP; PU; RP; RPB; TNP;
TxU-T; ViL; VtBrt; VtMiS. 9359

Marine Bible Society, Boston
  Second annual report of the
Marine Bible Society of Boston
and its vicinity. Presented at
their annual meeting, Nov. 6,
1822. Boston, James G. Bolles,
printer, 1822. 8 p. DLC; M;
MWA.   9360

[Marks, Richard]
  The retrospect; or, Review of
providential mercies... By Aliquis... From the 7th London ed.
Boston, Samuel T. Armstrong
and Crocker & Brewster, 1822.
236 p. Ct; InCW; MA; MB;
MBC; MoSpD; NjHo; RPB; ScU.
                                  9361
Marsh, John
  Blair's lectures on rhetoric
and belles-lettres, reduced to
question and answer. By Rev.

John Marsh. 2d ed. Hartford
(Conn.) Samuel G. Goodrich, E.
Clark, printer, Middletown, 1822.
144 p. CtHi; CtW; CtY;
MiGr; MiNazC; NjP; OCl; PU;
PWW; TBriK.   9362

Marshall, Elihu F.
  A spelling book of the Eng-
lish language... Concord [N. H.]
Hill & Moore, 1822. 156 p. MH;
MHingHi; Nh-Hi.   9363

Marshall, George, d. 1855
  Marshall's practical marine
gunnery: containing a view of
the magnitude, weight, description & use, of every article
used in the Sea gunner's department, in the navy of the United
States. Norfolk, Pr. by T. G.
Broughton and pub. by C. Hall,
1822. 136 p. CtY; DLC; DN;
MB; MH; NN; NcD; PPL.
                                  9364
Marshall, Mrs. [L. H. ?]
  Sketch of my friend's family,
intended to suggest some practical hints on religion and domestic manners. 6th ed. Hartford,
O. D. Cooke & sons, 1822. 126 p.
CtHi; NBuG.   9365

Marshall, Mary, b. 1780
  A portraiture of Shakerism,
exhibiting a general view of
their character and conduct, from
the first appearance of Ann Lee
in New-England, down to the
present time. [Concord, N. H.,]
Pr. for the author, 1822. 446 p.
CSmH; DLC; M; MB; MBAt; MH;
MHi; MLanc; MNan; MPeHi;
MSo; MWiW-C; MiU-C; MnDu;
NBuG; NCH; NN; NNUT; Nh;
NhD; NhM; OClW; OClWHi;
PPPrHi.   9366

Martin, Anthony B.
  Remarks on agriculture and
a method of improving soils, by
creating artificial manures,
founded on chemical and scien-

tific principles. Baltimore, J. D. Toy, printer, 1822. 19 p. DA; Vi. 9367

Martin, Michael
Life of Michael Martin, who was executed for highway robbery, December 20, 1821. As given by himself. 3d ed. Boston, Russell & Gardner, 1822. 71 p. DLC; M; MB; MHi; NjPT. 9368

Martin, Wheeler, 1765-1836
Thoughts, in five propositions on the following: vii. verse, II Chapter of Psalms, 'The wicked shall be turned into Hell, and all the nations that forget God,'' ...Providence, Pr. by Miller and Hutchens, 1822. 11 p. DLC; RPB. 9369

Martin, William
Le retour de Kips Hill. Arranged as a rondo for the piano forte. New York, A. & W. Geib [1822?] 6 p. NN; PP. 9370

Martyn, Henry, 1781-1812
Sermons by the late Rev. Henry Martyn, B.D., fellow of St. John's college, Cambridge... 1st Amer. from the original Calcutta ed. Boston, pub. for the benefit of the American Board of Commissioners for Foreign Missions, Crocker & Brewster, printers, 1822. 386 p. CBPSR; CSansS; CtHC; CtHT; GDC; GMM; ICP; ICU; IEG; KTW; KyLoP; MA; MB; MBAt; MBC; MDeeP; MH; MHi; MLy; MNt; MPiB; MS; MShM; MdBLC; MeBat; MoMM; MoS; MoSpD; NBLiHi; NCH; NHunt; NbCrD; NbOM; NcElon; NcSalL; NjPT; OCl; OO; RNR; RPB; TNMB; TxAuPT. 9371

Mary Hollis, an original tale. See Sedgwick, Catharine Maria.

Maryland (State)

Counter report relative to the Susquehannah Canal wing-dam, accompanied by the report of the committee of the House of Delegates, to which was recommitted the bill relating to said wing-dam. Annapolis, Pr. by Jehu Chandler [1822] 13 p. MdBJ-G. 9372

---- Documents respecting the Maryland Penitentiary. December session, 1822. Annapolis, J. Hughes, printer, 1822. [iv] p. MdHi. 9373

---- Laws made and passed by the General Assembly of the state of Maryland, at a session begun and held at the City of Annapolis on Monday the third day of December, eighteen hundred and twenty-one... Annapolis, Pr. by Jehu Chandler, printer to the state, 1821! [1822] 184 p. C; Ct; Ia; MdBB; MdHi; MdUL; Mo; MWCL; Nb; Nj; NNLI; Nv; PU-L; R; W. 9374

---- A list of invalid pensioners. December session, 1822. Annapolis, J. Hughes, printer, 1822. Bdsd. MdHi. 9375

---- Report of the auditor of the state. December session, 1822. Annapolis, J. Hughes, printer, 1822. [iv] p. MdHi. 9376

---- Report of the Committee appointed to inspect the wing-dam at the head of the Susquehanna Canal, with the evidence, &c. December session, 1821. Annapolis, Pr. by Jehu Chandler [1822] 19 p. MdHi. 9377

---- Report of the Committee of Claims, on the proceedings of Benjamin Harwood, esq. Treasurer of the Western Shore. December session, 1822. Annapolis, Jeremiah Hughes, printer, 1822. 4 p. MdHi. 9378

---- Report of the Committee of
Claims, relative to the proceedings of William Richardson, Esq.
Treasurer of the Eastern Shore
of Maryland. December session,
1822. Annapolis, J. Hughes,
printer, 1822. [vi] p. MdHi.
                                    9379

---- The report of the Committee of Grievances and Courts of
Justice, relative to the official
conduct of the honorable Abraham Shriver, associate judge of
the Fifth Judicial District...
Annapolis, Pr. by J. Chandler
[1822] 62 p. MdBP.   9380

---- Report of the Committee of
the Senate of Maryland, on internal improvement, to whom
was referred so much of the
executive communication as relates to that subject. December
session, 1821. Annapolis, J.
Chandler [1822?] 8 p. MdBE;
MdHi.   9381

---- Report of the Committee of
Ways and Means to the House of
Delegates of Maryland, on the
finances and resources of the
state, December session, 1821.
Annapolis, Chandler [1822?] 10 p.
NNC.   9382

---- Report of the House of
Delegates, by the Committee to
whom was referred, the executive communication relating to
the appointment of commissioners to inspect the Potomac River, with accompanying documents, to which is added Mr.
Millard's resolutions on internal
improvements. December session, 1821. Annapolis, J. Chandler [1822] 15 p. Parsons collection.   9383

---- Report of the State Agent,
for the Western Shore. December session, 1822. Annapolis,
J. Hughes, printer, 1822. [ii],

3, [iii] p. MdHi.   9384

---- Report of the Treasurer of
the Western Shore of Maryland
in obedience to an order of the
House of Delegates, 13th ins.
Respecting monies received for
duties on retailers of dry goods,
importers and wholesale merchants. As also of dealers in
lottery tickets. December session, 1822. Annapolis, J.
Hughes, printer, 1822. [iv] p.
MdHi.   9385

---- Report of the Treasurer of
the Western Shore of Maryland,
in obedience to an order of the
House, relative to the disbursements made in by the State on
account of the penitentiary, December session, 1821. Annapolis, Chandler [1822?] [4] p. fold.
table. NNC.   9386

---- Report of the Treasurer of
the Western Shore on the funded
stock. December session, 1822.
Annapolis, J. Hughes, printer,
1822. [iv] p. MdHi.   9387

---- Report of the Treasurer of
the Western Shore respecting his
proceedings, under the act of
December Session, 1821. Entitled An act, relating to the
Penitentiary of Maryland, and
authorizing the Treasurer of the
Western Shore, to constitute
stock, to the amount of twenty-
eight thousand dollars. December session, 1822. Annapolis,
J. Hughes, printer, 1822. [iv] p.
MdHi.   9388

---- Treasurer's report by order of the House of Delegates of
9th December, relative to the
revenue, the school fund, and
the annual expenditure of the
Judiciary, December session.
Annapolis, J. Hughes, printer,
1822. [iv], [1] p. MdHi.   9389

---- Votes and proceedings of the General Assembly of the state of Maryland at December session, 1821. Annapolis, Pr. by Jehu Chandler, 1821[!] [1822] 155 p. DLC; MdBB; MdBP; MdHi. 9390

---- Votes and proceedings of the Senate of the state of Maryland, December session, 1821. Annapolis, Pr. by J. Chandler, printer to the state, 1821[!] [1822] 80 p. MdHi. 9391

Maryland Circulating Library No. 2. Supplement to the catalogue of books, &c. belonging to the Maryland Circulating Library, corner of North Charles and Conewago Streets. Baltimore, December, 1822. 34, [2] p. MdHi. 9392

The Maryland resolutions. See Maxcy, Virgil.

Mason, John, 1646?-1694 Select remains of the Rev. John Mason; or, The Christian's pocket companion. A new ed. Rockville, Md., J. A. Bingham, 1822. 209 (i. e. 205) p. CtHT; DLC; MdBE; MdHi; OCIW. 9393

Mason, John, 1706-1763 A treatise on self knowledge, showing the nature and benefit of that important science and the way to attain it...To which are added, Questions adapted to the work, for the use of schools and academies. 3d ed., with notes. Boston, J. Loring, 1822. 196 p. CtHC; CtHT; MB; MH; MdW; NCaS; NGH; NNMHi; OMC; PU. 9394

Mason, John Mitchell, 1770-1829 Address, delivered at the organization of the faculty of Dickinson College, January 15th, 1822. Carlisle, G. Phillips, printer, 1822. 16 p. CSmH; DLC; KyDC; MnU; PHi; PPPrHi. 9395

---- Address delivered at the organization of Dickinson College, at Carlisle, Pennsylvania, January 15th, 1822. New-York, Pr. by Samuel Marks, 1822. 20 p. DLC; ICMe; NNC. 9396

---- The evangelical ministry exemplified in the Apostle Paul: A sermon preached in Murray-Street Church, December 2, 1821, on the occasion of resigning his charge of his congregation...New-York, Pub. at the Literary Rooms, Corn. of Broadway and Pine-Street; Abraham Paul, printer, 1822. 39 p. DLC; IEG; ICP; ICU; IObB; MA; MB; MBC; MH-AH; MHi; MWA; MdBD; NIC; NNC; NNUT; NjPT; NjR; OCHP; PHi; PPL. 9397

[Mason, Lowell, comp.] The Boston Handel and Haydn Society collection of church music; being a selection of the most approved psalm and hymn tunes, together with many beautiful extracts from the works of Haydn, Mozart, Beethoven, and other eminent modern composers...The whole harmonized for three and four voices, with a figured bass for the organ or piano forte...Boston, Richardson & Lord, 1822. 320, [3] p. (The compiler's name does not appear on the title-page of this edition.) ICN; MB; MBC; MBNEC; MH; MHi. 9398

Mason, William Powell, 1791-1867 A report of the case of Jeune Eugenie, determined in the Circuit Court of the United States, for the First circuit, at Boston, December, 1821. Boston, Wells and Lilly, 1822. 108 p.

CtHT-W; CtY; DLC; MB; MBAt;
MBNEH; MH; MWA; MdBB;
MiU-C; MoU; N-L; NBLiHi;
NNLI; PHi; PPL; RP; WBeloC.
9399

Massachusetts (State)
An act to establish the city of
Boston. Feb. 23, 1822. [Boston,
1822] Bdsd. MB; MH; MiU.
9400

---- An act to regulate the administration of justice within the
county of Suffolk, and for other
purposes. (with an act establishing the city of Boston). [1822?]
24, [3] p. M; RP.   9401

---- By His Excellency John
Brooks... A proclamation for a
day of public thanksgiving and
praise... fifth day of December
... Given... eighteenth day of October... eighteen hundred and
twenty two. [Boston, 1822]
Bdsd. MB; MBB.   9402

---- By His Excellency, John
Brooks, Governor of the Commonwealth of Massachusetts, A
Proclamation for a day of humiliation, fasting and prayer...I
do hereby appoint Thursday, 4th
of April...as a day of humiliation, fasting and prayer... Given
at... Council Chamber... Boston,
25th February, 1822. [Boston,
1822] Bdsd. MB; MBB.   9403

---- The constitution of the state
of Massachusetts, adopted 1780.
With the amendments annexed.
Printed by order of the House of
Representatives. Boston, Pr.
for B. Russell, printer to the
state, by Russell and Gardner,
1822. 86 p. Ct; ICartC;
KLindB; M; MB; MBAt; MBC;
MBevHi; MBr; MC; MHingHi;
MWA; MiU-C; MiU-L; MoHi;
NB; NNC; ViFbE.   9404

---- Commonwealth of Massachusetts... The Committee of

both houses of the legislature,
to whom... was referred a message of His Excellency the Governor, communicating sundry
resolutions... of the state of
Maryland, relative to the appropriation of a portion of the public lands... ask leave... to submit the following report. [Bos-
ton, 1822] 15 p. MB; MH.
9405

---- ---- [Another ed.] [Bos-
ton, 1822] 18 p. MB; MBC;
NIC.   9406

---- Free negroes and mulattoes. House of Representatives,
January 16, 1822. The Committee, directed by an order of the
House of Representatives, at the
last session of the Legislature
of this Commonwealth, to report
a bill concerning the admission
into this state of free negroes
and mulattoes, have considered
the matter referred to them, and
have agreed to the following report... Boston, 1822. 16 p. ICU;
MB; MH; MHi; MiD-B; MsJS;
Nh.   9407

---- Laws of the Commonwealth
of Massachusetts, passed at the
several sessions of the General
Court, beginning May, 1818...
and ending February, 1822. Vol.
VIII. Boston, Pr. for Benj.
Russell, printer to the state, by
Russell and Gardner, 1822. 751,
[18] p. MBeHi; MSaEC; Mi-L;
Mo; TxU-L.   9408

---- Laws of the Commonwealth
of Massachusetts, passed by the
General Court, at their session,
which commenced on Wednesday,
the ninth day of January, and
ended on Saturday, the twenty
third day of February, A.D.
eighteen and twenty-two. Boston,
Benj. Russell, 1822. [613]-751 p.
IaU-L; L; MKiTH; MPiBL; Mo;
Nj; T.   9409

---- Laws of the Commonwealth of Massachusetts, passed by the General Court, at their session, which commenced on Wednesday, the twenty-ninth of May, and ended on Saturday, the fifteenth of June, one thousand eight hundred and twenty two. Boston, Pr. for Benj. Russell, printer to the state, by Russell and Gardner, 1822. 36, [2] p. Ia; L. MDi; MKiTH; MMal; MdBB; Mi-L; Mo; NNLI; Nj; TxU-L. 9410

---- List of members of the House of Representatives. 1822. Bdsd. MHi. 9411

---- Report of the Committee of Valuation, January 7, 1822. 8 p. M; MHi. 9412

---- Report of the committee to whom was referred that part of His Excellency's message to the Legislature, which related to the state prison. Boston, 1822. 22 p. MH; PPAmP; RPB. 9413

---- Report on the merits of the claim of the State of Massachusetts, on the national government for expenses of the militia, during the late war, to the Governor and council of the Commonwealth. January, 1821. Boston, Pr. by Russell and Gardner, 1822. 30 p. Ct; CtHT-W; DLC; KHi; M; MB; MBAt; MH; MHi; MWA; MiD-B; NNC; Nh-Hi; PHi; PPAmP; WHi. 9414

---- Resolution, in regard to the settlement of the claim on the general government, War of 1812, transmitted to Hon. Francis Bayliss by John Brooks, Gov., Jan. 10, 1822. [2] p. MHi. 9415

---- Resolves of the General Court of the Commonwealth of Massachusetts, passed at their session, which commenced on Wednesday, the ninth day of January, and ended on Saturday, the twenty-third day of February, one thousand eight hundred and twenty-two. Boston, Pr. for Benjamin Russell, by Russell and Gardner, 1822. 387-490 [4] p. IaU-L; Nb; Nj. 9416

---- Resolves of the General Court of the Commonwealth of Massachusetts, passed at their session, which commenced on Wednesday, the twenty ninth day of May, and ended on Saturday, the fifteenth day of June, 1822. Boston, Pr. for Benjamin Russell, printer to the state, by Russell & Gardner, 1822. 63, [2] p. Ia; IaU-L; MDi; MKiTH; Nb; Nj. 9417

---- Rules and orders to be observed in the Senate of the Commonwealth of Massachusetts for the year 1822... Boston, Pr. for B. Russell, printer to the state, by Russell and Gardner, 1822. 32 p. MiD-B. 9418

---- Rules and regulations of the board of primary schools; revised February, 1822. Boston, Pr. by E. G. House, 1822. 20 p. MHi; NjR. 9419

---- Tax for the year 1822... Commonwealth of Massachusetts. In the year of our Lord eighteen hundred and twenty two. An act to apportion and assess a tax of seventy five thousand dollars... 20 p. MB. 9420

---- Ancient and Honourable Artillery Company
Rules and regulations... Boston, E. G. House, 1822. 32 p. MBAt; NN. 9421

Massachusetts Domestic Missionary Society
Fourth annual report of the

Massachusetts Domestic Missionary Society, and their address to the public. Boston, Crocker & Brewster, printers, 1822. 19 p. MB; MBAt; MH; MWA; MiD-B; NjPT. 9422

Massachusetts General Hospital, Boston

Address of the trustees of the Massachusetts General Hospital, to the subscribers and to the public. [Boston, 1822] 34 p. CtY; DLC; DNLM; ICJ; M; MB; MH; MHi; MnHi; PPL. 9423

---- Rules and regulations for the government of the Hospital, adopted November 1, 1822... Boston, Pr. by Russell and Gardner, 1822. 11-20 p. MBAt; MHi. 9424

Massachusetts Historical Society

Collections of the Massachusetts Historical Society. Vol. IX of the second series. Boston, Pr. by Phelps and Farnham, 1822. 372 p. IaHA; KyLxT; MBBC; MBevHi; MHa; MeHi. 9425

Massachusetts Medical Society

Acts of incorporation and acts regulating the practice of physick and surgery, with the by-laws and orders of the Massachusetts Medical Society. Boston, Pr. by Joseph W. Ingraham, 1822. 92 p. DLC; DNLM; IEN-M; MH-M; MHi; MeB; MiDW-M; OCIW. 9426

---- A catalogue of books, belonging to the Massachusetts Medical Society, 17th June, 1822. 12 p. [Boston, 1822] MB; MBC; MBM; MH-M; MHi; NNNAM. 9427

---- Medical dissertations delivered at the annual meeting of the Massachusetts Medical Society. Pub. by the society. 3d vol. Boston, Pr. by Joseph W. Ingraham, 1822. 469 p. IU;

KyLxT; MHi; MWA; MWat; MoSpD; NNC-M; OCG; OCIM; PU; WU-M. 9428

Massachusetts Missionary Society

Annual report, May 28, 1822. With a list of officers and report of Treasurer. Salem, Pr. by Warwick Palfray, Jun., 1822. 16 p. CSmH; NN. 9429

Massachusetts Peace Society

Sixth annual report of the Massachusetts Peace Society. [Boston, 1822?] 8 p. MB; BrMus. 9430

The Massachusetts register and United States calendar; for the year of our Lord 1823, and forty-seventh of American independence... Boston, pub. by James Loring and Richardson & Lord. Sold wholesale and retail at their book-stores, Cornhill. [1822?] 252 p. C; CtHT-W; GDC; ICN; ICU; InU; MB; MBB; MBD; MDovC; MH; MHi; MNF; MTop; MWA; MWHi; MdBP; MeB; MeBa; MiD-B; MnU; MoSpD; N; NBLiHi; NN; Nh; OCIWHi; P; RPB. 9431

Massachusetts-State Prison, Charlestown

Abstract of the number of convicts in the prison, the manner of employing them, together with the receipts and expenses of the institution. Sept. 30, 1818, 1822. Bdsd. MH. 9432

Massinger, Philip, 1583-1640.

...A new way to pay old debts; a comedy...Boston, Wells and Lilly, 1822. 102 p. DLC; MH; MeB; NN; PPL; TxU. 9433

Mather, Cotton

The biography of Samuel Whiting, minister of Lynn. Extracted from Magnalia Christi Americana:

by Cotton Mather. Boston, Pr.
by True and Greene, 1822. 12 p.
DLC.   9434

---- Essays to do good addressed to all Christians... A
new ed. , imp. by the Rev. Geo.
Burder. Lexington, Ky. , Thomas T. Skillman, 1822. 256 p.
KyDC; KyHi; KyLoP; KyU. 9435

---- Essays to do good addressed
to all Christians... New ed. , imp.
by Geo. Burder. Pr. for the
benefit of missions. From the
latest Boston and London ed.
Wilmington, R. Porter, 1822.
215, [1] p. CBPSR; DeHi; DeWI;
MB; NjP; PPL; PWW; TNJ;
TxShA.   9436

Mathews, Charles, 1776-1835
    La diligence. 1st Amer. from
the 12th London ed. New York,
E. M. Murden, 1822. 8 p. MA;
MH.   9437

---- Mathews at home; or,
Travels in air, on earth, and on
water. With all the comic songs.
(A corr. ed.) The Polly Packet;
with six copper-plate engravings,
and stories; from Mr. Mathews'
youthful days. New York, E. M.
Murden, 1822. 36 p. DLC; MA;
MB; MH; MWA; MiU-C; NN;
NAuCM; PHi; PU; RPB.   9438

---- ---- Corr. from the last
London ed.... New York, S.
King, 1822. 36 p. PPL.   9439

---- ---- 1st Amer. from the
12th London ed. ... New York,
E. M. Murden, 1822. 36 p.
PPL.   9440

---- Mathew's trip to Paris; or,
The dramatic tourist. With all
the songs, adventures, etc. as
performed by Mr. Mathews at
the English opera house. 1st
Amer. from the 12th London ed.

New York, E. M. Murden, 1822.
48 p. ICN; MA; MB; MWA.
                               9441

No entry   9442

Maturin, Charles Robert, 1782-
1824
    Bertram, or, The castle of
St. Aldobrand; a tragedy in five
acts. Philadelphia, T. H. Palmer, 1822. 67 p. MH; NN; PPL;
PU; RPB.   9443

[Maxcy, Virgil] 1785-1844
    The Maryland resolutions,
and the objections to them con-
sidered. By a citizen of Mary-
land. Baltimore, Pub. by E. J.
Coale & Co. , John D. Toy,
printer, 1822. 39 p. CtHT-W;
DLC; M; MB; MBAt; MBC; MH;
MWA; MdBE; MdBJ; MdBP;
MdHi; MiU-C; NN; OCl; OClWHi;
PHi; PPAmP; PPL; RPB; TxU;
Vi; WHi.   9444

May you like it. See Tayler,
Charles Benjamin.

Mead, Asa
    Report of the Rev. Asa Mead,
agent of the Young Men's Bible
Society of Washington City, Pr.
by order of the Board June 1822.
Washington City, Pr. by Anderson and Meehan, 1822. 45 p.
DLC.   9445

Meade, Richard Worsam
    Documents in relation to the
claim of Richard W. Meade, on
the government of Spain. Washington, Pr. by Gales & Seaton,
1822. 35 p. DLC; MH; PHi; PP.
                               9446
Medical and Chirurgical Faculty
of Maryland
    The act of incorporation and
supplementary acts, with the by-
laws of the Medical and Chir-

urgical Faculty of Maryland...
Baltimore, Pr. by John D. Toy,
1822. 48, [2] p. MdBM; MdBE;
MdHi; PPL.   9447

The medical practitioner's
pocket companion; or, A key to
the knowledge of diseases, and
of the appearances that denote
recovery or danger... Philadelphia, pub. by James Webster;
Wm. Brown, printer, 1822.
64, [4] p. DLC; DNLM; OO.
                              9448
Medical Society of the County of
Kings, Brooklyn
    Statutes regulating the prac-
tice of physic and surgery in
the State of New York, and the
by-laws of the Medical Society
of the County of Kings adopted
April 8, 1822. Brooklyn, A.
Spooner, 1822. 32 p. NBLiHi.
                              9449
Medical Society of the State of
New York
    Transactions of the Medical
Society of the State of New-York,
for the year 1822. Albany, Pr.
by Websters and Skinners, 1822.
12 p. NN; NNNAM; NjR.   9450

The medley. New York, S.
Wood & sons, Baltimore, S.S.
Wood & co., 1822. 28 p. DLC.
                              9451
A medley of joy and grief. See
Haight, Sarah (Rogers).

Meek, R.
    The female Sunday school
teacher; or, An account of the
life and happy death of Miss E.
Gillard...To which is added, the
history of Susan Smith. Boston,
Samuel T. Armstrong and
Crocker & Brewster. New York,
John P. Haven, 1822. 71 p. OO;
TWcW.   9452

Meineke, Christopher, 1782-1850
    The Brussel's waltz. Ar-
ranged for the piano forte by C.

Meineke. Baltimore, John Cole
[1822] [2] p. MdHi; MWA. 9453

Meline, Florant, 1790-1827
    Governor Joseph C. Yates
grand march. Published by the
Author [1822?] [2] p. MdHi;
NN.   9454

Melish, John, 1771-1822
    Catalogue of maps & geograph-
ical works, published and for
sale by John Melish. Philadel-
phia, 1822. 24 p. PHi; PPAmP.
                              9455
---- A geographical description
of the United States, with the
contiguous countries, including
Mexico and the West Indies; in-
tended as an accompaniment to
Melish's map of these countries
...A new ed., greatly improved.
Philadelphia, The author, 1822.
491, [15] p. CMont; DLC;
DeGE; GEU; IC; ICU; IGK; IaU;
In; KyBgW; MBAt; MBBC; MH;
MSha; Me; MeBa; MiD; MiGr;
MiK; MiU; MoSM; MoSpD; NNC;
NNCoCi; NRU; NSchU; NbU;
NcAS; NcU; NjR; OCY; OClWHi;
OHi; OO; OrP; PHi; TBriK;
TxHuT; TxU; WHi.   9456

---- A geographical description
of the world, intended as an accompaniment to the map of the
world...new ed., greatly improved. Philadelphia, the author, 1822. 289, [4] p. MB; Md;
NjR; TNP; ViRU.   9457

---- Northern section of the
United States, including Canada
&c. Philadelphia, 1822. 1 p.
Map. PHi.   9458

---- A statistical view of the
United States, containing a geographical description of the
United States, and of each state
and territory... Philadelphia, the
author, 1822. 45 p. OClWHi.
                              9459

---- The traveller's directory through the United States: containing a description of all the principal roads... with copious remarks on the rivers and other objects... Philadelphia, the author, 1822. 183 p. DLC; IaHA; InHi; MB; MH; MHi; MeHi; NUtHi; OCIWHi; PHi; PPL. 9460

---- Views on political economy, from the Description of the United States... [Philadelphia] 1822. 27 p. PHi. 9461

Memoir of Jonathan Leavitt. See Leavitt, Miss.

Memoir of Susan B. Marble, who died at New-Haven, Feb. 4, 1821. Aged nearly fourteen years. New-Haven, A. H. Maltby & Co., 1822. 24 p. CtY. 9462

Memoir of the life and happy death of Wilberforce Smith. Hartford, George Goodwin & sons, 1822. 16 p. CtHi. 9463

A memoir of the life and ministry of Mr. W. Bramwell... 1st Amer. from 2d London ed. New York, Pub. by N. Bangs & T. Mason, for the Methodist Episcopal Church, and to be had of the Methodist Preachers in their circuits and stations. 1822. 324 p. IU; MsJMC; MoS; NcD; Nh-Hi; OSW. 9464

A memoir of the Rev. William Tennent. See Boudinot, Elias.

Memoirs of the youthful days of Mr. Mathews, the celebrated comedian, lately arrived from England, interspersed with laughable tales, anecdotes, and original comic songs. Philadelphia, T. S. Manning, 1822. 24 p. CSmH; MB; PPAmP; PPL. 9465

The memorial of the subscribers interested in printing, paper-making, bookselling... [To Congress] [Philadelphia, 1822] 12 p. M. 9466

Meriam, Joseph, comp.
Wesleyan camp-meeting hymn-book for the use of those who love our Lord and Saviour Jesus Christ. Winchester, pub. Joseph Meriam, 1822. 144 p. MBNMHi; Nh-Hi. 9467

Merrill, Josiah G.
A sermon delivered June 26, 1821, at the ordination of the Rev. Stephen Merrill, to the pastoral care of the Congregational Church at Kittery Point, Maine. Portsmouth, T. H. Miller, printer, 1822. 16 p. CtSoP; MBC; MDeeP; MeB; Nh-Hi; RPB. 9468

[Merwin, Samuel]
Christian character exemplified, in the life of Adeline Marble, corresponding secretary of the "Female Juvenile Mite Society" of New-Haven; who died May the 3d, 1822. New-Haven, A. H. Maltby and co., 1822. 32 p. CSmH; CtHi; CtY; DLC; MWA; PHC; PHi; PPL. 9469

Messrs. Gales & Seaton, a letter. See Carey, Mathew.

A method of daily prayer, for the use of children and young persons, previous to Confirmation. Boston, Joseph W. Ingraham, 1822. 36 p. MBD; MdBD. 9470

Methodist Episcopal Church
Minutes taken at the several annual conferences of the Methodist Episcopal Church, commencing in December, 1821, and ending in November, 1822. Cincinnati, pub. by M. Ruter, for the Methodist Episcopal Church in the United States; Looker &

Reynolds, printers, 1822. 60 p.
OClWHi; PPM. 9471

---- Minutes taken at the several annual conferences of the Methodist Episcopal church for the year 1822. New York, Pub. by N. Bangs and T. Mason, for the Methodist Episcopal church. J. C. Totten, printer, 1822. 40 p. ICN; MHi; MnSH; NNMHi; TNS; TxGeoS. 9472

---- Missionary Society
The third annual report of the Missionary Society of the Methodist Episcopal Church. New-York, Pr. under the direction of the managers...J. D. Myers & W. Smith, printers, 1822. 22 p. NbHi. 9473

The Methodist harmonist. New York, Pub. by N. Bangs and T. Mason, Pr. by Myers & Smith, 1822. 247, 4 p. CtHT-W. 9474

Methodist Society
The minutes of the yearly conference of the Methodist Society, held in the City of New York, November, 1822. New York, pub. for the Society by Wm. M. Stilwell, J.W. Bell, printer, 1822. 24 p. NRivHi; PPiW. 9475

Metz, Julius
The vesper hymn. A Russian air. New York, Dubois & Stodart [1822] 5 p. DLC; MH; N; ViRVal. 9476

Miami University, Oxford, Ohio.
Miami University and Cincinnati College, by the Oxford Committee. Hamilton, pr. by James B. Camron, 1822. 20 p. OCHP; OClWHi. 9477

---- Report to the honorable, the Senate and House of Representatives of the state of Ohio. [1822] 4 p. OClWHi. 9478

Middlebrook's almanack for 1823. By Elijah Middlebrooks [sic] New-Haven, J. Babcock and son; Sidney's press [1822] 12 ll. CLU; Ct; CtHi; CtY; DLC; InU; MB; MWA; NBuG. 9479

Middlebury College, Middlebury, Vermont
Catalogue of the officers and students of Middlebury College, and Vermont Academy of Medicine in connexion, October, 1822. 16 p. DLC; NNNAM. 9480

Middlesex Harmonic Society
Sacred Concert. Order of performance...3d of November, 1822. [Boston, 1822] 8 p. MHi. 9481

Middling Interest Association, Boston, Mass.
The constitution of the Middling Interest Association. Boston, Pr. by True & Greene, 1822. 7 p. MHi. 9482

Milk for babes, or, A catechism in verse: for children...Hartford, G. Goodwin & Sons, 1822. 22 p. CtHi. 9483

---- From the 15th London ed. Portland, pub. by Wm. Hyde; A. Shirley, printer, 1822. 16 p. CtY; FStPHi; MBC; MeHi. 9484

Miller, A.E., ed.
Notices of the early history of South-Carolina. [Charleston, S. C.,] pr. by A. E. Miller, 1822. 14 p. DLC; MHi; MWA; NNS; ScC. 9485

Miller, George Benjamin
A sermon preached on the occasion of the death of Nathaniel Conkling, Esq., in the town of Minden, January 18, 1822. Johnstown [N. Y.] Pr. by Asa Child, 1822. 12 p. N; OCHP. 9486

Miller, Henry

An inaugural thesis on the relation between the sanguiferous and nervous systems, submitted to the examination of the Rev. Horace Holley, A. M.; A. A. S. President, the trustees and medical professors of Transylvania University, on the 12th day of March, 1822. For the degree of Doctor of Medicine. Lexington, Ky., Pr. by William Gibbes Hunt, 1822. 46 p. CSmH; CtY; DLC; DNLM; ICU; KyLxT; NNNAM; NBuU-M. 9487

---- An oration, pronounced on the anniversary of the KΛ Society of Hippocrates, in Lexington, Kentucky. Lexington, Ky., Pr. by Thomas T. Skillman, 1822. 13 p. CSmH; DNLM; ICU; NNNAM. 9488

Miller, Samuel
A sermon delivered in the Middle Church, New Haven, Conn. Sept. 12, 1822, at the ordination of the Rev. Messrs. William Goodell, William Richards, and Artemas Bishop, as evangelists and missionaries to the heathen. Boston, Crocker and Brewster, 1822. 46 p. Ct; CtHC; CtHT-W; CtSoP; IEG; KWiU; MAnP; MB; MBC; MH-AH; MeBat; MiD-B; MnHi; NCH; NcMHi; NjP; NjR; PHi; PPL; PPPrHi; RBr; RPB; ScCC; TU; TxH; VtMiM; VtMiS. 9489

Miller, Stephen Decatur, 1787-1838
Speech of the Hon. Stephen D. Miller, (of South Carolina) on the tariff. Delivered in the Senate of the United States on the 21st and 23d of Feb. 1822. On Mr. Clay's resolution in relation to the tariff. 37 p. ScU. 9490

Miller's planters' & merchants' almanac for 1823. Charleston, S.C., A.E. Miller [1822] 24 ll. Sc; ScC. 9491

---- Charleston, A. E. Miller [1822] 2d ed. 24 ll. ScC. 9492

---- Charleston, A.E. Miller [1822] 3d ed. 24 ll. MWA. 9493

Mills, Robert
Internal improvement of South-Carolina, particularly adapted to the low country... Columbia, State gazette office, 1822. 28 p. DLC; ScHi. 9494

Milman, Henry Hart
Belshazzar: a dramatic poem. Boston, Wells and Lilly, 1822. 125 p. DLC; MB; MBrZ; MCR; MH; MdBP; NIC; NNS; NbOP; PPL-R; TxU; ViAl; VtB; VtNofN. 9495

---- ---- New-York, Pr. for the booksellers, Wm. Grattan, printer, 1822. 108 p. DLC; MBL; MH; NNUT; Nh; NjP; NjR; PPL. 9496

---- The martyr of Antioch: a dramatic poem. New-York, Pr. for the booksellers, Wm. Grattan, printer, 1822. 108 p. KMK; MB; MLow; MdBP; NNS; NjP; PPL; ViRVal. 9497

Milner, Joseph, 1744-1797
The history of the church of Christ... 2d Amer. ed. comprising some account of the lives of the authors, and an original index. Boston, Samuel T. Armstrong and Crocker & Brewster; New York, John P. Haven, 1822. 5 v. CBPSR; CtHC; CtW; GMM; GU; IaDuU; InCW; KyBgW; KyHi; KyLoU; LNB; LNMus; MA; MH; MdBD; MeBat; MoK; MoSpD; MsJPED; NHunt; NjN; OM; OO; OW; PFal; ScSpW; TxAuPT; ViMiS; VtU. 9498

Milton, John
The poetical works of John

Milton; with the life of the au-
thor. New York, R. & W. A.
Bartow, 1822. 3 vols. CtHT;
GAuY; IAlS; IU; MA; MH;
NbOC; OMC; PPLT; ScCMu;
TNL; TNP; ViRUT; ViU; WHi.
9499

Ming's Hutchins' improved: be-
ing an almanac and ephemeris
for 1823. New-York, Alexander
Ming [1822] 18 ll. ABH; DLC;
MB; MBAt; MWA; NBLiHI; NHi;
NN; NRMA; NWhpHi; PHi;
RNHi.   9500

---- New-York, John C. Totten
[1822] 18 ll. DLC; MWA; NHi.
9501

Miniature almanack for 1823.
Boston, Lord & Richardson; J.
H. A. Frost, printer [1822] 14 ll.
MHi; NN.   9502

---- ---- 20 ll. MWA.   9503

Minor, Peter
    Notes on the cultivation and
management of tobacco, from the
plant bed to the prize; according
to the most approved practices
in Albemarle, and the adjacent
counties in Virginia. Baltimore,
Pr. by J. Robinson, 1822. 24 p.
DLC; N.   9504

Minutes of the proceedings and
trial, in the case of John Milton
Goodenow vs. Benjamin Tappan,
for defamation, in the Supreme
Court, Jefferson County, Ohio,
November term, A.D. 1822.
Steubenville, O., pr. by James
Wilson, 1822. 19, [1] p. OCIWHi.
9505

Mississippi (State)
    Constitution and form of gov-
ernment of the state of Mississippi. Natchez, Pr. by Andrew
Marschalk, 1822. 36 p. MWiW-
C; Ms-Ar.   9506

---- Journal of the House of
Representatives of the state of

Mississippi, at the fifth session
of the General Assembly. Held
in the Town of Columbia, June
1822. Columbia, Pr. by Peter
Isler, state printer, 1822. 186 p.
M; Ms; MsU; NN.   9507

---- Journal of the Senate of the
state of Mississippi at the fifth
session of the General Assembly
held in the Town of Columbia,
June, 1822. Columbia, Pr. by
Peter Isler, state printer, 1822.
151 p. CSmH; DLC; ICU; M;
Ms; MsU; NN; WHi.   9508

---- [Laws] Printed by P. Isler
--state printer. By authority.
Laws of the state of Mississippi.
[Columbia? 1822?] 408 p. DLC;
Ia; IaU-L; M; MH-L; MdBB;
MiU-L; Ms; Ms-Ar; NN; NNB;
NNLI; Or-SC.   9509

---- Laws of the state of Mississippi. Passed at the fifth
session of the General Assembly,
held in the town of Columbia.
Columbia, pr. by P. Isler,
state printer, 1822. 158, xxii p.,
[4] p. DLC; ICLaw; Ia; M;
MdBB; Ms; MsU; NNB; NNLI;
OCLaw.   9510

Mississippi Land Company, New
York
    To the Senate and House of
Representatives of the United
States of America, in Congress
assembled, the memorial of the
subscribers, in behalf of themselves and others, their associ-
ates, composing the Mississippi
Land Company, of New York.
[1822?] 11 p. MiU-C; WHi.
9511

Missouri (State)
    Acts of the first General As-
sembly of the state of Missouri,
passed at their second session,
began [sic] and held at the town
of St. Charles, on Monday, the

fifth day of November, in the
year of our Lord one thousand
eight hundred and twenty one...
St. Charles, Pr. by Robert
M'Cloud, printer to the state,
1822. 195, [1] p. DLC; I; ICLaw;
Mo; MoHi; MoSHi; NNB.   9512

---- Journal of the House of
Representatives of the state of
Missouri, at the first session of
the first General Assembly; be-
gun and held in the town of St.
Louis. On Monday the 18th Sep-
tember, 1820. St. Louis, Pr.
by Edward Charless & Co. at the
Republican office, 1822. 208 p.
MoHi; MoSL.   9513

---- Journal of the House of
Representatives the of [sic] state
of Missouri, at the second session of the first General Assembly; began and held in the town
of St. Charles, on Monday, the
5th November, 1821... St. Charles,
Pr. by Robert M'Cloud, printer
to the state, 1821! [1822] 203 p.
Mo; MoHi; MoSL.   9514

---- Journal of the Senate of the
state of Missouri, at the second
session of the first General Assembly; began and held in the
town of St. Charles, on Monday,
the 5th November, 1821. St.
Louis, Mo., Pr. by J.C. Cum-
mins, at the office of the Missouri Gazette, 1821! [1822] 216 p.
DLC; Mo; MoHi; MoSL.   9515

---- St. Charles, Nov. 5, 1822.
Yesterday at 4 o'clock, the Governor transmitted by Mr. Pettus,
his private secretary, to both
Houses of the General Assembly,
the following message. Bdsd.
MoHi.   9516

Mr. Way's case. Doubts of
the eligibility of this gentlemen,
to the mayoralty, having been
started, it was expected by every

one who knew him, that he
would immediately publish to his
fellow citizens, under his proper
signature, a plain unsophisti-
cated statement of all the material facts connected with his removal from the city... Plain
dealer. [1822] 1 p. DLC. 9517

The monastery. See Scott,
Sir Walter, bart.

Moncrieff, William Thomas
Monsieur Tonson: a farce,
in two acts... New York, E.M.
Murden, 1822. 42 p. MH; NjR.
9518
Monitor, ó Guia de los Franc-
mazones utilísimo... escrito en
Inglés por un Franc-mazon y
traducido al Castellano. Neuva-
York, En la imprenta de Joseph
Desnoues, E. Bliss y E. White,
1822. 272 p. PHi; PPFM.
9519
Monro, John, 1786-1851
Dear Kate thy charms were
like the rose. A favorite song.
New York, A. & W. Geib [1822]
3 p. Wolfe 5895.   9520

---- The smile of contentment
and love. Adapted to the much
admired air Kinlock of Kinlock.
Philadelphia, G.E. Blake [1822]
3 p. DLC; MWA; NBuG; NN;
PP; RPB.   9521

---- ---- New York, E. Riley
[1822?] 3 p. DLC; N.   9522

Monroe, James, Pres. U.S.
Views of the President of the
United States, on the subject of
internal improvements...Wash-
ington, Gales & Seaton, 1822.
80 p. MB.   9523

Monsigny, Pierre Alexandre,
1729-1817
Overture to The deserter.
Arranged for the piano forte.
New York, Geib & co. [1822?]

Montagu, Basil, 1770-1851
A digest of the law of part-
nership, with a collection of the
cases decided in the courts of
law and equity upon that subject.
1st Amer., from 2d and last
London ed. of 1822...New York,
George Lamson, 1822-24. 2 v.
DLC; Nj; TChU.   9525

---- ---- Philadelphia, H. C.
Carey & I. Lea, 1822. 2 v.
MH-L; Ms; MWCL; MsWJ; Nj;
NSyCA; ViU; W.   9526

---- A summary of the law of
lien. 1st Amer. from the last
London ed., imp. by a digest of
the American decisions. Exeter,
N.H., George Lamson; J.J.
Williams, printer, 1822. 236 p.
CU-Law; ICLaw; MAnP; MBS;
NNC-L; NRAL; NbCrD; Nh-Hi;
VtBrt.   9527

Montefiore, Joshua
Commercial and notorial
precedents: consisting of the
most approved forms, special
and common, required in the
daily transactions of business...
2d Amer., from the last London
ed... Philadelphia, H. C. Carey
& I. Lea; New York, H. C.
Carey & Co., 1822. 480 p.
CoCsL; MBS; MH; MWCL; PP;
PPB; PU-L; ViU; WU-L.   9528

Montgomery, James
The grounds of the Christian's
love to the church and the means
of promoting her prosperity...
A sermon, Philadelphia, S. Pot-
ter & co., 1822. 22 p. CtHT;
ICP; InID; NGH; NNG; PHi;
PPAmP; PPL; WHi.   9529

[Montgomery, James] 1771-1854
Prose by a poet. Philadel-
phia, Abraham Small, Wm.
Brown, printer, 1822. 2 v. in 1.

A monument of parental affection. See Gilpin, Joshua.

Moore, Humphrey
An address delivered at Hop-
kinton, before the Hillsborough
Society for the Promotion of
Agriculture and Domestic Manu-
factures, October 17, 1821...
Amherst, N.H., Pr. by E.
Mansur, 1822. 14 p. MBHo;
MH; MiD-B; Nh-Hi; NjR. 9531

---- A sermon, preached December 31, 1821, at the funeral of Rev. Jacob Burnap, D.D.
late pastor of the Church in
Merrimack, N.H. Amherst,
Pr. by Richard Boylston, 1822.
16 p. DLC; MBC; MB-FA;
MH-AH; Nh.   9532

Moore, Jacob Bailey
A topographical and histori-
cal sketch of the town of And-
over, in the county of Hills-
borough, and state of New Hamp-
shire. Concord [N.H.] Pr. by
Hill and Moore, 1822. 24 p.
CtSoP; DLC; IaHA; M; MB;
MBC; MBNEH; MC; MHi; MWA;
MdBJ; MeHi; MnHi; NBLiHi;
NSy; Nh; Nh-Hi; NhD; PHi;
RPB.   9533

Moore, Martin
Memoirs of the life and char-
acter of Rev. John Eliot, apostle
of the N. A. Indians. Boston,
pub. by T. Bedlington, Flagg &
Gould, printers, 1822. 174 p.
ArBaA; CSfCW; CtHC; CtHT-
W; DLC; GDC; IAlS; IC; ICMe;
ICN; IP; IaU; MA; MAJ; MAnP;
MB; MBC; MBL; MBNEH; MH;
MHi; MNF; MPiB; MdBE;
MdBP; MdCatS; MiD-B; MiU;
MnHi; MoSM; NCH; NNG;
NNMr; NSchU; NSy; NbU; Nh;
OCIWHi; OMC; PHi; PPL; RPB;
TU; Tx; ViAL; VtMiM; WHi. 9534

Moore, Thomas, 1779-1852
    Melodies, songs, sacred
songs, & national airs, containing several never before published in America.   New York,
G. Long, 1822. 277 p. Ct; MBC;
MChi.   9535

---- Oh woman. Philadelphia,
G. Willig [1822?] 3 p. MH;
MWA; NBuG.   9536

---- ---- Philadelphia, G. E.
Blake [1822?] [2] p. PU.   9537

Moran, Peter K., d. 1831
    The carrier pigeon.   New
York, P. K. Moran [1822?] 3 p.
MH; MWA; MdHi; N; NN; PPL;
RPB.   9538

---- Chit chat. New York, P.
K. Moran [1822] [2] p. DLC;
MWA.   9539

---- Crooskeen lawn.   New York,
Dubois & Stodart [1822] [2] p.
DLC; MB; MH; N; NN; PU;
RPB.   9540

---- The dove. A favorite song.
New York, P. K. Moran [1822]
3 p. MH; MWA; NN.   9541

---- A favorite Swiss waltz.
With variations for the harp or
piano forte.   Charleston, J.
Siegling [1822?] 5 p. NN.   9542

---- The fortune teller. New
York, P. K. Moran [1822] 3 p.
DLC; MH.   9543

---- "Go let me weep." As sung
by Mr. Earle at the oratorios.
New York, P. K. Moran [1822?]
3 p. MH; MWA; PPL.   9544

---- The Hebrew mourner.   As
sung at the sacred concerts by
Mrs. Fagan.   New York, P. K.
Moran [1822] 3 p. MH; MWA.
                                 9545

---- How blissful those mo-
ments! A favorite song. New
York, P. K. Moran [1822] 3 p.
DLC; MH; NBuG; NN; PPL.
                                 9546
---- I'll be a fairy. The words
by W. Roscoe, Esqr. of Liverpool. New York, P. K. Moran,
[1822?] 3 p. DLC; MH; NN.
                                 9547
---- Oh thou who dry'st the
mourner's tear. New York,
pub. by the Author [1822?] 7 p.
PP; RPB.   9548

---- Weep not for those. New
York, P. K. Moran [1822] 4 p.
MH; RPB.   9549

Moravians.
    Die täglichen Loosungen und
Lehrtexte der Brüdergemeine
für das Jahr 1823.   Philadelphia,
Gedruckt bey Conrad Zentler,
1822. [120] p. PNazMHi.   9550

Morgan, K. D.
    (Circular.) Washington, Pa.
Jan. 1st, 1822. Madam. You
are now addressed as a member
of a republic, blest by nature
with all the necessaries and
many of the luxuries of life [Re-
questing the women of America
to confine their purchases for
apparel to articles manufactures
in the United States and not that
manufactured in England] Washington, Pa. 1822. 1 p. DLC.
                                 9551
Morison, John, 1791-1859
    Is it well thee? A New Year's
question, affectionately addressed
to the immediate attention of
young people.   Boston, S. T.
Armstrong, 1822. 36 p. NN.
                                 9552
[Morse, Jedidiah]
    Ancient atlas adapted to
Morse's New school geography.
Boston, Richardson & Lord, J.
H. A. Frost, printers, [1822?]
MH; PPLT.   9553

---- Modern atlas adapted to
Morse's new school geography.
Boston, Richardson & Lord; J.
H. A. Frost, printers, 1822.
8 maps. MH; NWattJHi; RPB.
                                    9554
---- A new system of geogra-
phy, ancient and modern for the
use of schools, accompanied
with an atlas adapted to the
work... 23d ed. Boston, pub. by
Richardson & Lord, J. H. A.
Frost, printer, 1822. 278, 100
p. CtHT-W; ICU; InEvW;
InSbNHi; InU; MB; MBAt; MH;
MWHi; MiD-B; MoSpD; NBath;
NIl; NNC; NPV; OCIWHi; OO;
PPi; PWCHi; RNHi; RPB;
VtMiM.   9555

---- A new universal atlas of
the world, comprising in twenty
maps... New-Haven, Howe &
Spalding, 1822. [20] p. CtHi;
CtSoP; CtY; MA; MDeeP; MH;
MWiW; MdBP; MnHi; NIC; NUt;
NbHi; NcD; RNHi.   9556

---- A report to the secretary
of war of the United States, on
Indian affairs, comprising a nar-
rative of a tour performed in
the summer of 1820, under a
commission from the President
of the United States, for the pur-
pose of ascertaining, for the use
of government, the actual state
of the Indian tribes in our coun-
try. New Haven, Pr. by S.
Converse, 1822. 96, 400 p. C;
CSfCW; CL; CSt; CU; CoD;
CtHC; CtHi; CtHT; CtW; CtY;
GU-De; IC; ICN; ICU; Ia; In;
InHi; InU; KHayF; KHi; LN; _M;
MA; MB; MBAt; MH; MNF;
MWiW-C; Md; MdBE; MdBJ;
MdBP; MiD-B; MiU-C; MnU;
MoSHi; MsLE; NBB; NCH; NHi;
NIC; NN; NNC; NNUT; NRHi;
NSchU; NSyHi; NUt; NbU; NcU;
NdHi; Nh; NhD; NjR; O; OCHP;
OCIWHi; OkU; OrP; P;
PPAmP; PPL-R; PU; RPB;

ScC; ScU; Tx; TxH; TxU; Vi;
ViRuT; VtMiS; VtU; WBeloC;
WHi; WaPS; WaU.   9557

---- A sermon, delivered before
the American Board of Commissioners for Foreign Missions,
at their annual meeting in Springfield, Massachusetts, September
19, 1821. Ed. 2. Washington,
Davis and Force, 1822. 31 p.
MH-AH; PPPrHi; WHi.   9558

Morse, Royal, auctioneer, Cambridge, Mass.
    Auction of real estate... Cam-
bridge [Mass.] Mar. 18, 1822.
bdsd. MB.   9559

Morse, Sidney Edwards, 1794-
1871
    A new system of modern ge-
ography, or a view of the pres-
ent state of the world. Accom-
panied with an atlas. Boston,
G. Clark; New Haven, Howe &
Spalding, 1822. 676 p. Ct;
CtHT; CtMMHi; CtY; DLC; GU;
ICP; IGK; KHi; MA; MB;
MBAt; MDeeP; MH; MNF;
MWiW; MdBP; MdBS; MeB;
MiDU; MiGr; MiU; MsCliM;
NBLiHi; NNC; NRU; NSyU;
NcU; NcWsS; Nh-Hi; NjR;
OCIW; OCIWHi; OHi; OMC;
RNR; RWe; ScCC; ScCliTo; TU;
TxD-T; TxU-T; Vi; ViAlTh;
VtU.   9560

Morton, Thomas, 1764?-1838
    Speed the plough. A comedy.
In five acts. Philadelphia, T.
H. Palmer, 1822. 76 p. DLC;
MH.   9561

Moulton, Joseph W.
    Lots in Buffalo. Intending to
remove from this place, I offer
for sale, a House and 60 lots,
presenting 4,000 feet front, according to a subdivision of about
10 acres, on a map which may
be inspected at my office. Buf-

falo, Aug. 28, 1822. Bdsd.
(Imprint "Day's Press" stamped
without ink.) NBuHi.   9562

Moultrie, Alexander
Oration delivered on the 4th
of July, 1822, before the Cincinnati and Revolutionary Societies.
Charleston, Pr. by A. E. Miller,
1822. 16 p. MHi; WHi.   9563

Mount Carmel. See David,
pseud.

Mozart, Wolfgang Amadeus,
1756-1791
Favorite waltz. Composed by
Mozart.   Philadelphia, Geo. Wil-
lig [1822] p [1]-2. DLC; NBuG;
NN; PP.   9564

---- ---- For the piano forte.
New York, N. Thurston [1822]
[2] p. NN.   9565

---- ---- For the piano forte.
Charleston, J. Siegling [1822?]
2 p. NN.   9566

Muhlenberg, Henry
Reduction of all the genera
contained in the catalogue of
North American plants to the
natural families of the French
professor.   New York, James
V. Seaman, 1822. 415 p. MSaP.
                             9567

Murphy, Arthur, 1727-1805
Three weeks after marriage;
a comedy. Boston, Wells and
Lilly, etc. 1822. 48 p. DeGE;
MH; PPL; RPB.   9568

---- ... The way to keep him, a
comedy. Boston, Wells and
Lilly; and A. T. Goodrich & co.,
New-York, 1822. 123 p. CSt;
MH; MeB; PPL; ViU.   9569

Murray, Lindley, 1745-1826
An abridgment of L. Murray's
English grammar, with altera-
tions and improvements, de-

signed for the use of the younger
class of learners... 15th Boston
ed.   Boston, James Loring,
1822. OMC.   9570

---- Abridgement of Murray's
English grammar, with an appendix containing exercises in
orthography... Bellows Falls,
Blake, Cutler & Co., 1822. 108
p. MH; NPotT.   9571

---- ---- From the 20th English
ed., corr. by the author. Bur-
lington, Pr. by E. & T. Mills,
1822. 107, 1 p. VtMiS; VtU.
                             9572
---- Abridgement of Murray's
grammar, with additions from
Webster, Ash, Tooke, and oth-
ers.   New-Haven, Pr. by A. H.
Maltby and co., 1822. 120 p.
CtHi; CtHT-W; CtY; NcWsS.
                             9573
---- English exercises adapted
to Murray's English grammar
... 10th Boston from the 20th
English ed. Boston, James
Loring, 1822. 213 p. CSt; MH;
MHingHi.   9574

---- ---- From 20th English ed.
Exeter [N. H.] John J. Williams,
1822. 237, [2] p. MB; MH.
                             9575
---- English grammar, adapted
to the different classes of learn-
ers... stereotyped by B. and J.
Collins, from the last English
ed.   Bridgeport, Josiah B. Bald-
win, 1822. 312 p. CtSoP; WaSp.
                             9576
---- ---- Exeter, [N. H.] John
J. Williams, 1822. 309 p.
ArCH; ICN; MH; MHaHi; MNS;
PLFM.   9577

---- ---- From the last English
ed.   Raleigh, N. C., Pr. by J.
Gales & Son, 1822. 344 p.
NcElon; NcGw; NcWfC.   9578

---- ---- From the 28th English ed. Utica, William Williams, 1822. 237 p. MH; NNC; NUt; NUtHi.   9579

---- Murray's English grammar simplified. Designed to facilitate the study of the English language... Troy, N. Y. , pub. and sold by Z. Clark. Sold also by H. Stockwell and F. Adancourt, pr. by F. Adancourt, 1822. 176 p. Sylvester.   9580

---- The English reader: or, Pieces in prose and poetry, selected from the best writers... From the latest ed.   Albany, E. & E. Hosford, 1822. 264 p. CtHi; CtHT-W; ICHi; MWA; MWHi; NNC-T; Nh; OClWHi; WGr.   9581

---- ---- 3d Canandaigua ed. Canandaigua, N. Y. , J.D. Bemis & co. , 1822. 272 p. MWA; NCanHi; NRHi.   9582

---- ---- Exeter [N. H.] John J. Williams, 1822. 263 p. ICN; ICU; IU; MH; MHi; MWA; Nh; TxDaM.   9583

---- ---- Pittsburgh, R. Patterson & Lambdin; J. B. Butler, printer, 1822. xvi, 264 p. PAle.   9584

---- ---- From a late London ed.   Stockbridge, C. Webster, 1822. 274 p. MH.   9585

---- ---- Utica, William Williams, 1822. 263 p. (Stereotyped by H. & E. Phinney, Cooperstown.) NUt.   9586

---- English spelling-book, with reading lessons.   New York, Collins & Co. , 1822. 162 p. CtHT-W.   9587

---- Introduction to the English reader: or, A selection of pieces, in prose and poetry. New York, Evert Duyckinck, 1822. 166 p. DLC.   9588

---- ---- Philadelphia, Edwin J. Scott, 1822. xvi, 166 p. PLFM.
                                      9589
---- Key to the exercises adapted to Murray's English Grammar.   Exeter, N. H. , John J. Williams, 1822. 183 p. MAnP; MH; MeHi; Nh; PHi.
                                      9590
---- Sequel to the English reader... from the 4th English ed.   New York, Collins, 1822. 299 p. ICU.   9591

---- Sequel to the English reader, or, Elegant selections in prose and poetry.   From the 3d English ed.   Philadelphia, P. M. Lafourcade; I. Ashmead & co. , printers, 1822. 299 p. CSt; MH; Nptw; NRU-W; PHi; PPL; PPF; PLFM; PPeSchw; PU; PU-Penn.   9592

The musical cabinet, containing a selection of all the new and fashionable songs... Charlestown, T. M. Baker, 1822. 252 p. CtHT-W; MB; MBevHi; MHi; TxU.   9593

Musical Fund Society of Philadelphia.
    Constitution of the Musical Fund Society of Philadelphia established Feb. 29, 1820.   Philadelphia, Pr. by Thomas H. Palmer, 1822. 33 p. PHi; PPL.
                                      9594
Mutual Assurance Society
    At a general meeting of the members of the Mutual Assurance Society against fire on buildings of the state of Virginia, held at the capitol in the city of Richmond, on the 18th day of February, 1822.   [Richmond, 1822] 1 p. DLC.   9595

---- Statement, shewing the actual situation of the funds of the Towns' branch of the Mutual Assurance Society against fire on buildings of the state of Virginia, on the 19th day of January, 1822... Richmond, 19th January, 1822. [Followed by] Statement shewing the situation of the funds of the County branch of the Mutual Assurance Society against fire on buildings of the state of Virginia, on the 19th day of January, 1822... 19th January, 1822. [Richmond, 1822] 1 p. DLC.   9596

The mystic beauties of Free Masonry developed!! By an ancient brother. 1st Amer. ed. Salem [Mass.] pub. and sold by Henry Whipple; sold also by C. Whipple, Newburyport; Burrill and Hersey, printers, Haverhill, Mass., 1822. 108 p. CSmH; CtW; MB; MHa; MdBL; NNFM; PPL; RPMA.   9597

N

Narrative of a private soldier in His Majesty's 92d regiment of foot; written by himself; detailing many circumstances relative to the insurrection in Ireland in 1798; 1st Amer. ed. Philadelphia, pub. for the benefit of the United Foreign Missionary Society, 1822. 216 p. DLC; IObB; NjP; PMA; WNaE.   9598

Natchez, Mississippi
   Ordinances of the City of Natchez, and Mississippi State laws which relate to the City of Natchez. Published by order of the Corporation. Natchez, Pr. by Marschalk and Idol, 1822. 30 p. Heartman. McMurtrie. Mississippi Imprints, 165.   9599

The National calendar, and annals of the United States for 1823. By Peter Force. Washington City, Davis & Force [1822] 148 ll. CtY; DLC; DWP; InU; MBAt; MHi; NBLiHi; NNA; NjP; OCIWHi; PHi; PPL; PPi;   9600
National primer, adapted to the capacities of young beginners... Baltimore, Cushing & Brother, John Cushing & Co., [1822] 36 p. MdHi.   9601

Nautical almanac and ephemeris for the year 1824. Published annually. New-York, pub. by Richard Patten; Abraham Paul, printer, 1822. 73, [4] p. MSaP; MsWJ.   9602

[Neal, John] 1793-1876
   Logan, a family history... Philadelphia, H. C. Carey & I. Lea, 1822. 2 v. CtY; CtW; DLC; MH; MWA; MeHi; MiD-B; NN; PU; RPB; ViU; WHi.   9603

Neely, John I.
   To the editors of the Evansville Gazette, gentlemen, I have lately seen a hand bill, signed, Charles Dewey, dated the 18th inst. in which he complains that I (together with others) have not made a fair and correct statement of a conversation... Princeton, July 23, 1822. Bdsd. In.
                                          9604
The Negro servant. See Richmond, Legh.

Nelson, John, 1786-1871
   A sermon delivered at the funeral of the Rev. Edwards Whipple, late junior pastor of the church in Shrewsbury. September, 1822. Worcester, Pr. by W. Manning [1822] 19 p. DLC; M; MBAt; MBC; MH; MHi; MWA; MWHi; MiD-B; NN; PPPrHi; RPB.   9605

Der Neue Allentauner Calender auf 1823. Allentaun, Pa.,

George Hanke [1822] 18 11. DLC.
9606

Der Neue, Americanische Land-
wirthschafts-Calender auf 1823.
Von Carl Friedrich Egelmann.
Reading, Pa. , Johann Ritter und
Comp. [1822] 18 11. CLU; DLC;
MBAt; MWA; N; PAnL; PDoBHi;
PHi; PPL; PR; PRHi; P.   9607

Der Neue für den Staat von Ohio
eingerichtete Calender auf 1823.
Von Carl Friedrich Egelmann.
Canton, Eduard Schaeffer [1822]
18 11.   MWA.   9608

Der Neue Pennsylvanische Stadt-
und Land-Calender auf 1823.
Allentown, Pa. , Heinrich Ebner
und Comp. [1822] 18 11. CLU;
CtY; DLC; DeWint; MWA;
MnU; NjR; P; PAtM; PDoBHi;
PHi; PPG; PPL; PPeSchw; PU;
PRHi.   9609

A new and complete preceptor
for the violin... Philadelphia,
Klemm & brother [1822?] 30 p.
CSmH.   9610

New arithmetical tables, most of
which must necessarily be committed to memory, before any
considerable progress can be
made in learning arithmetic.
Philadelphia, Bennett & Walton,
J. Harding, printer, 1822. 18 p.
NjR.   9611

New-Bedford, Mass.
    Bye-laws for the town of New-
Bedford, as amended, passed in
town-meeting, May 6, 1822.
Bdsd.   MNBedf.   9612

---- To the qualified voters in
New-Bedford, in town meeting
assembled: The committee appointed on the first Monday in
last April, to consider the propriety of erecting a suitable
building for a market and town-
house... New-Bedford, May 6,

1822.   Bdsd.   MNBedf.   9613

New Brunswick (N. J.) almanac
for 1823.   By Joshua Sharp.
Philadelphia, Griggs & Dickinson
for Joseph C. Griggs, New
Brunswick [1822] 18 11. CtY;
MWA; NjMo; PHi.   9614

---- ---- [Philadelphia] Griggs
& Dickinson for Joseph C.
Griggs, New Brunswick (N. J.)
[1822] 18 11. CtY; MWA; NjHi;
NjR; PHi.   9615

The New Brunswick collection of
sacred music; being a selection
of tunes from the most approved
authors, designed for the use of
churches and singing societies...
New York, R. & W.A. Bartow,
& W. A. Bartow co. , Wm. Myer,
printer, 1822. 120 p.   NjR;
PPPrHi.   9616

New Castle County, Delaware
    Cases for trial and argument,
at the December term, A. D.
1822... Before the honorable, the
Court of Common pleas, to be
held at New-Castle, for the
County of New-Castle. Trials,
assigned for the first week of
the court, commencing Monday,
Dec. 16th, A. D. , 1822. New
Castle, Nov. 16th, 1822. 45 x
52 cm. Bdsd. DeHi.   9617

The New-England almanack, and
farmer's friend for 1823.   By
Nathan Daboll. New-London,
Samuel Green [1822] 16 11. CLU;
CtHT-W; CtHi; Ct; CtNlC;
CtY; DLC; InU; MB; MH; MWA;
N; NBuG; NHi; NN; NNC;
NjMoW; OCIWHi; PHi.   9618

The New-England farmer's diary
and almanac for 1823.   By Truman Abell. Windsor, Vt. ,
Simeon Ide for Ebenezer Hutch-
inson, Hartford [1822] 24 11.
CLU; CtY; DLC; InU; MH;

MWA; N; NN; NNA; NhHi; NjR; Vt; VtU; VtHi; BrMus. 9619

New England Guards
  Company orders. Boston, Aug. 13, 1822. Bdsd. MHi. 9620

New England Palladium, July 2, 1822
  To the public. The publication, in one of the papers of this city, of which is represented as appearing to be an honest history of some transactions between Messrs French and Tucker and myself, renders it proper that I also should give my narrative of some of the transactions... S. Upton. [Boston, 1822] 1 p. DLC. 9621

The New-England primer, improved: for the more easy attaining of the true reading of English. Albany, Pr. by Websters and Skinners, 1822. 71, [1] p. NAlbi; NHi; NRivHi; NSmB. 9622

---- Rochester, N.Y., Pr. by E. Peck & Co., 1822. 69 p. NRHi. 9623

The New-England primer improved. With the Assembly's shorter catechism. Philadelphia, Pr. for the booksellers, 1822. 32 l. PHi. 9623a

The New England primer, improved: for the more easy attaining of the true reading of English. To which is added the Assembly of divines' catechism. Troy, Pr. by Wm. S. Parker, and sold by him at the Troy bookstore, 1822. 71 p. MiU-C. 9624

The New-England primer, or an easy and pleasant guide to the art of reading, adorned with cuts, to which is added, the Catechism. Brookfield, Pr. by E. Merriam and Co., 1822. [62] p.

MAshlHi. 9625

---- Hanover, N.H., J. Hinds, 1822. 63 p. MH; NhD. 9626

---- Woodstock, Pr. by David Watson, 1822. 63 p. MWA; NhD; VtSL. 9626a

A New England tale. See Sedgwick, Catherine Maria.

New England Tract Society
  Sanctified afflictions. Andover, Pr. by Flagg and Gould, 1822. 16 p. PPL. 9627

New Hampshire (State)
  By the Governor a proclamation for a day of thanksgiving... I do hereby appoint Thursday the twenty-eighth day of November next, to be observed as a day of prayer and thanksgiving throughout this state... Concord, this twenty-eighth day of October, in the year of our Lord one thousand eight hundred and twenty-two... [Concord, 1822] 1 p. DLC. 9628

---- By the Governor. A proclamation for a fast... I do hereby appoint Thursday, the fourth day of April next, to be observed as a day devoted to a fasting, humiliation and prayer throughout this state... Given at the Council Chamber the fourth day of March, in the year of our Lord one thousand eight hundred and twenty-two... [Concord, 1822] 1 p. DLC. 9629

---- Journal of the House of Representatives of the state of New-Hampshire, at their session, begun and holden at Concord, on the first Wednesday of June, A.D. 1822. Concord, pub. by Hill & Moore [pr. by Geo. Hough, Concord] 1822. 409 p. DLC; Mi. 9630

---- Journal of the Senate of the State of New Hampshire, at their session, holden at the capitol in Concord, commencing on the first Wednesday of June, and ending on the fourth day of July, A.D. one thousand eight hundred and twenty-two. Concord [N.H.] pub. by Hill and Moore; Samuel T. Moses, printer, Exeter (N.H.) 1822. 222 p. DLC; IaHi; MeHi; Mi.   9631

---- The laws of the state of New-Hampshire. Vol. III. Concord, Pr. by Hill and Moore, for the state, 1822. 62, 4, [2] p. Ct; DLC; ICLaw; Ky; MBU-L; MdBB; Mi-L; Mo; Nb; T; TxU-L.   9632

---- Militia laws of the state of New Hampshire, in addition to the law for forming arranging and regulating the militia passed Dec. 22, 1820. Concord, pr. by Hill and Moore, 1822. 13 p. MH; MiD-B.   9633

---- The New-Hampshire agricultural repository. No. 1. Pub. by the State board of agriculture, under the patronage of the legislature of the state of New-Hampshire. Concord, Pr. by Hill and Moore, 1822. 135 p. DLC; IaAS; MB; MBHo; MH; MiD-B; Nh-Hi; NjR.   9634

---- Report of the committee appointed November session, 1820, to revise the probate laws of New Hampshire. (Pub. by order of the House of Representatives) Concord, Hill and Moore, 1822. 75 p. MH-L; Nh-Hi; NhD.
                                      9635

New Hampshire Baptist Domestick Mission Society
   The third annual report of the Board of Trustees of the New Hampshire Baptist Domestick Mission Society. Concord, Pr.

by Hill and Moore, 1822. 19 p. DLC.   9636

New Hampshire Bible Society
   Eleventh report... Amherst, N.H., Pr. by Richard Boylston, 1822. 24 p. MWA.   9637

New Hampshire Medical Society
   The charter, by-laws, regulations, and policy, of the New Hampshire Medical Society, with a list of the fellows and honorary members, and of the officers for the year commencing in June, 1822. Concord, Pr. by George Hough, for the Society, August 1822. 35, [1] p. DLC; IEN-M; MB; MH-M; OC; OCG; PU.
                                      9638

New Hampshire Missionary Society
   Report on the concerns of the New-Hampshire Cent Institution, for September 1822. By appointment of the trustees of the New-Hampshire Missionary Society. Amherst, Pr. by Richard Boylston, for the Society, 1822. 8 p. DLC.   9639

---- Twenty-first annual report of the trustees of the New-Hampshire Missionary Society... Concord, Pr. by George Hough, 1822. 22 p. MiD-B; N; NjR.
                                      9640

New Hampshire Musical Society
   Order of performance of the New Hampshire Musical Society, June 6, 1822. 8 p. DLC. 9641

The New-Hampshire register, and United States' calendar for 1823. Concord, George Hough [1822] 76 ll. CtY; ICN; InU; MB; MHi; MWA; MdBP; MiD-B; NHi; Nh; NhHi; N; NbHi; NhKe.   9642

New-Hampton Academy. New Hampshire.
   Catalogue of the officers and

students of New-Hampton Academy. November 30, 1822. Bdsd. MiU-C. 9643

New Haven
By-laws of the city of New-Haven, January, 1822. New Haven, Pr. by Gray & Hewit, 1822. 31 p. Ct; CtHi; CtY; MH-L; MHi. 9644

---- Proceedings of the city of New-Haven, in the removal of monuments from its ancient burying-ground, and in the opening of a new ground for burial. New-Haven, Conn., Gray & Hewit, 1822. 32 p. Ct; CtHi; CtY; DLC; M; MBC; MHi; NjR; PHi. 9645

New Haven, Conn. - Church of Christ in the United Societies of White-Haven and Fair-Haven
The constitution, profession of faith, and covenant of the Church of Christ, in the United Congregational Society in the city of New Haven. Together with a catalogue of the officers and members, from the Union, Nov. 1796, to April, 1822. New-Haven, A. H. Maltby and Co., 1822. 34 p. Ct; CtY; MH. 9646

New Haven. Social Library Company
A catalogue of books in the New-Haven Social Library; together with the constitution and by-laws of the company. [New Haven] Pr. by Nathan Whiting, 1822. 25 p. CtY; NN. 9647

New Jersey (State)
Journal of the proceedings of the Legislative council of the state of New-Jersey... Trenton... First sitting of the forty-seventh session. Bridgeton, Pr. by John Clarke & co., 1822. 74, 17 p. Nj; NjR. 9648

---- Private and temporary acts.

Acts of the forty-sixth General Assembly of the state of New-Jersey, at a session begun at Trenton, on Tuesday the twenty-third day of October, one thousand eight hundred and twenty-one. Trenton, Pr. by Joseph Justice, 1822. 44 p. IaU-L; In-SC; Nb; Nj; NjR; Nv. 9649

---- Public acts. Acts of the forty-sixth General Assembly of the state of New Jersey. At a session begun at Trenton, on Tuesday the twenty-third day of October, one thousand eight hundred and twenty-one. Trenton, (N. J.) Pr. by Joseph Justice, 1822. 21 p. IaU-L; In-SC; MdBB; Mi-L; Nb; Nj; NjR; R; W. 9650

---- Reports of cases argued and determined in the Supreme Court of judicature of the state of New-Jersey, by William Halstead, Jun., reporter. Trenton, Pr. by Joseph Justice, 1822-31. 7 vols. NNLI; Nj; ODaL. 9651

---- Rules & orders to be observed in the House of assembly of the state of New-Jersey. Adopted October 24, 1822. Trenton, Pr. by J.J. Wilson, 1822. 8 p. DLC. 9652

---- Votes and proceedings of the 47th General Assembly... at a session begun at Trenton, on the 22d day of October, 1822. Being the only sitting. Trenton, Pr. by James J. Wilson, 1822. 142 p. DLC; Nj; NjR. 9653

The New-Jersey almanac for 1823. By David Young. Elizabeth-Town, J. & E. Sanderson [1822] 18 ll. CtY; CLU; DLC; MB; MWA; NjHi; NjR; NjT. 9654

---- By Joshua Sharp. Trenton, George Sherman [1822] 18 ll.

DLC; MB; MWA; NBuG; NHi;
NjHi; NjR; PHi.   9655

New Jersey Bible Society
    Eleventh report of the New
Jersey Bible Society, Princeton,
Aug. 28, 1822. Trenton, Jo-
seph Justice, printer, 1822. 17 p.
NjR.   9656

New Jerusalem Church
    The liturgy of the New Jerusa-
lem Church. Philadelphia, pub.
for the use of the New Church
by T. S. Manning, printer, 1822.
101 p. MCNC; MH; PPL.   9657

---- Hymns for the use of the
New Church, signified by the New
Jerusalem in the Apocalypse.
Philadelphia, T. S. Manning, 1822.
224 p. MH; PPL.   9658

The new military guide. See
Farmer, John.

The New St. Tammany almanac
for 1823. By Wm. Collom.
Philadelphia, George W. Mentz
[1822] 18 ll. CtY; DLC; InU;
MWA; NjR; PHi; PPL.   9659

A new society for the benefit of
Indians. See American Society
for Promoting the Civilization
and General Improvement of the
Indian Tribes within the United
States.

New Year's address of the lamp-
lighter. "Give us but light,"
old Ajax sung, While clouds of
darkness o'er him hung...Bos-
ton, January 1, 1822. Bdsd.
MSaE.   9660

New York (City)
    Address of the Board of
Health of the city of New-York,
to their fellow citizens [June 10,
1822. New York, Van Pelt,
1822?] 8 p. NNC.   9661

---- Annual report of deaths in
the city and county of New York,
for the year 1821...New York,
Pr. by G. L. Birch, 1822. 11 p.
MBNEH; NBLiHi; NjR.   9662

---- The annual report of the
finance committee, in Common
Council, January 21, 1822.
[New York, 1822] 20 p. NjR.
                                 9663

New York (State)
    An act for regulating elec-
tions, passed April 17, 1822,
and an act apportioning the members of assembly of this state,
passed April 12, 1822, etc.
Albany, Packard & Van Benthuysen, 1822. 40 p. MH; NN;
NRHi; OCLaw.   9664

---- The act for the support of
common schools passed April
12, 1819, with extracts from acts
passed March 30, 1820, and
March 23, 1821, also, the act to
amend the act for the support of
common schools, passed April
17, 1822...Albany, Pr. by
Packard & Van Benthuysen,
1822. 38 p. MH; MWeA; N; P;
PPL; ViRUT; WHi.   9665

---- The act to amend the Act
for the support of common
schools, passed April 17, 1822
...Albany, Pr. by Packard &
Van Benthuysen, 1822. 16 p.
Sabin 53454   9666

---- An act to incorporate the
Farmers' Fire Insurance and
Loan Company. Passed Feb.
28, 1822. No imprint [1822?]
14 p. MBC.   9667

---- Acts passed at the forty-
third session of the legislature
of the state of New-York, respecting the canals from Lake
Erie to the Hudson River, and
from Lake Champlain to the
same. Utica, Pr. by William

Williams, 1822. 20, [3] p. N;
NcD. 9668

---- The annual report of the
Canal Commissioners of the State
of New York, presented to the
Legislature, the 27th February,
1822. Albany, Pr. by Cantine
& Leake, 1822. 32 p. DLC; N;
NN. 9669

---- Between Benjamin Prince,
public administrator in the city
of New York, appellant, and
George Hazleton, and Mary his
wife, appellees. Case on the
part of the appellant. (Relates to
the will of William Jones.)
New York, E. Conrad, 1822.
94 p. MB; NN. 9670

---- Case of the appellant (debt)
Court for trial of Impeachments
and Correction of Errors, (1821-
22; with Appendix). Albany,
1822. [4], 62, 68, 3 p. MH-L.
9671

---- Communication from the
Secretary of State, transmitting
the census of this state. Albany,
1822. 59 p. (In Assembly, Mar.
15, 1822. No. 150.) N; NN.
9672

---- Constitution of the state of
New-York, as amended. Can-
andaigua, Pr. by J.D. Bemis &
Co., 1822. 34, [1] p. ICN;
NCanHi. 9673

---- Constitution of the state of
New York, adopted in convention,
November 10th, 1821...Hudson,
Pub. by William E. Norman,
Wm. B. Stebbins, printer, 1822.
23 p. CSmH; N. 9674

---- ---- New-York, J.B. Jan-
sen, 1822. 24 p. DLC. 9675

---- Constitution of the state of
New York as amended. Penn
Yan, N.Y., Pr. by S.Q. Chad-
wick, 1822. 32 p. NjP. 9676

---- In the court for the trial
of impeachments and the correction of errors. Patrick Manahan, plaintiff in error, vs.
James Gibbons, James Maher,
Thomas Dawson, Thomas Moun-
sey, and Josiah Kerr, defend-
ants in error. Case on the
part of the plaintiff. Albany,
1822. 13 p. N. 9677

---- Journal of the assembly of
the state of New-York: at their
forty-fifth session, begun and
held at the capitol in the city of
Albany, the first day of January,
1822. Albany, Pr. by Cantine
and Leake, 1822. 1129, 59,
146, xxx p. NNLI. 9678

---- Journal of the Senate of the
state of New-York: at their
forty-fifth session, begun and
held at the capitol, in the city of
Albany, the first day of January,
1822. Albany, Pr. by Cantine
and Leake, 1822. 360, xiv p.
N; NNLI. 9679

---- Laws of the state of New
York, passed at the forty-fifth
session of the Legislature, begun and held at the city of Albany, the first day of January,
1822. Albany, Pr. by Cantine
and Leake, 1822. 367 p. In-SC;
MH-L; Ms; N-L; NTSC; NTiHi;
Nb; Nj; RPL; W; Wa-L. 9680

---- Laws of the state of New-
York, passed at the forty-fifth
session of the Legislature begun and held at the city of Albany, the first day of January,
1822. Albany, Pr. by Cantine
and Leake, for Websters & Skinners, and Wm. Gould & co.
1822. 367 p. Mi-L; NNLI;
NNebgL; NTSC; NUtSC. 9681

---- List of patents of lands,
&c. to be sold in January, 1822,
for arrears of quit rent. Al-

bany, Pr. by E. and E. Hosford [1822] iv, 2, 35 p. MiD-B; NN; NNNG; NSmB; NTiHi. 9682

---- Notice. In Chancery... In pursuance of a decretal order of the Court of Chancery, will be sold at public auction, at the house of John Burtiss, of Cowneck, in Queens County, on the thirtieth inst., ... land... New-York, 23d April, 1822. --Geo. Caines, Master in Chancery. Bdsd. NN. imp. catal. 9683

---- Report of the general committee to the Board of Agriculture; read and accepted, January 23d, 1822. Albany, Pr. by Packard & Van Benthuysen, 1822. 10 p. CSmH; MB. 9684

---- (Resolution, Apr. 10, 1822) that the attention of the national government be called to the importance of improving the navigation of the Hudson, opening free communication with the internal canal navigation of the state of New York. [Albany? 1822] 1 p. NN. 9685

---- Revised statute. Relating to the navigation of the New-York state canals. Chapter IX. Title IX. Article seventh. [1822?] 14 p. N. 9686

---- The revised twenty-five dollar act, passed April 5, 1813. And the fifty dollar act, passed April 10, 1818, with the several acts amending the same; together with a copious index. Ithaca, pr. by Spencer & Stockton, and sold by them at their bookstore, and by J.D. Bemis & Co. at the Canandaigua Bookstore, 1822. 32 p. NIC. 9687

---- Speech of His Excellency De Witt Clinton, to the Legislature of the state of New-York, at the opening of the session 2d January, 1822. [Albany, 1822] 8 p. DLC; MB; N; PHi; PPL. 9688

---- Speech of His Excellency the Governor at the opening of the present session of the Legislature, (Wed.) 2d Jan., 1822. [Albany, 1822] Broadside, pr. on white satin. MH. 9689

New-York almanack for 1823. [1822] 12 ll. NCooHi; WHi. 9690

New York and Brooklyn Steam Ferry Boat Co.
A statement of facts, with remarks, &c. In answer to a pamphlet, published at Brooklyn, in relation to the steam boat ferry. Pr. by A. Spooner, Brooklyn, 1822. 46 p. NB; NBLiHi; NHi; NJQ; NN; NSmb. 9691

New York & New Jersey almanac for 1823. By David Young. New-York, Daniel D. Smith [1822] 18 ll. MWA. 9692

---- ---- New-York, S. Marks [1822] 18 ll. Ct; CtY; MWA (two varieties); N; NHi; NjP; NjR. 9693

New York Bethel Union
First report of the New-York Bethel Union, presented at the public general meeting, December 31, 1821. With an appendix. Instituted June 4, 1821. New-York, pub. by order of the Society, at the office of the Christian Herald and Seaman's Magazine, E. B. Clayton, printer, 1822. 21 p. MBC; MMch; NNG; NjR. 9694

New York Eye and Ear Infirmary
First annual report of the New York Eye Infirmary, 45 Chatham-Street; founded, August, 1820 and supported by voluntary subscriptions. New-York, Pr. by

Mahlon Day, 1822. 15 p. DLC;
ICU; NNNAM; OCIWHi; OO.
9695

New York Female Auxiliary
Bible Society
Sixth annual report... and the
fourth annual report of the New
York Female Juvenile Bible As-
sociation, together with the
names of their subscribers and
donors, and the address of the
Rev. Mr. M'Murray. New York,
Daniel Fanshaw, 1822. 32 p.
MnHi.   9696

New York Free-School Society.
See Public School Society of
New York.

New York Friendly Association
of Master Book-Binders.
New York Friendly Associa-
tion of Master Book-Binders'
List of prices. A. D. 1822. New
York, pub. by the Society, 1822.
Bdsd. MWA.   9697

New York. General Theological
Seminary of the Protestant Episcopal Church
The constitution, act of incorporation, and statutes of the
General Theological Seminary of
the Protestant Episcopal Church
in the United States. New York,
Pr. by T. and J. Swords, 1822.
19 p. A-Ar; MBC; NN; NNC;
NNG; NNUT; PHi; ScCC.   9698

---- The constitution of the General Theological Seminary of the
Protestant Episcopal Church in
the United States of America
with the address and resolutions
of the board of trustees, at a
meeting held in New-York, December, 1821. New York, Pr.
by T. and J. Swords, 1822. 12 p.
A-Ar; MHi; NBuU-M; NCH;
NNUT; PHi; PPL; ScCC.   9699

New York Mechanic and Scientific Institution

Charter, constitution, and by-
laws of the New-York Mechanic
and Scientific Institution... New-
York, W. A. Mercein, printer,
1822. 20 p. DLC; NNC; NNMus.
9700

A New York merchant, pseud.
An exposition of some of the
evils arising from the auction
system. [New York] Van Pelt
and Spear [1822?] 16 p. M; N;
PPL.   9701

New York. New (i. e., Park)
Theatre
[Play bills, Jan. 1-July 5,
1822. New York, 1822] 154
bdsds. MB.   9702

The New York preceptor... New
York, pub. by Samuel Wood &
sons; and Samuel S. Wood &
co., [c1822] 68 p. MWA; NNC.
9703

The New York primer... New
York, pub. by Samuel S. &
William Wood; R. & G. S. Wood,
printers [1822] [1], 33 p. NNC.
9704

The New-York spelling-book; or,
Fourth book. New York, pub.
by Samuel S. & William Wood
[1822?] 160 p. MH; NNC. 9705

New York. Sunday School Union
Society
Sixth annual report of the New
York Sunday School Union So-
ciety. New York, Pr. for the
Society by J. Seymour, 1822.
11 p. WHi.   9706

New York. University of the
State of New York. College of
Physicians and Surgeons
Catalogue of the faculty and
students of the College of Physicians and Surgeons in the university of the state of New York.
New York, Pr. by Harris Sage,
1822. 8 p. OC.   9707

New York. Zion Church.

Second report of the managers of the Episcopal Missionary Association of Zion Church. New York, Pr. by Gray & Bunce, 1822. 12 p. MdBD.   9708

Newburyport Female Charitable Society
An account of the plan and regulation of the... Newburyport Female Charitable Society. Newburyport, E. W. Allen, 1822. 29 p. NN.   9709

Newell, John Lyman
New American arithmetic, in the coin of the United States, denominated federal money... Hartford, Pr. for the author, 1822. viii, 202 p. Ct; CtHT-W; DAU; DE; ICU; MDeeP; MH; MiU-C.   9710

Newport Mercury
Address of the carrier of the Newport Mercury, to its patrons. Jan. 1st, 1822. Bdsd. RNHi.   9711
The Newtonian reflector: or New-England almanac for 1823. By Anson Allen. Hartford, Roberts & Burr [1822] 12 ll. CLU; CtHi; DLC; InU; MWA; MB; NN; PPeSchw.   9712

---- or, Republican almanac for 1823. By Anson Allen. Hartford, Roberts & Burr [1822] 12 ll. Ct; CtHi; MWA; NHi; NN; WHi.   9713

Niagara, a poem. See M., A.

Nicholls, John
Recollections and reflections, personal and political, as connected with public affairs during the reign of George III... Philadelphia, H. C. Carey and I. Lea, 1822. 302 p. CtW; DLC; DeWi; ICMe; LNH; MBAt; MBL; MH; MHi; MiD; MiD-B; NNS; Nh-Hi; P; PFal; PPL; RP; ScC;

WHi.   9714

Nicks, John
John Nicks, tailor, respectfully informs the inhabitants of Redbook and its vicinity, that he has commenced the tailoring business, in all its various branches, near Dubois & Co. Store... Lower-Redhook, April 25, 1822. Pr. at the Ulster Plebian office-Kingston. Broadsheet. NKingS.   9715

Nightingale, John Charles, 1785?-1837?
The carnival of Venice. Arranged as a rondo for the piano forte. Philadelphia, G. Willig [1822?] 3 p. DLC; NN.   9716

The nightingale, or, A new and choice selection of the most admired songs. Albany, Pr. by G. J. Loomis & co., 1822. 105, 3 p.   N.   9717

Niles, Hezekiah, 1777-1839
Principles and acts of the revolution in America: or, An attempt to collect and preserve some of the speeches, orations, & proceedings, with sketches and remarks on men and things, and other fugitive or neglected pieces... Baltimore, Pr. and pub. for the editor, by W. O. Niles, 1822. 495 p. ArU; Ct; DLC; DeGE; GU; Ia; ICN; KU; LNT; M; MB; MdBE; MdToH; MeHi; MiU; MoSW; NNC; NSy; PPL; RNR; Wv.   9718

Nixon, Barnaby
Biographical and other extracts from the manuscript writings of Barnaby Nixon. New York, W. Alexander & son, 1822. [70] p. LNH.   9719

Noah, Mordecai Manuel, 1785-1851
An address delivered before

the General Society of Mechanics and Tradesmen of the city of New-York, at the opening of the Mechanic Institution... New-York, W. A. Mercein, 1822. 28 p. MB; NIC; NjR. 9720

---- Grecian captive; or, The fall of Athens... New York, E. M. Murden, June, 1822. 48 p. CtY; DLC; ICU; MB; MH; MWA; MdBJ; MiU-C; NIC; NN; NNC; PU; RPB. 9721

---- Marion; or, The hero of Lake George: a drama in three acts, founded on events of the Revolutionary war. New-York, E. Murden, 1822. 70 p. CSt; CtY; CU; DLC; ICU; MB; MH; MdBP; MiU-C; NIC; NGlf; PU; RPB. 9722

Nolcini, Charles, d. 1844
A military waltz. Composed for the piano forte. Boston, G. Graupner. Sold by John Ashton [1822?] p 2-3. Wolfe 6538A. 9723

Norami, Pietro
The washing day. New York, P. K. Moran [1822?] 3 p. Wolfe 6542. 9724

The North-American calendar; or, The Columbian almanac for 1823. Wilmington, Robert Porter [1822] 18 ll. CtY; DLC; DeU; MWA; NHi. 9725

North Carolina (State)
Annual report... to the General Assembly... December 10, 1822, together with Mr. Fulton's reports to the Board. Raleigh, Pr. by J. Gales & Son, 1822. 6 p. NcWfC. 9726

---- Debate on the convention question in the House of Commons of the Legislature of North-Carolina; Dec. 18, 19, 1821. Taken in short-hand by Joseph Gales. Raleigh, Pr. by J. Gales & Son, 1822. 78 p. Ct; ICJ; NcD; NcU; PHi. 9727

---- Journals of the Senate and House of Commons of the General Assembly of North Carolina, at its session in 1821... Raleigh, Pr. by Thos. Henderson, Jr., 1822. 107, 111 p. NcWsM. 9728

---- The laws of North Carolina, enacted in the year, 1821. Raleigh (N. C.), Pr. by Thomas Henderson, 1822. 83 p. IaU-L; MdBB; NcU; PPL; T; TxU. 9729

---- Proceedings of the Friends of convention at the meeting held in Raleigh, December, 1822. Raleigh, Pr. by Thomas Henderson, 1822. 7 p. DLC; MH; MiU-C; NcD. 9730

The North Carolina register and United States calendar for 1823. By Rev. Colin M'Iver. Raleigh, J. Gales & Son [1822] 77 ll. NcU. 9731

Der Northampton Bauern Calender auf 1823. Easton, Pa., Christian Jac. Huetter [1822] 18 ll. Drake 11366. 9732

The Northampton Farmer's almanac for 1823. Easton, Pa., Henry & William Hutter [1822] 18 ll. MWA. 9733

Northern Missionary Society
Report, of the board of directors of The Northern Missionary Society, at their annual meeting, in the city of Troy, September 4, 1822. Together with the treasurer's account, etc. Albany, Pr. by Charles R. and George Webster, 1822. 12 p. TxFwSB. 9734

Norton, Andrews
Address delivered before the
University in Cambridge at the
interment of Professor Frisbie,
July XII, MDCCCXXII. Cam-
bridge, Pr. at the University
Press by Hilliard and Metcalf,
1822. 24 p. CBPac; CtHC; DLC;
ICMe; IU; MBC; MBNEH;
MDeeP; MH; MHi; MWA; MeHi;
MiD-B; MoSpD; NcU; Nh-Hi;
PHi; PPAmP.   9735

Norton, Elijah
A missionary sermon, in
which the hidden riches of secret
places are discovered and made
to appear as unrighteous Mam-
mon...Woodstock, Pr. by David
Watson, 1822. 34 p. DLC; MBC;
VtU.   9736

Norton, Jacob
The duty of religious tolera-
tion...a sermon, delivered in
the South meeting house in Weymouth, Nov. 8, 1821...Boston,
Pr. by John Cotton, Jr., 1822.
28 p. IObB; MBAU; MBAt;
MBC.   9737

Norwich, Conn.
The by-laws of the city of
Norwich. Pub. by authority of
the city. Norwich, Robinson &
Dunham, 1822. 16 p. Ct; MHi.
                           9738
Norwich University. Northfield,
Vermont
Catalogue of the officers and
cadets of the American Literary,
Scientific, and Military Academy,
together with the prospectus and
internal regulations of the insti-
tution, &c. Norwich, Vt., No-
vember 1822. Woodstock, Pr.
by David Watson, 1822. 20 p.
DLC; MB; MBC; MH; NjPT;
WyHi.   9739

---- A journal of an excursion
made by the corps of cadets, of
the American Literary, Scien-

tific and Military Academy, un-
der Capt. Alden Partridge.
June, 1822. Concord [N.H.] Pr.
by Hill and Moore, 1822. 38 p.
DLC; MB; MBAt; MHi; Nh-Hi;
VtMiM.   9740

Notices of East Florida. See
Simmons, William Hayne.

The novels, tales, and ro-
mances of the author of Waverly.
See Scott, Sir Walter, bart.

Noyes, Thomas
A sermon preached in the
South Parish in Weymouth before
the Norfolk Auxiliary Society for
the Education of Pious Youth for
the Gospel Ministry, 1822. Dedham, B. Field, printer [1822]
30 p. MBC; MBD; MiD-B;
NNUT; NhD; VtMiM; WHi.
                           9741

O

O let me in this ae night.
Philadelphia, G. Willig [ca 1822]
1 l. DLC; NBuG; NHi; NN.
                           9742
---- Scottish song...variations
for the piano forte. Philadelphia, G.E. Blake [1822?] p 2-4.
Wolfe 108.   9743

---- A much admired Scotch air.
Philadelphia, J.L. Frederick
[1822?] p 2-3. DLC.   9744

O, what a row! or, The adventures of a steam packet. A new
comic song. New York, E.
Riley [1822?] 3 p. DLC; MH;
NN; PP; RPB.   9745

Oakley, George P.
The willow basket. Poughkeepsie, Paraclete Potter, 1822.
18 p. NP.   9746

The obligations of Christians to
attempt the conversion of the

Jews,...By a presbyter of the
Church of England. Salem,
Warwick Palfray, jun., 1822.
22 p. GDC; MBC; MSaE;
VtMiM.   9747

[O'Brien, John Maurice] 1786-
1865
  The powers and duties of the
town officer, as contained in the
statutes of Maine... Brunswick,
Pr. by Joseph Griffin, 1822.
324 p. CtY-L; ICU; MH-L;
MeBa; MeHi; MeWaC; NjP;
PWmpDS.   9748

Observations on electricity,
looming, and sound. See Hopkins, George F.

Observations on the nomination
of a candidate for the presidency.
Submitted for the consideration
of the members of the Legislature now in session, by a citizen of Ohio. [1822] 15 p. N;
ViU.   9749

Observations on the principles
of correct education. See Amicus, pseud.

Observations suggested by the
late occurrences in Charleston,
by a member of the Board of
Public Works, of the state of
South Carolina. Columbia, Pr.
at the State Gazette Office,
1822. 16 p. NBLiHi; ScU. 9750

Observations on the Susquehanna
River and Maryland Canal, addressed to the Legislatures of
Pennsylvania and Maryland.
Baltimore, Frederick G. Schaeffer, 1822. 29 p. MdBE; MdBP.
                              9751
O'Connolly, Patrick
  The Catholic faith, ever the
same, yesterday, to-day and to-
morrow, or an Irishman's ex-
postulation with an apostate,
the companion of his youth.

Boston, Pr. for the Author,
1822. 18 p. DGU.   9752

The odes of Horace in Cincinnati. See Peirce, Thomas.

Office-holders: observations
upon the duties and emoluments
of certain public offices. New
York, 1822. 26 p. ICU; M;
PPL; WHi.   9753

Oh Charlie is my darling and O
Peggy is my darling. A favor-
ite Scotch song. Philadelphia,
G. E. Blake [ca 1822] [2] p.
MWA.   9754

Ohio (State)
  An act for disciplining the militia of the state of Ohio,
passed February 2, 1822; together with the rules and articles
of war, for the government of
the army of the United States.
Columbus, pr. at the office of
the Columbus Gazette, by P. H.
Olmsted, 1822. 77 p. MH-L;
MiU-L; NNB.   9755

---- Acts of a general nature,
passed at the first session of
the 20th General Assembly of
the state of Ohio, begun and
held in the town of Columbus,
Dec. 3, 1821... Vol. XX. Columbus, Pr. at the office of the
Columbus Gazette, by P. H.
Olmsted, 1822. 88, 16 p. MH-
L; NNB; NNLI; OCLaw.   9756

---- Acts of a local nature,
passed at the first session of
the twentieth General Assembly
of the state of Ohio, begun and
held in the town of Columbus,
December 3, 1821... Vol. XX.
Columbus, pr. at the office of
the Columbus Gazette, by P. H.
Olmsted, 1822. 95 p. MH-L;
NN; NNLI; OCLaw; Vi.   9757

---- Acts passed at the second

session of the twentieth General
Assembly of the state of Ohio,
begun and held in the town of
Columbus, May 20, 1822. Vol.
XXI. Columbus, pr. at the office of the Columbus Gazette, by
P. H. Olmsted, 1822. 8 p. CtY-L; MH-L; RPL.   9758

---- A bill for the establishment
and support of common schools,
reported by the commissioners
of common schools. 1822. 24 p.
DLC.   9759

---- Inaugural speech of Jeremiah Morrow, Esq., governor
of the state of Ohio, to the
twenty-first General Assembly,
December 28, 1822. Columbus,
pr. at the office of the Columbus
Gazette, by P. H. Olmsted, 1822.
6 p. OCLaw; OHi.   9760

---- Journal of the House of
Representatives of the state of
Ohio; being the first session of
the twentieth General Assembly,
begun and held at the town of
Columbus, in the county of
Franklin, Monday, December
third, one thousand eight hundred
and twenty one... Columbus, pr.
at the office of the Columbus
Gazette, by P. H. Olmsted, 1822.
330, 15 p. O-LR; OU.   9761

---- Journal of the Senate of the
state of Ohio; being the first session of the twentieth General Assembly, begun and held in the
town of Columbus, in the county
of Franklin, Monday, December
3, 1821. Columbus, pr. at the
office of the Columbus Gazette,
by P. H. Olmsted, 1821[!]
[1822] 326 p. OO.   9762

---- Journal of the Senate of
the state of Ohio; being the second session of the twentieth General Assembly, begun and held
in the town of Columbus, in the

county of Franklin, Monday,
May 20, 1822. Columbus, Pr.
at the office of the Columbus
Gazette, by P. H. Olmsted, 1822.
14 p. CtY-L; OU.   9763

---- Message. Fellows citizens of the Senate and House of
Representatives. [Columbus,
1822] 4 p. OCLaw; OClWHi.
                                 9764
---- Mr. Atwater from the committee on schools and school
lands, made the following report.
(The committee to whom was referred so much of the Governor's message as relates to
schools and school lands... now
beg leave further to report:)
[Columbus? 1822?] 4 p. DLC;
N.   9765

---- Report and resolutions on
the subject of the Maryland Report, etc., relative to school
lands. Columbus, pr. at the office of the Columbus Gazette,
by P. H. Olmsted, 1822. 20 p.
OClWHi.   9766

---- Report of the commissioners, of common schools. Columbus, Pr. at the office of the
Columbus Gazette by P. H. Olmsted, 1822. 18 p. DLC; N;
OCLaw.   9767

---- Report of the committee of
finance, [to whom was referred
so much of the Governor's message as relates to the revenue
of the state, together with reports of the auditor and treasurer, for the years 1820 and
1821] [Columbus, 1822] 7 p.
WHi.   9768

---- Report of the Committee
on canals. Columbus, Pr. at
the office of the Columbus Gazette by P. H. Olmsted, 1822.
15 p. DLC; N; OCHP; OClWHi.
                                 9769

---- Report of the committee to whom was committed the resolutions relative to the appointment of a committee, to revise the laws of a general nature, now in force in this state. [1822?] 6 p. NN. 9770

---- Report of the committee who were appointed to inquire into the expediency of providing by law, for the holding of a court in bank by the judges of the Supreme Court; and also for publication of the reports of the decision of such court. [Columbus? 1822?] 8 p. OCLaw. 9771

---- Report... on the proceedings of the General Assembly of Ohio... on a National Bank... per order Warren Dutton. 6 p. MB. 9772

The Ohio almanac for 1823. Canton, Edward Schaeffer [1822] 18 ll. DLC; MWA; OMans. 9773

Ohio Bible Society
Tenth report of the trustees of the Ohio Bible Society, with the treasurer's account, and extracts from the minutes of said society, held at Zanesville, September 4th, 1822. Pr. by Horatio J. Cox [Zanesville, 1822] 8 p. OCIWHi. 9774

The Ohio register, and western calendar for 1823. By William Lusk. Ripley, James Finley & Co., printers [1822] 20 ll. NN. 9775

O'Keeffe, Miss
Patriarchal times; or, The land of Canaan... From the 3d London ed. New-York, pub. by A. T. Goodrich; D. Fanshaw, printer, 1822. 2 v. CtHT-W; GDC; KWiU; MB; NNS; PMA; PPDrop. 9776

O'Keeffe, John, 1747-1833
Dead alive; a comic opera in

two acts. Philadelphia, T. H. Palmer, 1822. 32 p. MB; MH; PU. 9777

---- The prisoner at large; a comedy, in two acts. Philadelphia, T. H. Palmer, 1822. 31 p. MH. 9778

---- Wild oats; the strolling gentleman. A comedy. Boston, Wells and Lilly, Court Street, 1822. 115 p. CtHT-W; DLC; MeB; PPL; WM. 9779

O'Meara, Barry Edward, 1786-1836
Napoleon in exile; or, A voice from St. Helena... Philadelphia, H. C. Carey and I. Lea, 1822. 2 v. CSfP; CoD; DeGE; GEU; KyLxT; MBrigStJ; NNUT; NWM; P; PPL; ScC; ScU; ViAl; ViR; ViRA. 9780

---- ---- Philadelphia, Jehu Burton, printer, 1822. 2 v. in 1. LNL; MiDSH; MdBD; OCl; OkU; PHi; PPAmP; PP; PPL; PPWa; PRea; ViU. 9781

---- ---- 2d ed. Philadelphia, J. Crissy, 1822. 2 v. CtW; DLC; InGrD; KyLx; LU; MH; MnS; MnU; NNC; NjP; OCU; P; PFal; PLFM; PRea; PV; TNJ; TxWFM; WJan. 9782

---- Memoirs of military and political life of Napoleon Bonaparte from his origin to his death on the rock of St. Helena ...Hartford, Goodrich, 1822. 395 p. Ct; CtW; DLC; GU; KMar; KWiU; MBC; MNe; MSwan; MnSSt; NCH; NGH; NNNAM; NjP; OCl; OcIW; OCIWHi; OU; ScC; VtVe; VtU. 9783

On intemperance... Philadelphia, Pr. for the Religious Tract and Book Society of the Evangelical Lutheran Congregation of St.

John's Church.   Joseph Rakestraw, printer, 1822. 40 p.
MWA; PPLT; ScCMu.   9784

On the internal improvement of
Virginia; with Mr. Moore's report to the Board of Public Works,
on the improvement of the navigation of Appomattox River...
Richmond, Pr. for the author,
at the sign of Franklin's Head,
Market-Bridge, 1822. 59 p. DLC.
                              9785
On worship, ministry and prayer.
Philadelphia, B. & T. Kite, 1822.
16 p. PSC-Hi; ScCC.   9786

---- 2d ed. Philadelphia, to be
had of Benjamin & Thomas Kite,
1822. 16 p. NcD.   9787

Oneida County Medical Society
   By-laws of the Oneida Medical
Society, as revised and adopted
Jan. 1, 1822.   Utica, 1822. 8 p.
WHi.   9788

Ontwa, the son of the forest.
See Whiting, Henry.

Opie, Mrs. Amelia (Aldersen)
   Madeline, a tale.   Philadelphia, Carey & Lea, 1822. 2 v.
in 1.   MNS; PHi.   9789

---- Temper, or, Domestic
scenes, a tale.   Boston, Bradford and Read, [etc.] 1822. 2 v.
NjR. (Vol. 1 only)   9790

Oratorio, to be performed at the
Rev. Dr. Nichols' Meeting-
House, Portland, Wednesday eve-
ning, October 23, 1822. A.W.
Thayer, printer. 7 p. MeHi.
                             9791
Original poetic effusions... See
Grenville, A. S.

The orphan girl; to which is
added an account of Sarah Bar-
row.   Hartford, G. Goodwin &
Sons, 1822. 22 p. CtHi.   9792

Osbourn, James
   Divine communications; or,
Spiritual letters to faithful men.
Baltimore, John D. Toy, 1822.
158 p. NcD.   9793

---- Thoughts of peace in time
of war; or, God's goodness to
Israel in the worst of times...
Baltimore, pub. by the Author,
John D. Toy, printer, 1822.
291 p. MdHi; NcD.   9794

Osgood, Emery
   A Masonic discourse, delivered at the installation of
Mexico Lodge of Free and Accepted Mason, No. 307, in the
town of Mexico, Oswego County,
N.Y. Sept. 17, A.L. 5818. Detroit, Repr. by Sheldon and
Reed, 1822. 12 p. MiD-B. 9795

Osgood, Samuel
   The tenets of Freemasonry:
illustrated in a sermon preached
at the consecration of Orient
Lodge, in East-Hartford, Conn.,
Sept. 25, 1822.   Hartford,
Goodsell & Wells, printers, 1822.
15 p.   CBPSR; Ct; CtHC; CtHi;
IaCrM; MBC; MH-AH; NGH;
RHi; Vt.   9796

Otway, Thomas, 1652-1685
   Venice preserved, a tragedy
...Boston, Wells and Lilly, 1822.
88 p. MH; MeB; PPL; TxU.
                             9797
Ousatonic Canal Company
   Proposals for the stock of the
...[New Haven, A.H. Maltby &
Co., printer, 1822?] 16 p. CtHi;
CtY.   9798

Owenson, Sydney, 1783?-1859
   Friend of my soul.   New
York, E. Riley [1822?] 1 l. NHi.
                             9799

                P

Pacificus, Philo, pseud.   See

Worcester, Noah.

Paddy's trip to America. See
Talbot, Charles S.

Paine, Emerson, 1766-1851
Sermons, delivered at Middle-
borough, first precinct, Lord's
day, June 9, 1822... To which is
added The result of the ecclesiastical council... Plymouth
[Mass.] A. Danforth, 1822. 31 p.
CBPSR; CtHC; MAnP; MB;
MBC; MWA; RPB.   9800

Paine, Thomas, 1737-1809
El derecho del hombre, para
el uso y provecho del género
humano. Traducido del inglés
por Santiago Felipe Puglia.
Philadelphia, Matias Carey, 1822.
168 p. DLC; MH.   9801

Paley, William
The principles of moral and
political philosophy. 10th Amer.
ed. Canandaigua, J. D. Bemis
and co., 1822. 427 p. N;
NCanHi; NN; TxH.   9802

---- A treatise on the law of
principal and agent, chiefly with
reference to mercantile transac-
tions. A new ed. with additions
by Niel Gow. Philadelphia,
Abraham Small, 1822. 375 p.
CtHT; CtW; GU-L; IU; Ia;
IaDaGL; In-SC; Ky; KyLoU-L;
M; MWCL; N-L; NNLI; NNU;
NcD; NjP; PP; ViU.   9803

---- ---- A new ed., with con-
siderable additions, by Niel Gow.
2d Amer. ed., imp. Exeter,
N. H., G. Lamson, J. J. Willi-
ams, printer, 1822. 427 p. CLU;
CU; G; Ky; LNT-L; MB; MH-
L; MiDU-L; Nh-Hi; PU-L; TU;
WU-L; WvU.   9804

Palmer, Benjamin Morgan, 1781-
1847
Religion profitable: with a

special reference to the case of
servants. A sermon, preached
on September 22, 1822, in the
Circular Church, Charleston,
S. C. Charleston, S. C., J. R.
Schenck, printer, 1822. 21 p.
ScCC; ScHi.   9805

---- The upright character and
peaceful end of the righteous.
A sermon, preached in the Independent Church at Ponpon...
14th of April, 1822, on the occasion of the death of the Rev.
Loammi Floyd... Charleston,
S. C., William Riley, printer,
1822. 24 p. MBC; RPB.   9806

Panormo, Francis, 1764-1844
The bird waltz. For the pi-
ano forte or harp. Charleston,
J. Siegling [1822?] 3 p. NN.
          9807
The parent's assistant, and Sun-
day school book. Boston, Cum-
mings and Hilliard, 1822. 32 p.
MB; MCarl; MdBD.   9808

The parents' assistant; or,
Young child's catechism. Com-
piled principally from Blair,
Martinet, and others. By an in-
structor. Woodstock, Pr. by
David Watson, 1822, 72 p. MH.
          9809
Paris, John Ayrton, 1785-1856
Pharmacologia; or, The his-
tory of medicinal substances,...
From the last London ed., with
a general English index. New
York, F. & R. Lockwood, 1822.
426 p. CSt-L; CoCsE; CtW; GU-
M; ICJ; ICU; KyLoCP; MB;
MBM; MBP; MBU-M; MdBM;
MeB; MiU; NBM; NGH; NNNAM;
NRAM; NTRPI; NbU-M; OC;
OCLloyd; OClM; PPC; TNV.
          9810
Parke, Uriah
The farmers' and mechanics
practical arithmetic... Win-
chester, Va., Pr. by Samuel H.
Davis, 1822. 207 p. DAU; NcD;

ViWin. 9811

Parke, William Thomas, 1762-1847
Johnny came a courting me. Philadelphia, G. E. Blake [1822] [2] p. MH. 9812

Parker, Daniel
Report of the paymaster general to the Secretary of war... [Washington, Pr. by Davis & Force, 1822] 31 p. PPL. 9813

Parker, Edward L.
A sermon, delivered at Bedford, N. H. March 26, 1822, occasioned by the sudden death of James Parker, Esq. Amherst, Pr. by Richard Boylston, 1822. 16 p. DLC; ICN; MB; Nh; Nh-Hi. 9814

Parmly, Eleazar
An essay on the disorders and treatment of the teeth. 3d ed. Pr. for the author; and published by Henry Durell and Co. New York, and T. and G. Underwood, Medical Booksellers, Fleet St., London, 1822. 88 p. CoFcS; GHi; IEN-D; MBM; MdUM; NNC-M; PPL; PU-D; ViNoM. 9815

Parry, John, 1776-1851
I never will deceive thee. A ballad. Philadelphia, G. E. Blake, [1822?] [2] p. NN; PPL; PU. 9816

---- They're a' a noddin. A favorite Scotch song. Philadelphia, Geo. Willig [1822] [2] p. DLC; MH; MWA; NN; PPL; PU; RPB. 9817

---- Two wives; or, A hint to husbands: a comic musical drama in one act. New York, E. M. Murden, 1822. 27 p. PU. 9818

Parsons, Isaac
Sermon, occasioned by the death of Mrs. Carile Mary Whit-more, wife of the Rev. Zolva Whitmore, who died at North-Guilford; preached at East-Haddam, the following Lord's Day, Sept. 29th, 1822. Middletown (Conn.) Pr. by E. & H. Clark, 1822. 23 p. Ct; CtHC; CtHi; ICU; MBC; MH; MHolliHi; MWA; NRMA; OCIW. 9819

A pastoral letter from the rector of Trinity church. See Croswell, Harry.

Patching, Tallcut
A religious convincement and plea, for the baptism and communion of the spirit, and that which is of material bread, wine and water rejected as Jewish rites... Buffalo, Pr. for the author, by H. A. Salisbury, 1822. 457 p. CSmH; NBuG; NBuHi. 9820

Patton, Robert Bridges, 1794-1839
Das deutsche Lesebach. No. 1. Auszuge aus Engel's Philosoph fur die Welt enthaltend. Middlebury, J. W. Copeland, 1822. 24 p. MB; MH. 9821

[Paulding, James Kirke] 1778-1860
A sketch of old England, by a New-England man... New-York, C. Wiley, 1822. 2 v. in 1. C; CSmH; Ct; CtW; CtY; DLC; DeWI; ICN; ICU; IU; Ia; KyLx; LNT; LU; MA; MB; MBL; MH; MLy; MMeT; MNS; MS; MWA; MdBE; MdBJ; MiD-B; MtU; NBLiHi; NBu; NCH; NIC; NNC; NNS; NcU; NhD; NjP; NjR; P; PNt; PPA; PPAmP; PPL; PPT; PU; RPB; ScCC; ScSoh; ScU; TxU; VtU; WHi. 9822

Paxton, George
Illustrations of the Holy Scriptures in three parts. Philadelphia, James E. Moore, J. Harding, printer, 1822. 2 v. CSansS;

CtHT; ICP; KKc; MB; MBC; MdW; OO; PLT; PCC; PPLT; PPiW; TNJ. 9823

---- Illustrations of the Holy Scriptures; in three parts. Philadelphia, James Moore, publisher; Griggs and Dickinson, printers, 1822. 2 v. GDC; KKc; MdW; NSchU. 9824

---- ---- Philadelphia, David Hogan, Griggs & Dickinson, printer, 1822. 2 v. MiU; NcMHi; NjR; OrpWB; PWW; ScDuE; TxAuPT; ViRUT. 9825

Paxton, John Adems
The New Orleans directory and register, containing the names, professions and residences, of all the heads of families and persons in business of the city and suburbs. New Orleans, Benj. Levy & co., 1822. 200 p. CSmH; DLC; LNH; LNP; ICHi; MWA; NN; NIC. 9826

Payne, J.W.H.
The unfortunate lovers, or The affecting history of Selim and Almena, a Turkish tale from "The bride of Abydos" of Lord Byron. New York, S. King, 1822. 26 p. MH. 9827

Payne, John Howard
Adeline, the victim of seduction, a melo drama in three acts, altered from the French and adapted to the English stage. New York, E.M. Murden, 1822. 41 p. CtY; ICU; IU; Ia; MBAt; MH; NCH; NIC; NN; NNC; PHi; PU. 9828

Payson, Edward
An address to seamen. [Newburyport, Charles Whipple, 1822] 12 p. NjR. 9829

Pearce, William
Hartford-bridge; or, The

skirts of the camp. An operatic farce, in two acts. New York, S. King, 1822. 36 p. MH; OO; RNR. 9830

Peaslee, Reuben
The experience, Christian and ministerial of Reuben Peaslee. Haverhill, Burrill & Hersey, 1822. 33 p. MHa. 9831

Peck, John, 1735?-1812
A descant on Universalism; a poem. To which is added A few questions to the believers in universal salvation. New Haven, pr. and sold at no. 4 Glebe building, 1822. 24 p. Ct; CtHC; CtY; MB; MH; MMeT-Hi; MPiB; OCIWHi. 9832

---- ---- New York, Larkin Moors, 1822. 29, [4] p. MiD. 9833

[Peirce, Thomas] 1786-1850
The odes of Horace in Cincinnati [pseud.] as published in the 'Western spy and literary cadet," during the year 1821. Cincinnati, pr. at Harrison's Press, 1822. 117 p. CSmH; DLC; NN; O; OCHP; OCIWHi; OFH; RPB. 9834

Pelton, Samuel
The absurdities of Methodism. New York, E. Bliss & E. White, 1822. 268 p. CtW; MB; MBBC; NjMD; NjR; PPL; PPPrHi; TxDaM. 9835

Pen Owen. See Hook, James.

Penn, William
The harmony of divine and heavenly doctrines, demonstrated in sundry declarations on a variety of subjects. Preached at the Quakers' meetings in London. 1st Amer. from 3d London ed. New York, Repub. by Refine Weekes, M. Day, printer, 1822. 155 p. InRchE; MH; NBF; NjR; PHC; PPL; PSC-Hi. 9836

Pennsylvania

An act for the regulation of the militia of the commonwealth of Pennsylvania, passed the second day of April, one thousand eight hundred and twenty-two... Harrisburg, Pr. by W. Greer, 1822. 67 p. DLC; OCLaw; P; PHi; PU-L.   9837

---- Acts of Assembly, concerning the Lancaster, Elizabethtown and Middletown turnpike road. Lancaster, Pr. by John Bear, 1822. 22 p. CSmH; P; PHi.
9838

---- Acts of assembly and ordinances relating to the water works. [Harrisburg, 1822] 20 p. PPAmP.   9839

---- Acts of General Assembly of the Commonwealth of Pennsylvania, passed at a session which was begun and held at the Borough of Harrisburg, on Tuesday, the fourth day of December, in the year of our Lord, one thousand eight hundred and twenty one... Harrisburg, Pr. by C. Gleim, 1822. 330 p. DLC; IaU-L; InSC; Ky; MdBB; Mi-L; Mo; MSaEC; Nb; Nc-S; Nj; NNLI; Nv; P; PLL; PPAmP; PPLR; PU; RPL; T; TxU-L; W.   9840

---- Documents accompanying the report of the Committee on Roads, Bridges and Inland Navigation, read in the Senate of Pennsylvania, on the 23rd of March, 1822. Harrisburg, Pr. by Charles Mowry, 1822. 192 p. MiU; P; PHi; PPi; PPL.   9841

---- Fourth annual report of the controllers of the public schools of the first school district of the state of Pennsylvania. With their accounts. Philadelphia, Pr. by order of the Board of Control. 1822. 13 p. PNazMHi; PPL.   9842

---- Governor's message delivered to the legislature of Pennsylvania, Dec. 5th, 1822. [Harrisburg, 1822] 11 p. DLC; PPAmP.   9843

---- Journal of the Senate of the Commonwealth of Pennsylvania, which commenced at Harrisburg, the fourth day of December, in the year of our Lord, one thousand eight hundred and twenty one... Vol. XXXII. Harrisburg, Pr. by Charles Mowry, 1822. viii, 852, xx p. CSmH; MoHi; P.   9844

---- Journal of the thirty second House of Representatives of the Commonwealth of Pennsylvania. Commenced at Harrisburg, Tuesday, the fourth of December, in the year of our Lord, one thousand eight hundred and twenty one... Harrisburg, Pr. by John S. Wiestling, 1822. 1196, xiii, 3, li p. MoHi; P; WHi.
9845
---- Receipts and payments at the Treasury of Pennsylvania from the first day of December, one thousand eight hundred and twenty one to the thirtieth day of November, one thousand eight hundred and twenty two, inclusive. Harrisburg, Pr. by Mowry and Cameron, 1822. 467 p. P.   9846

---- Regulations for the uniform & equipments for the militia officers of the commonwealth... Philadelphia, Pr. by Clark & Raser, 1822. 11 p. PPAmP.
9847
---- Report of Mr. Stevenson, chairman of the Committee on Domestic Manufactures, read, Tuesday, Dec. 24, 1822. Harrisburg, Pr. by John S. Wiestling, 1822. iii, 8 p. P; PPAmP; PPL.   9848

---- Report of the Committee of Ways and Means on the petition of distillers, Jan. 23, 1822. [Harrisburg, 1822] 6 p. PHi.
9849

---- Report of the finances of the Commonwealth of Pennsylvania, for the year 1822, made to the legislature. Harrisburg, Pr. by John S. Wiestling, 1822. vii, 36 p. P.
9850

---- Report of the names of all persons holding offices under this commonwealth, by appointment of the governor, to which salaries or emoluments are attached, designating the office or offices held by each officer and the date of his appointment. Harrisburg, Pr. by John S. Wiestling, 1822. 90 p. P; PPAmP.
9851

---- Report on roads, bridges and canals; read in the Senate, March 23, 1822. Mr. Raguet, chairman. [Harrisburg] Pr. by Charles Mowry, 1822. 18 p. DLC; DeGE; MiU; P; PHi; PPAmP; PPL; PPi.
9852

---- Report on the finances of the Commonwealth of Pennsylvania for the year 1822...Harrisburg, Pr. by Greer & Minshall, 1822. 36, vii p. PPL.
9853

---- Report on the subject of education, read in the Senate of Pennsylvania, March 1, 1822. Mr. Wurts, Chairman. Harrisburg, Pr. by Charles Mowry, 1822. 24 p. NNC; PLFM; PPAmP; PPL; Tx; TNP.
9854

---- Report on the subject of weights and measures, read in the Senate, March 1, 1822. Harrisburg, Pr. by Charles Mowry, 1822. 3 p. PPAmP.
9855

---- Report relative to actual settlers, read in the Senate, March 21, 1822. Harrisburg, Pr. by Charles Mowry, 1822. 19 p. PHi; PPAmP; PPL.
9856

---- Report relative to executive patronage, read in the Senate, March 25, 1822. Mr. Hill, chairman [Harrisburg, 1822] 27 p. DLC; PPAmP.
9857

---- Tagebuch des zwei und dreissigsten Hauses der Reprasentanten der Republik Pennsylvanien. Reading, pr. by C.A. Bruckman, 1821[!] [1822] Seidensticker p. 214.
9858

---- Statement of the Turnpike Company of the Commonwealth. [Harrisburg, 1822] 8 p. P.
9859

---- Tagebuch des drei und dreissigsten Hauses der Repräsentanten der Republik Pennsylvanien. Easton [Pa.] C.J. Hütter, 1822. Seidensticker p. 215
9860

---- Tagebuch des Senats der Republik Pennsylvanien, 1821-22. Harrisburg, Pr. by Henry C. Martthen, 1822. Seidensticker, p. 216.
9861

---- Titles of the Acts passed by the Legislature of the Commonwealth of Pennsylvania at the session of 1821-22. Harrisburg, Pr. by Charles Mowry, 1822. xiii p. P.
9862

Pennsylvania Academy of Fine Arts
  Eleventh annual exhibition of the Pennsylvania Academy of the Fine Arts. Philadelphia, Hickman and Hazzard, 1822. 24 p. MHi; PMA.
9863

The Pennsylvania agricultural almanack for 1823. Lancaster, Pa., William Albright [1822]

18 ll. MWA; PHi.   9864

The Pennsylvania almanac, and
rural economist's assistant for
1823. By Charles F. Egelman
[sic]. Harrisburg, Pa., John
Wyeth, J.S. Wiestling and C.
Gleim [1822] 18 ll. InU; MWA;
PHi; PLF.   9865

The Pennsylvania almanac for
1823. By John Ward. Philadelphia, M'Carty & Davis [1822]
18 ll. MWA; NjR; PHi.   9866

---- ---- Philadelphia, Isaac
Pugh [1822] 18 ll. MWA; NjT;
PPL.   9867

---- Philadelphia, Richards
Johnson [1822] Drake 11369.
                                 9868
Pennsylvania & New Jersey al-
manac for 1823. By Joshua
Sharp. Philadelphia, D. Dick-
inson [1822] 18 ll. DLC; InU;
MWA; NjR; PDoBHi; PHi. 9869

Pennsylvania Infirmary for Diseases of the Eye and Ear
    The Pennsylvania Infirmary
for Diseases of the Eye and Ear
established at Philadelphia.
Philadelphia, Pr. by order of
the Society, William Fry, printer, 1822. 6 p. PHi; PPAmP;
PPC; RNR.   9870

Pennsylvania Institution for the
Deaf & Dumb
    Documents in relation to the
dismissal of David G. Seixas,
from the Pennsylvania Institution
for the Deaf and Dumb; published for the information of the
contributors. Philadelphia, Pr.
by order of the Board of Directors, 1822. 48 p. NN; P; PHi;
PPL; ScC.   9871

---- Second annual report...
[Philadelphia, 1822?] 20 p.
(T.-p. mutilated.) PPL.   9872

Pepe, Guglielmo, barone, 1782-
1855
    A narrative of the political
and military events which took
place at Naples, in 1820 and
1821; with observations explanatory of the national conduct in
general and his own in particular...New York, J.V. Seaman,
1822. 130 p. CU; PV; VtMiM.
                                 9873
Percival, James Gates, 1795-
1856
    Clio. Charleston, S. Bab-
cock & co., [etc.] 1822. 2 v in
1. CtHT-W; CtHi; CtY; DLC;
MB; MBC; MH; MNF; MdBP;
MeBat; MnU; NN; NcD; PU;
RPB; ScU.   9874

---- Oration delivered before
the Φ B K Society, September
10th, 1822, on some of the moral and political truths derivable
from the study of history. New
Haven, A.H. Maltby and Co.,
1822. 19 p. CtHC; CtHT-W;
CtY; DLC; MB; MBAt; MBC;
MH; MHi; MiD-B; NCH; NNC;
NTEW; OMC; RPB; WHi. 9875

---- Prometheus, part 2, with
other poems...New Haven, A.
H. Maltby & co., 1822. 108 p.
C; CtHT-W; CtY; LNHT; MBC;
MH; MsJMC; NCH.   9876

Percy, Sholto, pseud. See
Robertson, Joseph Clinton, 1788-
1852.

Percy, Thomas, 1729-1811, bp.
of Dromore
    A key to the New Testament
...From the last London ed.
Baltimore, E.J. Coale & Co.,
Toy, printer, 1822. 148 p. DLC;
ICU; IObB; MH; MdAS; MdBE;
MdBJ; MdBD; MiSch; MdHi;
NSyU; ULC.   9877

Periclean Society of Alexandria
    Constitution and by-laws of

the Periclean Society of Alexandria. Revised January 23d,
1822. Alexandria, D.C., Pr.
by Rounsavell and Pittman, 1822.
9 p. DLC.   9878

Perkins, Charles
    An oration, pronounced at the
request of the citizens of Norwich, Conn. on the anniversary
of American Independence, July
4th, 1822. Norwich, Conn.,
Pr. by Robinson & Dunham,
1822. 24 p. A-Ar; Ct; DLC;
NCH; Nh; PHi.   9879

Perkins, Nathan
    A half century sermon, de-
livered at West-Hartford, on the
13th day of October, 1822...
Hartford, Pr. by George Good-
win, 1822. 24 p. Ct; CtHC;
CtHT-W; CtHi; GDC; IaHa;
MBC; MBNEH; MHi; MiD-B;
Nh; PPPrHi; RPB; WHi; BrMus.
                            9880
Perossier, James W.
    O lady love awake. A ro-
mance. New York, A. & W.
Geib [1822?] [2] p. DLC.   9881

Perrault, Charles
    Cinderella; or, The little
glass slipper. Illustrated with
elegant engravings. Philadelphia, Mary Charles, 1822. 8 l.
PP.   9882

Perrin, Jean Baptiste
    A grammar of the French
tongue; grounded upon the decisions of the French Academy.
Philadelphia, Hickman & Hazard,
1822. 346 p. MH; OWoC.
                            9883

Perry, David, b. 1741
    Recollections of an old soldier.
The life of Captain David Perry,
a soldier of the French and Revolutionary wars. Windsor, Vt.,
Pr. at the Republican & Yeoman
printing office, 1822. 55 p.

DLC; MH; MiD-B; MiU-C; NN;
NRHi; RHi; RPB; VtU.   9884

Peters, Absalom, 1793-1869
    A sermon, preached at Ben-
nington, Vt., on the Lord's day,
Sept. 29, 1822. Bennington, Pr.
by T. Andrews, 1822. iv, 21 p.
CtY; MBC; MH-AH; VtHi;
VtMiM.   9885

The phantom barge. See Thomson, Charles West.

Phi Beta Kappa Society. New
Hampshire Alpha
    Catalogue of the members of
the New Hampshire, Alpha of
the Phi Beta Kappa Society,
Dartmouth College. Haverhill,
Mass., Burill and Hersey,
printers, 1822. 15 p. DLC;
GDC; MBAt; NhD.   9886

Philadelphia (City)
    Ordinances of the corporation
...passed since the 3d day of
August, 1820. Philadelphia,
Lydia R. Bailey, 1822. p. 163-
208. PPL.   9887

---- Report of the Watering Com-
mittee, read in Select Council,
Nov. 12, 1818... Philadelphia,
Pr. by William Fry, 1822. 42 p.
PPL.   9888

---- Report of the Watering
Committee, to the select and
common councils. Read January
24, 1822. Philadelphia, Pr. by
Lydia R. Bailey, 1822. 22, [1] p.
PPL; THi.   9889

Philadelphia Bank
    Statement of the accounts of
the Philadelphia Bank. [Phila-
delphia, 1822] 23 p. PHi. 9890

The Philadelphia directory and
register, for 1822. Philadelphia,
M'Carty & Davis, 1822. DLC;
MWA; NN; PHi; PP; PPL. 9891

Philadelphia Dispensary for the Medical Relief of the Poor
Rules... with a list of contributors... for 1822. [Philadelphia, 1822?] 11 p. PPL. 9892

Philadelphia. First Unitarian Church
Catalogue of books in the library of the First Society of Unitarian Christians in... Philadelphia. [Philadelphia] 1822. 12 p. PPAmP. 9893

---- Friends' Asylum for the Insane
State of the Asylum for the relief of persons deprived of the use of their reason. Published by direction of the contributors, fourth-month, 1822. Philadelphia, Pr. by Solomon W. Conrad, 1822. 15 p. Ct; MiU-C; PPAmP. 9894

The Philadelphia grand waltz. New York, A. & W. Geib [1822?] 3 p. NN. 9895

---- Law Academy
Constitution and by-laws of the Law Academy... Philadelphia, Thomas H. Palmer, 1822. 16 p. Sabin 61765. 9896

---- New Theatre
Fundamental rules and regulations of the stockholders in the New Theatre in the city of Philadelphia... [Philadelphia] Pr. by Thomas Desilver, 1822. 8 p. PHi. 9897

---- ---- Playbills from Dec. 2, 1822, to Apr. 30, 1823. [Philadelphia, Thos. Desilver, 1822-3] 45 bdsds. DLC; PPL. 9898

Philadelphia Orphan Society
Seventh annual report of the Philadelphia Orphan Society, read at the anniversary meeting, January 1, 1822. Philadelphia,

J. H. Cunningham, printer, 1822. 21 p. DLC; PPL. 9899

Philadelphia. St. Mary's Church
To the Honourable the Senate and House of Representatives of the Commonwealth of Pennsylvania: The memorial of the undersigned... [Philadelphia, 1822] 46 p. PPL. 9900

---- Seventh Presbyterian Church
The charter... Philadelphia, Pr. by John Bioren, 1822. 8 p. PPPrHi. 9901

---- Southern Dispensary for the Medical Relief of the Poor
Rules... with a list of contributors... for 1822. [Philadelphia, 1822?] 11 p. PPL. 9902

---- Spring Garden District
An ordinance, for raising supplies to defray the expenses for completing the general survey, and the expense attending the repairs of public pumps, the public highways and expenses for 1822. [Philadelphia, 1822] 1 p. PHi. 9903

Philadelphia Sunday and Adult School Union
The fifth report... read... May 21, 182(?) Philadelphia, 1822. 88 p. MHi. 9904

Philadelphia Theatre
[Playbills] January 2 to April 10, 1822. [Philadelphia, Thomas Desilver] 40 bdsds. PU. 9905

Philadelphia. Walnut Street Theatre
Playbills; from Jan. 1 to April 23, 1822. Philadelphia, 1822. 57 bdsds. PPL. 9906

Philip, Alexander Philip Wilson
A treatise on indigestion and its consequences, called nervous

and billious complaints... Philadelphia, Benjamin & Thomas Kite, 1822. viii, 205 p. Nh.
9907

---- ---- Philadelphia, H. C. Carey & I. Lea; Harrisburg, Pr. by Wm. Greer, 1822. viii, 205 p. IU-M; MB; MBM; MBU-M; MdBM; NBuG; NBMS; NNNAM; NbU-M; OC; OClM; PPC.
9908

Philip, or, The aborigines, a drama, in three acts. New-York, Pr. 1822. 48 p. MH; NN.
9909

Philipps, Thomas, 1774-1841
Away with this pouting and sadness. An Irish melody. Philadelphia, Geo. Willig, 1822. 3 p. MWA; NBuG; NN.   9910

---- Elementary practices for singing. Boston, Thomas Badger Jr. [1822] 4 p. MWA.   9911

---- The hunter's horn. A new sporting cavatina. New York, E. Riley [1822?] 3 p. NN; RPB.
9912

---- Julia loves. A canzonett. Philadelphia, G. Willig, 1822. 3 p. NN; RNR.   9913

---- The last bugle. A martial ballad. Philadelphia, G. Willig [1822] 3 p. DLC; MB; MH; MWA; NBuG; NN; PP; PPL; RPB.
9914

---- This blooming rose. A ballad. Boston, E.W. Jackson, [1822?] [2] p. RPB.   9915

[Phillips, Sir Richard] 1767-1840
A general view of the manners, customs, and curiosities of nations; including a geographical description of the earth. New-Haven, John Babcock & son, 1822. 2 v. CtW; CtY; ICP; MA; MAm; MDeeP; MdBL; NNS;

PHi; PP; PU; RP.   9916

[----] A grammar of natural and experimental philosophy... From the 12th London ed., imp. and enl. Hartford, pub. by Huntington and Hopkins, Sidney's press, New Haven, 1822. 216 p. CtHT-W; CtHi; NNE.   9917

[----] ---- From the 12th London ed., imp. and enl. Hartford, S. G. Goodrich, 1822. 216 p. DLC; MA; MDeeP; MWBor; MWBorHi; NjR; PHi; PU; VtMiM.   9918

[----] ---- From the 12th London ed., imp. and enl. New-Haven, John Babcock and Son, and S. Babcock and Co.; Charleston, S. C., Sidney's press, New-Haven, 1822. 216 p. CtHi; CtW; IaDuP; MB; MH; MNS; MPeHi; NNC; OClWHi; PPL; RPB.   9919

[----] The universal preceptor; being a general grammar of arts, sciences, and useful knowledge. 4th Amer. ed., with additions and improvements. Philadelphia, E. Parker, 1822. 316 p. CtHT-W; DLC; GB; MB; MH; MiDSH; NUtHi; P; RPB.
9920

[----] The wonders of the world. In numbers. - no. 1. Abridged from the 10th London ed. New-Haven, J. Babcock and son; and S. Babcock and co., Charleston, S. C., 1822. 32 p. CtY; MB; MWA; NNC.   9921

Phillipps, Samuel March, 1780-1862
A treatise on the law of evidence... Volume the second. Boston, Wells and Lilly, Court Street, 1822. 371 p. (Vol. 1 is New York, Gould & Banks, 1820.) FU-L; GColu; GDC; InHuP; KyLoUL; MnU; NNLI. 9922

Phillips Academy, Andover,
Mass.
Order of exercises for exhibition at Phillips Academy, Andover, August 20, 1822. Bdsd.
MHi.　　　　　　　　　9923

Phinney's calendar, or western almanac for 1823. By Andrew Beers. Cooperstown, H. & E. Phinney [1822] 18 ll. ICN; NHi.
　　　　　　　　　　　9924
---- ---- Cooperstown, H. & E. Phinney, and sold by them [1822] 18 ll. DLC; InU; MWA; MiD-B; N; NN; NCooHi; NR; NRMA; NIC; WHi.　　9925

Pickering, David
A discourse, delivered at the Universalist Church, in the city of Hudson, N.Y. December 27, 1821. Hudson, Pr. by Ashbel Stoddard, 1822. 56 p. N.　9926

---- ---- 2d ed. Hudson, Ashbel Stoddard, 1822. 56 p. PPL; RPB.　　　　　　　　　9927

---- A discourse, delivered at the Universalist Church, in the city of Hudson, on Sabbath evening, October 6, 1822. Hudson, Pr. by Ashbel Stoddard, 1822. 22 p. MMeT-Hi.　　　　　9928

---- Psalms and hymns, for social and private worship: carefully selected from the best authors. Hudson, Pr. by Ashbel Stoddard, 1822. [425] p. DLC; IObB; MBAt; MMeT-Hi; PPL; RHi; RNHi; RPB.　　　9929

---- Salvation of Judas Iscariot. A discourse, delivered at the Universalist Church, in the city of Hudson, on Sabbath evening, October 6, 1822. By David Pickering...Hudson, Pr. by Ashbel Stoddard, 1822. 20 p. MMeT-Hi; N.　　　　　9930

---- A sermon, delivered at the Universalist Church, in the city of Hudson, December 25, 1821. Being the anniversary of Jesus Christ. Hudson, Pr. by Ashbel Stoddard, 1822. 15 p. MMeT-Hi; N.　　　　　　　　　9931

[Pickering, Henry] 1781-1838
Elegiac stanzas [by Henry Pickering. Salem, Mass., 1822?] [4] p. MSaE.　9932

[----] The ruins of Paestum: and other compositions in verse. Salem, Mass., Cushing and Appleton, 1822. 128 p. DLC; ICP; MB; MBev; MH; MPiB; MS; MSa; MSaE; MWH; MnU; NNC; PPAmP; PPL; PU; RPB; TxU; VtMiM; WHi.　　　　　9933

Pickering, Timothy
An address delivered before the Massachusetts Agricultural Society at the Brighton cattle show, Oct. 9th, 1822. [Boston? 1822] 26 p. MH.　　9934

Pierce, John
Ministerial fidelity described in a discourse delivered at Canton...January 30, 1822, at the ordination of the Rev. Benjamin Huntoon. Boston, Pr. by True & Greene, 1822. 28 p. CtHC; DLC; ICMe; ICT; MBAt; MBAU; MBC; MBNEH; MH; MHi; MiD-B.　　　　　　　　　9935

Pike, James
An English spelling book; or, An introduction to the art of reading. 3d ed. Boston, Munroe & Francis, 1822. 172 p. DLC; MB; MH; MeHi; TxU-T.
　　　　　　　　　　　9936
Pike, Joseph, 1657-1729
An epistle to the national meeting of Friends, in Dublin, concerning good order and discipline in the church. Philadelphia, Solomon W. Conrad, 1822.

23 p. MBC; PSC-Hi; PPeSchw.
9937

Pike, Nicholas
A new and complete system of
arithmetick. Composed for the
use of the citizens of the United
States... 4th ed. , rev. , corr. ,
and imp. by Chester Dewey.
Troy, N. Y. , Wm. S. Parker,
1822. 532 p. DAU; IaFd; MA;
MH; MWA; NNC; PPL.   9938

Pike, Samuel, 1717?-1773
Religious cases of conscience,
answered in an evangelical man-
ner, at the casuistical lecture...
To which is now added, The spir-
itual companion, or the professing
Christian tried at the bar of
God's word... Middletown (Conn.)
Pr. and pub. by E. & H. Clark,
1822. 436 p. CtMMHi; CtSoP;
CtW; ICP; MBC; NSyU; NbCrD;
NcAS; NcRSh.   9939

Pike, Stephen, comp.
The teacher's assistant, or,
A system of practical arithmetic
... Philadelphia, pub. by Johnson
and Warner, and for sale at
their book-stores in Philadelphia
& Richmond, Va. , 1822. 198 p.
DLC; NcU.   9940

---- ---- A new ed. , with corr.
and add. by the author. Philadelphia, Benjamin Warner; Stereotyped by B. and J. Collins,
1822. 198 p. CSt; PLFM;
PPeSchw.   9941

---- ---- ---- Philadelphia,
McCarty & Davis, 1822. 198 p.
MNS; PU.   9942

[Pinckney, Thomas]
Reflections, occasioned by the
late disturbances in Charleston.
By Achates. Charleston, A. E.
Miller, 1822. 30 p. MB; MH;
NN; NcU; Sc; ScC; ScCC; ScU.
9943
The pious stranger. Meditations

and reflections on various sub-
jects... Albany, Pr. by E. & E.
Hosford, 1822. 294 p. ICT;
KyBgW; MiD-B; PPL; TNP.
9944
The pirate. See Scott, Sir
Walter, bart.

Pittsburgh almanac for 1823. By
John Armstrong. Pittsburgh, R.
Patterson & Lambdin, J. B. But-
ler, printer [1822] 18 ll. DLC;
InHi; MWA.   9945

The Pittsburgh magazine almanac
for 1823. By John Armstrong.
Pittsburgh, R. Patterson [1822]
30 ll. OMC.   9946

---- Pittsburgh, R. Patterson &
Lambdin; J. B. Butler, printer
[1822] 30 ll. OClWHi; OHi; PPi;
WHi.   9947

Pius VII, Pope
Discourse of His Eminence
Cardinal Chiaramonti, Bishop of
Imoa, now Pope Pius VII. Addressed to his diocesans on
Christmas day, 1797. Translated from the Italian. Baltimore, pub. by Joseph S. Williams; William Ogden Niles,
printer, 1822. 12 p. DGU;
PPCHi.   9948

Plan of the city of Washington,
seat of government of the United
States. Entered according to the
Act of Congress on the 12 day of
November 1822, by S. A. Elliot,
of the District of Columbia.
Map. ScMar.   9949

Planche, James Robinson, 1796-
1880
All in the dark; or, The banks
of the Elbe. A musical farce,
in two acts. New York, E. M.
Murden, 1822. 52 p. MB; MH;
MWA; NIC-L.   9950

Plantou, Anthony
Observations on the yellow
fever, with an account of a new
mode of treatment & cure for the
same, as well as for putrid &
malignant diseases in general...
Philadelphia, 1822. 58 p.
NNNAM; PPAmP; PU; PPM;
PPL; PPWa; PHi.   9951

---- ---- 2d ed. Philadelphia,
1822. 58 p. NRU-M; LNH; PPC;
RPB.   9952

Pleyel, Camille, 1788-1855
The crusaders farewell. A
romance from the French. Philadelphia, G. Willig [1822?] p [2]-
4. NN.   9953

Pleyel, Ignaz Joseph, 1757-1831
The wreath you wove. New
York, P. K. Moran [1822] [2] p.
MWA.   9954

Pleyel Society, Nantucket
Order of performance of the
Pleyel Society, Nantucket, June
9, 1822. [Nantucket? 1822] 4 p.
MH.   9955

Plutarchus.
Plutarch's Lives, translated
from the original Greek; with
notes critical and historical, and
a life of Plutarch. A new ed.
New York, Samuel Campbell &
son (etc.) 1822. 8 v. ArCH;
CoGP; DLC; IU; LNB; LNL;
MA; MB; MDeeP; MSher; MWar;
NPStA; NhPet; OO; PAtM; RBr;
TJoS; TxGaiC; ViRUT; ViU.
                          9956
---- ---- A new ed. , carefully
corr. , and the index much
amended, and accurately revised
throughout. Philadelphia, Hick-
man & Hazzard, 1822. 4 v.
IaScM; LNB; MA; MH-AH;
MdBL; MoSpD; NPV; NStc;
NcAS; Nj; NjP; OM; PPA; PHi;
PPWi; PPins; PU; RPB; ScCC.
                          9957

---- ---- New ed. Philadelphia,
H. C. Carey & I. Lea, 1822. 8 v
CtW; MA; TNP.   9958

Pocket companion; or, Every
man his own lawyer...Ed. 7.
Philadelphia, S. Roberts, 1822.
88 p. PAtM; PHi; PU.   9959

The pocket selection of hymns,
for the use of evangelical
churches, and religious assem-
blies, in the United States, being
a collection from the best authors. Frederick County, Md.,
Pr. and pub. by Matthias Bart-
gis at Pleasant Dale Paper Mills,
1822. 245 p. DLC; IEG; MdBD;
NNU.   9960

[Pocock, Isaac], 1782-1835
The Magpie; or, The maid of
Palaiseau. A melo-drama. Bos-
ton, Wells and Lilly, 1822. 61 p.
CtY; MH; MMal; MWA; RPB.
                          9961
---- Montrose; or, The chil-
dren of the mist. A musical
drama, in three acts. Balti-
more, J. Robinson, 1822. 60 p.
DLC; MH.   9962

Poetry for children. New-
Haven, pub. for J. Babcock &
Son, and S. Babcock & Co. ,
Charleston, S. C. Sidney's
press, 1822. 30, [1] p. CtHi.
                          9963
Pollet, Jean-Joseph-Benôit,
1753?-1818
Come rest in this bosom.
Baltimore, John Cole [1822?] 5 p.
NN; RPB.   9964

---- ---- Philadelphia, B. Carr,
[1822?] [2] p. MdHi; NN; PP.
                          9965
---- ---- Arranged with an accompaniment for the harp or piano forte. New York, A. & W.
Geib [1822?] [2] p. MH; RPB;
ViHi.   9966

---- Fleuve du Tage. Baltimore,
Publie par l'Auteur [1822?] 4 p.
MdHi; MWA.   9967

---- ---- A favorite French air.
Come rest in this bosom. Phila-
delphia, G. E. Blake [1822?] 8 p.
DLC; MH; MWA; RPB.   9968

---- ---- ---- Come rest in
this bosom. Philadelphia, J. L.
Frederick [1822?] 6 p. DLC.
                              9969
---- Variations sur l'air Fleuve
du Tage. Pour harp ou piano
forte. New York, P. K. Moran
[1822?] 8 p. DLC; RPB.   9970

Pomeroy, Jonathan L.
  A reply to a pamphlet en-
titled "Objections to Unitarian
Christianity considered." Boston,
Crocker & Brewster, 1822. 22 p.
CBPac; ICN; MBC; MWA. 9971

Pomeroy, S. W.
  Remarks, by S. W. Pomeroy,
on green crops, manuring with,
by turning them in. Boston,
Wells & Lilly, 1822. 8 p. MeB.
                              9972
Poor Robin's almanac for 1823.
By Joshua Sharp. Philadelphia,
D. Dickinson [1822] 18 ll. CtY;
DLC; InU; MWA; NHi; NjR; N;
P; PHi; PPL.   9973

Poor Sarah. See, Boudinot,
Elias.

Poor Will's almanac for 1823.
By William Collom. Philadelphia,
Kimber and Sharpless [1822] 18
ll. CtY; DLC; IU; MWA; NHi;
NjR; NjGlaN; PHi; PP; WHi.
                              9974
Poor Will's pocket almanack for
1823. Philadelphia, Kimber &
Sharpless [1822] 24 ll. DLC;
MWA; PHC; PHi.   9975

Pope, Alexander
  An essay on man. Exeter,

J. J. Williams, 1822. 48 p. MH.
                              9976
Porney, Mr., pseud. See Py-
ron du Martre, Antoine.

Porter, Anna Maria
  Roche-blanche; or, The
hunters of the Pyrenees: a romance. Boston, Wells & Lilly,
1822. 2 v. DLC; MFai; MH;
NCH; NcU.   9977

Porter, David
  Journal of a cruise made to
the Pacific Ocean by Captain
David Porter, in the United
States frigate Essex, in the
years 1812, 1813, and 1814. 2d
ed. New York, Wiley & Halsted,
1822. 2 v. CMary; CSfA; CU;
CtHT-W; DLC; DeWI; In; LNH;
M; MB; MH; MLanc; MLow;
MLy; MNBedf; MNBedfHi;
MdAN; MeHi; Mi; Mi-Mus;
MiD; MiU; MnHi; MoS; NCH;
NIC-L; NNA; NNC; NNPrM;
NWM; NjP; OC; OCHP; OClWHi;
P; PHi; PPAmP; PPGi; PPL;
PPWI; RNR; RP; RPA; RPB;
ScC; ScU; TxU; ViFre; ViU.
                              9978
Porter, Jane, 1776-1850
  Bannockburn; a novel, being
a sequel to the Scottish chiefs.
Philadelphia, E. T. Scott, 1822.
2 v. MBAt; MH; MNBedfHi; MU;
NGH; PLFM; PU; WHi.   9979

---- The Scottish chiefs, a romance. 5 v. in 2. Hartford,
pub. by Silas Andrus; P. B.
Gleason & Co., printers, 1822.
2 v. MFiHi; NIC-L; PPeSchw;
WGr.   9980

Porter, Noah, 1781-1866
  Memorial of a revival. A
sermon, delivered in Farmington,
at the anniversary Thanksgiving,
December 6, 1821. Hartford,
G. Goodwin & sons, 1822. 23 p.
Ct; CtHC; CtHi; ICN; MBC;
MiD-B; MiU-C; RBr.   9981

Porteus, Bielby, bp.
A summary of the principal
evidences for the truth and divine origin of the Christian revelation...A new ed., with questions for the examination of pupils. Concord, Hill and Moore,
1822. 140 p. CtHC; ICP; MH;
VtMiM.   9982

---- ---- Exeter, J. J. Williams,
1822. 131 p. MH; NhD; Nh-Hi.
                                9983
Portland, Maine
Rules and regulations for the
government of the public schools
in Portland. Portland, Pr. by
Todd and Smith, 1822. 10 p.
MeHi.   9984

---- First Universalist Church
of Christ
The profession of faith, bond
of union and peace, and church
organization and government, of
the First Universalist Church of
Christ. Portland, Pr. by Todd
& Smith, 1822. 8 p. MeHi. 9985

---- Portland Athenaeum
Regulations and by-laws of
the Portland Athenaeum and read-
ing-room. Instituted December
17, 1819. Portland, Thayer,
Tappan and Stickney, printers,
1822. 6 p. NNC.   9986

A postscript to the Rev. Mr.
Harold's address to the Roman
Catholics of Philadelphia [1822]
32 p. MdW.   9987

Pounder's Wesleyan almanack for
1823. Philadelphia, Jonathan
Pounder [1822] 16 ll. MWA;
PHi.   9988

Powell, John Joseph
Essay upon the law of con-
tracts and agreements...5th
Amer. ed., rev. and corr.
Exeter, N. H., Pub. by George
Lamson, J. J. Williams, printer,

1822-3. 2 v. in 1. DLC; IaU-L;
MH-L; MWH; NNLI; NcElon;
TU.   9989

----An essay upon the learning
of devises, from their inception
by writing, to their consumma-
tion by the death of the devisor
...3d Amer. ed. Exeter, N.H.,
Pub. by George Lamson; J. J.
Williams, printer, 1822. 523,
xxvi p. MH-L; MSaEC; Md;
NNC-L; NbU-L; NhD; Nh-Hi.
                                9990
The power of Grace, exemplified
in the sickness and death of
Anna Emery. Andover, Flagg
& Gould, printers, 1822. 24 p.
MeB.   9991

Powers, Grant, 1784-1841
The Kingdom of Christ. A
sermon delivered at the ordination of the Rev. Elderkin J.
Boardman, to the pastoral care
of the Church of Christ in Bak-
ersfield, Vermont. July 4, 1822.
Haverhill, N. H., Pr. by Sylvester T. Goss, 1822. 31 p.
Ct; MA; MBC; RHi; VtMiM.
                                9992

Powers, H. P.
The angel's salutation to the
shepherds. A Christmas ser-
mon delivered in Trinity Church,
Newark (N. J.) on the 25th De-
cember, 1821. Newark, The New
Jersey Eagle, 1822. 17 p.
OClWHi.   9993

The powers and duties of the
town officer. See O'Brien,
John Maurice.

The powers of fancy and other
poems. Baltimore, Pr. by
Joseph Robinson, 1822. 93 p.
MdHi; RPB.   9994

The practical American gardener, exhibiting the time for every
kind of work; and for every
month of the year. By an old

gardener. Baltimore, Pub. by
Fielding Lucas, Jr., 1822. 424 p.
InLPU; MdBE; MSaP; RPB;
ScCMu.   9995

Precedents for the use of justices of the peace: being a general collection of forms of practice; adapted to the existing laws
of Pennsylvania... Reading, Pa.,
George Getz, 1822. 142 p. P;
PAtM; PHDHi; PReaHi.   9996

[Prentiss, Charles] 1774-1820
    History of the United States of
America; with a brief account of
some of the principal empires and
states of ancient and modern
times. Stereotype ed., cor.
and improved: with questions.
Keene, N.H., J. Prentiss, 1822.
276 p. Ct; DGU; DLC; KyLoF;
M; MB; MBNEH; MBev; MBevHi;
MH; MPlyP; MShM; MWA;
MdBMSJ; MiPh; MShM; MnDu;
NRMA; Nh; NhHi; OCIWHi; TNP;
WJan.   9997

Prentice, Josiah
    Sermon delivered at North-
wood, December 30, 1821, being
the last Sabbath in the year.
Exeter, Samuel T. Moses, 1822.
19 p. Nh-Hi.   9998

Presbyterian Church in the USA
    The constitution of the Presby-
terian Church in the United
States of America; containing the
confession of faith, the cate-
cisms... Stereotyped ed. Elizabethtown, N.J., pub. by Mervin
Hale, Abraham Paul, printer,
1822. 466 p. CU; ICU; MB; NN;
NPtjerHi; NcMHi; NjN; PPPrHi;
VtMiS; WManiHFC.   9999

---- ---- Stereotype ed. Utica,
William Williams, 1822. [2],
466 p. CBPSR; CoD; CtHT-W;
CtSoP; DGU; GDC; IaDmD;
InCW; MBC; MdBS; MoSpD; N;
NBuG; NCH; NOg; NUtHi;

NcMHi; OCIWH; PPPrHi; WaT.
                                   10000
---- Minutes of the General As-
sembly of the Presbyterian
Church in the United States of
America: with an appendix,
A.D. 1822. Philadelphia, Wm.
Bradford, 1822. 64 p. DLC;
InU; M; MNe; MiD-B; MsTS;
NcD; NcMHi; WHi.   10001

---- A narrative of the state of
religion, within the bounds of
the General Assembly... [Phila-
delphia, W. Bradford, 1822] 8 p.
Ct; MB; MBC; MWA; NjR.
                                   10002
---- Rules of the General As-
sembly of the Presbyterian
Church. Philadelphia, Wm.
Bradford, 1822. 4 p. PPPrHi.
                                   10003
---- Associate Synod of North
America
    ... Minutes of the Associate
Synod... 1822... Carlisle, Pa.,
Holcomb & Tizzard, 1822. 32 p.
PPiXT.   10004

---- Grand River and Portage
Presbyteries
    Confession of faith, covenant,
and articles of practice, adopted
May 1, 1822, by the presbyteries of Grand River and Portage, for the churches under their
care. Warren (Ohio), Pr. by
Hapgood and Quinby, 1822. 8 p.
OCIWHi; OO.   10005

---- Philadelphia Synod.
    Pastoral letter, Nov. 1, 1822.
[Lancaster, 1822] 8 p. PPPrHi.
                                   10006
---- Second Presbytery of the
Carolinas & Georgia
    Pastoral letter addressed par-
ticularly to the churches, both
settled & vacant, under the care
of the Second Presbytery of the
Carolinas & Georgia. Augusta,
Ga., Pr. at the Herald office,
by Wm. J. Bunce, 1822. 15 p.

PPPrHi.   10007

Presbyterian Education Society
   Fourth report of the Board of
Directors of the Presbyterian
Education Society, presented at
the annual meeting May 5, 1822.
Newark, N. J. , Pr. by John
Tuttle & Co. , 1822. 40 p.
NSmB.   10008

A present for an apprentice.
See Barnard, Sir John.

Pressley, John Taylor, 1795-1870
   The pastor's duty. A sermon,
delivered at the opening of the
associated reformed synod, of
the Carolinas and Georgia.
Steel-Creek, 2nd April, 1821.
Augusta, Ga. , Pr. by Wm. J.
Bunce, 1822. 18 p. PPPrHi.
                           10009
The primrose. New York, Samuel Wood & sons; and Samuel S.
Wood & Co. , Baltimore, 1822.
21 p. CtNwchA; MH; TxSaWi.
                           10010
Prince, William
   Fellow citizens, in presenting
myself as a candidate to the
citizens of the first congressional district, I had naturally to
expect, that all my conduct, for
a period of twenty eight years
during which I have resided
among you would be closely examined, and thoroughly scruti-
nized by my enemies... July 20th,
1822. [Vincennes? 1822] Bdsd. In.
                           10011
Prince, William, 1766-1842
   Catalogue of fruit and ornamental trees and plants, bulbous
flower roots, greenhouse plants,
...cultivated at the Linnaean botanic garden...21st ed. New
York, 1822. 140 p. MH; NNC.
                           10012
Prince & Mills, firm
   A treatise and catalogue of
fruit and ornamental trees,
shrubs, &c. cultivated at the Old

American Nursery. Flushing
Landing, near New-York...
February, 1822. 34 p. NjR.
                           10013
Princeton Theological Seminary
   A brief account of the rise,
progress and present state of
the theological seminary of the
Presbyterian church in the United
States at Princeton; including
the consistution of the said semi-
nary; a catalogue of those who
have been members, and a list
of the present officers and stu-
dents.   Philadelphia, A. Finley,
1822. 87, 20 p. DHEW; LU;
MBC; MH; MLow; MoWgT;
NCH; NjJ; NjP; NjR; OCIWHi;
PLT; PPPrHi.   10014

---- A catalogue of those who
have been members of the Theological Seminary, of the Presbyterian Church...together with
the present officers and students.
January, 1822. Trenton, Pr. by
George Sherman, 1822. 13 p.
CSmH; CtHT-W.   10015

---- Tenth annual report of the
Board of Directors...[Philadel-
phia, Pr. by William Bradford,
1822] 8 p. MH; NjPT.   10016

Princeton University
   Catalogue of the officers and
students of Nassau Hall, December, 1822. 15 p. NjP; TNP.
                           10017
Proctor, John W.
   Address to the Danvers Auxiliary Society, for suppressing
intemperance and other vices,
and promoting temperance and
general morality, April 24,
1821.   Salem, Pr. by John D.
Cushing and Bros. , 1822. 19 p.
MB; MBC; MSaE; MiD-B.
                           10018
The prodigal daughter. Baltimore, Pr. for the purchaser,
1822. 8 p. MdBP.   10019

A Professor
    O let me in this ae night. A
Scotch song.   Arranged for the
piano forte.   New York, E.
Riley [1822?] [2] p. MWA;
NBuG.   10020

Prominent features of a northern
tour.   Written from a brief di-
ary kept in travelling from
Charleston, S. C. to, and through
Rhode-Island, Massachusetts,
New-Hampshire, Vermont, Lower
and Upper Canada, New York,
Maine... and back... Charleston,
Pr. for the author, by C. C.
Sebring, 1822. 48 p. MB; MMal;
MiU-C; NcU; Nh-Hi; PPL; ScC.
                               10021
Property Guards. Baltimore.
    Constitution and by-laws of
the Property Guards of the city
of Baltimore.   Company formed,
A.D. 1810, 2d ed.   Baltimore,
Pr. by B. Edes, 1822. 20 p.
MdBE.   10022

Prose by a poet.   See   Montgomery, James, 1771-1854.

The prospect before us.   See
Carey, Mathew.

Protestant Episcopal Church in
the USA
    The Book of Common Prayer,
and administration of the sacra-
ments, and other rites and
ceremonies of the Church...
Stereo. by E. & J. White. Albany, E. & E. Hosford, 1822.
360, 105 p. CtHT; MBD; MWA;
N; RP.   10023

---- ---- Baltimore, E.J.
Coale & Co., 1822. 360, 105
[1] p.   ICP; MB; MBD; MCET;
MWA; MdBE.   10024

---- ---- Stereotyped by D. &
G. Bruce, New-York.   Philadelphia, Pub. by S. Potter & Co.,
for the Common Prayer-book

Society of Pennsylvania, W.
Fry, printer, 1818 [i. e. 1822]
304 p. ViU.   10025

---- Domestic & Foreign Missionary Society
    The address of the board of
directors of the Domestic and
Foreign Missionary Society of
the Protestant Episcopal Church
in the United States of America,
to the members of the said
church, Feb. 16, 1822. [Phila-
delphia, 1822] 16 p. CtHT; MHi;
NNG; PHi; PPL; WHi.   10026

---- Maryland (Diocese)
    A compilation for the use of
the members of the Protestant
Episcopal Church, in Maryland,
consisting of the Constitution and
Canons of the Church in the
United States.   The Constitution
and Canons of the Church of
Maryland; with a connected
statement of all testimonials required of candidates for Holy
Orders, and the laws of the
state of Maryland respecting the
duties of Clergy and Vestries.
Baltimore, Pr. by Joseph Robinson, 1822. 69 p. DGU; GDC;
MBD; MdBE; MdBP; MdHi.
                               10027
---- ---- Journal of a convention
of the Protestant Episcopal
Church in the diocese of Maryland, held in St. John's Church,
City of Washington, June 5th,
6th, 7th, 8th, 1822. Washington, Pr. by Davis and Force,
1822. 46 p. DLC; MBD; NBuDD.
                               10028
---- New Jersey (Diocese)
    Journal of the proceedings of
the thirty-ninth annual convention of the Protestant Episcopal
Church in the state of New Jersey... Shrewsbury... New Brunswick, Wm. Myer, printer, 1822.
39 p. NN; NjR; PPL.   10029

---- New York (Diocese)
Journal of the proceedings of the thirty-sixth convention of the Protestant Episcopal Church in the state of New-York; held in St. Paul's Church, in the city of Troy, on Tuesday, October 15th, and Wednesday, October 16th, A.D. 1822. New-York, Pr. by T. & J. Swords, 1822. 72 p. MBD; MiD-MCh; NBuDD; NGH.
10030

---- North Carolina (Diocese)
Journal of the proceedings of the sixth annual convention... in the Supreme Court Room, City of Raleigh, 1822. Newbern, Pr. by Pasteur & Watson, 1822. 32, [1] p.   NN.   10031

---- Ohio (Diocese)
Journal of the proceedings of the fifth annual convention of the Protestant Episcopal church in the state of Ohio; held at Worthington, June 5, 6, 7, 1822. Delaware, Ohio, pr. by Griswold & Howard, at the office of the Delaware Patron, 1822. 34 p. MBD; NN; OCIWHi.   10032

---- Pennsylvania (Diocese)
Journal of the thirty-eighth convention of the Protestant Episcopal Church in the state of Pennsylvania, held in St. Peter's Church in the city of Philadelphia, on Tuesday, Wednesday and Thursday the 7th, 8th, and 9th of May, 1822. Philadelphia, pub. by order of the convention; J. Harding, printer, 1822. 33 p. MBD; NBuDD; PPL.   10033

---- ---- Tenth annual report of the trustees of the Society of the Protestant Episcopal Church for the Advancement of Christianity in Pennsylvania... Jan. 7, 1822. Philadelphia, Pr. by Jesper Harding, 1822. 12 p. PPL.
10034

---- South Carolina (Diocese)

Journal of the proceedings of the 34th annual convention of the Protestant Episcopal Church in the diocese of South Carolina... 1822, Charleston, Pr. by A.E. Miller, 1822. 44 p. MBD; NN.
10035

---- Vermont (Diocese)
Journal of the proceedings of the convention of the Protestant Episcopal Church in the state of Vermont. Bellows Falls, Pr. by Blake, Cutler and Co., 1822. 6 p. MBD; MWA; Vt.   10036

Protestant Episcopal Female Tract Society of Baltimore
... The conversion of Augustine. Chiefly abridged from his own confessions. [Baltimore, pub. by the Protestant Episcopal Female Tract Society of Baltimore; pr. by John D. Toy, Sept. 1822] 11, [1] p. MdHi. 10037

---- ... Eleonora, or, The young Christian. [Baltimore, pub. by the Protestant Episcopal Female Tract Society of Baltimore; printer, John D. Toy, July, 1822.] 12 p. MdHi.   10038

---- ... Gilbert Ainslie; or, The Moss-side family. [Baltimore, pub. by the Protestant Episcopal Female Tract Society of Baltimore; printer, John D. Toy, Aug. 1822] 12 p. MdHi. 10039

---- ... An important discovery, or, "Temper is everything." [Baltimore, pub. by the Protestant Episcopal Female Tract Society of Baltimore; printed by John D. Toy, Nov. 1822.] 20 p. MdHi.   10040

---- ... The little missionary. [Baltimore, pub. by the Protestant Episcopal Female Tract Society of Baltimore; pr. by John D. Toy, Sept. 1822.] 12 p. MdHi.   10041

---- ... The twins. [Baltimore,
Pub. by the Protestant Episco-
pal Female Tract Society of
Baltimore; Pr. by John D. Toy,
Dec. 1822] 4 p. MdHi.   10042

Protestant Episcopal Theological
Seminary in Virginia.
    Circular of the board of man-
agers of the Theological School
of the Diocese of Virginia...
Winchester, Va., Pr. by Samuel
Davis, 1822. 24 p. DLC; NN;
PPL.   10043

Protestant Episcopal Theological
Seminary of Maryland
    Address of the Board of Trus-
tees of the Protestant Episcopal
Theological Seminary of Maryland, to the members of the
church in this diocese.   Georgetown, D. C., James C. Dunn,
printer, 1822. 25 p. A-Ar;
CSmH; DLC; DWP; MdBD;
MdHi; PPL.   10044

Proudfit, Alexander Moncrief,
1770-1843
    The duties of the watchman
upon the walls of Zion; a sermon, preached before the synod,
at Galway, February 13, 1822.
Salem, N. Y., Pr. by H. Dodd
and co., 1822. 38 p. CSmH;
DLC; ICP; MB; MBC; MH-AH;
MWA; N; NN; PPPrHi; PPiXT.
                          10045
---- The universal extension of
Messiah's kingdom.   A sermon,
delivered in the North church,
New-Haven, Conn., Sept. 12,
1822, before the American Board
of Commissioners for Foreign
Missions, at their annual meet-
ing.   Boston, Crocker & Brews-
ter, 1822. 27 p. CBPSR; Ct;
CtHC; KWiU; MA; MBC; MH-
AH; MHi; MNF; MeBat; MeHi;
MiD-B; NCH; NNMr; NcMHi;
OO; PPL; PPPrHi; RBr; RPB;
ViRUT.   10046

Providence.   Town Council.
    Licence to keep and sell gun
powder in the town of Providence... [Providence, 1822]
Bdsd. RPJCB.   10047

---- Young Men's Baptist Education Society
    ... Constitution... [Providence,
1822] Bdsd. RPB.   10048

The provost.   See Galt, John.

Psallonian Society, Providence.
    Select oratorio to be per-
formed by the Psallonian Society,
October 30th, 1822, at the Second Baptist Meeting-House.
[Providence] Brown and Danforth,
printer [1822] 8 p. RPB.10049

Public defaulters brought to light.
See   Giles, William Branch.

Public School Society of New
York
    A list of the members, sub-
scribers and trustees, of the
Free-School Society of New
York.   New York, Pr. by James
and John Harper, 1822. 12 p.
DLC.   10050

Puglia, James Philip
    El desengaño del hombre,
compuesto por Santiago Felipe
Puglia, maestro de la lengua
Castellana en esta metropoli...
Filadelfia, H. C. Carey e I. Lea
... Año, 1822. 257 p. TxSaO.
                          10051
---- Forgery defeated; or, A
new plan for invalidating and de-
tecting all attempts of the kind
... Philadelphia, J. F. Hurtel,
1822.   30 p. PPAmP; PHi; WHi.
                          10052
Puglia, Santiago Felipe.   See
Puglia, James Philip.

The pulpit made free; and an
ability or license to preach made
common to all Christians... by a

layman... New York, R. N. Henry,
1822. viii, 112 p. MB; NGH;
NNG; PPL; PSC-Hi.   10053

[Pyron du Martre, Antoine]
Syllabaire françois; or, A
French spelling book... By Mr.
Porney... Philadelphia, Collins
& Croft, 1822. 151 p. IAlS;
IaDuCM; KyU; PU-Penn; VtU.
10054

Q

Questions adapted to Blair's
Rhetoric abridged. See Blake,
John Lauris.

Questions adapted to Murray's
observations on the principles of
good reading. Portsmouth,
N.H., Pr. by T.H. Miller,
1822. 8 p. Nh-Hi.   10055

Questions and answers upon the
truths of the Christian religion;
being the second part of the Geneva Catechism. Pr. for the
trustees of the Publishing Fund,
by Hilliard and Metcalf. Sold
by Cummings & Hilliard, Boston
and other agents of the Publishing Fund, December, 1822. 67 p.
MA; MBAt; MBAU; MH; MWA;
PPPrHi.   10056

Questions on natural philosophy
for the use of the scholars of
the Salem Street Academy, in
Boston and other schools.
Adapted to "Conversations on nat-
ural philosophy." Boston, Jos.
W. Ingraham, 1822. 28 p.
CSmH; DLC; MH; MLow;
MMhHi; NNC; PHi.   10057

Quincy, Josiah, 1772-1864
Remarks, on some of the provisions of the laws of Massachusetts, affecting poverty, vice,
and crime... Cambridge, Pr. at
the University Press, by Hilliard
& Metcalf, 1822. 28 p. CBPac;

Ct; CtHC; CtHT-W; DLC; ICJ;
ICN; ICT; ICU; IU; LNH; M;
MB; MBAt; MBC; MDeeP; MH;
MHi; MWA; MWCL; MiD-B;
MnU; MoSHi; NNC; NNUT;
NRAB; PHi; PPL; RPB; Vi;
WHi.   10058

R

[Racine, Jean Baptiste] 1639-
1699
... The distrest mother, a
tragedy... Boston, Wells & Lilly,
New York, A. T. Goodrich & co.,
1822. 72 p. CtHT-W; DLC; MH;
MMal; MeB; PPL; PU; TxU.
10059

Radcliffe, Richard, comp.
The president's tour, a col-
lection of addresses made to
James Munroe, Esq. President
of the United States, on his tour
through the Northern and Middle
States, A.D. 1817, accompanied
with answers from the President
... New Ipswich, N.H., Pr. by
Salmon Wilder, 1822. 76 p.
DLC; MBNEH; Nh-Hi; Vi.
10060

The rainbow; or, Lights and
shadows of fashionable life. Illustrated by 'Three single gentlemen rolled into one." Baltimore, Pub. by E.J. Coale &
Co.; Wm. Wooddy, printer, 1822
166 p. MdBJ; MdBP; MdHi;
PU.   10061

Ramsbotham, John
Practical observations on
midwifery... Philadelphia, H.C.
Carey and I. Lea, 1822. 379 p.
CSt-L; ICJ; ICU-R; Ia; InU-M;
LNoP; MBM; MNBedf; MNF;
MdBJ-W; MdBM; MiDW-M;
NBMS; NBuU-M; NClsM;
NNMSCQ; NNNAM; Nh; OC;
OClM; PPC; ScCMu.
10062

Randel, John, Jun.
Description of a direct route
for the Erie Canal at its Eastern

termination... Albany, Pr. by G.
J. Loomis & Co., 1822. 72 p.
CSmH; MB; MH-BA; MWo;
MeU; N; NBu; NN; NNE; PPL;
WHi. 10063

Randell, Joshua
The doctrine of election illustrated. Windsor, Pr. by Simeon Ide, May, 1822. 25 p. DLC;
MeLB. 10064

Ravenscroft, Edward, fl. 1671-
1697
The anatomist; or, The sham
doctor. A farce. In two acts.
Philadelphia, T. H. Palmer,
1822. 32 p. DLC; MH. 10065

Read & think. Major Dewey has
come forward a second time as
will be seen by what follows,
and has completely controverted
the injurious charges which his
political enemies have circulated
... Bdsd. In. 10066

The reasons of the appeal court
of equity for confirming the de-
cree of the circuit court, in the
case of Isaac Carr & others, vs.
James Green, pub. with a member of Charleston bar. Charleston, Pr. and sold by Archibald
E. Miller, 1822. 26 p. MH-L;
MiD-B. 10067

Recreations of George Taletell.
See Holmes, Isaac Edward.

Reed, Ephraim
Musical monitor, or, New-
York collection of devotional
church music; united with The
elementary class-book, being an
introduction to the science of music...2d rev. ed. Ithaca, Pr.
by A. P. Searing & Co., 1822.
iv, 215, [1] p. MWA; NIC.
10068
Reekers, John Joseph
Decimal tables of interest,
reduced to the denary scale of

notation. A method concise,
easy and mathematically accur-
ate. Stereotype ed. Baltimore,
Pr. for the author by William
Woody, 1822. 19 p. DLC;
MdBP. 10069

Reeve, William, 1757-1815
Giles Scroggins' ghost. With
an introduction and variations
for the piano forte. New York,
Rd. Meetz [1822] 15 p. MWA.
10070
---- My Marie's ee's o' the
deep, deep blue! A Scottish
ballad. Baltimore, John Cole
[1822?] 3 p. DLC; MH; MWA;
MdHi; NN. 10071

Reflections occasioned by a public execution at Boston, April
25, 1822. 12 p. MWA; MiD-B.
10072
Reflections, occasioned by the
late disturbances in Charleston.
See Pinckney, Thomas.

Reflections upon the perils and
difficulties of the winter navigation of the Delaware. See
Jones, William.

Reformed Church in America
The acts and proceedings of
the General synod of the Re-
formed Dutch Church in North
America, at New York, June,
1822. New-York, Pr. by Geo.
Forman, 1822. 69 p. IaPeC;
MiD-B; NcMHi; NjR. 10073

---- Psalms & hymns with the
catechism, confession of faith &
liturgy of the Reformed Dutch
Church in North America. New
York, Daniel D. Smith, 1822.
523 p. InRch. 10074

Reformed Church in the United
States
Gott gewidmete Dank-Emp-
findungen bey der Ecksteintegung
der zu erbauden Reformirten

Salems Kirche, nahe bey Hägerstaun, auf den 27sten, May, 1822.
Hagerstaun, Gruber & May,
1822. 8 p. PP. 10075

---- Zion's Classis
Verlandlungen der Zions-
Classis. 1822. Hanover, Pa.,
gedruckt bey Dan. Phil. Lanbe.
1822. DLC. 10076

A refutation of the calumnies
circulated against the southern
and western states. See Holland, Edwin Clifford.

Reid, Samuel Chester
The New-York telegraph and
signal book. Signals established
between the telegraph on Staten-
Island, and the shipping belonging to the port of New-York.
New-York, Pr. for the author,
1822. 71+ p. MH. 10077

Reid, Thomas
The works of Thomas Reid...
with an account of his life and
writings, by Dugald Stewart...
New York, E. Duyckinck, Col-
lins and Hannay and R. and W.
A. Bartow; J. & J. Harper,
printers, 1822. 3 v. CtHT;
CtNwchA; CtW; GEU; GU; ICU;
IEG; IJ; IJI; IU; IaMpI; InGrD;
KyBgW; KyDC; KyLoP; MCM;
MH; MLaw; MWH; MdBJ; MdBL;
MdW; MeLewB; MoS; MoSpD;
NGeno; NNC; NNG; NNUT;
NSyU; NWM; NbLW; NcMHi; Nj;
OBerB; OO; OWoC; PPP; PPT;
PU; PPiD; PPiW; ScOrC;
TJaL; TMeSC; TNDL; TNP;
Vi; ViRU; VtWinds. 10078

Rejoinder to the reply of Rev.
Mr. Harold. See Carey,
Mathew.

Relfe, John, 1763-1837
Mary's dream, or Sandy's
ghost. A favorite song. Arranged for the piano forte. New

York, E. Riley [1822?] [2] p.
DLC; NN; RPB. 10079

Religion exemplified, in the life
of poor Sarah [Rogers, an Indi-
an] Taken from the Boston Recorder. [colophon:] [Boston]
Pr. and sold by Lincoln & Edmands [1822?] 12 p. MB.
10080

Remarks addressed to the con-
sciencious[!] of all denominations, on the subject of praying
for one another. Boston, John
Cotton, Jr., printer, 1822. 12 p.
CBPac; ICMe; MBC; MH; MWA.
10081

Remarks on religious association. See Laicus, pseud.

Remarks on the address of the
Honourable John Quincy Adams,
delivered at Washington, July 4,
1821. New-York, Pr. by G. L.
Birch, 1822. 30 p. DLC; ICN;
LNH; MWA; MWiW; MdBJ;
NNC; ViL. 10082

Remarks on the censures of the
government of the United States.
See Gore, Christopher.

Remarks on the doctrine of the
influence of the Holy Spirit. To
which are added observations on
the efficacy and universality of
the Grace of God. New-York,
Pr. by Samuel Wood & Sons,
1822. 15 p. NNFL. 10083

Remarks on the project of establishing a line of packets between Boston and Liverpool.
[1822] 20 p. (Date 1822 supplied
by MWA. Latest date in text is
1821.) MWA; PPL. 10084

Remarks upon the art of teaching and learning; designed for
those who give, and those who
receive instruction... By a gentleman, residing at the city of
Washington, D.C. Boston, Pr.

by Thomas Badger, jr., 1822.
31 p. M; MH; MWA; NNG;
OMC; RPB.   10085

Remarks upon the Report of the
managers of the Unitarian Society for the distribution of books,
with an appendix, containing
some strictures upon a reply
lately published in the Boston
Christian Register, to a pamphlet
written by the Rev. Mr. Hawley
of Washington. By a Trinitarian.
Baltimore, J. Robinson, 1822.
8 p. MdBD.   10086

Remarks upon the writings of
Swedenborg; with extracts from
the works of different authors.
Bath (Me.) pub. for the com-
piler. 1822. 38 p. CSmH;
MCNC; MWA; PPL.   10087

Renwick, James
    Outlines of natural philosophy:
being the heads of a course of
lectures, delivered in Columbia
College. New York, C. S. Van
Winkle, printer, 1822-23. 2 vols.
CtHT-W; MB; MH; NIC; NNC;
NWM; RNR; TNP.   10088

Report of a cause tried in the
District Court of Philadelphia,
April 24, 1822, John Keen vs.
Philip Rice, involving the right
of New-Jersey to oyster-beds in
the Maurice River Cove. Bridgeton, W. N. J., Pr. by J. Clarke
and Co., 1822. 28 p. NjR.10089

Report of proceedings in the Dis-
trict Court of the United States
for the southern district of New-
York, on a suit brought by the
United States against Daniel D.
Tompkins June 3, 1822. New
York, Pr. by C. S. Van Winkle,
1822. 54 p. KHi; MH-L; Mi-L;
N; N-L; NNC; NbU.   10090

Report of the case of Joshua
Stow vs. Sherman Converse, for

a libel; containing a history of
two trials before the superior
court and some account of the
proceedings before the Supreme
court of errors. New Haven,
Pr. by S. Converse, 1822. 183
(i. e. 179) p. CtHi; Ct; CtM;
CtY; DLC; Ia; MB; MBAt; MH;
MWA; MoU; NHi; NIC-L; NN;
NNC-L; NNUT; NPV; OCIWHi;
PP; PPL.   10091

A report of the evidence in the
case, John Atkins, appellant, vs.
Calvin Sanger, et al. executors,
relative to the will of the late
Mrs. Badger, of Natick; which
was disallowed before the Supreme court of probate, at the
October term, 1822. Dedham,
Pr. by H. & W. H. Mann [1822?]
84 p. DLC; KWiU; MB; MBAt;
MBNEH.   10092

Report on the penitentiary system in the United States... New-
York, Pr. by Mahlon Day, 1822.
101, 107 p. MWA.   10093

A resident of Frederick. See
H., J.

The retrospect. See Marks,
Richard.

Revere, John, 1787-1847
    An inquiry into the origin and
effects of sulphurous fumiga-
tions, in the cure of rheumatism,
gout, diseases of the skin, palsy,
etc. Baltimore, pub. by E. J.
Coale & Co., John D. Toy,
printer, 1822. [5], 63, [6] p.
DGU; DLC; MdBM; MdBP;
MWA; NNNAM.   10094

Review of the "Life of Michael
Martin, who was executed for
highway robbery, Dec. 20, 1821,
as given by himself." See
Colman, Henry.

A review of the whole truth;

containing an examination of the causes which led to the rise of the new Methodist Society in New York... New York, J. Robinson, pr. , 1822. 35 p. PPL.
    10095

Review of three pamphlets. See Carey, Mathew.

Reynolds, Frederic, 1764-1841
    The exile; a comedy, in three acts. Philadelphia, T. H. Palmer, 1822. 59 p. MH; NN; NIC; PU.
    10096

---- The will. A comedy, in five acts. Philadelphia, T. H. Palmer, 1822. 71 p. MB; MWA; MH; NN; PPL.   10097

Rhode Island (State)
    At the General Assembly of the state of Rhode Island and Providence Plantations, begun and holden [by adjournment] at Providence, within and for said state, on the second Monday of January, in the year of our Lord, one thousand eight hundred and twenty-two... Providence, Jones and Wheeler, state printers, 1822. 46 p. C; DLC; Ia; In-Sc; MdBB; Mi; RNCH.   10098

---- At the General Assembly of the state of Rhode Island and Providence Plantations, begun and holden at Newport, within and for said state, on the first Wednesday of May, in the year of our Lord, one thousand eight hundred and twenty-two... Providence, Jones and Wheeler, state printers, 1822. 53 p. C; DLC; Ia; In-SC; MdBB; Mi; R; RNCH.
    10099

---- At the General Assembly of the state of Rhode Island and Providence Plantations, begun and holden [by adjournment] at Newport, within and for said state, on the second Monday of June, in the year of our Lord, one thousand eight hundred and

twenty-two...[Providence, 1822] 57 p. C; DLC; Ia; In-SC; MdBB; Mi; R; RNCH.   10100

---- At the General Assembly of the state of Rhode Island and Providence Plantations, begun and holden at Providence, within and for said state, on the last Monday of October, in the year of our Lord, one thousand eight hundred and twenty-two... Providence, Jones and Wheeler, state printers, 1822. 57 p. C; DLC; Ia; In-SC; MdBB; Mi; R; RNCH.   10101

---- The public laws of the state of Rhode Island and Providence Plantations, as revised by a committee, and finally enacted by the Honorable General Assembly at their session in January, 1822. Providence, Miller and Hutchens [1822] 524, xlvi p. C; CSmH; CSt; DLC; G; IU; IaU; L; MB; MSaEC; MdBB; Mi; MnHi; MnU; Nb; NN; Nv; OCLaw; OrSc; PP; PPL; R; RJa; RNCH; RNR; RP; RPL; RPaw; RWoH; WaU; Wy. 10102

---- Public laws of the state of Rhode Island and Providence Plantations, passed at and since the session of the General Assembly in January, A.D. , 1822. Providence, Jones and Wheeler, state printers, 1822. 525-599, 2 p. DLC; In-Sc; MB; MdBB; Ms; RNCH; RPA.   10103

Rhode-Island almanack for 1823. By Isaac Bickerstaff. Providence, Brown and Danforth [1822] 14 ll. CLU; DLC; InU; MB; MH; MWA; MnU; N; NBuG; NHi; NjMoW; NjR; OClWHi; PHi; PPL; RP; RPA; RPB; RHi; RU; WHi.   10104

Rhode Island Historical Society
    The charter, constitution and

circular of the Rhode-Island His-
torical Society.   Incorporated
June, A.D. 1822.   Providence,
Pr. by Jones & Wheeler [1822]
8 p.   DLC; MHi; NhD; RHi;
RNHi; RPA; RPB.   10105

Rhode-Island register and United
States calendar for 1823. Providence, Brown and Danforth
[1822] 48 ll. In; MH; MWA; N;
RHi; RP; RPB; WHi.   10106

Rhode Island Republican
    Carrier's New Year's address
of the Rhode Island Republican.
Newport, January 1, 1822. Bdsd.
RNHi.   10107

Richmond alarm.   Andover,
Flagg & Gould, printers, 1822.
12 p. MeB.   10108

[Richmond, Legh] 1772-1827
    The Dairyman's daughter: ex-
tracted from an interesting nar-
rative, communicated by a clergy-
man of the Church of England.
No. XXII.   Lexington, Ky.,
Thomas T. Skillman, 1822. 24 p.
(Private Library of John Wilson
Townsend, Lexington, Ky.)
                            10109
---- Memoir of Miss Hannah
Sinclair...To which is added her
letter on the principles of the
Christian faith.   Baltimore, Cush-
ing & Jewett, 1822. DLC; NN.
                            10110
[----] ...The negro servant.
Communicated by a clergyman of
the Church of England.   Phila-
delphia, Sunday and adult school
union [1822?] 20 p. DLC. 10111

Ridgely, G.W.
    An oration delivered in the
chapel of Transylvania University, at Lexington, Kentucky, on
the fourth day of July, 1822.
Lexington, Pr. by Wm. Gibbes
Hunt, 1822. 14 p. ICU; KyU;
N; PPAmP.   10112

Riley, Edward, 1769-1829
    Catalogue of music publised
[sic] & sold by E. Riley, New
York [1822] 4 p. NN.   10113

Riley, Edward C., d 1871?
    Cherry-cheek'd Patty.   Ar-
ranged for the piano forte. New
York, E. Riley [1822] 3 p. DLC;
MH; N; NN.   10114

Ritchie, William
    Two sermons, delivered be-
for the First Church and Society
in Needham, December 16, 1821.
Dedham, Pr. by H. & W.H.
Mann, 1822. 22 p. CtSoP; MBC;
MHi; MiD-B; N; NNUT; RPB;
WHi.   10115

Robbins, Archibald
    A journal, comprising an ac-
count of the loss of the brig
Commerce, of Hartford (Conn.)
James Riley, master, upon the
Western coast of Africa, August
28th, 1815...15th ed. Hartford,
Silas Andrus; stereotyped by
Starr, New York, 1822. 275 p.
CtEhad; NcWfC.   10116

Robbins, Asher, 1757-1845
    Address to the Rhode Island
Society for the Encouragement of
Domestic Industry, delivered at
Pawtuxet, Oct. 16, 1822. Provi-
dence, Miller and Hutchens,
1822. 54 p. DLC; MH-BA;
MiD-B; MWA; NN; PPL; RHi;
RNHi; RP; RPB.   10117

Robbins, Thomas
    An address delivered before
a number of military companies
assembled at Hartford, to celebrate our national independence,
July 4, 1822. Hartford, Goodsell and Wells, printers, 1822.
16 p. CtHi; CtSoP; MH-AH;
MWA; NUtHi.   10118

[Robertson, Joseph Clinton]-
1788-1852

The Percy anecdotes, original and select, by Sholto and Reuben Percy, brothers of the Benedictine monastery, Mont Benger. Eloquence.   New-York, pub. by Richard Scott, Myers & Smith, printers, 1822. 143 p. MSa.
10119
[----] ---- Humanity, pub. by Richard Scott, West-Chester County.   New York, S. Marks, printer, 1822. 144 p. RBr; ViAl.   10120

Robertson, William, 1721-1793
An historical disquisition concerning the knowledge which the ancients had of India... Albany, Pr. and pub. by E. and E. Hosford, 1822. 330, xiii p. GEU; GMWa; InCW; MB; MBBC; MC; MDeeP; MWA; MdW; MeAu; N; NBCP; NHi; NN; NjN; OO; PWc; RP; RPB; TNP; ViL; Wv.
10121
---- The history of America... From the latest London ed; in which is included, the posthumous volume, containing the history of Virginia, to the year 1688; and of New-England, to the year 1652... Albany, E. & E. Hosford, 1822. 2 v. ArLSJ; CtHC; DLC; GEU; GMWa; ICU; IHi; IaGG; IaSlB; InCW; LNH; MDi; MH; MHi; MNS; MNan; MWA; MWo; MdW; Me; MeAu; N; NBuG; NCaS; NOsw; NjN; OSW; PWc; RHi; RP; RPB; ScDuE; TNP; TxDaM; ViL; ViRVal; WMV.   10122

---- ---- 2d Amer. from 10th London ed; in which was included the posthumous volume, containing the history of Virginia to the year 1688, and of New England to the year 1652, to which is added the declaration of American independence with a correct facsimile of the signatures.   Philadelphia, Robert Desilver, 253 Market street, 1822.

2 v. CtW; IaB; KyOw; LNL; MB; MNe; MdBP; NcHil; P; PV; RKi; RPB; RPJCB.   10123

---- The history of Scotland, during the reigns of Queen Mary and King James VI.   Albany, E. and E. Hosford, 1822. 2 v. CtHC; GEU; GMWa; KyLoS; MB; MC; MH; MPiB; MWA; MdW; MeAu; MeHi; NCaS; NN; NR; NjN; O; OO; PPL; ScDuE; TMeSC; TNP.   10124

---- The history of the reign of the Emperor Charles V, with a view of the progress of society in Europe, from the subversion of the Roman Empire to the beginning of the sixteenth century. Albany, E. and E. Hosford, 1822. 3 vols. CtHT; GAuY; GMWa; ICP; InLW; MAbD; MB; MH; MWA; MdW; MsG; NCaS; NGcA; NPtw; NcA; NcGu; PHC; PRosC; PSC; PWc; RPB; ScP; TNP; ViAl; ViL; ViU; VtMiM; Wv.   10125

Robinson, Ralph
The discouragements and encouragements of the gospel ministry: a sermon, preached at Hanover, in Paris, N. Y., May 19, 1822.   Utica, Pr. by T. Walker, 1822. 20 p. CSmH; MBC; PPPrHi.   10126

Robinson, Robert C.
An address, delivered at Cummington, before Orion Lodge, June 25, A. L. 5822... Northampton [Mass.] Sylvester Judd, Jr., 1822. 16 p. MB.   10127

[Rocafuerte, Vicente] 1783-1847
Bosquejo ligerísimo de la revolución de Méjico, desde el grito de Iguala hasta la proclamación imperial de Iturbide, por un verdadero americano... Philadelphia, Teracrouef y Naroajeb, 1822. 300 p. CL;

C-S; CU-B; CtY; DLC; MH;
NIC; PPAmP; PPL.   10128

---- Memoria político-instruc-
tiva, enviada desde Filadelfia en
agosto de 1821 a los gefes in-
dependientes del Anáhuac llamado
por los Españoles Nueva España.
Impresa en Filadelfia, 1822.
150 p. Colon. Impresos en español publicados en Filadelfia
1800-1835, item 61.   10129

Roche, Manning B.
     A sermon on the character and
mission of the son of man...
Philadelphia, Pr. by Jacob Frick
& Co., 1822. 16 p. DLC; MB;
PBa.   10130

Roche, Regina Maria (Dalton)
     The children of the abbey. A
tale. Hartford, Pr. by Goodsell and Wells, 1822. 2 v. CtHi;
IObB; MBAt; MBC; MPlyA;
NRU; TxBrdD; WaU.   10131

Rogers, Daniel
     The New York City Hall re-
corder for the year 1821. Containing reports of the most interesting trials and decisions
which have arisen in the various
courts of judicature...New York,
Pr. by E.B. Clayton, 1822. iv,
212 p. CLSU; NNU; PScrLL.
                            10132
Rogers, Patrick Kerr, 1776-
1828
     An introduction to the mathe-
matical principles of natural
philosophy, adapted to the use of
beginners; and arranged more
particularly for the convenience
of the junior students of William
and Mary College, Virginia.
Richmond, Shepherd & Pollard,
printers, 1822. 144 p. MCM;
MiU; PPF; RPB; ViW.   10133

Romeyn, John Brodhead, 1777-
1825
     The duty and reward of hon-

ouring God. A sermon, delivered in the Presbyterian
Church, Cedar-Street, New York,
on the 22d of December, 1821,
the anniversary of the landing of
the Pilgrims of New England.
New York, F. & R. Lockwood,
1822. 30 p. DLC; MB; MBC;
MH-AH; MWA; MeLewB; NNC;
NNG; NNUT; PHi; PPPrHi;
WHi.   10134

Ronaldson, James
     Specimen of printing type
from the letter foundry of James
Ronaldson. Philadelphia, 1822.
MB; NN; NNC; NNC-Atf; PHi;
PPAmP; PPF; PPL.
                            10135
Rood, Pamela A.
     An account of the last sick-
ness and death of Mr. George
W. Thompson, who departed this
life Sept. 11, 1821. Enfield,
N.H., Pr. by Ebenezer Chase,
1822. 12 p. Nh.   10136

Rosa, a melo-drama. See
Hyer, William G.

Roslin Castle. New York, E.
Riley [1822?] 1 l. DLC; NHi.
                            10137
Ross, James, 1744-1827
     Onomasia: or, Philadelphia
vocabulary, with the signs of
quantity; comprising, sententiae
pueriles, Catonis disticha, col-
lectiones poeticae selectae, materia medica, a sketch of mythology...Philadelphia, Pr. for
the author, by Lydia R. Bailey,
1822. 110 p. DLC; NjR; PHi;
PPL; PU; ViU.   10138

[----] Victoria neo-aureliana...
Philadelphia, L.R. Bailey, 1822.
12 p. NN; PPL.   10139

---- ---- Editionem hanc se-
cundam editit Ja. Boss...Phila-
delphia, Lydia R. Bailey, 1822.
12 p. NN; PPL.   10140

Rossini, Gioacchino Antonio,
1792-1868
The barber of Seville: a
comic opera, in three acts.
Philadelphia, H. C. Carey and I.
Lea, 1822. 74 p. MB; MH; PU.
                                10141
---- The celebrated cavatina Di
tanti palpiti. Baltimore, John
Cole [1822] 3 p. MdHi; MWA;
NN; RPB.   10142

---- The celebrated piano forte
song. Philadelphia, G. E. Blake
[1822?] 4 p. MH; RPB.   10143

---- Di tanti palpiti. Arranged
with variations for the piano
forte by William Martin. New
York, A. & W. Geib [ca 1822]
9 p. DLC; NN.   10144

---- ---- With variations for the
piano forte... Philadelphia, G.
Willig [1822] 13, 3 p. MWA; NN;
PP; PP-K; PPL; RPB.   10145

The round table... Albany, January, 1822. 16 p. (Caption title of
vol. 1, no. 1 at the end of p.
16 is, Albany, Pr. by E. and
E. Hosford. Probably only this
no. issued.) MB; NN.   10146

Rousseau, Jean-Jacques, 1712-
1778
Absence. The words adapted
to the favorite air of Rousseau's
dream. New York, E. Riley,
[1822] 1 l. MWA.   10147

---- El contrato social; o, Prin-
cipios del derecho politico.
Nueva ed. , rev. y corr. Fila-
delfia, Impr. de H. C. Carey &
I. Lea, 1822. 180 p. CU-B; MB;
PPL.   10148

Rowe, Nicholas
   ... Jane Shore. A tragedy...
Boston, Wells and Lilly; New
York, A. T. Goodrich and co. ,
1822. 76 p. DLC; PPL.   10149

Rowland, Thomas
An oration, by Thomas Rowland, esq. delivered in the Protestant Church of Detroit, July
4th, 1822. Detroit, Pr. by
Sheldon and Reed [1822?] 15 p.
MiD-B.   10150

Rowson, Susanna (Haswell) 1762-
1824
Biblical dialogues between a
father and his family comprising
sacred history. Boston, Rich-
ardson and Lord, 1822. 2 v.
CoFcS; DLC; ICU; MB; MBAt;
MBC; MH; MMal; MNt; MW;
MWA; MoSpD; NCaS; OMC; PU;
RP; RPB; WBeloC.   10151

---- Exercises in history, chron-
ology, and biography. Boston,
Richardson & Lord, 1822. 170 p.
CtHT-W; MH.   10152

Roxbury, Mass. Baptist Meeting House
Order of exercises at Roxbury, April 10, 1822. [Boston?
1822?] Bdsd. WHi.   10153

---- First Baptist Church of
Christ
A declaration of the articles
of faith of the First Baptist
Church of Christ in Roxbury.
Boston, Pr. by Lincoln & Ed-
mands, 1822. 6 p. MWA.
                                10154
---- First Church
A concert, at the Rev. Dr.
Porter's meeting-house, in Rox-
bury... March 31st. Boston, T.
Badger, Jr. , 1822. 7 p. MB.
                                10155
---- First Universalist Church
The declaration of faith, com-
pact and platform, adopted by the
First Universalist Church of
Christ in Roxbury. Boston, Pr.
by Henry Bowen, 1822. 4 p. MB.
Sabin 73643.   10156

Ruddiman, Thomas, 1674-1757

Rudiments of the Latin tongue ... ed. 27 rev. Philadelphia, Abraham Small, 1822. 156 p. CtHT-W; MH; OTifH; PPL; ScNC.   10157

Ruffner, Henry, 1789-1861
Strictures on a book entitled, "An apology for the book of Psalms, by Gilbert M'Master." Lexington, Va., Pr. by Valentine M. Mason, 1822. 56 p. DLC.   10158

Rufus Plummer, Eleazer Pierce [4 columns of 99, 104, 104, 103 names in alphabetical order, being a list of those qualified to vote in the town affairs of Portland, Maine, March 23, 1822] Portland, Me. Bdsd. MeHi.
10159
The ruins of Paestum. See Pickering, Henry.

Rules and regulations for the sword exercise of the cavalry. See M., J. G. L.

[Rundell, Mrs. Maria Eliza (Ketelby),] 1745-1828
American domestic cookery, formed on principles of economy; for the use of private families ...Baltimore, Pub. by Fielding Lucas, Jun.; Matchett, printer, 1822. 347 p. MdHi.   10160

[Russell, William]
The history of modern Europe: with an account of the decline & fall of the Roman Empire; and a view of the progress of society, from the rise of the modern kingdoms to the Peace of Paris, in 1763. A new ed. with A continuation, extending to the pacification of Paris in 1815... Philadelphia, Abraham Small, 1822. 6 v. CPalt; CtHT; FPe; GU; IalS; ICP; ICU; IaPeC; LNB; LNT; MA; MB; MH; MdAN; MdW; Me; MoS; MsJMC; NIC;

NN; NNC; NPV; NcWsS; NjP; OAU; ODaB; OUr; PPA; PU; RBr; ScNC; TxShA; Vi; ViRU; VtU; WCr.   10161

[----] ---- A new ed., with a continuation... In six volumes. Vol. VI. Keene, N.H., John Prentiss, 1822. MB.   10162

Ryan, James
A key to the second New York edition of Bonnycastle's algebra; and also adapted to the former American and latest London editions of that work. New York, George Long; J. Seymour, printer, 1822. 261 p. CtHT-W; DLC; GU-M; InThR; MH; MeB; PHi; PMA; NjR.   10163

S

[S., R.]
Jachin y Boaz; ó Una llave autentica para la puerta de Framasonería ... Traducida al español por Eduardo Barry. Filadelfia, H. C. Carey y I. Lea, 1822. 83 p. MB; NNFM; PHi.
10164
Sabine, James
Solemn feasts, solemn vows. A sermon preached to Essex street Church and Society, in Boylston Hall, Boston, on Thanksgiving day, December 5, 1822... Boston, George Clark, 1822. 16 p. MB; MBAt; MH; MiD-B; RPB; TxHuT.   10165

Sackett, John H.
An enquiry into the origin and tendency of political institutions ... Pronounced before the Tammany Society...13th May, 1822. New York, Pr. by Van Pelt and Spear, 1822. 19 p. NB; NN; PPL.   10166

Saint Peter's School, Baltimore.
Address of the Trustees of St. Peter's School to the congre-

gation of St. Peter's Church and
to the public. [1822] 6 p. MdHi.
                              10167
Saint-Pierre, Jacques Henri
Bernardin de, 1737-1814
   Paul and Virginia, translated
from the French of Bernardin
Saint-Pierre, by Helen Maria
Williams. New York, H.I. Me-
garey & W.B. Gilley; W. Grat-
tan, printer, 1822. (C. P. Wil-
liams collections Greenville,
Miss.)   10168

Salem, Massachusetts
   Bill of mortality for the town
of Salem, 1821. Salem, Janu-
ary 1, 1822. Bdsd. MSaE.
                              10169
---- Expenses of the town of
Salem from March 1821-March,
1822...Jona P. Saunders, Town
Clerk. Bdsd. MSaE.   10170

---- Order of the Board of
Health defining the duties of the
superintendent and regulating the
fees for the burial of the dead.
Salem, 1822. Bdsd. MSaE.
                              10171
---- Rules, orders, and by-
laws, made by the freeholders
and inhabitants of the town of
Salem. Salem, Pr. by W. & S.
B. Ives, 1822. 20 p. MB;
MSaE; PPL.   10172

---- Active Fire Club
   The constitution of the Active
Fire-Club, Associated in Salem
on the third Thursday in February, 1806. Revised May 15,
1822. Salem, Pr. by Warwick
Palfray, Jr. 1822. 15 p. MSaE.
                              10173
---- List of members. Salem,
1822. Bdsd. MSaE.   10174

Salem Gazette
   Carrier's New Year Address.
1822. Bdsd. MSaE.   10175

Salem Grammar School

   Order of exercises at the an-
nual exhibition of the Salem
Grammar School, Thursday, Ap-
ril 25, 1822. Bdsd. MSaE.
                              10176
Salem. First Baptist Church
   A summary declaration of the
faith and practice of the Baptist
Church of Christ in Salem...
3d ed. Salem, Warwick Palfray,
Jr., printer, 1822. 16 p. MB;
MSaE.   10177

---- Hamilton Fire Club
   Names and places of residence
of members. 1822. Bdsd.
MSaE.   10178

---- Navigation School
   Charts, pilots, nautical books,
instruments and stationery.
School room on Essex Street,
opposite Newbury St. Samuel
Lambert. 182[2] Bdsd. MSaE.
                              10179
Sampson, Ezra
   Beauties of the Bible, being
a selection from the Old and
New Testaments... Lansingburgh,
pub. by Tracy & Bliss, stereo-
typed by D. & G. Bruce, New
York, 1822. 282 p. MBrZ;
MNBedf; N; NCH; NhM; ViRUT;
VtMiS.   10180

Sandham, Miss
   The school-fellows; a moral
tale. Boston, Pr. by J. H. A.
Frost, pub. by Leonard C.
Bowles, 1822. 267 p. IObB;
MPlyA.   10181

Sargent, John
   Memoir of Rev. Henry Mar-
tyn, B.D., late fellow of St.
John's college, Cambridge, and
chaplain to the Honorable East
India Company. 4th Amer. ed.
Hartford, G. Goodwin & sons,
printers, 1822. 375 p. CtHi;
GAU; ICU; KyLx; MBev-F;
MWar; MoSpD; MsWp; NcRSh;
NjP; OM; RPB; RWe; TNP;

TxH; TxHuT; ViAl; ViU;
BrMus.   10182

Saurin, Jacques, 1677-1730
Sermons translated from the
original French of the late Rev.
James Saurin...Wheeling, Va.,
Davis & M'Carty, 1822. 316 p.
KSalW; TCollSM; WvW.   10183

Sawyer, Joshua, 1789-1869
An address to the brethren of
Mount Vernon Lodge, at their
annual celebration of St. John the
Baptist, at Johnson, June 25,
1821. Burlington, Vt., E. & T.
Mills, printers, 1822. 11 p.
VtHi.   10184

Schabaelje, Jan Philipsen
Die Wandlende Seele; Das ist;
Gespräche der Wandlenden Seele
mit Adam, Noah und Simon
Cleophas...Harrisburg, Gedruckt
bey John S. Wiestling, 1822.
454 p. INGo; MiU-C; P; PHC;
PHi.   10185

Schiller, Johann Christoph Friedrich von, 1759-1805
The robbers; a tragedy in five
acts...Baltimore, J. Robinson,
1822. 60 p. MH.   10186

Schoolcraft, Henry Rowe, 1793-
1864
A memoir on the geological
position of a fossil tree, discovered in the secondary rocks
of the river Des Plaines...Al-
bany, Pr. by E. and E. Hosford, 1822. 18 p. DI-GS; DLC;
DNLM; MB; MWA; MiD-B; N;
NNC; NNM; PPAN.   10187

Schuylkill Navigation Company
Report of the president and
managers...to the stockholders.
Philadelphia, Pr. by James Kay,
Jun. & co., [1822] 11 p. MH-
BA; PPL.   10188

Schuylkill Permanent Bridge

Company, Philadelphia
By-laws, rules and regulations of the corporation...to
which are prefixed the act of the
legislature authorizing the incorporation... Philadelphia, Pr.
by William Fry, 1822. 40 p.
PHi; PPAmP.   10189

Scott, John, 1777-1834
The life of the Rev. Thomas
Scott, D.D. Boston, S.T. Arm-
strong and Crocker & Brewster;
New York, J.P. Haven, 1822.
457 p. Ar-Hi; CBPSR; CSfMI;
CU; CtHT; CtW; DLC; GDC;
GOgU; ICartC; KWiU; MA; MB;
MBNEH; MBev-F; MBrZ; MH-
AH; MNe; MPeaI; MWA; MeB;
MiU; MoSpD; NAnge; NNUT;
NjP; PFal; PPL; PPLT; RBa;
ViU; VtMiM.   10190

Scott, Thomas
Essays on the most important
subjects in religion. Middletown (Conn.) E.H. Clark, 1822.
500 p. ICP; IaFairP; TWcW;
ViRU.   10191

---- Treatises on various theological subjects, published at
different times, and now collected into volumes. Vol. II. From
the Philadelphia ed. Middletown (Conn.) E. & H. Clark,
1822. 500 p. ICP; ScCoB.
                                 10192
---- The well bred horse Ball,
a beautiful dark sorrell...will
stand the ensuing season one
half of his time at the stable of
the subscriber, and the remaind-
er of his time at John Moore's
in Vincennes...March 19, 1822.
Bdsd. In.   10193

[Scott, Sir Walter, bart.]1771-
1832
The fortunes of Nigel; a romance...Albany, Webster, 1822.
2 v. in 1. NCH.   10194

[----] ---- New York, Pr. for
the booksellers, 1822. 2 v.
KyLxT; RBr.   10195

[----] ---- In two volumes.
Philadelphia, Edwin T. Scott,
D. Dickinson, printer, 1822. 2 v.
CtY; MeWebr; NIC; NcNb; PPL.
                               10196
[----] ---- Philadelphia, H. C.
Carey and I. Lea; New York,
H. C. Carey & Co., 1822. 2 v.
DLC; IaBo; PPL; RPB; ScSoh.
                               10197
---- Guy Mannering. Hartford,
Samuel G. Goodrich and Hunting-
ton and Hopkins, 1822. 268 p.
MNF.   10198

[----] ---- or, The astrologer,
by the author of Waverly and
The antiquary. Philadelphia, J.
Conrad, 1822. 2 v. NN; OCIWHi.
                               10199
---- Halidon Hill; a dramatic
sketch, from Scottish history.
New York, Samuel Campbell and
son; E. B. Clayton, printer,
1822. 70, [1] p. CtHT-W; DLC;
MBAt; MH; NBLiHi; NN; NjP;
OO; PU.   10200

---- ---- Philadelphia, H. C.
Carey & I. Lea, 1822. 107, [1] p.
CtHT; DLC; LNH; MB; MH;
MNF; NIC; NcAS; Nh; OO; PPL;
PU; RPB; ScC; ScSoh; ViAl.
                               10201
[----] The monastery; a ro-
mance, by the author of Waver-
ly, etc. New York, pub. by E.
Duyckinck, J. & J. Harper,
printers, 1822. 2 v. RJPHL;
WvBe.   10202

[----] The novels, tales, and ro-
mances of the author of Waverley. Boston, S. H. Parker,
1822-24. 17 v. MH.   10203

[----] The pirate; a romance.
Albany, Pr. by E. and E. Hosford, 1822. 2 v. NFai; VtMiM;

WMOSC.   10204

[----] ---- Boston, S.H. Parker,
1822. 407 p. DLC.   10205

---- ---- Boston, Wells & Lilly,
and Munroe & Francis, 1822.
2 v. in 1. KPea; MBilHi;
MFiHi; MH; RBr.   10206

---- ---- Hartford, Samuel G.
Goodrich and Huntington and
Hopkins, 1822. 305 p. CtHC;
MNF; RNHi.   10207

[----] ---- In two volumes.
New York, Wm. Borradaile,
Samuel Marks, printer, 1822.
2 v. IaDuU; MeWebr.   10208

[----] ---- New York, Pr. for
the booksellers by J. Seymour,
1822. 2 v. DLC; MBAt; MBC;
MDeeP; MWA; NIC; NN; PPL.
                               10209
[----] ---- Philadelphia, H. C.
Carey & I. Lea, 1822. 2 v.
(Vol. 1 has imprint, 'M. Carey
& Sons') MBev; NRU; OAU;
PHatU; PFal; PPL; RPB; ViAl;
ViU.   10210

[----] Tales of my landlord:
third series. Philadelphia,
James Maxwell, 1822. 3 v.
MeWebr; NN; PPL; RPB.
                               10211
---- Waverly; or, 'Tis sixty
years since. Hartford, Samuel
G. Goodrich and Huntington and
Hopkins, 1822. 282 p. MNF.
                               10212
[----] ---- By the author of
Guy Mannering... New-York, E.
Duyckinck, 1822. 2 v. MB;
MBoy; RJa.   10213

A Scriptural exposition of the
declaration in the parable of the
sheep and goats; by a friend to
truth. New York, Bolmore,
printers, 1822. 16 p. CSansS;
CtY; MCNC; MdBD.   10214

A scripture peace tract...Boston, Pr. by Jonathan Howe, 1822. 8 p. MWA. 10215

The seaman's devotional assistant, intended to aid masters and seamen in the daily worship of almighty God, on board their vessels at sea...From the London ed. with add. and alterations. New-York, pub. by the Society for Promoting the Gospel among seamen in the port of New-York; and may be had of E. Bliss & E. White, at the office of the Christian Herald and Seamen's Magazine; Gray & Bunce, printers, 1822. 139 p. MB; PPWa. 10216

[Sedgwick, Catharine Maria] Mary Hollis. An original tale. New York, Pr. by Van Pelt & Spear, for New York Unitarian Book Society, 1822. 22 p. ICME; MH. (Wright 2354) 10217

[----] A New-England tale; or, Sketches of New-England character and manners. New York, E. Bliss & E. White, 1822. 277 p. CSmH; CtY; DLC; MB; MF; MH; MWA; MnU; N; NNS; NjP; PU; RPB; TNV; ViAl; VtMiM; WaU. 10218

[----] ---- 2d ed. New York, E. Bliss & E. White, 1822. 285 p. CoU; CtHT-W; ICN; ICU; MA; MB; MBAt; MH; MMh; MNS; MStoc; MWA; MWH; NCH; UU. 10219

[Sedgwick, Henry Dwight] 1785-1831 The English practice: A statement showing some of the evils and absurdities of the practice of the English common law, as adopted in several of the United States, and particularly in the state of New-York. New-York, Pr. by J. Seymour, 1822.

71 p. IObB; IaU-L; LU; MB; MBAt; MH; MHi; MWCL; NGeno; NNC; NjR; OCLaw; P; PPAmP; PPL; PU-L. 10220

[Seixas, David G.] Letters to C.C. Biddle, Wm. McIlvaine, Mary Corvgille, and John Bacon connected with the dismissal of David G. Seixas, the founder and late principal of the Pennsylvania Institution for the Deaf and Dumb...[Philadelphia, 1822] 28 p. DLC; DNLM; P. 10221

A selection of hymns. See Henshaw, John Prentiss Kewley.

A selection of hymns for the use of Evangelical Lutheran Churches. Hagerstown, (Md.) W.D. Bell, 1822. 344 p. RPB. 10222

A selection of hymns for the use of Sunday schools. New York, Wickham, 1822. 88 p. ICN; NNUT. 10223

Selection of the New Testament rules, given by our Lord and his apostles, to the Church of Christ, for their only rule of government and practice. Haverhill, Pr. by Sylvester T. Goss, 1822. 12 p. Nh-Hi. 10224

Selections from the Chronicles of Boston. See Webster, Redford.

Self examination. New York, Day, 1822. 12 p. PPFYR. 10225

Semple, Robert Baylor, 1769-1831 The faithful servant of God exemplified in the life and death of Samuel L. Stranghan, late minister of the gospel, Northumberland county, Va., compiled at the request of the Dover association...Richmond, Shepherd &

Pollard, printers, 1822. 74 p.
OCIWHi; Vi; ViRU; ViU; ViW.
10226

Sergeant, John, 1779-1852
Speech of Mr. Sergeant in the
House of Representatives, March
7th, 1822, on the bill to establish an uniform system of bankruptcy throughout the United
States. [Washington, D. Rapine,
printer, 1822?] 41 p. DLC; M;
MB; MdBP; NjP; PPAmP; PPL.
10227

Sergeant, Thomas
Constitutional law. Being a
collection of points arising upon
the Constitution and jurisprudence
of the United States and which
have been settled by judicial decision and practice. Philadelphia, Abraham Small, 1822.
415 p. C; CSfLaw; CU; DLC;
GMilvC; ICU; In-SC; ICU;
KyLoU-L; L; LU; M; MB; MH;
MNF; MWCL; MdBB; NICL;
NNS; NWM; Nj; PP; PPL;
PPB; PPiM; Sc-Sc; ScCC; ViU;
WaU.   10228

A series of numbers addressed
to the public. See Columbian
(A).

The seven wonders of the world;
and other magnificent buildings,
&c. ... New York, Samuel Wood
& sons, and Samuel S. Wood &
co, Baltimore, 1822. 42, [3] p.
CtNwchA; MH.   10229

[Sewall, Henry Devereux]
An appeal from the denuncia-
tions of the Rev. Dr. Mason,
against rational Christians; ad-
dressed to all who acknowledge
the religion of Jesus Christ...
By a Unitarian of New York.
New York, pub. by the New
York Unitarian Book Society,
Van Pelt and Spear, printers,
1822. 24 p. CBPac; DLC; ICMe;
MAbD; MBAt; MBC; MH; MHi;
MWA; MeBat; NIC; NNS; NNUT;

Nh; NjP; NjPT; PHi; PPAmP;
PPPrHi; PPiW; RPB.   10230

Seymour's almanac for 1823.
By Matthew Seymour. Norwalk,
Philo Price [1822] 12 ll. Ct;
CtHi; MWA; NbHi.   10231

Shakespeare, William, 1564-1616
As you like it, a comedy...
Boston, Wells & Lilly, etc.,
1822. 100 p. DLC; MH; MeB;
PPL.   10232

---- ... Coriolanus; or, The
Roman matron, a tragedy...
Boston, Wells and Lilly; New
York, A. T. Goodrich & co.,
1822. 88 p. CSt; LNH; MB; MH;
MeB; PPL; ViU.   10233

---- Hamlet, a tragedy... Boston, Wells and Lilly, 1822. 154
p. MH; PU.   10234

---- King John. A historical
play. Boston, Wells and Lilly,
1822. 88 p. CU; MWA; MeB.
10235
---- King Lear; a tragedy; altered from Shakespeare by Nathan Tate. Boston, Wells and
Lilly, etc., 1822. 108 p. MB;
MH; MeB; PPL; PU.   10236

---- Macbeth; a tragedy, in five
acts. Philadelphia, T.H. Palmer, 1822. 56 p. MH.   10237

---- The merry wives of Windsor, a comedy. Boston, Wells
and Lilly, etc, 1822. 106 p.
MB; MH; MeB; PP; PPL.
10238
---- ---- New York, Dunigan,
1822. 108 p. PU.   10239

---- Othello... Boston, Wells &
Lilly; New-York, A. T. Goodrich
& co., 1822. 108 p. MB; PPL;
PU.   10240

---- ... Richard the Third, a

tragedy... Boston, Wells and Lilly, 1822. 100 p. DLC; MH; NNC; PPL.   10241

---- Romeo and Juliet. A tragedy. Boston, Wells & Lilly, 1822. 95 p. MeB; PPL; PU.   10242

Sharp, Granville
Religious Tracts, No. 34. Published by "The Society of the Protestant Episcopal Church for the Advancement of Christianity in Pennsylvania," for the "Episcopal Female Tract Society of Philadelphia." Plain arguments by way of question and answer, from the Gospel history, and certain scriptural passages, for the divinity of Christ; compiled from Dr. Burgess's edition of Granville Sharp's Remarks on the use of the definite article in the Greek text of the New Testament. Philadelphia, 1822. 12 p. MdHi.   10243

Sharp, T.
The heavenly sisters; or Biographical sketches of the lives of thirty eminently pious females, partly extracted from the works of Gibbons, Germont, & others, & partly original. New Haven, N. Whiting, 1822. 144 p. Ct; CtHi; CtHT-W; CtY; DLC; ICartC; IaU; MDeeP; OHi.   10244

---- ---- New York, Henry Durell & Co., 1822. 158 p. CtHT-W; IU; NRU; PPPrHi; ScC; ScNC.   10245

Shaw, Henry Moore
A discourse delivered before the Masonic fraternity, assembled at Brownville, Jefferson Co. to celebrate the anniversary of St. John the Evangelist, Dec. 27, A. L. 5821. Albany, Pr. by G. J. Loomis & Co., 1822. 20 p. N; PPPrHi; WHi.   10246

---- A sermon delivered... December 12, 1821... Sacket's Harbor, N. Y., Pr. by Mathew M. Cole, 1822. 14 p.   N.   10247

Shaw, Jeremiah
Remarks upon three of Mr. Ballou's principal wide-spread publications: presenting ... a clear view of the ridiculous absurdity of his self-styled arguments for proof of universal salvation. Concord, George Hough, 1822. 26 p. DLC; MBC; MDeeP; MH-AH; MNe; MWA; NNUT; Nh-Hi.   10248

Shaw, Joshua
United States directory for the use of travellers and merchants... Philadelphia, Pr. by J. Maxwell [1822] 156 p.   DLC; GU-De; MBNEH; MH; P; PP PPL; PHi; PPPCity. 10249

Shaw, Oliver, 1779-1848
There's nothing true but heav'n.   3d ed. A favorite song. Providence, Shaw [1822?] p [1]-2. DLC; MB; MH; PP; RPB.   10250

Sheet almanack for 1823.   New-London, Samuel Green.   Advertised in the "Connecticut Gazette," December 25, 1822.   10251

The shepherd and his flock... Hartford, Geo. Goodwin & Sons, 1822. 36 p. CtHi.   10252

Sheridan, Mrs. Frances (Chamberlaine)
The history of Nourjahad. With a biographical preface. Philadelphia, Hickman & Hazzard, 1822. 55 p. IObB; MH.   10253

Sheridan, Richard Brinsley Butler, 1751-1816
The critic, or A tragedy rehearsed, a dramatic piece. Boston, Wells and Lilly, etc., 1822. 68 p. MH; RPB.   10254

---- The duenna, an opera...
Boston, Wells and Lilly; New
York, A. T. Goodrich & co.,
1822. 83 p. CU; MH; MeB;
NNC; PPL; ViU.   10255

---- The rivals, a comedy...
Boston, Wells and Lilly, 1822.
117 p. DLC; MB; MH; MeB;
NNC; PPL; TxU.   10256

---- ---- New-York, S. King,
1822. 110 p. MH.   10257

Sheriff's sale. By virtue of a
writ... on Monday, the 27th inst.
...Caleb North, Sheriff. Philadelphia, May 16, 1822. Bdsd.
PPL.   10258

Sherwood, Mrs. Mary Martha
(Butt) 1775-1851
    The ayah and lady. An Indi-
an story...from the 3d London
ed.   Boston, S. T. Armstrong
and Crocker & Brewster; New
York, J. P. Haven, 1822. 104 p.
CoU; MHad; MnU.   10259

---- Dazee, or, The re-captured
negro. Newburyport, W. & J.
Gilman, 1822. 47, [1] p. MB;
OCIWHi.   10260

---- History of Emily and her
brothers...Hartford, G. Goodwin
& Sons, 1822. 22 p. CtHi.
                                  10261
---- History of Henry Fairchild
and Charles Trueman. New
York, D. H. Wickham, 1822. 36
p. MScitHi.   10262

---- History of Little George
and his penny. Hudson, Wm.
E. Norman, printer, 1822. 24 p.
Maxwell Hurley, Beverly Hills,
Calif. Cat. XIII, p. 21.   10263

---- History of little Henry and
his bearer. Hartford, George
Goodwin & Sons, 1822. 52 p.

CtHi.   10264

---- ---- Boston, Lincoln &
Edmands, 1822. 36 p. MB.
                                  10265
---- The orphan boy, and The
caskets, by the author of "The
Raven and the dove," &c. Boston, Lincoln & Edmands, 1822.
34 p. MB; NN.   10266

---- The orphan boy...Hart-
ford, George Goodwin, 1822. 34
p. CtHi.   10267

---- The re-captured negro.
Philadelphia, Pub. by the Protestant Episcopal Sunday and
Adult School Society of Philadelphia.   Jesper Harding printer,
1822. 67 p. NN; TxU.   10268

Sheys, Briant
    The American book-keeper,
comprising a system of book-
keeping, by single and double entry: adapted to the merchant,
farmer, and mechanic...New-
York, Daniel D. Smith; S.
Marks, printer, 1822. 160 p.
MB.   10269

Shield, William, 1748-1829
    The midshipman. New York,
E. Riley [1822?] 1 l. DLC; NHi;
RPB.   10270

---- Tell her I'll love her. New
York, E. Riley [1822?] [2] p.
DLC; NN.   10271

---- The wealthy fool. New
York, E. Riley [1822?] 3 p. CtY;
MH; N; NBuG; NN.   10272

Shooting match. At the new tav-
ern in South Salem...To Eben
Thrasher's then repair,
You'll find good sport and liquors
    there,
For best of ball and powder, hop
To Derby Square, at Weller's
    Shop.

Salem, Nov. 1822. Bdsd. MSaE.
10273

A short account of the life of Jesse Cadbury, of Birmingham, England, son of Richard and Elizabeth Cadbury, who died 9th month 19, 1818, aged about thirteen years... Philadelphia, Pr. by Joseph Rakestraw, for the Female Tract Association of Friends, and to be had of Richard Johnson, 1822. 12 p. InRchE.
10274

A short address to the Roman Catholic congregation of St. Mary's Church, on the approaching election for trustees. Written in consequence of the two late addresses from the pastor and lay trustees of the said church. By an Irish Catholic. Philadelphia, Pr. for Bernard Dornin, 1822. 8 p. DLC; PHi; PPAmP.
10275

Short review of a project for uniting the courts of law and equity. See South Carolinian, pseud.

A short system of practical arithmetic. See Kinne, William.

Shreve, Joseph
    The speller's guide... Brownsville (Pa.) Jackson & Harvey, 1822. 175, [3] p. OCIWHi.
10276

Sias, Solomon
    A discourse delivered at St. Johnsbury, before Harmony Lodge of free and accepted Masons at the anniversary of St. John, the Baptist, June 24th, A. L. 5822. Danville, Pr. by E. Eaton, 1822. 15 p. IaCrM; LNMas; MBC; NNFM; PPFM; RPMA; VtHi.
10277

[Sigourney, Mrs. Lydia Howard (Huntley)] 1791-1865

Traits of the aborigines of America. A poem. Cambridge, from the University Press, Hilliard and Metcalf, printers; sold by Cummings & Hilliard, Boston, 1822. 284 p. CoCsC; CtHT; CtSoP; DLC; GEU; IC; ICN; ICU; IE; IaMp; KMK; KyDC; MA; MB; MBC; MBL; MH; MMal; MNBedf; MSa; MWA; MWiW; MdBE; MdBL; MdBP; MiU-C; MnSM; MoSpD; NIC; NNC; NNS; NSmB; NTEW; NbHi; NbU; NjP; OCHP; OHi; OkHi; P; PHi; PPAN; PWGWHi; RNR; RPB; TxU; VtMiM; VtU; WHi; WM.
10278

[Simmons, Amelia]
    American cookery; or, The art of dressing viands, fish, poultry, and vegetables; and the best mode of making puff-pastes, pies, tarts, puddings, custards, pickles, and preserves, and all kinds of cakes, from the imperial plumb to plain cake, adapted to this country, and all grades of life. By an American orphan. New York, W. Beastall, 1822. 72 p. MH.
10279

Simmons, James Wright, 1790-1858
    Blue beard; or, The marshal of France: a poem. Philadelphia, Moses Thomas, J. Maxwell, printer, 1822. 110 p. PPAmP.
10280

---- Valdemar, or The castle of the cliff, a tragedy. Philadelphia, H. C. Carey and I. Lea, 1822. 50 p. MH.
10281

[Simmons, William Hayne] 1784-1870
    Notices of East Florida, with an account of the Seminole nation of Indians. By a recent traveller in the province. Charleston, Pr. for the author by A. E. Miller, 1822. 105, [1] p. DLC;

F; MB; NN; NNS; OCHP;
PPAmP; PPL; ScC; ScCC.
10282
Simond, Louis
Switzerland; or, A journal of
a tour and residence in that
country in the years 1817, 1818,
and 1819... Boston, Wells and
Lilly, 1822. 2 vol. CtW; DLC;
FTU; GU; IaDaM; KyDC; M;
MA; MB; MBAt; MBC; MBev;
MH; MH-AH; MHi; MLanc;
MLow; MNF; MNBedf; MNe; MS;
MSa; MTa; MWal; MeBaT;
MnM; NBu; NCH; NGeno; NNS;
NPStA; NhD; NjP; P; PHatU;
PCC; PNt; PPA; PU; PPL;
RNR; RP; RPB; ScC; ScU; TNJ;
Vi; ViRUT; VtU.   10283

Sinclair, Hannah, 1780-1818
A letter on the principles of
the Christian faith.   From the
14th Edinburgh ed.   Baltimore,
pub. by Fielding Lucas, Jr.,
John D. Toy, printer, 1822.
112 p. DLC; MdBE; MdHi; MB;
MiGr; NbOP.   10284

Sir Andrew Wylie, of that ilk.
See Galt, John.

[Siret, Louis Pierre] 1745-1797
Epitome historiae Graecae,
cum appendice De diis et heroi-
bus, poeticio [auctore Josepho
Juvencio.] Accedit dictionarium
latino-anglicum.   Ed. 1. americana.   Novi-Portus, A.H. Maltby et soc., 1822. 112 p. CU;
MB; MH; NNC.   10285

Six hundred questions deduced
from Goldsmith's History of England, calculated to instruct young
persons in the causes, consequences, and particulars of
events in English history. Boston, Munroe and Francis, 1822.
72 p. MH; MMhHi.   10286

The sketch book of Geoffrey
Crayon.   See Irving,Washington.

A sketch of old England.   See
Paulding, James Kirke.

Sketch of the life and character
of the late Rev. Joseph Mottey,
of Lynnfield.   From the Christian Deciple, Nov. and Dec.
1821.   Boston, Pr. by Phelps
and Farnham, 1822. 16 p. MHi;
MWA.   10287

Sketches of the domestic man-
ners and institutions of the Ro-
mans... Philadelphia, H.C.
Carey & I. Lea, 1822. 230 p.
CtHT; KyLx; MB; MH; NCH;
NNS; OCl; PHi; PPA; PHatU;
PPL; RPA; RPB; ScC; ViU;
VtU.   10288

Skillman, Thomas T., publisher
Tracts on religious subjects.
Lexington, Ky., Thomas T.
Skillman, 1822. 288 p. KyLxT.
10289
Smith, Adam
The theory of moral senti-
ments; or an essay towards an
analysis of the principles, by
which men naturally judge con-
cerning the conduct and charac-
ter, first of their neighbors
and afterwards of themselves...
New York, Evert Duyckinck,
George Long, Samuel Campbell,
James A. Burtus, 1822. 2 v.
ArBaA; CoCsC; FTa; GDC; IJI;
InLPU; MBradJ; MH-BA; MY;
MiU-C; NcMHi; Nj; OCiv; OO;
PPT; PPWa; PPins; RPA;
ScCC; ScNC; TSewU; WM.
10290
Smith, Charles B.
The defining spelling book,
being a collection of words used
by men of letters, concisely ex-
plained... Lexington, Ky., Pr. by
William Gibbes Hunt, 1822.
225 p. Present location un-
known; above info. from Albert
H. Allen. Pierson, 410. 10291

Smith, David

Sermon, delivered at Durham, Feb. 24th, 1822, at the funeral of Mr. Isaac Prentiss, of Boston, and Mr. John T. Palmer, from Europe; who were drowned, in consequence of the fall of a bridge, while the stage-coach was passing over it. Middletown (Conn.) E. & H. Clark, 1822. 16 p. Ct; CtHi; ICMe; MBC; MWA; MiD-B; OCIW; PHi.   10292

Smith, Elias
The medical pocket-book, family physician, and sick man's guide to health; containing a short description of vegetable medicines... Boston, Bowen, 1822. 168 p. MB; MH-M; PPC.   10293

Smith, Henry Barney
An oration, delivered at Dorchester, on the Fourth of July, 1822. Boston, Pr. by True & Greene, 1822. 18 p. DLC; MBAt; NNC.   10294

Smith, James, 1771-1841
The National Vaccine Institution. To the citizens of the United States... Baltimore, 1822. [2] p. MBCo.   10295

Smith, James Edward, 1759-1828
A grammar of botany, illustrative of artificial, as well as natural classification with an explanation of Jussieu's system. New-York, James V. Seaman, J. & H. Harper, printers, 1822. 264 p. CSfA; CtHT-W; CtW; DLC; ICU; IEN-M; IdHi; KyDC; LU; MAA; MAnP; MB; MBHo; MH; MNBedf; MNe; MSaP; MiGr; MiU-C; MnHi; MnU; NCH; NN; NNC; NNNBG; NcU; O; OCLloyd; OMC; OU; OUrC; PPL; PPi; RNR; RP; VtU; WU; WaPS; WyU.   10296

Smith, John Broadfoot
A few imperfect rhymes on

the sovereignty of Jehovah, designed as a help to the feeble lamps of Christ's flock, and a check to Dagonism. Cincinnati, Looker & Reynolds, printers, 1822. 56 p. OCIWHi; RPB.
                                  10297

Smith, Mishael
The history of Daniel, the prophet, the son of Josiah, King of Judah. Charleston, S.C., E. Thayer and W.P. Bason, 1822. 310 p. OO; PWcHi; ScDuE; TxU; ViU.   10298

Smith, Robert Archibald, 1780-1829
The harper of the mull. A favorite Scotch song. New York, E. Riley [1822?] [2] p. DLC; MH; MWA; N; NN; NRU-Mus.
                                  10299

Smith, Stephen Renssalaer, 1788-1850
A sermon delivered at the dedication of the "Free Church," Clinton, November 14, 1821. Utica, 1822. 8 p. MMeT-Hi; NUt.   10300

---- A sermon, delivered in Union Village, Paris (N.Y.) the first Sunday in May, 1822... Onondaga, Pr. for the author, 1822. 15 p. NHi.   10301

Smollett, Tobias George, 1721-1771
The history of England, from the revolution in 1688, to the death of George II. A new ed. with the authors last corr. and imp. Philadelphia, Edward Parker, William Brown, printer, 1822. 2 v. ArBaA; CBPSR; CtHT; IaDmD; MBBC; MLei; MNF; MdBJ; MiEalC; MoFuWc; NAlf; NNNAM; NJQ; NRU; Nj; OO; RBr; RKi; RP; ScCC; ScDuE; TNJ; TxMinw; Vi; VtBrt; WHi; WM; WyU. 10302

Society for Propagating the Gospel Among the Indians
  Report of the Select Committee of the Society for Propagating the Gospel Among the Indians.   Cambridge [Mass.] Pr.
by Hilliard and Metcalf, 1822.
28 p. WHi.   10303

Society for the Prevention of
Pauperism in the City of Baltimore
  Views of the Society...Balti-
more, Pr. by Thomas Maund,
1822. 36 p. MdBP.   10304

Society for the Prevention of
Pauperism in the City of New
York.
  Report on the penitentiary sys-
tem in the United States, pre-
pared under a resolution of the
Society for the Prevention of
Pauperism, in the city of New-
York.   New-York, Pr. by Mah-
lon Day, 1822. 101, 107 p. Ct;
CtHT-W; DLC; IaE; KyLx; MB;
MBC; MH; MNBedf; MWA;
MiD-B; NN; NNG; NjP; NjR;
PHi; PP; PPAmP; PPL; RPB;
ScCC.   10305

Some account of J.S.   See Sullivan, James.

Some passages in the life of Mr.
Adam Blair.   See   Lockhart,
John Gibson.

Somerville, William Clarke,
1790-1826
  Letters from an American in
Paris, on the causes and conse-
quences of the French revolution.
Baltimore, E.J. Coale & Co.;
J.D. Toy, printer, 1822. 67 p.
CtY; MdBE; MdHi.   10306

[----] Letters from Paris, on
the causes and consequences of
the French Revolution.   Baltimore, E.J. Coale, 1822. 390 p.
CtW; CtHT-W; DLC; InND;

KyLx; MA; MB; MD; MSa;
MdBE; MdBL; MdBS; MdCatS;
MdHi; MNe; MiD; NCH; NNC;
NbOP; NjP; RPA; BrMus.
                             10307
Song, for the celebration of the
4th of July.   See   Harris,
Thaddeus Mason.

Songs of Zion: or, The Christian's new hymn book, for the
use of the Methodists.   Ed. 2.
Baltimore, Cushing and Jewett,
1822. 240 p. CtW; NNUT.
                             10308
The songster's museum; or, A
new selection of the most popular songs, moral sentimental,
humourous, and patriotic.   Albany, Pr. by G.J. Loomis &
co., 1822. 245 + 7 p. N.
                             10309
South-Carolina (State)
  Acts and resolutions of the
General Assembly of the state of
South-Carolina, passed in December 1821. Columbia, Pr. by
Daniel Faust, 1822. 112 p. DLC;
IaU-L; In-SC; MdBB; Mi-L; Nb;
Nj; Nv; W.   10310

---- Reports of cases deter-
mined in the Constitutional court
of South Carolina...By D.J. Mc-
Cord, Columbia, S.C., D.
Faust, state printer, 1822-30.
4 v. CLSU; CSfBar; CSt; CU;
DLC; F-SC; KyLxFL; LNBA;
LNL-L; MBU-L; MWCL; MdBB;
MdUL; Me-LR; Mn; Ms; MoU;
NNIA; NNLI; Nc-S; OCIW;
PPiAL; PU-L; RPL; ScCliP;
ScU; TChCL; WOshL; WaU.
                             10311
South Carolinian, pseud.
  Short review of a project for
uniting the Courts of Law and
Equity in this state [S.C.] in
which the expediency of such a
measure is briefly considered.
Charleston, S.C., Duke &
Browne, printer, 1822. 12 p.
ScC.   10312

Souza-Botelho, Adélaide Marie
Emilie (Filleul) marquise de,
1761-1836
   Helen de Tournon: a novel...
Translated from the French.
Boston, Wells and Lilly, 1822.
231 p. MB; MHi.   10313

Sparhawk, Ebenezer
   A discourse delivered Jan. 18,
1794, at the interment of Benjamin Shattuck, Esq. an eminent
physician in Templeton...Boston,
Pr. by E. & W. Bellamy, 1822.
24 p. MBAt; MBM; MH; MHi;
MWA; MiD-B.   10314

[Sparks, Jared] 1789-1866
   Eighth and ninth letters to the
Rev. Samuel Miller on his
charges against Unitarians. Bal-
timore, Toy, 1822. 44 p.
MBAt; MH; P; PPAmP.   10315

[----] Five letters on atonement,
in which the opinions of Trinitarians and Unitarians are examined with reference to their
moral tendency. By a Unitarian
of Baltimore. Baltimore, pub.
by the Baltimore Unitarian Book
Society; sold by F. Lucas, Jr.,
& N. G. Maxwell, Market St.;
John D. Toy, printer, 1822. 93 p.
MdHi; MsU.   10316

---- A sermon, preached in the
hall of the House of Representatives in Congress, Washington
city, March 3, 1822; occasioned
by the death of the Hon. Wm.
Pinkney, late a member of the
Senate of the United States.
Washington, Davis and Force,
1822. 15 p. DLC; ICMe; IEG;
M; MBAt; MBAU; MBC; MH;
MHi; NN; RPB.   10317

---- A sermon preached in the
Hall of the House of Representa-
tivs in Congress, Washington
City, March 3, 1822, occasioned
by the death of the Hon. Wm.

Pinkney...2d ed.   Baltimore,
pub. by the Baltimore Unitarian
Book Society; sold by F. Lucas,
Jr., and N. G. Maxwell; John D.
Toy, printer, 1822. 23 p.
CSmH; CtY; DLC; ICMe; MB;
MBAU; MWA; MH; MdBP; MHi;
MdHi; MiD-B; PPAmP.   10318

The Spectator; with notes and a
general index...Philadelphia,
Hickman & Hazzard, 1822. 769 p.
CtHT; IAl; KyLoP; LNDil; MH;
NRU-W; NcWsS.   10319

Spencer, J., comp.
   New songs for the use of
Christians, selected by J. Spencer and E. B. Rollins. Woodstock, Pr. by David Watson,
1822. 72 p. KBB; RPB. 10320

Spencer, John C.
   Correspondence between John
C. Spencer, Esq. and James
Hillhouse, Esq., commissioner
of the school fund of the state of
Connecticut...[Canandaigua,
1822] 8 p. MB; NN.   10321

A spiritual exposition of the declaration, in the parable of the
sheep and goats; Matthew XXV.
46. By a friend to truth. New
York, Bolmore, printer, 1822.
16 p. MBC.   10322

Spooner, William Jones
   An address delivered at Cam-
bridge, before the Society of
Phi Beta Kappa, at their annual
meeting, August 29, 1822. Bos-
ton, Oliver Everett, Hilliard &
Metcalf, printers, 1822. 34 p.
A-Ar; DLC; ICU; MBAt; MH;
MHi; MLaw; MnHi; NCH; NNC;
RPB.   10323

Spooner's Brooklyn directory,
for the year 1822. Brooklyn,
N. Y., Alden Spooner, 1822. 71
p. NB; NBLiHi; NHi; NN.
                                   10324

[Sprague, William Buell] 1795-
1876
   Letters on practical subjects,
from a clergyman of New England, to his daughter. Hartford,
Huntington & Hopkins, 1822. 136
p. CBPac; CtHi; CtHT-W; MA;
MB; MH; MHub; MiU-C;
TxAuPT.   10325

Spring, Gardiner, 1785-1873
   Essays on the distinguishing
traits of Christian character...
3d ed. New York, J. Seymour,
1822. 134 p. CtW; LNH;
NbCrD; OO.   10326

Spring flowers; or, Easy lessons
for young children. New-Haven,
pub. by J. Babcock and Son, and
S. Babcock and Co., Charleston,
S. C. Sidney's Press, 1822. 31
p. CtHi.   10327

Sproat, P. W.
   The savage beauty, a satirical
allegorical novel. Philadelphia,
Pr. by S. Roberts, 1822. 136 p.
DLC; ICU; MB; MBAt; MH;
MWA; NHi; NN; OClWHi; PU.
                             10328
---- The temple of sensibility.
A Parnassian wreath... Philadel-
phia, Pr. by S. Roberts, 1822.
36 p. ICU; MH.   10329

The spy. See Cooper, James
Fenimore.

Squier, Miles Powell
   The death and resurrection of
the believer. A sermon, de-
livered at the funeral of Mrs.
Almira James, wife of Mr.
Aaron James, who died at Buf-
falo (N. Y.) Jan. 28, 1822, in
the twenty-fourth year of her
age. Buffalo, Pr. by David M.
Day [1822] 16 p. ICN; MWA.
                             10330
Stanford, John
   An address delivered in the
Orphan Asylum, New-York, Feb-

ruary 5, 1822, on the conflagra-
tion of the Orphan House in the
city of Philadelphia on the 23rd
of Jan. New-York, E. Conrad,
1822. 11 p. MBC; MH; NHi;
NN; NRAB; NjR; OClWHi; RPB;
VtMiS.   10331

Stansbury, Daniel
   Tables to facilitate the necessary calculations in nautical
astronomy; more particularly designed to enable navigators to de-
termine their longitude from lu-
nar observations... New York,
Pr. for the author, sold by Collins & co., 1822. 339, [1] p.
DLC; NNG; PHC; ScCC. 10332

Stansbury, Philip, 1802?-1870
   A pedestrian tour of two
thousand three hundred miles,
in North America. To the Lakes
--the Canadas,--and the New
England states. Performed in
the autumn of 1821... New-York,
J. D. Myers & W. Smith, 1822.
274 p. CSmH; CtHT; CtSoP;
CtY; DLC; ICN; ICU; IU; IaSc;
MA; MB; MH; MS; MWA; MiD;
MiU-C; MnHi; MoS; MoSM;
NBu; NHi; NIC; NN; NNA; NNS;
NNia; NTi; Nh-Hi; NjR; O; OC;
OMC; PHi; PPL; PPi; RP;
ScU; WHi.   10333

State of New-York agricultural
almanack for 1823. Albany,
Daniel Steele & Son; Packard &
Van Benthuysen, printers [1822]
24 ll. CtLHi; DLC; IU; MWA;
NBuHi; NHi; NN; NR; NjR;
VtU; WHi.   10334

State of New-York agricultural
almanac for 1823. By S. South-
wick. Albany, Stephen W. Johnson, Jun.; E. and E. Hosford,
printers [1822] 24 ll. DLC; MB;
NCooHi; N; NN.   10335

Staughton, William, 1770-1829
   Address delivered at the open-

ing of the Columbian College in
the District of Columbia, Janu-
ary 9, 1822; by the president...
Washington city, Anderson and
Meehan, 1822. 31 p. DLC; IEG;
KyLoF; LNB; M; MB; MBC;
MBNEB; MH; MdBP; NHC-S;
NRAB; NjR; OC; OCHP; PHi;
PPAmP; PU; PPPrHi; RPB;
ScU; ViRU.   10336

Stearns, Samuel
    A sermon, delivered at the
funeral of the Rev. Eliab Stone,
late senior pastor of the North
Church in Reading, September 3,
1822. Salem, Pr. by John D.
Cushing and Brothers, 1822. 32
p. MB-FA; MBAt; MBC;
MBNEH; MH; MHi; MSaE;
MiD-B; Nh-Hi; NjR; PHi; RPB.
                              10337

Steel, John H.
    Report on the geological struc-
ture of the county of Saratoga, in
the state of New York; together
with remarks on the nature and
properties of the various soils
and modes of culture... Saratoga
Springs, G. M. Davison, printer,
1822. 56 p. MB.   10338

Steele's Albany almanack for
1823. By Andrew Beers. Albany, D. Steele & Son; Packard
& Van Benthuysen, printers
[1822] 18 ll. NCooHi; N.   10339

Steibelt, Daniel, 1765-1823
    Sonata. For the piano forte
with an accompaniment for the
violin. Philadelphia, B. Carr
[1822?] 11, 2 p. Wolfe 8560.
                              10340

Stevens, Beriah
    A new and concise system of
arithmetic, containing vulgar,
decimal, and logarithmetic; calculated for the use of the inhabitants of the U.S. ... Saratoga
Springs, N.Y., G. M. Davison,
1822. 423 p. CtHT-W; DAU;
InDanN; MB; MH.   10341

Stevens, Ebenezer
    Statement of the claim of
Ebenezer Stevens, Austin L.
Sands, Joshua Sands and Robert
Morris. [1822?] 20 p. MB;
NbU.   10342

Stevenson, John Andrew, 1761-
1833
    The bells of St. Petersburg.
New York, P. K. Moran [1822]
[2] p. RPB.   10343

---- Farewell but whenever you
welcome the hour. New York,
E. Riley [1822?] [3] p. MWA;
NBuG; RPB.   10344

---- Lord Ullin's daughter. A
favorite ballad. Baltimore, John
Cole [1822?] [2] p. MWA;
MdHi; NN.   10345

---- Love and friendship. New
York, P. K. Moran [1822] [2] p.
N.   10346

---- Music. New York, E.
Riley [1822?] 1 l. NN; PP.
                              10347
---- To ladies eyes. A favor-
ite Irish melody. New York,
E. Riley [1822?] [2] p. MWA;
N; NN.   10348

---- The Young May moon. Baltimore, Carr [1822?] 1 l. MWA;
NN.   10349

Stewart, David, 1772-1839
    An anniversary oration de-
livered before the Philokrisean
Society of Baltimore. Baltimore, Pr. by Richard J. Matchett, 1822. 22 p. CSmH;
MdBE; MdHi.   10350

Stewart, Dugald
    Elements of the philosophy of
the human mind. Albany, E.
and E. Hosford, 1822. 2 v. in 1.
CStclU; Ct; CtHT; GU; ICMe;
ICP; IEG; IaDaSA; InCW; InNd;

KM; MAm; MB; MFi; MH;
MdBM; MeBa; MiDU; MiU; MiV;
N; NCaS; NbU; OHi; OO; OkU;
PPAmP; PPWe; RP; ScCMu;
ViRU; VtMiM.   10351

---- ---- Boston, Wells and
Lilly; E. & E. Hosford, printer,
1822. 563 p. NSyU.   10352

---- A general view of the progress of metaphysical, ethical,
and political philosophy... Boston, Wells and Lilly, 1822. 2 pts
in 1. CtHC; CtW; GOgU; MAnP;
MB; MH; MPiB; MdBP; MoSW;
MsJMC; NCH; NNC; NjP; RNR;
OCIW; OWoC; PPAmP; PPLT;
PU; ScC; ScCoT; TNP.   10353

Stewart, Mordecai
     The youth's guide... containing
mensuration, book-keeping, geography, arithmetic, grammar,
writing letters, complimentary
and promissory notes... 2d ed.
Baltimore, R. J. Matchett, 1822.
InU.   10354

Stilwell, James
     Life and sufferings of James
Stilwell, a deaf and dumb man
who was 10 years in France un-
der the celebrated Abbe Sicard
... Baltimore, Pr. by William
Ogden Niles, 1822. 12 p. MNF.
                               10355
Stoddards diary; or Columbia al-
manack for 1823. By Andrew
Beers. Hudson, Ashbel Stoddard
[1822] 12 ll. CtNhHi; MWA;
NBuG; NN; NHi; PHi; ViU.
                               10356
Storace, Stephen, 1763-1796
     The Revolutionary soldier's
lullaby. New York, E. Riley
[1822?] [2] p. DLC; NN. 10357

Storrs, Richard Salter, 1787-
1873
     A discourse delivered at North
Bridgewater, May 28, 1822, at
the funeral of Mrs. Mary Hallam

Huntington wife of the Rev. Dan-
iel Huntington... Boston, Pr. by
Crocker & Brewster, 1822. 20 p.
CtHC; ICP; MBC; MH-AH;
MSabra; MWA; MeBat; MiD-B;
NBLiHi; RPB; ScCC.   10358

---- A sermon, delivered at
North Bridgewater, Oct. 31,
1821, at the ordination of the
Rev. Daniel Temple, and Rev.
Isaac Bird, as evangelists and
missionaries to the heathen.
Boston, Crocker & Brewster,
printers, 1822. 52 p. CSt; CtY;
CtHC; DLC; ICP; KWiU; M;
MA; MB; MBC; MH; MPiB;
MWA; MeB; MeBat; MiD-B;
NCH; NHi; NN; NNUT; NjR;
OCIWHi; OO; PPPrHi; RBr;
RPB; VtMiM.   10359

Story of the third old man.   See
Golgolam, al Hafiz, pseud.

The strangers' guide to the City
of Charleston.   Charleston,
S. C. , 1822.   Sabin 12092.
                               10360
The strayed lamb.   Andover,
Flagg & Gould, printers, 1822.
12 p. MeB.   10361

Streeter, Russell
     A discourse, delivered at the
evening meeting, of the First
Universalist Society, in Portland
the fourth Sabbath in December,
1821.   Portland, Pr. at the Argus Office, by Thomas Todd,
1822. 16 p. LU; MMeT; MMeT-
Hi; MWA; MeHi; MeP; PPL;
BrMus.   10362

---- The rich man and Lazarus!
An explanatory sermon, de-
livered on the third Sabbath in
July, 1822, before the First Uni-
versalist Society in Portland,
(Me.)... Portland, Pr. by Todd
and Smith, 1822. 16 p. MMeT-
Hi; MWA; MeBaT; MeHi;
MeLewB; MeP; MiD-B; PPL;

BrMus.   10363

Strictures on strictures of William Hogan. See Catholic of the olden time, pseud.

Strong, James
    An eulogium, pronounced by the Hon. James Strong, at Hudson, N. Y., upon the late Lieut. Com. Allen, of the U. S. Navy, who was killed in an engagement between the U. S. Schooner Alligator, and three piratical vessels, off Matanzas. New York, W. Grattan, and T. Longworth, 1822. 15 p. PHi.   10364

Strong, Paschal Neilson, 1793-1825
    The pestilence, a punishment for public sins. A sermon, preached in the Middle Dutch Church. Nov. 17, 1822, after the cessation of the yellow fever, which prevailed in New York in 1822. New-York, H. Sage, 1822. 26 p. DLC; MB; MBC; MH; MWA; NHi; NN; NNUT; NjR; PLT; WHi.   10365

Strong, Titus, 1787-1855
    The scholar's guide, to the history of the Bible; or an abridgment of the scriptures of the Old and New Testament... Greenfield, Clark & Tyler; Denio & Phelps, printers, 1822. 319 p. CtW; MB; MDeeP; MH; MPiB; N; NhPet.   10366

---- A sermon, delivered at Northampton, before Jerusalem Lodge, June 25, A. L. 5822... Northampton, Mass., Pr. by S. Judd, Jr., 1822. 22 p. CSmH; MNF; MWA.   10367

---- The young scholar's manual, or, Companion to the spelling book, consisting of easy lessons in the several branches of early education. 3d ed. Greenfield,

Mass., Denio & Phelps, 1822. 90 p. MA; MDeeP; MWA.   10368

Stuart, Moses
    Letters on the eternal generation of the Son of God, addressed to the Rev. Samuel Miller, D.D. Andover, Mark Newman; Flagg and Gould, printers, 1822. 166 p. CBPac; CSansS; CtHC; CtW; CtY; DLC; GDC; ICMe; ICN; ICP; ICT; IEG; IU; MA; MAnHi; MAnP; MB; MBAU; MBAt; MBC; MH; MHi; MMeT-Hi; MWiW; MeBat; MeLewB; MiD-B; MnHi; MoSpD; NNUT; NcMHi; NjR; OO; OkU; PCC; PHi; PPL; PPLT; PPP; PPPrHi; ViRUT; VtU; WHi.   10369

Stubborn facts. Andover, Flagg & Gould, printers, 1822. 26 p. MeB.   10370

Sturm, Christopher Christian, 1740-1786
    Reflections on the works of God in nature and Providence... From a late London revised and corr. ed. Baltimore, Armstrong and Plaskitt; A. Paul, printer, New York, 1822. 626 p. ArBaA; ICU; IP; Md; MdAS; MdBE; NNiaU.   10371

---- ---- For every day in the year. New-York, Pub. by N. Bangs and T. Mason, for the Methodist Episcopal Church. A. Paul, printer, 1822. 626 p. LNT; MeBaT; MsJMC; NcGA; TU; TxD-T.   10372

[Sullivan, James?]
    Some account of J. S. extracted from a letter written by him in Jamaica to a citizen of Philadelphia... Philadelphia, [J. R. A. Skerrett, printer] 1822. 8 p. InRchE; NcD; PSC-Hi; ScCC.   10373

[Sullivan, William] supposed author
    History of the United States of America.   See [Prentiss, Charles].

Sulpitius, Servius, pseud.
    Remarks of Servius Sulpitius, on an address, delivered at Washington, July 4, 1821 by John Quincy Adams, Secretary of State.   Taken from the Alexandria Gazette.   Alexandria, Pr. by John Shaw, Jr., 1822. 31 p. DLC; PPL; TxU.   10374

The Sultana.   See Bailey, Jonathan.

Summary of the perseuctions of the Rev. Wm. Hogan.   See Episcopalian, pseud.

Summerfield, John
    A sermon, preached in the Reformed Dutch Church, in Nassau-street, in behalf of the New-York Institution for the Instruction of the Deaf and Dumb; to which is added, an appendix, with information relative to the institution.   New-York, E. Conrad, 1822. 27, 16 p. CtHT; DLC; IEG; IObB; In; MBAt; MBC; MH; MiD-B; NHi; NN; NNC; NNG; NNMHi; NNUT; OClWHi; PHi; PPL; PPPrHi.
                                10375
---- ---- 2d ed.   New York, Pr. by J. Seymour, 1822. 40 p. MWo; MnHi; NHi; NN.   10376

The Sunday school children, to which is added The value of the Bible.   Hartford, George Goodwin & Sons, 1822. 34 p. MWal; WHi.   10377

The Sunday school hymn book. 5th ed.   Philadelphia, pub. by the Sunday and Adult School Union.   And for sale at their depository, 29 N. Fourth Street,

R. Piggot, Agent. I. Ashmead & Co., printers, 1822. [125] p. NcWsM.   10378

The Sunday school spelling-book; compiled with a view as well to teach children to spell and read and to contribute to their moral and religious instruction.   Philadelphia, pub. by the Episcopal Sunday and Adult School Society of Philadelphia, and for sale at their depository, No. 177, Chestnut Street, J. Crissy & G. Goodman, printers, 1822. 144, [2] p. (Private collection of Dr. J. A. Nietz, University of Pittsburgh.   10379

The Sunday sliding party; or, Examples of the awful consequences of Sabbath-breaking. Hartford, G. Goodwin & Sons, 1822. 22 p. CtHi.   10380

The surprising adventures of four Russian sailors, at the Island of Spitzbergen.   New-York, pub. by Samuel Wood and Sons; and Samuel S. Wood & Co., Baltimore, 1822. 36 p. MBAt; MNoanHi; PPL.   10381

Susquehannah and Saint Lawrence Canal
    Report of a committee appointed for the purpose of ascertaining the most eligible route for a canal from the Seneca Lake to the Erie Canal. Geneva, N. Y., Pr. by James Bogert, 1822. 22 p. N; NGH.   10382

Sutton (N. H.) Baptist Church
    Confession of faith, articles of church government, and covenant.   Concord, N. H., Pr. by George Hough, 1822. 12 p. Nh-Hi.   10383

[Swaim, William]
    A treatise on Swaim's panacea; being a recent discovery for the

cure of scrofula, or king's evil, mercurial disease, deep-seated syphilis. Philadelphia, Clark & Raser, 1822. 138 p. IEN-M; NBMS; PPL.   10384

---- ---- Philadelphia, Clark & Raser, printers, 1822. 84 p. MNBedf; NNNAM; PPL.   10385

Swan, Frederick W.
    Remarkable visionary dreams of a mulatto boy in Northfield, Mass., by the name of Frederick W. Swan, aged thirteen years; together with a sketch of his life, sickness, conversion, and triumphant death. Chesterfield, N.H., Joseph Meriam, 1822. 19 p. MNF.   10386

Swayne, Justice
    Vindication of the liberty of conscience and the rights of justices, in relation to witnesses. Wilmington, Del., "Freepress," 1822. 7 p. DeWI.   10387

Swift, Zephaniah, 1759-1823
    A digest of the laws of the state of Connecticut... New Haven, S. Converse, 1822[-23] 2 v. Ar-Sc; C-L; CU; Ct; CtY; CtW; CU; IU; Ia; KU; M; MH-L; MSaEC; MWCL; Mi-L; MiDU-L; MnU; NN; Nb; NcD; Nj; Nv; OCLaw; OClWHi; OO; Or-SC; R; Wa-L; WaU.   10388

The sword of justice wielded by mercy. A dialogue between the inspectors of the State prison, in New-York, and a convict on the day of his liberation. New-York, office of the Gospel Herald, 1822. 11 p. MiU-C.   10389

Swords's pocket almanack, Christian's calendar for 1823. By Joel Sanford. New-York, T. & J. Swords [1822] 8 ll. PHi.
                                      10390
---- ---- New-York, T. & J.

Swords [1822] 40 ll. IU; MWA; NHi; NNG; NNS; NjR; PHi; PPL.   10391

Symptoms of a falling church, and how to build up Zion. By a minister of the Baptist Church, in connection with the Rev. Mr. John Buzzell, of Parsonsfield (Me.) ... Philadelphia, J. Young, 1822. 18 p. MB.   10392

Synge, Edward
    Religious tracts. An answer to all the excuses and pretences which men ordinarily make for their not coming to the Holy Communion... Charleston, Protestant Episcopal Society for the Advancement of Christianity in South-Carolina, A.E. Miller, printer, 1822. 42 p. RPB.
                                      10393

T

Tables containing the assays, weights & values of the principal gold and silver coins of all countries... converted into the currency of the United States. Philadelphia, H.C. Carey & I. Lea, 1822. 8 p. PU-Mus.
                                      10394

Tacitus, Cornelius
    The works of Cornelius Tacitus; with an essay on his life and genius, notes, supplements, &c. By Arthur Murphy, Esq. 2d Amer. from the London ed. with the author's last corrections. Baltimore, F. Lucas, Jr., E.J. Coale & Co., Cushing & Jewett, N.G. Maxwell, Armstrong & Plaskitt, Joseph Robinson, John and Thomas Vance, Abner Neale, 1822. 6 v. GEU.   10395

---- ---- 2d Amer. from the London ed., with the author's last corrections. Boston, Pr. for Wells & Lilly, Richardson

& Lord, Munroe & Francis, Lincoln & Edmonds, Oliver Everett, Cummings & Hilliard, Charles Ewer, Timothy Bedlington, 1822. 6 v. MWo; MoSM; MoSpD; RPB. 10396

---- ---- 2d Amer. ed. , from the London ed. , with corrections. Georgetown, Gideon Davis, 1822, 6 v. MoS. 10397

---- ---- 2d Amer. from the London ed. , with the author's last corrections. Lexington, W.W. Worseley, 1822. 6 v. Townsend. 10398

---- ---- from the London ed. , with the author's last corrections. New York, Peter A. Mesier, Collins & co. , 1822. 6 v. DLC; LNH; Mi; NCaS; TNP; TU; ViPet; ViRUT. 10399

---- ---- 2d Amer. from the London ed. , with the author's last corrections. Philadelphia, H. C. Carey and I. Lea (and others), 1822. 6 v. CSt; CtB; CtW; CtWins; DeGE; ICU; IaDL; KyLoN; KyLxT; MoSW; NcBe; OAU; OCl; OBevB; OSW; PPF; PPL; PRosC; PU; TJoT; TxU; Vi; ViNo; VtU. 10400

---- ---- 2d Amer. from the London ed. with the author's corrections. Pittsburgh, Patterson & Lambdin, 1822. 6 v. IaGG; PW. 10401

---- ---- 2d Amer. , from the London ed. Washington, Davis & Force, 1822. 6 v. KyDC. 10402

[Talbot, Charles S.]
  Paddy's trip to America; or, The husband with three wives: a farce, in two acts. New-York, pr. for the author, 1822. 48 p. (Author supplied from Frank P. Hill's "American Plays," No. 286.) MH; MWA; MiU-C; RPB. 10403

---- Paddy's trip to America; or, The husband with two wives. A farce... Rochester, N. Y. , Pr. for the author, 1822. 48 p. NN. 10404

Talcot, Joseph
  American practical catechism, for use of schools, compiled by the aid of persons of various denominations; to which are annexed instructive lessons for youth. Philadelphia, Pr. by Jos. Rakestraw, 1822. 36 p. IObB; PHi; PSC-Hi; Pu-Penn. 10405

Tales of Glauber-Spa. By several American authors. In two volumes. New York, J. & J. Harper, 1822. 2 v. KyU. 10406

Tales of my landlord. See Scott, Sir Walter, bart.

Taletell, George, pseud. See Holmes, Isaac Edward.

Tappan, Benjamin, 1788-1836
  A sermon delivered in Winthrop, September 25, 1822; before the Kennebec Missionary Society, at their first annual meeting. Hallowell, Goodale, Glazier and Co. , printers, 1822. 20 p. MBC; MH-AH; MeBaT; MeLewB; NNMR; NjPT; RPB. 10407

Tappan, William Bingham, 1794-1849
  Lyrics. By William B. Tappan... Philadelphia, H.C. Carey and I. Lea; New York, H. C. Carey & co. , 1822. 132 p. CtY; DLC; MB; MH; MWA; MdBP; NGH; NHi; NNC; NNUT; Nh-Hi; NjR; P; PHi; PPL; PU; RPB. 10408

---- Poems, by William B. Tappan. Philadelphia, James Crissy, 1822. 252 p. CtHC; DLC; ICU; IEN; IU; MH; MWA;

MWHi; MnU; MnW; Md; NCH;
NN; NNUT; NTi; Nh-Hi; NjP;
P; PPL; PU; RPB; ViAl; Vt.
10409

Tatham, James
A grammar, in which the orthography, etymology, syntax
and prosody of the Latin language are minutely detailed...
Philadelphia, Kimber & Sharpless, 1822. 140 p. DLC; NjP;
PU. 10410

Taunton, Mass.
Committee to inquire into the
cause of the increase of pauperism. Report made and ac-
cepted at the town-meeting hold-
en in Taunton, May 6, 1822. 7 p.
NN. 10411

[Tayler, Charles Benjamin]
1797-1875
May you like it. By a coun-
try curate... Philadelphia, J.
Conrad, 1822. 272 p. DLC; MB;
NN; PAtM; PPL; VtU. 10412

Taylor, Mrs. Ann (Martin)
1757-1830
Retrospection: a tale...
Philadelphia, Collins and Croft,
1822. 173 p. DLC; IObB; IaDa;
MBAt. 10413

Taylor, Creed, 1766-1836
Journal of the law-school,
and of the moot-court attached
to it; at Needham, in Virginia.
Richmond, Pr. by J. & G. Coch-
ran, 1822. 371 p. DLC; Ia; MH-
L; MiL; MnU; NcD; Nv;
OCLaw; Vi; ViHi; ViU; ViU-L;
ViW; WaU. 10414

Taylor, Isaac, 1759-1829
Scenes in Europe, for the
amusement and instruction of
little tarry-at-home travellers.
1st Amer., from 3d London ed.
Philadelphia, U. Hunt, 1822. 93
p. DLC; NNS; OHi; PHi; RPB;
TxH. 10415

Taylor, Jane, 1783-1824
Original poems for infant
minds... Philadelphia, Desilver,
1822. 180 p. PU. 10416

---- ---- By several young persons. Philadelphia, Thomas
Town, 1822. 180 p. MnU; NjR.
10417

Taylor, John, 1753-1824
Tyranny unmasked... Washing-
ton City, Davis and Force, 1822.
349 p. ArU; CSmH; CU; CtY;
DLC; ICU; IU; IaU; In; KyLx;
KyLxT; MB; MH; MNF; Md;
MdBE; MdBP; MiD-B; MiU-C;
MnU; NBuG; NCH; NHi; NN;
NNS; NcAS; NjP; OCHP; OMC;
OO; PHi; PPL; RPB; TNV;
TxU; Vi; ViU; VtU; WHi.
10418

Taylor, John Bianchi, 1801-
1876
They're a'noddin. A favourite Scotch ballad. Arranged with
an accompaniment for the piano
forte or harp. Baltimore, John
Cole [1822?] p [1]-2. DLC;
RPB. 10419

Taylor, Richard
A trip to camp meeting: or,
A portrait of the American Anti-
christ in a dialogue between
Methodist preachers and Quak-
ers. Philadelphia, Pr. by John
Young, 1822. 64 p. VtU. 10420

Taylor, Robert Barraud, 1774-
1834
The validity of the title of
R. S. Hackley, to Florida lands.
[New York? 1822?] 15 p. MdHi.
10421

The templar, to which is added,
The tales of Passaic. By a
gnetleman of New York. Hacken-
sack, N. J., J. Spencer and E.
Murden, 1822. 127 p. CtY; MH;
NHi; PU. 10422

Templi Carmina. Songs of the
temple, or Bridgewater collec-

tion of sacred music. 10th ed.
Boston, Richardson & Lord, Pr.
by J. H. A. Frost, 1822. 333 p.
DLC; MBevHi; MEab; MS; MWA;
RPaw.   10423

Tennant, William
The thane of Fife; a poem in
six cantos. Philadelphia, Hick-
man and Hazzard, 1822. 178 p.
MB; MBAt; MH; MWA; NNC;
NjP; RPB.   10424

Tennessee (State)
Acts passed at the second
session of the fourteenth General
Assembly of the state of Tennes-
see. G. Wilson & Heiskell &
Brown, public printers. Knoxville,
Tenn., Pr. by Heiskell & Brown,
1822. 176, xxvi p. DLC; Ky; L;
MH-L; MdBB; Mi-L; Mo; Ms;
NN; NNB; NNLI; Nb; Nj; Nv;
Or-SC; RPL; TU; TU-M.   10425

---- Journal of the House of
Representatives at the second
session of the fourteenth General
Assembly of the state of Tennessee. Begun and held at Murfreesborough, on Monday the
twenty-second day of July, one
thousand eight hundred and twenty-two. Printed for G. Wilson,
and Heiskell & Brown, printers
to the state. Nashville, Tenn.,
Pr. by George Wilson, 1822.
166 p. DLC; MWA; T; TMeC;
TNV; TU.   10426

---- Journal of the Senate at the
second session of the fourteenth
General Assembly of the state of
Tennessee, begun and held at
Murfreesborough, on Monday the
twenty-second day of July, one
thousand eight hundred and twenty-two. Printed for G. Wilson
and Heiskell & Brown, printers
to the state. Nashville, Ten.,
pr. by George Wilson [1822]
218 p. DLC; MWA; NN; TMeC.
                               10427

The Tennessee farmer: or
Farmer Jackson in New York.
[New York, 1822?] 8 p. N.
                               10428
Tenterden, Charles Abbott, 1st
baron. See Abbott, Charles.

Texier de La Pommeraye, Ar-
naud
Abridgment of a French and
English grammar. 1st ed.
Philadelphia, 1822. 272 p. ABBS;
CtW; DLC; ICartC; NjP; PHi;
PPAmP; PPL.   10429

Thacher, James, 1754-1844
The American orchardist; or,
A practical treatise on the cul-
ture and management of apple
and other fruit trees... Boston,
J. W. Ingraham, 1822. 226 p.
CU; Ct; DLC; ICJ; MAnHi; MB;
MBAt; MBC; MBev-F; MBHo;
MDeeP; MH; MMeT; MPlyP;
MWA; MeU; NIC; NNNAM; NcRA
NhPet; OO; OrCA; PPWa; PU;
RNR; RPB.   10430

Thacher, Moses
A sermon, preached in Fox-
borough, at the funeral of Mrs.
Shubael Pratt... Dedham, Pr. at
the Register Office, 1822. 21 p.
DLC; M; MAbD; MBC; MBAt;
MTa; MTaHi; MiD-B; NBLiHi;
OCIWHi; RPB.   10431

Thayer, Caroline Matilda.
Letter to the members of the
Methodist Episcopal Church in
the city of New-York... Cincinnati, repub. by the New-Jerusa-
lem Society of Cincinnati, Looker & Reynolds, printers, 1822.
24 p. MB; MH.   10432

Thiersch, Friedrich Wilhelm
von, 1784-1860
Greek tables; or, A method
of teaching the Greek paradigm
in a more simple and fundamental manner... Andover, Godman
press, Flagg and Gould, 1822.

86 p. CtHT-W; DLC; IES; MAnP; MB; MBC; MH; MWiW; MdBD; NBuG; NNC; NjR; OCl.   10433

Thomas, Daniel
A sermon, preached at the funeral of Doctor Daniel Sawin, who departed this life, April 29, 1822: aged XXXVI years. Boston, Pr. at the Office of the New-England Galaxy, 1822. 16 p. MAbD; MBAt; MBC; MWA.
10434

Thomas, Robert
The modern practice of physic...6th Amer. from the 7th London ed. New York, Collins & Co., J. & J. Harper, printers, 1822. xv, 1050 p. CoCsE; DLC; GWay; ICJ; ICU; IEN-M; IU-M; LNoP; LNT-M; MH-M; MdBJ; MdBM; NBM; NBuU-M; NNNAM; NRAM; OCU-M; OO; PPC; PPL; RNR; RPM; ScCMeS; TNP; TxDaBM; WMAM.   10435

---- A treatise on domestic medicine...1st Amer. ed. rev. by David Hosack, M.D. New York, Collins & Co., A. Paul, printer, 1822. 500 p. CSfCMS; F; GU-M; ICJ; IEN-M; MeB; MiU; NBM; NGH; NNNAM; NbU-M; NcD; OCLloyd; PPC; WU-M.   10436

Thompson, Gabriel H.
Plane sliding sector, or, Trigonometrical scale, designed for practical geometry, trigonometry, navigation, and surveying. Boston, Pr. by H. Bowen, 1822. 10 p. ICJ.   10437

Thompson, Otis, 1776-1859
An address, delivered before the Bristol County Agricultural Society on their first anniversary at Taunton, October 30, 1822. 16 p. CSmH; MTaHi; Nh; RPB.
10438
---- Brief remarks upon Rev. Thomas Andros's strictures on

the review of his essay. Providence, Miller and Hutchens, 1822. 32 p. MBC; RHi; RPB; BrMus.   10439

---- A sermon, preached at Attleborough, Mass., March 25, 1821. Occasioned by the death of Mrs. Lucy Atkinson, consort of Samuel Atkinson, Esq., of Chillicothe, Ohio. Providence, Miller and Hutchens, 1822. 12 p. MBC; MTaHi; MWA; MiD-B; RHi.   10440

---- A sermon, preached at the interment of Deacon John Brown, who departed this life June 19, 1822, in the eighty-fifth year of his age. Providence, Brown and Danforth, 1822. 15 p. CBPSR; MB; MBC; MWA; MiD-B; NCH; RPB.   10441

---- A sermon, preached at the ordination of the Rev. Silas Shores, to the pastoral care of the Second Congregational Church in Falmouth, July 21, 1822, with charge. Taunton, A. Danforth, 1822. 23 p. CSmH; MB; MBC; RPB; ScCC; BrMus.
10442
Thompson, Pishey
A catalogue of books on sale, by Pishey Thompson, Pennsylvania Avenue, Washington City. ...Dec. 1, 1822. 23 p. Nh.
10443
[Thomson, Charles West] 1798-1879
The phantom barge, and other poems. By the author of "The limner..." Philadelphia, E. Littell, 1822. 171 p. DLC; PPL.   10444

Thomson, James
The seasons, by James Thomson, to which is prefixed a life of the author, by Samuel Johnson. Vol. 2. Providence, Jos. McIntire, 1822. MPlyA. 10445

---- ---- Boston, pub. by T.
Bedlington, John Roberts, Bela
Marsh and Thomas Wells [Thay-
er, Tappan & Stickney, printers]
1822. 196 p. DLC; ICN; ICU;
MWA; MWiW; MeBa; NL;
NSsA; NjP; NjR; OCel; OMC;
PPL; VtBrt.   10446

Thomson, Samuel, 1769-1843
  A narrative of the life and
medical discoveries of Samuel
Thomson...Boston, Pr. for the
author, by E.G. House, 1822.
204 p. ICJ; MnU; OCIWHi; PPL.
                              10447
---- New guide to health; or,
Botanic family physician. Containing a complete system of
practice, upon a plan entirely
new;...Boston, Pr. for the author, by E.G. House, 1822. 300
p. Nh-Hi.   10448

Thorburn, J.M. & Company,
New York
  Catalogue of kitchen garden,
field, and flower seeds, bulbous
roots, &c. sold by G. Thorburn
and Son, ...New-York, B.
Young, 1822. 51 p. NN; OO.
                              10449
The three witnesses. See Hillhouse, William.

Timothy, Baron
  ...Catalogue of extensive and
valuable collection of metalick
fossils...Boston, Pr. by Joseph
W. Ingram, printer, 1822. 15 p.
NjR.   10450

To gentlemen residing in the vicinity of the Erie Canal. See
Eaton, Amos.

To the citizens of Baltimore.
Baltimore, T. Maund, printer,
1822. 8 p. MdHi.   10451

To the citizens of the state of
Mississippi. See Cato, pseud.

To the electors of Brunswick,
Lunenburg and Mecklenburg
Counties. Washington, May 5th,
1822. Fellow-Citizens...2 p.
NcU.   10452

To the electors of Montgomery
County. See Bacon, Henry.

To the free and independent
citizens of the Town of Boston.
Saturday, March 2, 1822. [Bos-
ton, Mass.? 1822?] Bdsd. WHi.
                              10453
To the freeholders of Albermarle. See Cocke, Charles.

To the people. Bdsd. In.
                              10454
To the president and managers
of the Union Canal Company of
Pennsylvania. See Baldwin,
Loammi.

To the public of Charleston.
Charleston, Pr. by C.C. Sebring, 1822. 16 p. PPAmP.
                              10455
To the voters of the City of
Washington. Some vile invendi-
aries, who have no regard either
for truth or decency, having
labored to calumniate Captain
Thomas Carbery, for the purpose of injuring his election, it
is deemed proper by some of
his friends, to give the lie direct,
to so much thereof as relates to
his military career... They,
therefore, beg leave to offer to
the citizens the following certificates... [Washington, 1822]
Bdsd. DLC.   10456

To the voters of the first congressional district. Fellow citizens...You will be called to the
polls in a few days to discharge
the important duty of selecting a
proper person to represent you
in the congress of the United
States---William Prince and
Charles Dewey have tendered to

you their services... An American. Bdsd. In.   10457

Todd, Ambrose S.
An address, delivered before the members of Union Lodge of free and accepted Masons; occasioned by the death of Wm. Cooke, esq., of Danbury. New Haven, A. H. Maltby and Co., 1822. 14 p. CtHi; MH; PPFM.
10458

Torrey, Jesse
The herald of knowledge; or, an address to the citizens of the United States, proposing a new system of national instruction. Washington, Pr. for the author, by A. Way, Jun., 1822. 34 p. DGU; DHEW; DLC; MB; MWA; MeBat; N.   10459

Torrey, William Turner
A discourse, delivered before the Charitable Society of Plymouth, January, 1822. Boston, Crocker & Brewster, printers, 1822. 16 p. MBC; MPlyP; MWA; MWey.   10460

---- A sermon, delivered in Plymouth, Dec. 23, 1821, on the Lord's day after the anniversary of the landing of the fathers. Boston, Crocker & Brewster, printers, 1822. 24 p. CSt; CtHC; MBC; MH; MMal; MPlyP; MWA; MWey; MeHi; NNC; RPB. 10461

The tour of Doctor Syntax in search of a wife: a hudibrastic poem. Repr. from the last London ed. Philadelphia, J. Clarke, printer, 1822. 213 p. Library of Geo. C. Blight, Haymarket, Va.   10462

Tovar Salcedo, Antonia, trans.
Reynaldo y Elena; o, La sacerdotisa peruana. Novela histórica traducida del francés por Doña Antonia Tovar y Salcedo. Filadelfia, H. C. Carey y I. Lea,

1822. 132 p. C-S; MdBD; PPA.
10463
Town, Salem
A system of speculative masonry... being a course of lectures, delivered before the Grand Chapter of the state of New York, at their annual meetings, held in Temple chapter room, in the city of Albany. 2d ed. Salem, N. Y., Pr. by H. Dodd and Co., 1822. 288 p. MB; MCon; MSa; MiD-B; NCooHi; NNFM; OCM; ODaM; VtMiS.   10464

Town and country almanack for 1823. By Joshua Sharp. Alexandria, John A. Stewart [1822] 20 ll. DLC.   10465

The town & country almanac for 1823. By John Sharp. Baltimore, Cushing & Jewett; John D. Toy, printer [1822] 18 ll. MWA; PHC; PHi.   10466

Townsend, Micajah
The promise of Paradise. A funeral sermon, preached at Alburgh, Vt. on the 22d of April, 1822, on the death of Philyer Loop, Esq., Aet. 44. Burlington, E. & T. Mills, 1822. 22 p. Ready, 104.   10467

Townsend, Shearjashub Bourne
An oration on the aids of genius; delivered at Providence, September 3, 1822, before the United Brothers' Society, of Brown University. Providence, Brown and Danforth, printers, 1822. 21 p. MBBC; MBC; MH; MHi; MW; MiU; RBr; RHi; RP; RPB.   10468

Tract Association of the Society of Friends of New York
Fifth annual report, Committee of Management, of the Tract Association of the Society of Friends of New York. New York,

Pr. by Mahlon Day, 1822. 7 p.
MWA.   10469

Traits of the aborigines of America. See Sigourney, Mrs.
Lydia Howard (Huntley).

Transylvania University
    A catalogue of the officers
and students of Transylvania University, Lexington, Kentucky,
January, 1822. 18 p. CtY;
KyLxT; MWA; N; NN; PPAmP.
                            10470
---- Catalogus senatus academici, eorum qui munera et officia
gesserunt, quique alicujus gradus
laurea donati sunt in Universi-
tate Transylvaniensi, Lexingtoniae in Republica Kentuckiensi.
Lexingtoniae, Guielmo Gibbes
Hunt, Typographo. MDCCCXXII.
12 p. KyLxT; M; MH; N; PHi;
PPAmP; WHi.   10471

---- Clarissimo Johanni Adair,
Armigero Gubernatori; Honora-
tissimo Gulielmo Taylor Barry,
LLD, Armigero, Vice-Guberna-
tori; senatoribus et delegatis
Reipublicae Kentuckiensis...
Aulae Academicae Lexingtoniae,
In Republicae Kentuckiensi, Sexto
Idus Sulii, Anno Salutis
MDCCCXII, E Typis Guliemi
Gibbes Hunt. 19 p. KyLxT; MH;
MWA; NN; PPAmP; WHi. 10472

---- Order of Exercises at Commencement. Transylvania University, July 10th, 1822. Bdsd.
PPAmP.   10473

A treatise on Swaim's panacea.
See Swaim, William.

Trial: Commonwealth vs. J.T.
Buckingham, on an indictment
for a libel, before the Municipal
court of the city of Boston, December term, 1822...Boston,
pub. at the office of the New-
England galaxy [1822] 60 p. C;

CSmH; Ct; DLC; ICLaw; ICMe;
ICN; LU-L; MB; MBAt; MBC;
MBNEH; MH; MNBedf; MWA;
MeLewB; Mi-L; MiD-B; MiU;
MnU; MoU; NBLiHi; NIC; NNC-
L; NNLI; NPV; Nh; NjR; PPB;
RHi; RP; RPB; TxDaM; TxU.
                            10474
Trial of Benjamin Shaw, John
Alley Junior, Jonathan Buffum,
and Preserved Sprague, for ri-
ots and disturbance of public
worship, in the society of
Quakers, at Lynn, Massachu-
setts, before the court of com-
mon pleas, held at Ipswich,
Massachusetts, March 16th, 1822.
Salem, Cushing & Appleton,
1822. 32 p. DLC; NNLI; NjR;
PSC-Hi.   10475

Trial of Gamaliel H. Ward, on
an indictment in the usual form
of hard words and law expres-
sions, for taking a horse from
a stable in Salem, and returning
him again. (With prefatory note
to the public,) January, 1822.
[Salem, Mass. , 1822] 22 p.
MHi; MSaE.   10476

Trial of John Blaisdell, on an
indictment for the murder of
John Wadleigh, at the Superior
Court of Judicature, holden at
Exeter, September 1822. Re-
ported by a member of the bar.
Pr. at Exeter [1822] 60 p.
DLC; MB; Nh; Nh-Hi; PP.
                            10477
Trial of John Lechler, for the
murder of his wife, Mary Lech-
ler, before the court of oyer
and terminer, held for the coun-
ty of Lancaster, on the nine-
teenth day of August, 1822; con-
taining all the evidence with the
particulars of the murder of
Mrs. Haag...reported by Daniel
Fuller. Lancaster, Pa. , Pr. by
Hugh Maxwell, 1822. 64 p. MH-
L; MdBB; PP; PPB; PPL;
PPiU.   10478

Trial of Lieutenant Joel Abbot, by the general court martial, holden on board the U. S. ship Independence, at the Navy yard, Charlestown, Massachusetts. On allegations made against him by Captain David Porter, navy commissioner. Washington, Davis and Force, 1822. 152 p. CSmH; DLC; M; MB; MH-L; MdAN; MdBP; NNIA; Nh-Hi; PPAmP; Vi; W. 10479

Trial of Lieutenant Joel Abbot, by the general naval court martial, holden on board the U. S. ship Independence, at the Navy yard, Charlestown, Massachusetts, on allegations made against him, by Capt. David Porter, navy commissioner. Reported by F.W. Waldo... To which is added, an appendix, containing sundry documents in relation to the management of affairs on the Boston station. Boston, Pr. by Russell & Gardner, 1822. 164, 72 p. C; CtY; DLC; ICLaw; In-SC; LNH; M; MBNEH; MBS; MH; MHi; MLy; MSaEC; MSaP; MWA; MdAN; MdBB; MeB; MnU; MoU; NNLI; NcD; Nh; OCHP; PHi; PPB; PPPrHi; RNHi; RP; WHi. 10480

The trial of the Rev. William Hogan, for an assault and battery on Mary Connell... The whole taken in short hand, by Joseph A. Dowling, stenographer. Philadelphia, R. Desilver, 1822. 272, 8 p. DGU; DLC; MBAt; MBrigStJ; MH-L; MdBL; MdW; MdHi; MoU; NIC-L; PHi; PPAmP; PPB; PPL; PV. 10481

Trials between E. M. Blunt vs. I. Greenwood for a libel and E. M. Blunt vs. R. Patten for infringement on copyright. New York, 1822. [12] p. NIC-L. 10482

Tribute of affection to John Roulstone. See Capen, Lemuel.

Trimmer, Mrs. Sarah (Kirby)
The robins: or, Fabulous histories, designed for the instruction of children, respecting their treatment of animals. Boston, Munroe and Francis, 1822. 234 p. MH; MHi; TJoT. 10483

Troup, Robert, 1757-1832
A letter to the Honorable Brockholst Livingston, esq., one of the justices of the Supreme court of the United States, on the lake canal policy of the state of New-York... Albany, Pr. by Packard & Van Benthuysen, 1822. 38, 34, 42, 5 p. CSmH; Ct; CtHC; DLC; ICJ; ICN; IU; MB; MBAt; MH; MHi; MWA; MeU; N; NBu; NBuG; NIC; NN; NNC; NRHi; NRU; NbU; NcD; Nh-Hi; NjR; OCHP; OCIWHi; P; PHi; PP; PPAmP; PPF; PPL; PU; RPB; ScU; Vi; WHi; WU. 10484

The true Christian faith in our Lord Jesus Christ, plainly asserted. New-York, Pr. by Mahlon Day, 1822. 12 p. MWA. 10485

---- Philadelphia, to be had of Benjamin & Thomas Kite, 1822. 16 p. NNG; NjR; PHC; PSC-Hi; PPL. 10486

True Reformed Dutch Church in the United States of America
Reasons assigned by a number of ministers, elders, and deacons, for declaring themselves the True Reformed Dutch Church, in the United States of America. Hackensack, N. J., Pr. by John C. Spencer, at the office of the Hackensakc Newsman, 1822. 19 p. MB; NNUT; NjR. 10487

---- ---- [Ed. 2] Hackensack, N. J., Pr. by John G. Spencer, at the office of the Hackensack Newsman, 1822. 11 p. NjR. 10488

Trumbull, Henry
  History of the discovery of
America; of the landing of our
forefathers at Plymouth, and of
their most remarkable engage-
ments with the Indians in New
England, from their first landing
in 1620, until the final subjuga-
tion of natives in 1679... Boston,
pub. by George Clark, pr. by
Jonathan Howe, 1822. 252 p.
CoCsC; FSaW; IRo; MB; MBC;
MBNEH; MPeHi; MnDa; NN; OO;
Vi.   10489

The trumpet march, grand march
& pastoral in the grand proces-
sion of the coronation of Henry
5th.   New York, E. Riley
[1822?] [3] p. NN.   10490

Truth advocated.   See Vindex,
pseud.

Tucker, Benjamin
  An epitome of ancient and
modern history.   A new ed.
Philadelphia, J. Anderson, print-
er, for D. Hogan, 1822. 368 p.
IObB; IEG; MH; MNBedf;
MdBS; MoCgS; NSyU; OCIW;
OSW; PPAmP; PWW; TNP.
                                 10491
[Tucker, George] 1775-1861
  Essays on various subjects of
taste, morals, and national poli-
cy... By a citizen of Virginia.
Georgetown, D.C., J. Milligan,
1822. 350 p. DLC; MB; MoSW;
PPL; ViL.   10492

Turford, Hugh
  The grounds of a holy life...
to which is added Paul's speech
to the Bishop of Cretia.   New
York, Pr. by Samuel Wood and
Sons, 1822. 102, [2] p. InRchE;
PHC; PHi.   10493

Turner, Edward
  A discourse, delivered at the
dedication of the First Universalist Meetinghouse in Westminster,

Massachusetts, July 3, 1821.
Boston, Pr. by Jonathan Howe,
1822. 16 p. MB; MMeT-Hi;
MWA; RPB.   10494

---- The substance of a discourse, delivered at the public
recognition of the First Universalist Church in Roxbury, Jan.
4, 1822.   Charlestown, J. Howe,
1822. 15 p. CSmH; ICN; MBAt;
NN.   10495

[Turner, Juliana Frances]
  The harp of the beech woods
... Montrose, Pa., Adam Wal-
die, 1822. 156 p. PU.   10496

Turner, R.
  A new introduction to book-
keeping, after the Italian method
...With a waste book... Salem,
pub. by Cushing & Appleton, T.
C. Cushing, printer, 1822. 54 p.
MHaHi; MLaw.   10497

The two apprentices.   Andover,
Flagg & Gould, printers, 1822.
8 p. MeB.   10498

The two lambs.   Andover, Pr.
by Flagg & Gould, 1822. 12 p.
MeB.   10499

U

The Ulster County farmer's almanac for 1823.   By Andrew
Beers.   Kingston, John Tappan
[1822] 18 ll. MWA; N; NN; NHi.
                                 10500

Ulster County Republican nomi-
nations.   At a meeting of the
Republican delegates, from the
several towns in Ulster County,
held at the Court-House, in Kings
ton on the 21st day of October,
1822:   pursuant to adjournment-
Conrad Bevier, Chairman.
Kingston, N.Y., E.J. Roberts,
printer [1822] Bdsd. NKings.
                                 10501

The unfortunate concubine, or
History of Jane Shore, mistress
to Edward IV, king of England,
showing how she came to be concubine to the king.   With an account of her untimely end.   New
York, S. King, 1822. 34 p. MH.
                              10502

Union Board of Delegates from
Male Sunday Schools of Balti-
more.
    Fourth annual report Union
Board Delegates [for the year
1821.   Baltimore, 1822] 17 p.
N.   10503

Union Canal Company of Pennsylvania
    Report of the president and
managers...to the stockholders
...1822.   Philadelphia, Pr. by
order of the company, [1822] 8 p.
ICJ; MH-BA; MnHi; WU. 10504

Unitas, pseud.
    ...A friendly letter to a mem-
ber of the Episcopal Church in
Maryland...[Baltimore?] Vestry
of the Parish of St. Peter's
[1822] 7 p. MdBE.   10505

United Brethren in Christ
    Lehr- und Zucht-Ordnung der
Vereinigten Brüder in Christo.
Hägerstaun, Gruber und May,
1822. 81 p. PLFM.   10506

United Foreign Missionary Society.
    The fifth report of the United
Foreign Missionary Society, presented at the annual meeting,
held in the City of New York, on
Wednesday, May 8, 1822. New
York, Pr. by Daniel Fanshaw,
1822. 96 p. DLC; GDC; MB;
MHi; NcMHi; NjR; PLT. 10507

United States
    An act for ascertaining claims
and titles to land within the territory of Florida. April 18, 1822.
Read, and referred to the Com-

mittee on the Public Lands in
the House of Representatives.
[Washington, 1822] (S. 62) DLC.
                              10508

---- An act further to establish
the compensation of officers of
the customs, and to alter certain collection districts, and for
other purposes. Feb. 1, 1822.
Pr. by order of the House of
Representatives. [Washington,
1822] 9p. (S. 9) DNA.   10509

---- An act to abolish the
United States' Trading establish-
ment with the Indian tribes.
Referred to the Committee on
Indian Affairs in the House of
Representatives, April 2, 1822.
[Washington, 1822] (S. 57) 4 p.
DNA.   10510

---- An act to amend an act,
entitled "An act to regulate trade
and intercourse with the Indian
tribes, and to preserve peace on
the frontiers," approved thirtieth
March, one thousand eight hundred and two.   Read, and referred to the Committee on Indian affairs, in the House of Representatives, May 8, 1822.
[Washington, 1822] (S. 79) 4 p.
DNA.   10511

---- An act to authorize and en-
power the Corporation of the
City of Washington, in the District of Columbia, to drain the
low grounds on and near the public reservations, and to improve
and ornament certain parts of
such reservations.   Reported by
the Committee for the District
of Columbia, without amendment,
and ordered to lie on the table
in the House of Representatives,
April 18, 1822. [Washington,
1822] (S. 80) DNA.   10512

---- An act to provide for the
collection of duties on imports

and tonnage in Florida, and for other purposes. April 2, 1822. Read twice, and referred to the Committee on Commerce in the House of Representatives. [Washington, 1822] (S. 69) 5 p. DNA.
10513

---- Acts passed at the first session of the seventeenth Congress of the United States. Washington, Pr. by Davis and Force, 1822. 151 p. ICN; MGlCH; MiD-B; NjR; PU-L.   10514

---- Adjutant General's office, Washington, July 16th, 1822. Orders. (No. 47) 7 p. MdHi; PPL.   10515

---- Aggregate amount of each description of persons in the United States and their territories according to the census... of 1820 and 1821. Together with a list of the taxable inhabitants, (etc.) of the state of Pennsylvania in the year 1821. Also a summary of the census... of New York... 1821 with Coxe's statement of the arts and manufactures of the United States. Prepared by order of the Secretary of the Treasury, in obedience to a resolution of Congress. Philadelphia, 1822. [8] p. M; NjP; PPL; PU.
10516

---- Amendment proposed by Mr. Rich to the bill, in addition to the act, entitled "An act for the prompt settlement of public accounts. April 18, 1822. Adopted, and ordered to be printed. [Washington, 1822] (H.R. 131) DLC.
10517

---- Amendment proposed by Mr. Tracy to the bill to establish an uniform system of bankruptcy throughout the United States. [Washington, 1822] [Jan. 1822] (H.R. 1) DLC.   10518

---- Amendment proposed by Mr. Trimble to the bill for the pre-

servation and repair of the Cumberland Road. February 5, 1822. Read, and ordered to lie upon the table. [Washington, 1822] (H.R. 50) DLC.   10519

---- Amendment proposed by Mr. Woodson, in committee of the whole, to the bill to establish an uniform system of bankruptcy throughout the United States. January 22, 1822. [Washington, 1822] (H.R. 1) DLC.   10520

---- Amendment proposed by the Committee on Pensions and Revolutionary Claims, to the Bill authorizing payment of certain certificates. January 17, 1822. Committed to a committee of the whole House to-morrow. [Washington, 1822] (H.R. 12) DLC.
10521

---- Amendment proposed by Mr. Walker, of Alabama, to the bill for the es-"tablishment of a territorial government in Florida," --to form the two first sections. March 4, 1822 in Senate of the United States. [Washington, 1822] (S. 39) 2 p. DNA. 10522

---- Amendment proposed to the bill providing for the examination of the titles to land in that part of Louisiana situated between the Rio Honde and the Sabine River. March 26, 1822. [Washington, 1822] (H.R. 123) DLC.   10523

---- Amendments proposed by the Committee on the Public Lands to the bill from the Senate, "for ascertaining Claims and Titles to Land within the territory of Florida." April 26, 1822. In the House of Representatives. [The amendments refer to the engrossed bill from the Senate.] [Washington, 1822] (S. 62) 3 p. DNA.   10524

---- Amendments proposed to

the standing rules and orders of the House of Representatives of the U.S. March 4, 1822. Read and order to lie on the table. [Washington, 1822] 3 p. (56) DLC; PU. 10525

---- Amendments reported by the Committee on Commerce to the bill from the Senate, entitled "An act further to establish the compensation of officers of the Customs, and to alter certain collection districts, and for other purposes." March 5, 1822. Read, and, with the bill, committed to a committee of the whole House to-morrow. [Washington, 1822] 1 p. (S. 9) DNA. 10526

---- Amendments reported by the Committee on Naval Affairs to the bill, entitled "A bill to incorporate the United States' Naval Fraternal Association, for the relief of the families of deceased Officers." Dec. 31, 1822. Read, and ordered to lie on the table. [Washington, 1822] (H.R. 82) DLC. 10527

---- Annual report of the Commissioners of the Sinking Fund. Feb. 7, 1822. Referred to the Committee of Ways and Means. Washington, Pr. by Gales & Seaton, 1822. 25 p. (53) DLC; PU. 10528

---- A bill allowing a drawback on the exportation of cordage manufactured in the United States from foreign hemp. February 28, 1822. [Washington, 1822] 5 p. (S. 58) DNA. 10529

---- A bill allowing a drawback on the exportation of cordage manufactured in the United States from foreign hemp. December 16, 1822. [Washington, 1822] 5 p. (S. 6) DNA. 10530

---- A bill altering the compen-sation of the members of Congress and Delegates of Territories; and, also, the salaries of the Clerks, and Doorkeepers, &c. of each House of Congress. April 20, 1822. Read twice and committed to a Committee of the whole House on Monday next. [Washington, 1822] (H.R. 175) DLC. 10531

---- A bill appropriating moneys for the purpose of repairing the National Road from Cumberland to Wheeling. December 20, 1822. [Washington, 1822] 2 p. (S. 16) DNA. 10532

---- A bill authorizing the establishment of a Penitentiary within the District of Columbia. Feb. 5, 1822. Read the first and second time, and committed to a committee of the whole on Friday next. [Washington, 1822] (H.R. 78) DLC. 10533

---- A bill authorizing the location of certain school lands in the state of Indiana. April 6, 1822. Read twice, and committed to the committee of the whole House to which is committed the bill for the relief of James Brisban. [Washington, 1822] (H.R. 158) DLC. 10534

---- A bill authorizing the payment of a sum of money to John Gooding and James Williams. Feb. 4, 1822. Mr. Pleasants, from the Committee on Naval Affairs, to whom the subject was referred, reported the following bill, which was read, and passed to the second reading. [Washington, 1822] 1 p. (S. 37) DNA. 10535

---- A bill authorizing the payment of a sum of money to Thomas Shields. January 2, 1822. Mr. Pleasants, from the Committee on Naval Affairs, to whom was referred the memorial of Thomas Shields, made a report, accompanied by the following bill, which was read, and passed to the second reading. [Washington, 1822] 1 p. (S. 10) DNA.   10536

---- A bill authorizing the President of the United States to employ an additional force for the suppression of piracy. Dec. 12, 1822. Mr. Pleasants, from the Committee on Naval Affairs, reported the following bill, which was twice read by unanimous consent. [Washington, 1822] 1 p. (S. 5) DNA.   10537

---- A bill authorizing the Secretary of the Treasury to exchange a stock bearing an interest of five per cent for certain stocks bearing an interest of six and seven per cents. March 20, 1822. [Washington, 1822] (H. R. 15) DLC.   10538

---- A bill authorizing the transfer of certain Certificates of the Funded Debt of the United States. January 17, 1822. [Washington, 1822] 1 p. (S. 20) DNA.   10539

---- A bill concerning Abner L. Duncan. April 18, 1822. Read twice, and committed to a committee of the whole House tomorrow. [Washington, 1822] (H. R. 169) DLC.   10540

---- A bill concerning invalid pensions. February 19, 1822. Read twice, and committed to a Committee of the whole House to-morrow. [Washington, 1822] (H. R. 91) DLC.   10541

---- A bill concerning invalid pensions. December 16, 1822. Read twice, and committed to a Committee of the whole House to-morrow. [Washington, 1822] (H. R. 195) DLC.   10542

---- A bill concerning pre-emption rights in the territory of Arkansas. April 3, 1822. Read twice, and committed to the committee of the whole House to which is committed the bill for the relief of Clement B. Penrose. [Washington, 1822] (H. R. 151) DLC.   10543

---- A bill concerning pre-emption rights in the territory of Arkansas. April 3, 1822. Read twice, and committed to the committee of the whole House to which is committed the bill for the relief of Clement B. Penrose. Dec. 12, 1822. Ordered to be re-printed. [Washington, 1822] (H. R. 151) DLC.   10544

---- A bill concerning the apportionment of Representatives in the State of Alabama. December 20, 1822. Read twice, and committed to a committee of the whole House to-morrow. [Washington, 1822] (H. R. 202) DLC.
                    10545

---- A bill concerning the commerce and navigation of Florida. February 28, 1822. [Washington, 1822] 4 p. (S. 61) DNA. 10546

---- A bill concerning the disbursement of public money. April 20, 1822. Read twice, and committed to a committee of the whole House on the state of the Union. [Washington, 1822] (H. R. 174) DLC.   10547

---- A bill concerning the disbursement of public money. April 20, 1822. Read twice, and committed to a committee of the whole House on the state of the Union. Dec. 9, 1822. Reprinted by order of the House of Representatives. [Washington, 1822] (H. R. 174) DLC.   10548

No entry   10549

---- A bill concerning the lands
to be granted to the state of
Missouri, for the purposes of
education, and other public uses.
December 10, 1822. [Washing-
ton, 1822] 3 p. (S. 2) DNA.
                                10550
---- A bill concerning the Military Academy.   March 4, 1822.
Read twice, and committed to a
Committee of the whole House
on the state of the Union. [Wash-
ington, 1822] (H.R. 104.) DLC.
                                10551
---- ---- March 4, 1822. Read
twice, and committed to a Committee of the whole House on the
state of the Union.   December
12, 1822. Ordered to be reprinted. [Washington, 1822]
(H.R. 104) DLC.   10552

---- A bill concerning the pro-
cess of execution issuing from
the Sixth Circuit Court of the
United States, for the District of
Georgia.   January 14, 1822.
[Washington, 1822] 1 p. (S. 15)
DNA.   10553

---- A bill confirming certain
claims to land in the state of Illinois.   February 25, 1822.
[Washington, 1822] 2 p. (S. 56)
DNA.   10554

---- ---- March 5, 1822. Read
twice, and committed to a Committee of the whole House, to-
morrow. [Washington, 1822]
(H.R. 107) DLC.   10555

---- ---- March 5, 1822. Read
twice, and committed to a committee of the whole House to-

morrow.   Dec. 12, 1822. Ordered to be reprinted. [Washing-
ton, 1822] (H.R. 107) DLC.
                                10556
---- A bill confirming claims to
Lots in the town of Mobile, and
to Land in the former Province
of West Florida, which claims
have been reported favorably on
by the Commissioners appointed
by the United States. April 18,
1822. Read twice, and committed to the committee of the
whole House to which is committed the bill for the relief of
Clement B. Penrose. [Washing-
ton, 1822] (H.R. 170) DLC.
                                10557
---- A bill confirming the title
of the Marquis de Maison Rouge.
January 16, 1822. [Washington,
1822] 2 p. (S. 17) DNA. 10558

---- A bill confirming the title
to a tract of land to Alzira Di-
brieu and Sophia Hancock. April
5, 1822. Read, and ordered to
lie on the table. [Washington,
1822] (H.R. 157) DLC. 10559

---- A bill directing the sale of
certain tracts of land in the
state of Ohio, heretofore re-
served on account of salt springs.
March 28, 1822.   Read twice,
and committed to the committee
of the whole on Bill No. 126,
providing for the sale of public
lands in Florida.   Dec. 12,
1822. Printed by order of the
House of Representatives. [Wash-
ington, 1822] (H.R. 139) DLC.
                                10560
---- A bill enabling the claimants to lands within the limits
of the state of Missouri to institute proceedings to try the validity of their claims.   March 11,
1822. Read twice, and committed to the Committee of the
whole House to which is committed the "bill granting to the state
of Alabama, and territory of Ar-

kansas, the right of pre-emption to certain quarter sections of land." [Washington, 1822] (H.R. 117) DLC.   10561

---- ---- March 11, 1822. Read twice, and committed to a committee of the whole House to which is committed the "bill granting to the state of Alabama, and territory of Arkansas, the right of pre-emption to certain quarter sections of land." December 10, 1822. Re-printed by order of the House of Representatives. [Washington, 1822] (H.R. 117) DLC.   10562

---- A bill extending the time for locating Virginia Military Land Warrants, and returning surveys thereon to the General Land Office. December 17, 1822. Read twice, and committed to a committee of the whole House tomorrow. [Washington, 1822] (H.R. 196) DLC.   10563

---- A bill fixing the compensation of the Commissioner of the Public Buildings. April 8, 1822. Read twice, and committed to a committee of the whole House tomorrow. [Washington, 1822] (H.R. 162) DLC.   10564

---- A bill for ascertaining claims and titles to land within the territories of East and West Florida. March 1, 1822. [Washington, 1822] 7 p. (S. 62) DNA.   10565

---- A bill for laying out, and making, a road, from the lower Rapids of the Miami of Lake Erie to the western boundary of the Connecticut Western Reserve, in the state of Ohio, agreeable to the provisions of the treaty of Brownstown. March 8, 1822. Read twice, and committed to a Committee of the whole House tomorrow. [Washington, 1822]

(H.R. 112) DLC.   10566

---- A bill for laying out, and making, a road, from the lower Rapids of the Miami of Lake Erie to the western boundary of the Connecticut Western Reserve, in the state of Ohio, agreeable to the provisions of the treaty of Brownstown. March 8, 1822. Read twice, and committed to a committee of the whole House tomorrow. Dec. 12, 1822. Ordered to be reprinted. [Washington, 1822] (H.R. 112) DLC.   10567

---- A bill for the apportionment of Representatives among the several states, according to the Fourth Census. January 7, 1822. Read twice, and committed to a Committee of the whole House on Thursday next. [Washington, 1822] (H.R. 26) DLC.   10568

---- A bill for the benefit of George Shannon. Dec. 16, 1822. [Washington, 1822] 2 p. (S. 9) DNA.   10569

---- A bill for the benefit of Thomas Pendergrass. April 8, 1822. [Washington, 1822] 1 p. (S. 83) DNA.   10570

---- A bill for the better organization of the district court of the United States within the state of Louisiana. March 8, 1822. [Washington, 1822] 3 p. (S. 68) DNA.   10571

---- A bill for the disposition of certain special Bank deposites. April 26, 1822. [Washington, 1822] 2 p. (S. 88) DNA. 10572

---- A bill for the establishment of a territorial government in Florida. January 22, 1822. Read twice, and committed to a committee of the whole House tomorrow. [Washington, 1822]

(H.R. 51) DLC. 10573

---- A bill for the establishment of a territorial government in Florida. February 6, 1822. [Washington, 1822] 12 p. (S. 39) DNA. 10574

---- A bill for the preservation and repair of the Cumberland Road. January 21, 1822. Read twice, and committed to the committee of the whole to which is committed the bill to procure the necessary surveys, plans, and estimates, on the subject of roads and canals. [Washington, 1822] (H.R. 50) DLC. 10575

---- A bill for the preservation and repair of the Cumberland Road. December 18, 1822. Read twice, and committed to a committee of the whole House to-morrow. [Washington, 1822] (H.R. 192) DLC. 10576

---- A bill for the release of Amos Muzzy and Benjamin White from imprisonment. February 11, 1822. Read twice, and committed to a committee of the whole House to-morrow. [Washington, 1822] (H.R. 83) DLC. 10577

---- A bill for the release of Amos Muzzy and Benjamin White from imprisonment. December 17, 1822. [Washington, 1822] 1 p. (S. 13) DNA. 10578

---- A bill for the relief of Alexander Humphrey and Sylvester Humphrey. March 11, 1822. [Washington, 1822] 1 p. (S. 70) DNA. 10579

---- ---- December 23, 1822. [Washington, 1822] 1 p. (S. 18) DNA. 10580

---- A bill for the relief of Andrew Mitchell. Feb. 28, 1822. [Washington, 1822] 1 p. (S. 59) DNA. 10581

---- A bill for the relief of Anthony Kennedy. January 8, 1822. Read twice, and committed to a Committee of the whole House to-morrow. [Washington, 1822] (H.R. 28) DLC. 10582

---- A bill for the relief of Benjamin Stephenson. March 29, 1822. Read twice, and committed to a committee of the whole House to-morrow. [Washington, 1822] (H.R. 141) DLC. 10583

---- A bill for the relief of certain distillers, within the sixth collection district of Pennsylvania. January 28, 1822. Read twice, and committed to the Committee of the whole House, to which is committed the bill for the relief of sundry citizens of Baltimore. [Washington, 1822] (H.R. 57) DLC. 10584

---- A bill for the relief of certain persons who have paid duties on certain goods imported into Castine. February 1, 1822. Read twice, and committed to a committee of the whole House to-morrow. [Washington, 1822] (H.R. 69) DLC. 10585

---- A bill for the relief of certain purchasers of public lands, as amended by the Committee on the Public Lands. January 21, 1822. Read twice, and committed to the committee to which is committed the bill to provide for paying to the state of Missouri three per cent of the nett proceed of the sales of public lands within the same. [Washington, 1822] (H.R. 7) DLC. 10586

---- A bill for the relief of Charles A. Swearingen. January 28, 1822. Read twice, and com-

mitted to a committee of the whole House to-morrow. [Washington, 1822] (H. R. 61) DLC.
10587
---- A bill for the relief of Charles Campbell. March 1, 1822. Read twice, and committed to a Committee of the whole House to-morrow. [Washington, 1822] (H. R. 101) DLC. 10588

---- A bill for the relief of Clarence Mulford. April 8, 1822. Mr. Ruggles, from the Committee of Claims, to which was referred the petition of Clarence Mulford, made a report, accompanied by the following bill, which was read, and passed to the second reading. [Washington, 1822] 1 p. (S. 82) DNA. 10589

---- A bill for the relief of Clement B. Penrose. February 20, 1822. Read twice, and committed to a committee of the whole House to-morrow. [Washington, 1822] (H. R. 93) DLC.
10590
---- A bill for the relief of Daniel Carroll, of Duddington, and others. February 28, 1822. [Washington, 1822] 1 p. (S. 60) DNA. 10591

---- A bill for the relief of Daniel Seward. December 27, 1822. [Washington, 1822] 2 p. (S. 20) DNA. 10592

---- A bill for the relief of David Cooper. April 11, 1822. [Washington, 1822] 1 p. (S. 86) DNA. 10593

---- A bill for the relief of Ebenezer Stevens, and others. January 24, 1822. [Washington, 1822] 2 p. (S. 28) DNA. 10594

---- A bill for the relief of Ebenezer Stevens and others. December 20, 1822. [Washington,

1822] 1 p. (S. 15) DNA. 10595

---- A bill for the relief of Edmund Kinsey and William Smiley. February 12, 1822. Read twice, and committed to the committee of the whole House to-morrow. [Washington, 1822] (H. R. 84) DLC. 10596

---- A bill for the relief of George B. R. Gove. December 31, 1822. Read twice, and committed to a committee of the whole House to-morrow. [Washington, 1822] (H. R. 209) DLC.
10597
---- A bill for the relief of Henry Lee. April 28, 1822. Read twice, and committed to a committee of the whole House to-morrow. [Washington, 1822] (H. R. 179) DLC. 10598

---- A bill for the relief of Holden W. Prout, administrator on the estate of Joshua W. Prout, deceased. February 25, 1822. 1 p. (S. 54) DNA. 10599

---- A bill for the relief of Jacob Babbitt. February 20, 1822. [Washington, 1822] 2 p. (S. 52) DNA. 10600

---- ---- December 16, 1822. [Washington, 1822] 2 p. (S. 7) DNA. 10601

---- A bill for the relief of James Barron. April 9, 1822. Read twice and committed to a committee of the whole House to-morrow. [Washington, 1822] (H. R. 164) DLC. 10602

---- A bill for the relief of James Brisban. February 15, 1822. Read twice, and committed to a committee of the whole House to-morrow. [Washington, 1822] (H. R. 89) DLC. 10603

---- A bill for the relief of
James H. Clark.   January 21,
1822. [Washington, 1822] 1 p.
(S. 22) DNA.   10604

---- A bill for the relief of
James McFarland. January 8,
1822.   Read twice and committed to the committee to which is
committed the bill for the relief
of Benjamin Freeland and John
M. Jenkins. [Washington, 1822]
(H.R. 20) DLC.   10605

---- A bill for the relief of
James May and the representatives of William Macomb. January 2, 1822. Read twice, and
committed to a Committee of the
whole House to-morrow. [Wash-
ington, 1822] (H.R. 16) DLC.
                                10606
---- A bill for the relief of
James Miller, John C. Elliot,
Noah Hampton, James Erwin,
and Jonathan Hampton. March 12,
1822.   Read twice, and committed to a committee of the
whole House to-morrow. [Wash-
ington, 1822] (H.R. 118) DLC.
                                10607
---- A bill for the relief of
James Morrison.   March 21,
1822. [Washington, 1822] 1 p.
(S. 77) DLC.   10608

---- A bill for the relief of
James Pierce.   February 25,
1822. Read twice, and committed to a Committee of the whole
House to-morrow. [Washington,
1822] (H.R. 97) DLC.   10609

---- A bill for the relief of
James Ross.   January 18, 1822.
Read twice, and committed to a
committee of the whole House
to-morrow. [Washington, 1822]
(H.R. 45) DLC.   10610

---- A bill for the relief of
James Ross.   January 18, 1822.
Read twice, and committed to a

committee of the whole House
to-morrow.   Dec. 12, 1822. Ordered to be reprinted. [Wash-
ington, 1822] (H.R. 45) DLC.
                                10611
---- A bill for the relief of
John Baptist Belfort and others.
April 10, 1822. [Washington,
1822] 2 p. (S. 84) DNA. 10612

---- A bill for the relief of
John Buhler.   December 27,
1822. [Washington, 1822] 2 p.
(S. 21) DNA.   10613

---- A bill for the relief of
John Byers.   January 9, 1822.
Read twice and committed to a
committee of the whole House to-
morrow. [Washington, 1822]
(H.R. 31) DLC.   10614

---- ---- December 17, 1822.
[Washington, 1822] 2 p. (S. 10)
DNA.   10615

---- A bill for the relief of
John Jenkins.   December 17,
1822.   Read twice, and committed to a committee of the whole
House to-morrow. [Washington,
1822] (H.R. 198) DLC. 10616

---- A bill for the relief of
John Post and Farly Fuller.
March 8, 1822.   Read twice,
and committed to the Committee
of the whole House to which is
committed the bill for the release of Amos Muzzy and Benjamin White. [Washington,
1822] (H.R. 111) DLC. 10617

---- A bill for the relief of
Jonathan N. Bailey. January
80, 1822.   Read twice, and committed to the committee of the
whole House to which is committed the bill for the relief of Benjamin Freeland and John M. Jenkins. [Washington, 1822] (H.R.
66) DLC.   10618

---- A bill for the relief of Joseph Bainbridge. March 21, 1822. Read twice, and committed to a committee of the whole House to-morrow. [Washington, 1822] (H. R. 132) DLC.   10619

---- A bill for the relief of Joseph C. Boyd. March 5, 1822. [Washington, 1822] 1 p. (S. 65) DNA.   10620

---- A bill for the relief of Joseph Forrest. April 22, 1822. [Washington, 1822] 1 p. (S. 87) DNA.   10621

---- A bill for the relief of Joseph Forrest. December 30, 1822. [Washington, 1822] 1 p. (S. 22) DNA.   10622

---- A bill for the relief of Joshua Russell. December 31, 1822. [Washington, 1822] 1 p. (S. 33) DNA.   10623

---- A bill for the relief of Josiah Hook, Junior. January 10, 1822. [Washington, 1822] 1 p. (S. 13) DNA.   10624

---- A bill for the relief of Matthew McNair. February 15, 1822. [Washington, 1822] 1 p. (S. 47) DNA.   10625

---- A bill for the relief of Nathan Branson. January 17, 1822. Read twice, and committed to a committee of the whole House to-morrow. [Washington, 1822] (H. R. 44) DLC.   10626

---- ---- December 12, 1822. Read twice, and committed to a committee of the whole House to-morrow. [Washington, 1822] (H. R. 189) DLC.   10627

---- A bill for the relief of Peter Cadwell and James Britten. February 28, 1822. Read twice, and committed to a committee of the whole House to-morrow. [Washington, 1822] (H. R. 99) DLC.   10628

---- A bill for the relief of Reuben Hickman and Fielding Hickman. February 1, 1822. Read twice, and committed to a committee of the whole House on Monday next. [Washington, 1822] (H. R. 72) DLC.   10629

---- A bill for the relief of Robert Purdy. January 28, 1822. Read twice, and committed to a committee of the whole House on Monday next. [Washington, 1822] (H. R. 60) DLC.   10630

---- ---- Dec. 23, 1822. [Washington, 1822] 1 p. (S. 17) DNA.   10631

---- A bill for the relief of Sally Vance. April 2, 1822. Read twice, and committed to the committee of the whole House to which is committed the bill for the relief of the legal representatives of Maria Therese, &c. [Washington, 1822] (H. R. 145) DLC.   10632

---- A bill for the relief of Samuel H. Walley and Henry G. Foster. February 19, 1822. [Washington, 1822] 2 p. (S. 49) DNA.   10633

---- ---- December 16, 1822. [Washington, 1822] 1 p. (S. 8) DNA.   10634

---- A bill for the relief of Samuel Walker. February 7, 1822. [Washington, 1822] 1 p. DNA.   10635

---- A bill for the relief of Stephen Howard, jr. March 18, 1822. Read twice, and committed to a Committee of the whole

House to-morrow. [Washington, 1822] (H.R. 127) DLC.   10636

---- A bill for the relief of Susan Berzat, widow, and the legal representatives of Gabriel Berzat, deceased. February 28, 1822. Read twice, and committed to a Committee of the whole House on Monday next. [Washington, 1822] (H.R. 96) DLC. 10637

---- A bill for the relief of Thaddeus Mayhew. January 4, 1822. Read twice, and committed to a committee of the whole House to-morrow. December 11, 1822. Committed to a committee of the whole House to-morrow. [Washington, 1822] (H.R. 23) DLC.   10638

---- A bill for the relief of the heirs and representatives of Alexander Montgomery. January 18, 1822. [Washington, 1822] 2 p. (S. 21) DNA.   10639

---- A bill for the relief of the heirs and representatives of Alexander Montgomery, deceased. December 17, 1822. [Washington, 1822] 2 p. (S. 12) DNA.   10640

---- A bill for the relief of the heirs or legal representative of William T. Nimmo. December 18, 1822. Read twice, and committed to a committee of the whole House to-morrow. [Washington, 1822] (H.R. 200) DLC.   10641

---- A bill for the relief of the legal representatives of Greenberry H. Murphy. April 8, 1822. [Washington, 1822] 1 p. (S. 81) DNA.   10642

---- A bill for the relief of the legal representatives of John Girault. January 22, 1822. Read twice, and committed to a

committee of the whole House to-morrow. [Washington, 1822] (H.R. 54) DLC.   10643

---- A bill for the relief of the legal representatives of John Guthry, deceased. January 31, 1822. Read twice, and committed to a committee of the whole House to-morrow. [Washington, 1822] (H.R. 67) DLC.   10644

---- A bill for the relief of the legal representatives of Joseph Hodgson, dec'd. March 18, 1822. [Washington, 1822] 1 p. (S. 73) DNA.   10645

---- A bill for the relief of the legal representatives of Marie Therese. January 31, 1822. Read twice, and committed to a committee of the whole House to-morrow. [Washington, 1822] (H.R. 68) DLC.   10646

---- A bill for the relief of the mother and unmarried sister of Lieutenant William H. Allen, deceased. December 31, 1822. Read twice, and committed to a committee of the whole House to-morrow. [Washington, 1822] (H.R. 208) DLC.   10647

---- A bill for the relief of the officers and volunteers engaged in the late campaign against the Seminole Indians. April 8, 1822. Read twice, and committed to the committee of the whole House, to which is committed the report of the Committee of Claims, in the case of sundry sufferers during the late war on the Niagara frontier. [Washington, 1822] (H.R. 152) DLC.   10648

---- A bill for the relief of the President and Directors of the Planters' Bank of New Orleans. January 29, 1822. Mr. Ruggles, from the Committee of Claims, to whom the subject was referred, reported the following bill, which was read, and passed to the second reading. [Washington, 1822] 1 p. (S. 30) DNA. 10649

---- A bill for the relief of the Registers and of the Receivers of public money of the several Land Offices. April 8, 1822. Read twice, and committed to the committee of the whole House to which is committed the bill from the Senate, granting a right of pre-emption to Noble Osborne and William Doake. [Washington, 1822] (H.R. 150) DLC. 10650

---- A bill for the relief of the representatives of Elisha Winter and William Winter. April 10, 1822. Mr. Eaton, from the Committee on Public Lands, to which the subject was referred, reported the following bill, which was read, and passed to the second reading. [Washington, 1822] 3 p. (S. 85) DNA. 10651

---- A bill for the relief of the representatives of John Donnelson, Thomas Carr, and others. February 1, 1822. [Washington, 1822] 1 p. (S. 36) DNA. 10652

---- ---- December 17, 1822. [Washington, 1822] 1 p. (S. 11) DNA. 10653

---- A bill for the relief of the sureties of Joseph Pettipool. March 1, 1822. [Washington, 1822] 1 p. (S. 63) DNA. 10654

---- A bill for the relief of Thomas W. Bacot. March 12, 1822. [Washington, 1822] 1 p. (S. 71) DNA. 10655

---- A bill for the relief of Trapman Johucke and Co. March 6, 1822. Read twice, and committed to a Committee of the whole House, to which is committed the bill for the relief of Nathaniel Bronson. [Washington, 1822] (H.R. 108) DLC. 10656

---- A bill for the relief of William Bartlett and John Stearns, owners of the schooner Angler, and Nathaniel Carver, owner of the schooner Harmony, and others. [Washington, 1822] (H.R. 43) DLC. 10657

---- A bill for the relief of William E. Meek. January 14, 1822. Read twice, and committed to a committee of the whole House to-morrow. [Washington, 1822] (H.R. 36) DLC. 10658

---- A bill for the relief of William N. Earle. January 28, 1822. Read twice, and committed to a committee of the whole House to-morrow. [Washington, 1822] (H.R. 58) DLC. 10659

---- A bill for the relief of William Nott, Stephen Henderson, and Nathaniel Cox, syndics of the creditors of George T. Phillips, late of the city of New Orleans, deceased. February 6, 1822. [Washington, 1822] 2 p. (S. 40) DNA. 10660

---- A bill for the relief of William Sayles. December 11, 1822. Read twice, and committed to a committee of the whole House to-morrow. [Washington, 1822] (H.R. 188) DLC. 10661

---- A bill for the relief of William Thompson. February 19, 1822. Read twice and committed to a Committee of the whole House, to-morrow. [Washington, 1822] (H.R. 92) DLC. 10662

---- A bill for the relief of William Whitehead and others. February 2, 1822. Read twice, and committed to the Committee of the whole House, to which is committed the bill for the relief of certain persons who have paid duties on certain goods imported into Castine. [Washington, 1822] (H. R. 73) DLC.   10663

---- A bill for the relief of Woodson Wren. December 20, 1822. Read twice, and committed to a committee of the whole House to-morrow. [Washington, 1822] (H. R. 204) DLC.   10664

---- A bill further regulating the compensation of Postmasters, and for other purposes. April 8, 1822. Read twice, and committed to a Committee of the whole House, to-morrow. [Washington, 1822] (H. R. 161) DLC.
10665
---- A bill further regulating the compensation of Postmasters, and for other purposes. April 8, 1822. Read twice, and committed to a committee of the whole House to-morrow. Dec. 12, 1822. Ordered to be reprinted. [Washington, 1822] (H. R. 161) DLC.   10666

---- A bill further to amend the several acts relative to the Treasury, War, and Navy, Departments. March 8, 1822. Read, and ordered to lie upon the table. [Washington, 1822] (H. R. 113) DLC.   10667

---- A bill further to continue in force and perpetuate an act passed on the twentieth day of April, in the year one thousand eight hundred and eighteen, entitled "An act supplementary to an act, entitled "An act to regulate the collection of duties on imports and tonnage," passed the second day of March, one thousand seven hundred and ninety-nine. March 8, 1822. [Wash-

ington, 1822] 1 p. (S. 67) DNA.
10668
---- A bill further to regulate the Post office department. April 17, 1822. Read the first and second time, and committed to a committee of the whole House to-morrow. [Washington, 1822] (H. R. 173) DLC.   10669

---- A bill granting a right of pre-emption to Noble Osborne and William Doake. January 28, 1822. [Washington, 1822] 2 p. (S. 29) DNA.   10670

---- A bill granting a section of the public lands to George Shannon. February 20, 1822. [Washington, 1822] 2 p. (S. 51) DNA.
10671
---- A bill granting a tract of land to William Conner and wife, and to their children. February 19, 1822. [Washington, 1822] 2 p. (S. 50) DNA.   10672

---- A bill granting the right of pre-emption to actual settlers on the Public Lands in the state of Illinois. February 13, 1822. [Washington, 1822] 3 p. (S. 46) DNA.   10673

---- A bill granting to the corporation of the city of Mobile, in the state of Alabama, certain lots of ground in the said city. February 11, 1822. [Washington, 1822] 1 p. (S. 43) DNA. 10674

---- A bill granting to the state of Alabama, and to the territory of Arkansas, the right of pre-emption to certain quarter sections of land. January 9, 1822. Read and committed to a committee of the whole House to-morrow. [Washington, 1822] (H. R. 30) DLC.   10675

---- A bill in addition to "An act to continue in force 'An act to protect the commerce of the United States, and punish the crime of piracy,' and, also, to make further provision for punishing the crime of piracy." April 2, 1822. Read twice, and committed to a Committee of the whole House to-morrow. December 12, 1822. Printed by order of the House of Representatives. [Washington, 1822] (H.R. 147) DLC.   10676

---- A bill in addition to the act concerning navigation. April 30, 1822. [Washington, 1822] 2 p. (S. 89) DNA.   10677

---- A bill in addition to the act, entitled "An act for the prompt settlement of Public Accounts." March 24, 1822. Read, and ordered to lie upon the table. [Washington, 1822] (H.R. 131) DLC.   10678

---- A bill in addition to the act, entitled "An act to reduce and fix the military peace establishment of the United States," passed March second, eighteen hundred and twenty-one. February 4, 1822. Read twice, and committed to the Committee of the whole on the state of the Union. [Washington, 1822] (H.R. 76) DLC.   10679

---- A bill in addition to the act, entitled "An act to reduce and fix the Military Peace Establishment of the United States," passed second March, eighteen hundred and twenty-one. April 16, 1822. The above bill being under consideration, Mr. Cannon proposed to amend the same, by inserting the following, as section second: [Washington, 1822] (H.R. 76) DLC.   10680

---- A bill making an appropriation to defray the expenses of

Missions to the Independent Nations on the American continent. April 1, 1822. Read twice, and committed to a committee of the whole House on the state of the Union. [Washington, 1822] (H.R. 143) DLC.   10681

---- A bill making appropriations for the Cumberland Road. Dec. 18, 1822. Read twice, and committed to a committee of the whole House to-morrow. [Washington, 1822] (H.R. 193) DLC.   10682

---- A bill making appropriations for the military service of the United States for the year eighteen hundred and twenty-two. February 19, 1822. Read twice, and committed to a committee of the whole House on the state of the Union. [Washington, 1822] (H.R. 90) DLC.   10683

---- A bill making appropriations for the public buildings. March 25, 1822. Read twice, and committed to the Committee of the whole House to which is committed the bill making appropriations for the support of government for the year 1822. [Washington, 1822] (H.R. 135) DLC.   10684

---- A bill making appropriations for the support of Government, for the year one thousand eight hundred and twenty-two. February 6, 1822. Read twice, and committed to a committee of the whole House to-morrow. [Washington, 1822] (H.R. 79) DLC.   10685

---- A bill making appropriations for the support of the navy of the United States for the year one thousand eight hundred and twenty-two. March 8, 1822. Read twice, and committed to the committee of the whole House, to which is committed the bill making appropriations for the support of government for the year one thousand eight hundred and twenty two. [Washington, 1822] (H. R. 116) DLC.   10686

---- A bill making further appropriations for the military service of the United States, for the year eighteen hundred and twenty-two, and for other purposes. April 8, 1822. Read twice and committed to a committee of the whole House to-morrow. [Washington, 1822] (H. R. 163) DLC.   10687

---- A bill making partial appropriations for the support of the Navy of the United States, during the year one thousand eight hundred and twenty-two. January 29, 1822. Read twice, and committed to a committee of the whole House to-morrow. [Washington, 1822] (H. R. 64) DLC.   10688

---- A bill making provision for the survey and disposal of the public lands in the territory of Florida. March 18, 1822. Read twice, and committed to a Committee of the whole House to-morrow. [Washington, 1822] (H. R. 126) DLC.   10689

---- A bill prescribing the mode of commencing, prosecuting, and deciding controversies between States. January 10, 1822 in Senate of the United States. [Washington, 1822] (S. 14) 7 p. DNA.   10690

---- A bill providing a compensation to receivers of public money for their services in transmitting public money to safe places of deposite. April 3, 1822. Read twice, and committed to the committee of the whole House to

which is committed the bill from the Senate, granting a right of pre-emption to Noble Osborne and William Doake. [Washington, 1822] (H. R. 149) DLC.   10691

---- A bill providing for recording and examining titles and claims to land in the territory of Florida. March 19, 1822. Read twice, and committed to the Committee of the whole House to which is committed the bill requiring surveyors' general to give bond and security for the faithful disbursement of public money, and to limit their term of office. [Washington, 1822] (H. R. 129) DLC.   10692

---- A bill providing for the disposal of the public lands in the state of Mississippi, and for the better organization of the land districts in the states of Alabama and Mississippi. January 8, 1822. Read twice and committed to a committee of the whole House to-morrow. [Washington, 1822] (H. R. 29) DLC.   10693

---- A bill providing for the examination of the titles to land in that part of the state of Louisiana situated between the Rio Hondo and the Sabine river. March 15, 1822. Read twice, and committed to the committee of the whole House to which is committed the bill to authorize the state of Illinois to open a canal through the public land, &c, &c. [Washington, 1822] (H. R. 123) DLC.   10694

---- A bill providing for the examination of the titles to land in that part of the state of Louisiana situated between the Rio Hondo and the Sabine river. March 15, 1822. Read twice, and committed to the committee of the whole House to which is committed the bill to authorize the state

of Illinois to open a canal through
the public land, &c, &c.   December 11, 1822, reprinted by order
of the House, and committed to
a committee of the whole House
to-morrow. [Washington, 1822]
(H. R. 123) DLC.   10695

---- A bill providing for the payment of the salaries of Public
Officers, and for other purposes.
April 18, 1822. Read twice,
and committed to the Committee
of the whole House on the state
of the Union. [Washington, 1822]
(H. R. 171) DLC.   10696

---- A bill providing for the payment of the salaries of Public
Officers, and for other purposes.
April 18, 1822. Read twice, and
committed to the committee of
the whole House on the state of
the Union.   Dec. 12, 1822. Ordered to be reprinted. [Washing-
ton, 1822] (H. R. 171) DLC.
                             10697
---- A bill relinquishing the
right and title of the United States
to certain lots of ground to the
President and Commissioners of
the town of Tuscaloosa, in the
state of Alabama.   April 18,
1822. Read twice, and committed to a committee of the whole
House to-morrow. [Washington,
1822] (H. R. 168) DLC.   10698

----A bill requiring Surveyors
General to give bond and security for the faithful disbursement
of public money, and to limit
their term of office.   January 10,
1822. Read twice and committed
to a Committee of the whole
House to-morrow. [Washington,
1822] (H. R. 32) DLC.   10699

---- A bill restoring to the ship
Diana the privileges of a Sea-
letter Vessel.   January 15, 1822.
Read twice, and committed to a
committee of the whole House to-

morrow. [Washington, 1822]
(H. R. 38) DLC.   10700

---- A bill securing to mechanics, and others, payment for
their labor and materials, in
erecting any house, or other
building, within the county of
Washington, in the District of
Columbia.   March 12, 1822.
Read twice, and committed to a
Committee of the whole House to-
morrow. [Washington, 1822]
(H. R. 120) DLC.   10701

---- A bill securing to mechanics, and others, payment for
their labor and materials, in
erecting any house, or other
building, within the county of
Washington, in the District of
Columbia.   March 12, 1822.
Read twice, and committed to a
Committee of the whole House to-
morrow.   Dec. 12, 1822. Ordered to be re-printed. [Washing-
ton, 1822] (H. R. 120) DLC.
                             10702
---- A bill supplemental to an
act, entitled "An act to authorize
the appointment of commissioners
to lay out the road therein mentioned." January 16, 1822 in
Senate of the United States.
[Washington, 1822] (S. 19) 1 p.
DNA.   10703

---- A bill supplemental to an
act, entitled "An act authorizing
the disposal of certain lots of
public ground in the city of New
Orleans and town of Mobile."
January 30, 1822, in Senate of
the United States. [Washington,
1822] (S. 33) 1 p. DNA. 10704

---- A bill supplemental to an
act, entitled "An act to authorize
the appointment of Commissioners to lay out the road therein
mentioned." January 31, 1822
in Senate of the United States.
[Washington, 1822] (S. 34)

1 p. DNA.   10705

---- A bill supplementary to an
act, entitled "An act to alter the
terms of the district court in
Alabama." January 28, 1822. In
Senate of the United States.
[Washington, 1822] (S. 25) 1 p.
DNA.   10706

---- A bill supplementary to an
act, entitled "An act to set apart
and dispose of certain public
lands for the encouragement of
the cultivation of the vine and
olive." March 26, 1822. In Senate of the United States. [Wash-
ington, 1822] (S. 78) 2 p. DNA.
                           10707
---- A bill supplementary to "An
act for the better organization of
the courts of the United States
within the state of New York."
February 12, 1822. Read twice,
and committed to a committee
of the whole House to-morrow.
[Washington, 1822] (H.R. 86)
DLC.   10708

---- A bill supplementary to "An
act relating to the ransom of
American captives of the late
war." January 2, 1822. Read
twice and committed to a committee of the whole House on
Monday next. [Washington, 1822]
(H.R. 18) DLC.   10709

---- A bill supplementary to,
and to amend an act entitled "An
act to regulate the collection of
duties on imports and tonnage,"
passed second March, one thousand seven hundred and ninety-
nine, and to repeal an act supplementary thereto, passed
twentieth April, one thousand
eight hundred and eighteen, and
for other purposes.   March 12,
1822.   Read twice, and committed to a committee of the whole
House to-morrow. [Washington,
1822] (H.R. 119) DLC.   10710

---- ---- March 12, 1822.
Read twice, and committed to a
committee of the whole House to-
morrow.   December 9, 1822.
Committee of the whole dis-
charged, and re-committed to
the Committee of Ways and
Means. [Washington, 1822]
(H.R. 119) DLC.   10711

---- ---- December 18, 1822.
Read twice, and committed to a
committee of the whole House to-
morrow. [Washington, 1822]
(H.R. 94) DLC.   10712

---- A bill supplementary to the
act, entitled "An act for the relief of the purchasers of public
lands prior to the first day of
July, eighteen hundred and twenty." March 8, 1822 in Senate of
the United States. [Washington,
1822] (S. 66) 3 p. DNA. 10713

---- A bill supplementary to the
acts to provide for certain per-
sons engaged in the Land and
Naval service of the United
States in the Revolutionary war.
January 15, 1822. Read twice,
and committed to a committee of
the whole House to-morrow.
[Washington, 1822] (H.R. 37)
DLC.   10714

---- A bill supplementary to the
acts to provide for certain persons engaged in the land and
naval service of the United States
in the Revolutionary war. [Jan.
1822] [Washington, 1822] (H.R.
37) DLC.   10715

---- A bill supplementary to the
acts to provide for certain persons engaged in the Land and
Naval service of the United States
in the Revolutionary War. December 27, 1822. Read twice,
and committed to a Committee
of the whole House to-morrow.
[Washington, 1822] (H.R. 207)

DLC. 10716

---- A bill to abolish imprisonment for debt. March 5, 1822. Read twice, and committed to a Committee of the whole House to-morrow. [Washington, 1822] (H.R. 106) DLC. 10717

---- A bill to abolish imprisonment for debt. December 10, 1822, in Senate of the United States. [Washington, 1822] (S. 1) 1 p. DNA. 10718

---- A bill to abolish imprisonment for debt. March 5, 1822. Read twice, and committed to a committee of the whole House to-morrow. Dec. 12, 1822. Ordered to be reprinted. [Washington, 1822] (H.R. 106) DLC. 10719

---- A bill to alter the Judicial Districts of Pennsylvania, and for other purposes. March 2, 1822. Read twice, and committed to a Committee of the whole House on Monday next. [Washington, 1822] (H.R. 102) DLC. 10720

---- A bill to alter the times and places of holding the district court in the district of New Jersey. March 20, 1822. In Senate of the United States. [Washington, 1822] (S. 76) 1 p. DNA. 10721

---- A bill to alter the times of holding courts in the Western District of Virginia, and for other purposes. January 29, 1822. Read twice, and committed to a committee of the whole House to-morrow. [Washington, 1822] (H.R. 63) DLC. 10722

---- A bill to abolish the United States' Trading Establishment with the Indian tribes and to provide for opening the trade to individuals. February 25, 1822. In Senate of the United States.

[Washington, 1822] (S. 57) 8 p. DNA. 10723

---- A bill to amend an act, entitled "An act further to regulate the entry of merchandise imported into the United States from any adjacent territory." April 1, 1822. Read twice and committed to the committee of the whole House, to which is committed the "Act to make perpetual an act passed the 3d day of March, 1817, entitled 'An act to continue in force an act, entitled 'An act further to provide for the collection of duties on imports and tonnage, passed the 3d day of March, 1815, and for other purposes. Dec. 12, 1822. Pr. by order of the House of Representatives. [Washington, 1822] (H.R. 146) DLC. 10724

---- A bill to amend the act, entitled, "An act to incorporate the Subscribers to the Bank of the United States." January 24, 1822, in Senate of the United States. [Washington, 1822] (S. 27) 2 p. DNA. 10725

---- A bill to amend an act, entitled "An act to regulate trade and intercourse with the Indian tribes, and to preserve peace on the frontiers," approved thirtieth March, one thousand eight hundred and two. April 2, 1822. In Senate of the United States. [Washington, 1822] (S. 79) 4 p. DNA. 10726

---- A bill to amend the act granting the right of pre-emption to certain settlers in the state of Louisiana, and for other purposes. Jan. 15, 1822. In Senate of the United States. [Washington, 1822] (S. 16) 3 p. DNA. 10727

---- A bill to amend the laws in force, as to the issuing of original writs, and final process, in the Circuit Courts of the United States within the state of Tennessee.   March 1, 1822. In Senate of the United States. [Washington, 1822] (S. 64) 2 p. DNA.   10728

---- A bill to authorize and empower the Corporation of the city of Washington, in the District of Columbia, to drain the low grounds on and near the public reservations, and to improve and ornament certain parts of such reservations.   April 8, 1822. In Senate of the United States. [Washington, 1822] (S. 80) 3 p. DNA.   10729

---- A bill to authorize the building a light-house at Stonington Point, in the state of Connecticut.   February 18, 1822. In Senate of the United States. [Washington, 1822] (S. 45) 2 p. DNA.   10730

---- A bill to authorize the Commissioner of the General Land Office to remit the instalments due on certain lots in Shawneetown, in the state of Illinois. Jan. 22, 1822. In Senate of the United States. [Washington, 1822] (S. 24) 1 p. DNA.   10731

---- A bill to authorize the holding of a District Court at Louisville, in Kentucky.   Jan. 18, 1822. Read twice, and committed to a committee of the whole House to-morrow. [Washington, 1822] (H.R. 46) DLC.   10732

---- A bill to authorize the holding of a District Court at Louisville, in Kentucky. Jan. 18, 1822. Read twice, and committed to a committee of the whole House to-morrow.   Dec. 12, 1822. Ordered to be reprinted. [Washington, 1822] (H.R. 46) DLC.
                                10733
---- A bill to authorize the lay-

ing out, and opening, of a road from Wheeling, in the state of Virginia, to the seat of government of the state of Missouri. Dec. 18, 1822. Read twice, and committed to a Committee of the whole House to-morrow. [Washington, 1822] (H.R. 201) DLC.
                                10734
---- A bill to authorize the occupation of the Columbia River. January 18, 1822. Read twice, and committed to a Committee of the whole House to-morrow. [Washington, 1822] (H.R. 47) DLC.   10735

---- A bill to authorize the occupation of the Columbia River. January 18, 1822. Read twice, and committed to a Committee of the whole House to-morrow. Dec. 11, 1822.   Committee of the whole reported progress, leave granted to sit again, and bill ordered to be reprinted. [Washington, 1822] (H.R. 47) DLC.   10736

---- A bill to authorize the paving of Pennsylvania Avenue. Feb. 26, 1822, in Senate of the United States. [Washington, 1822] (S. 55) 2 p. DNA.   10737

---- A bill to authorize the purchase of a number of copies of the sixth volume of the Laws of the United States.   Dec. 12, 1822, in Senate of the United States. [Washington, 1822] (S. 4) 2 p. DNA.   10738

---- A bill to authorize the state of Illinois to open a Canal through the Public Lands, to connect the Illinois River and Lake Michigan. January 14, 1822. Read twice, and committed to a committee of the whole House to-morrow. [Washington, 1822] (H.R. 34) DLC.   10739

---- A bill to authorize the state of Illinois to open a canal through the public lands to connect the Illinois River and Lake Michigan. January 24, 1822. In Senate of the United States. [Washington, 1822] (S. 26) 2 p. DNA.   10740

---- A bill to confirm certain claims to lots in the village of Peoria, in the state of Illinois. April 12, 1822. Read twice, and committed to a Committee of the whole House to-morrow. Dec. 12, 1822. Ordered to be re-printed. [Washington, 1822] (H.R. 167) DLC.   10741

---- A bill to continue in force "An act declaring the assent of Congress to certain acts of the states of Maryland and Georgia." January 4, 1822. Read twice, and committed to a committee of the whole House to-morrow. [Washington, 1822] (H.R. 25) DLC.   10742

---- A bill to continue the present mode of supplying the Army of the United States. December 17, 1822. Read twice, and committed to a Committee of the whole House to-morrow. [Washington, 1822] (H.R. 197) DLC.
                                   10743

---- A bill to define admiralty and maritime jurisdiction. Feb. 18, 1822. In Senate of the United States. [Washington, 1822] (S. 44) 2 p. DNA.   10744

---- A bill to designate the boundaries of a Land District, and for the establishment of a Land Office, in the state of Indiana. Feb. 1, 1822. In Senate of the United States. [Washington, 1822] (S. 35) 3 p. DNA.   10745

---- A bill to enable the holders of French, British, and Spanish titles to lands within the state of

Louisiana, which have not been recognized as valid by the government of the United States, to institute proceedings to try the validity thereof, and for other purposes. Dec. 11, 1822. In Senate of the United States. [Washington, 1822] (S. 3) 10 p. DNA.   10746

---- A bill to enable the holders of incomplete French and Spanish titles to lands within that part of the late province of Louisiana, which is now comprised within the limits of the state of Missouri, to institute proceedings to try the validity thereof, and to obtain complete titles for the same when found to be valid. April 8, 1822. Ordered to be reprinted as amended. [Washington, 1822] (S. 42) 10 p. DNA.
                                   10747

---- A bill to enable the holders of incomplete French and Spanish titles to lands within that part of the late province of Louisiana, which is now comprised within the limits of the state of Missouri, to institute proceedings to try the validity thereof, and to obtain complete titles for the same, when found to be valid. Dec. 11, 1822. Pr. by order of the House of Representatives, with amendments, reported at the last session, by the Committee on the Public Lands, thereto. [Washington, 1822] (S. 42) 11 p. DNA.   10748

---- A bill to enable the inhabitants of the District of Columbia to form a frame of government. March 21, 1822. Read twice, and committed to a Committee of the whole House to-morrow. [Washington, 1822] (H.R. 133) DLC.   10749

---- ---- March 21, 1822. Read twice, and committed to a com-

mittee of the whole House, to-morrow. Dec. 12, 1822. Ordered to be reprinted. [Washington, 1822] (H.R. 133) DLC.
10750

---- A bill to enable the proprietors of lands held by titles derived from the United States to obtain copies of papers from the proper department, and to declare the effect of such copies. March 2, 1822. Read twice and committed to a committee of the whole House on Monday next. [Washington, 1822] (H.R. 103) DLC.   10751

---- A bill to establish an additional land office in the state of Illinois. Feb. 15, 1822. [Washington, 1822] (S. 48) 1 p. DNA.
10752

---- A bill to establish an additional land office in the territory of Michigan. April 10, 1822. Read twice, and committed to the committee of the whole House to which is committed the bill from the Senate, entitled "An act to authorize the Commissioner of the General Land Office to remit the instalments due on certain lots in Shawneetown, in the state of Illinois." Dec. 12, 1822. Ordered to be reprinted. [Washington, 1822] (H.R. 165) DLC.
10753

---- A bill to establish certain Roads, and to discontinue others. April 22, 1822. Read twice, and committed to a committee of the whole House to-morrow. [Washington, 1822] (H.R. 177) DLC.
10754

---- A bill to establish on the Western Waters a National Armory. March 19, 1822. [Washington, 1822] (S. 75) 1 p. DNA.
10755

---- A bill to establish the District of Blakeley. January 2, 1822. [Washington, 1822] (S. 11) 1 p. DNA.   10756

---- A bill to extend the Charter of the Mechanics' Bank of Alexandria, in the District of Columbia. January 17, 1822. Read twice, and committed to a Committee of the whole House on Monday next. [Washington, 1822] (H.R. 40) DLC.   10757

---- A bill to extend the Charter of the Mechanics' Bank of Alexandria, in the District of Columbia. Dec. 19, 1822. [Washington, 1822] (S. 14) 1 p. DNA.
10758

---- A bill to extend the jurisdiction of Justices of the Peace, in the recovery of debts, in the District of Columbia. Jan. 16, 1822. Read twice and committed to a committee of the whole House on Saturday next. [Washington, 1822] (H.R. 39) DLC.
10759

---- A bill to fix, and render permanent, the Naval Peace Establishment of the United States. March 29, 1822. Read, and committed to a committee of the whole House on the state of the Union. [Washington, 1822] (H.R. 140) DLC.   10760

---- A bill to incorporate the inhabitants of Georgetown, and to repeal all acts heretofore passed for that purpose. March 22, 1822. Read twice, and committed to the Committee of the whole House to which is committed the bill to repeal part of an act, passed by the state of Maryland in the year seventeen hundred and eighty four, and now in force in Georgetown, &c, &c. [Washington, 1822] (H.R. 134) DLC.
10761

---- A bill to incorporate the United States Naval Fraternal Association, for the relief of the families of deceased officers. February 8, 1822. Read twice, and committed to a committee

of the whole House to-morrow.
[Washington, 1822] (H.R. 82)
DLC.   10762

---- A bill to incorporate the
United States Naval Fraternal
Association, for the relief of the
families of deceased officers.
Feb. 8, 1822. Read twice, and
committed to a committee of the
whole House to-morrow. Dec. 12,
1822. Ordered to be reprinted.
[Washington, 1822] (H.R. 82)
DLC.   10763

---- A bill to keep in repair the
Cumberland Road.   January 8,
1822. Mr. Johnson, of Kentucky,
from the Committee on Roads and
Canals, reported the following
bill, which was read, and passed
to the second reading. [Washing-
ton, 1822] (S. 12) 3 p. DNA.
                              10764

---- A bill to limit the Compensation of Marshals in certain
cases, and for other purposes.
February 1, 1822. Read twice,
and committed to the committee
of the whole, to which is committed, the Bill to provide for
the sale of lands conveyed to the
United States, and for sales under executions at the suit of the
United States. [Washington, 1822]
(H.R. 71) DLC.   10765

---- ---- February 1, 1822.
Read twice, and committed to the
committee of the whole, to which
is committed the Bill to provide
for the sale of lands conveyed to
the United States, and for sales
under executions at the suit of
the United States. Dec. 12, 1822.
Ordered to be reprinted. [Wash-
ington, 1822] (H.R. 71) DLC.
                              10766

---- A bill to perfect certain lo-
cations and sales of Public Lands
in Missouri. Feb. 21, 1822.
[Washington, 1822] (S. 53) 2 p.
DNA.   10767

---- A bill to make perpetual
an act, passed the third day of
March, eighteen hundred and
seventeen, entitled "An act to
continue in force an act, entitled 'An act further to provide
for the collection of duties on
imports and tonnage,' passed
third day of March, eighteen
hundred and fifteen, and for other purposes." March 15, 1822.
Read twice, and committed to a
committee of the whole House to-
morrow. [Washington, 1822]
(H.R. 122) DLC.   10768

---- ---- March 15, 1822.
Read twice, and committed to a
committee of the whole House to-
morrow. Dec. 12, 1822. Ordered to be reprinted. [Washing-
ton, 1822] (H.R. 122) DLC.
                              10769

---- A bill to prevent war
among the Indian tribes within
the territorial limits of the
United States.   March 18, 1822.
[Washington, 1822] (S. 72) 1 p.
DNA.   10770

---- A bill to procure the necessary Surveys, Plans, and Estimates, on the subject of Roads
and Canals. Jan. 2, 1822.
Read twice, and committed to a
Committee of the whole House
on the third Monday of January
instant. [Washington, 1822]
(H.R. 19) DLC.   10771

---- ---- Jan. 2, 1822. Read
twice, and committed to a Committee of the whole House on the
third Monday of January instant.
Dec. 12, 1822. Ordered to be
re-printed. [Washington, 1822]
(H.R. 19) DLC.   10772

---- A bill to provide for annu-
ities to the Ottawas, Pottawata-
mies, Kickapoos, Choctaws,
Kaskaskias, to Mushalatubbee,
and to carry into effect the treaty

of Saganaw.   April 24, 1822.
Read twice, and committed to a
committee of the whole House to-
morrow. [Washington, 1822]
(H.R. 181) DLC.   10773

---- A bill to provide for cloth-
ing the Militia when called into
the service of the United States.
Jan. 18, 1822. Read twice, and
committed to the committee of the
whole to which is committed the
Bill to provide for the discipline
of the Militia of the United States.
[Washington, 1822] (H.R. 48)
DLC.   10774

---- ---- ---- Dec. 10, 1822.
Reported from the committee of
the whole without amendment--
ordered to lie on the table, and
to be re-printed. [Washington,
1822] (H.R. 48) DLC.   10775

---- A bill to provide for delivering up persons held to labor
or service in any of the states
or territories, who shall escape
into any other state or territory.
Jan. 14, 1822. Read twice, and
committed to a Committee of the
whole House to-morrow. [Wash-
ington, 1822] (H.R. 35) DLC.
                             10776
---- ---- ---- Dec. 28, 1822.
Reprinted by order of the House
of Representatives, as amended
by a select committee on the
first of April last; and committed to a committee of the whole
House on the second of January
next. The parts to be stricken
out are embraced in brackets;
the additions are printed in ital-
ics. [Washington, 1822] (H.R.
35) DLC.   10777

---- A bill to provide for instructing and disciplining the Mid-
shipmen in the Navy of the United
States.   Mar. 27, 1822. Read
twice, and committed to a Committee of the whole House to-

morrow. [Washington, 1822]
(H.R. 136) DLC.   10778

---- ---- ---- Dec. 12, 1822.
Ordered to be re-printed. [Wash-
ington, 1822] (H.R. 136) DLC.
                             10779
---- A bill to provide for paying
to the state of Alabama three
per centum of the nett proceeds,
arising from the sales of the
public lands within the same.
Jan. 29, 1822. [Washington,
1822] (S. 31) 2 p. DNA. 10780

---- A bill to provide for paying to the state of Mississippi,
three per cent of the nett proceeds arising from the sales of
the public lands within the same.
January 16, 1822. [Washington,
1822] (S. 18) 2 p. DNA. 10781

---- A bill to provide for sick
and disabled seamen.   March 8,
1822. Read twice, and committed to a Committee of the whole
House to-morrow. [Washington,
1822] (H.R. 115) DLC.   10782

---- A bill to provide for the
appointment of an additional
Judge for the Michigan Territory,
and for other purposes. April 1,
1822. Read twice, and committed to a committee of the whole
House to-morrow. [Washington,
1822] (H.R. 144) DLC.   10783

---- A bill to provide for the
collection of duties on imports
and tonnage in Florida, and for
other purposes. March 11, 1822.
Mr. Holmes, of Maine, from the
Committee on Finance, reported
the following bill; which was
twice read by unanimous consent.
[Washington, 1822] (S. 69) 3 p.
DNA.   10784

---- A bill to provide for the
Discipline of the Militia of the
United States. January 3, 1822.

Read twice, and committed to a
Committee of the whole House
to-morrow. [Washington, 1822]
(H. R. 21) DLC.   10785

---- A bill to provide for the
Discipline of the Militia of the
United States: Jan. 3, 1822.
Read twice, and committed to a
Committee of the whole House to-
morrow.   Dec. 9, 1822. Recommitted to the Committee on the
subject of the Militia.   December
12, 1822. Reported with amend-
ments--ordered to lie on the
table, and printed as amended.
[Washington, 1822] (H. R. 21)
DLC.   10786

---- A bill to provide for the
sale of Lands conveyed to the
United States, and for sales under
executions at the suit of the
United States.   February 1, 1822.
Read twice, and committed to a
Committee of the whole House
to-morrow. [Washington, 1822]
(H. R. 70) DLC.   10787

---- ---- ---- Dec. 12, 1822.
Ordered to be reprinted. [Wash-
ington, 1822] (H. R. 70) DLC.
                                 10788
---- A bill to reduce the annual
compensation of certain officers
of government.   April 24, 1822.
Read twice, and committed to
the committee of the whole House,
to which is committed the bill,
altering the compensation of the
members of Congress and delegates from Territories: and, also,
the salaries of the Clerks and
Doorkeepers, &c. of each House
of Congress. [Washington, 1822]
(H. R. 180) DLC.   10789

---- ---- ---- Dec. 12, 1822.
Ordered to be reprinted. [Wash-
ington, 1822] (H. R. 180) DLC.
                                 10790
---- A bill to reduce the monthly allowance to the pensioners

placed upon the pension roll under the acts of 1818 and 1820.
April 22, 1822. Read twice,
and committed to the committee
of the whole House to which is
committed the Bill concerning
the disbursement of public money.
Dec. 12, 1822. Pr. by order of
the House of Representatives.
[Washington, 1822] (H. R. 178)
DLC.   10791

---- A bill to regulate the fees
of the Register of Wills in the
several counties within the District of Columbia.   February 2,
1822. Read twice, and committed to the committee of the
whole House on Monday next.
[Washington, 1822] (H. R. 74)
DLC.   10792

---- A bill to regulate the intercourse with the Indian tribes
within the United States and territories thereof. Jan. 17, 1822.
Read twice, and committed to a
committee of the whole House to-
morrow.   [Washington, 1822]
(H. R. 41) DLC.   10793

---- A bill to relieve the people
of Florida from the operation of
certain ordinances.   April 30,
1822. [Washington, 1822] (S. 90)
1 p. DNA.   10794

---- A bill to remit the duties on
a sword imported for Captain
Thomas Macdonough, of the
United States' Navy. Jan. 22,
1822. Read twice, and committed to the Committee of the
whole House, to which is committed the bill for the relief of
Gad Worthington. [Washington,
1822] (H. R. 53) DLC.   10795

---- A bill to repeal part of an
act passed by the state of Maryland in the year one thousand
seven hundred and eighty-four,
and now in force in Georgetown,

in the District of Columbia, entitled "An act for an addition to Georgetown, in Montgomery county." Jan. 8, 1822. Read twice and committed to a committee of the whole House on Thursday next. [Washington, 1822] (H. R. 22) DLC.   10796

---- A bill to repeal a part of the act entitled "An act to lessen the compensation for Marshals, Clerks, and Attorneys, in the cases therein mentioned." Mar. 1, 1822. Read twice, and committed to the Committee of the whole House, to which is committed the "Bill to limit the compensation of Marshals, in certain cases." [Washington, 1822] (H. R. 100) DLC.   10797

---- ---- ---- Dec. 12, 1822. Ordered to be reprinted. [Washington, 1822] (H. R. 100) DLC.   10798

----A bill to repeal the act, entitled, "An Act to encourage vaccination." Apr. 18, 1822. Read, and ordered to lie on the table. [Washington, 1822] (H. R. 172) DLC.   10799

---- A bill to repeal the fourteenth section of "An act to reduce and fix the military peace establishment," passed the second day of March, one thousand eight hundred and twenty-one. March 18, 1822. [Washington, 1822] (S. 74) 1 p. DNA.   10800

---- A bill to revive and amend the several acts imposing duties on imports and tonnage. March 4, 1822. Read twice, and committed to a Committee of the whole House on the state of the Union. [Washington, 1822] (H. R. 105) DLC.   10801

---- A bill to revive and continue in force certain acts concerning the allowance of Pensions up-

on a relinquishment of Bounty Lands. March 30, 1822. Read, and ordered to lie upon the table. [Washington, 1822] (H. R. 142) DLC.   10802

---- A bill to revive and continue in force certain acts for the adjustment of Land Claims in the Territory of Michigan. April 4, 1822. Read, and ordered to lie on the table. [Washington, 1822] (H. R. 153) DLC.   10803

---- A bill to revive, and continue in force, certain acts for the adjustment of land claims, in the Territory of Michigan. Dec. 24, 1822. Read twice, and committed to the committee of the whole House to which is committed the "bill to confirm certain claims to lots in the village of Peoria, in the state of Illinois." [Washington, 1822] (H. R. 206) DLC.   10804

---- A bill to reward Lieutenant Gregory, his officers and companions. Feb. 5, 1822. [Washington, 1822] (S. 38) 1 p. DNA.   10805

---- A bill vesting in the respective states the right of the United States to all fines assessed for the non-performance of militia duty during the last war. Jan. 22, 1822. [Washington, 1822] (S. 23) 2 p. DNA.   10806

---- The Committee of Claims, to whom was referred the petition of Matthew M'Nair, Report: [Washington, 1822] (43) 1 p. DLC; NjP.   10807

---- Congressional directory for the second session of the 17th Congress...Washington City, Pr. by Daniel Rapine, Agt, 1822. 47 p. DLC; MiD-B; NUtHi; PPL.   10808

---- Constitution of the United

States of America, as proposed
by the convention held at Philadelphia, Sept. 17, 1787, and
since ratified by the several
states: with amendments thereto...Washington, Pr. by Gales
& Seaton, 1822. 49 p. MiD-B.
                              10809
---- Declaration of Independence.
New York, Pub. by John Trumbull, Sept. 10th, 1822. Bdsd.
MHi.   10810

---- Document submitted by Mr.
Holmes, of Mississippi in relation to the Natchez Hospital.
April 26, 1822. Ordered to be
printed for the use of the Senate.
Washington, Pr. by Gales & Seaton, 1822. (90) 4 p. DLC; NjP.
                              10811
---- Documents accompanying
the bill making further appropriations for the military service of
the United States for the year
1822, and for other purposes.
April 8, 1822. Pr. by order of
the House of Representatives.
Washington, Pr. by Gales & Seaton, 1822. 44 p. 2 bdsds. (107)
DLC; NjP.   10812

---- Documents accompanying
the message of the President of
the United States, to both Houses,
at the commencement of the
second session of the 70th Congress.   December 3, 1822. Ordered to lie on the table. Washington, Pr. by Gales & Seaton,
1822. (13-91) 79 p. 13 bdsds.
(2) [!] [1] DLC; NjP.   10813

---- Documents accompanying
the message of the President of
the United States, to both Houses,
at the commencement of the
second session of the 17th Congress.   December 3, 1822. Pr.
by order of the Senate of the
United States. Washington, Pr.
by Gales & Seaton, 1822. 91 p.
DNA; R.   10814

---- Documents relative to Indian trade.   Submitted to the Senate by the Committee on Indian
Affairs. Feb. 11, 1822. Pr. by
order of the Senate... Washington, Pr. by Gales & Seaton,
1822. 62 p. 10 bdsd. (60) DLC;
GU-De; NNLI; Nh-Hi; NjP.
                              10815
---- Documents to be annexed
to the Report of the Committee
of Claims in the case of John
Anderson, et al. Dec. 30, 1822.
Pr. by order of the House of
Representatives of the United
States. [Washington, 1822] 20 p.
(7) [!] DLC; NjP.   10816

---- Documents to be annexed
to the report of the Committee
on Pensions and Revolutionary
Claims, No. 27, in the case of
Richard G. Morris. March 4,
1822. Pr. by order of the House
of Representatives. Washington,
1822. 4 p. (27)[!] DLC; PU.
                              10817
---- Documents to be annexed to
the Report on the petition of
Jonathan Battelle. Feb. 6, 1822.
Pr. by order of the House of
Representatives. [Washington,
1822] 5 p. (25)[!] DLC; G; PU.
                              10818
---- General return of the Army
of the United States, under the
command of Major General Jacob Brown; showing its strength
by regiments and corps, and by
posts and garrisons. March 12,
1822. Washington, Pr. by Gales
& Seaton, 1822. 2 p. (1st sess.,
17th, no. 67) G; NNLI; Nj; O;
TxU.   10819

---- General return of the Army
of the United States, under the
command of Major General Jacob Brown; shewing its strength
by posts and garrisons. March
12, 1822. Laid before the House
by the Committee on Military
Affairs, and ordered to be

printed. Washington, Pr. by Gales & Seaton, 1822. 2 p. 2 bdsds. (92) DLC; NjP. 10820

---- In Senate of the United States, January 2, 1822. The Committee on Naval Affairs, to whom was referred the memorial of Thomas Shields, have had the same under consideration, and thereupon submit the following, Report: [Washington, 1822] (6) 2 p. DLC; NjP. 10821

---- In Senate of the United States, January 2, 1822. The Committee of Claims, to whom was referred the petition of Joseph Janney, Report: [Washington, 1822] (5) 1 p. DLC; NjP. 10822

---- In Senate of the United States, January 3, 1822. The Committee of Finance, to whom was referred the memorial of Paul Lanusse and F. Bailey Blanchard, merchants, of New Orleans, praying for certificates of debenture on certain goods exported from the port of New Orleans in 1819, Report: [Washington, 1822] (7) 1 p. DLC; NjP. 10823

---- In Senate of the United States, Jan. 8, 1822. The Committee of Finance, to whom was referred the memorial of the Trustees of the Transylvania University, praying for a repeal of the duties on books imported into the United States... [Washington, [1822] (8) 3 p. DLC; NjP. 10824

---- In Senate of the United States, Jan. 10, 1822. Mr. Smith, from the Committee on the Judiciary, to which was referred the petition of Josiah Hook, made the following Report: [Washington, 1822] (9) 1 p. DLC; NjP. 10825

---- In Senate of the United States, Jan. 14, 1822. Mr. Johnson, of Louisiana, from the Committee on Indian Affairs, laid before the Senate the following... [Washington, 1822] (10) 12 p. 1 bdsd. DLC; NjP. 10826

---- In Senate of the United States, January 16, 1822. The Committee on Public Lands, to whom was referred the memorial of Daniel W. Coxe, of the city of Philadelphia, praying the confirmation of the title to a tract of land in Louisiana, granted by the Spanish government to the Marquis de Maison Rouge. Report: [Washington, 1822] (14) 1 p. DLC; NjP. 10827

---- In Senate of the United States, Jan. 16, 1822. The Committee of Finance, to whom was referred the petition of George Simpson, praying compensation for his services in negotiating a loan, Report: Washington, 1822. (13) 3 p. DLC; NjP. 10828

---- In Senate of the United States, Jan. 18, 1822. Mr. Benton, from the Committee on Public Lands, to whom was referred the bill concerning the lands and salt springs to be granted to the state of Missouri, for the purpose of education, and for other public uses, reported the same with the following amendment... [Washington, 1822] (S. 1) 1 p. DLC. 10829

---- In Senate of the United States, Jan. 18, 1822. Mr. Lowrie, from the Committee on Public Lands, to whom was referred the bill supplementary to the several acts for adjusting the claims to land, and establishing land offices, in the districts of the island of New Orleans, reported the same with the following amendments... [Washington, 1822] (S. 2) 1 p. DLC.   10830

---- In Senate of the United States, Jan. 21, 1822. Mr. King, of New York, from the committee appointed on the part of the Senate, jointly with the committee on the part of the House of Representatives, to revise the rules and orders by which the business of the two Houses shall be regulated, reported... [Washington, 1822] (16) 1 p. DLC; NjP.   10831

---- In Senate of the United States, Jan. 22, 1822. The Committee on Public Lands, to whom was referred the petition of John Caldwell and others, purchasers of lots in Shawneetown, in the state of Illinois, report... [Washington, 1822] (18) 1 p. DLC; NjP.   10832

---- In Senate of the United States, Jan. 22, 1822. The Committee of Claims, to whom was referred the petition of Rebecca Hodgson, report... [Washington, 1822] (17) 1 p. DLC; NjP. 10833

---- In Senate of the United States, Jan. 28, 1822. Mr. Thomas, from the Committee on Public Lands, to whom was referred the bill for the relief of Richard Matson, reported the same with the following amendment... [Washington, 1822] (S. 4) 1 p. DLC.   10834

---- In Senate of the United States, Jan. 28, 1822. Mr. Eaton, from the Committee on Public Lands, to whom was referred the petition of Noble Osborne and William Doake, praying a right of pre-emption, made the following Report... [Washington, 1822] (19) 1 p. DLC; NjP.   10835

---- In Senate of the United States, Jan. 28, 1822. Mr. Eaton, from the Committee on Finance, to whom was referred the petition of Wm. Nott, and others, in behalf of the creditors of George T. Philips, made the following Report... [Washington, 1822] (20) 2 p. DLC; NjP.   10836

---- In Senate of the United States, Jan. 29, 1822. The Committee of Claims, to whom was referred the petition of the President and Directors of the Planters' Bank of New Orleans, Report... [Washington, 1822] (23) 2 p. DLC; NjP.   10837

---- In Senate of the United States, Jan. 29, 1822. The Committee on Public Lands, to whom was referred the memorial of William Corrie, in behalf of Adam Corrie, submit the following Report... [Washington, 1822] (22) 1 p. DLC; NjP.   10838

---- In Senate of the United States, Jan. 30, 1822. The Committee on Public Lands, to whom was referred the petition of the Mayor, Aldermen, and inhabitants of the city of New Orleans, Report... [Washington, 1822] (25) 1 p. DLC; NjP.   10839

---- In Senate of the United States, February 1, 1822. The Committee of Claims, to whom was referred the memorial of Eliza Dill, Jane Jervis, and of Louisa St. Clair Robb, daughters of the late General S. Clair, Report... [Washington, 1822] (28) 1 p. DLC; NjP.   10840

---- In Senate of the United States, Feb. 1, 1822. Mr. Eaton, from the Committee on Public Lands, to whom was referred the petition of Nicholas Ware, and Wm. A. Carr, executors of

Thomas Carr, deceased, made
the following Report...[Washington, 1822] (29) 2 p. DLC; NjP.
10841

---- In Senate of the United
States, Feb. 4, 1822. The Committee on Naval Affairs, to whom
was referred the petition of John
Gooding and James Williams,
have had the same under consideration, and thereupon submit the
following Report...[Washington,
1822] (31) 2 p. DLC; NjP.
10842

---- In Senate of the United
States, Feb. 5, 1822. The Committee of Finance, to whom was
referred the petition of Henry I.
Jones, praying relief from a
judgment on a debenture bond,
Report...[Washington, 1822] (33)
1 p. DLC; NjP. 10843

---- In Senate of the United
States, Feb. 5, 1822. The Committee of Finance, to whom was
referred the petition of Henry W.
Delavan & Co. praying relief
from several appraisements of
goods imported into the port of
New York, Report...[Washington,
1822] (34) 1 p. DLC; NjP. 10844

---- In Senate of the United
States, Feb. 5, 1822. The Committee on Naval Affairs, to whom
was referred the petition of
William Vaughan, have duly considered that subject, and Report
...[Washington, 1822] (32) 1 p.
DLC; NjP. 10845

---- In Senate of the United
States, Feb. 5, 1822. The Committee on the Judiciary, to which
was referred "An act to provide
for the due execution of the laws
of the United States within the
state of Missouri, and for the
establishment of a district court
therein," report...[Washington,
1822] (35) 1 p. DLC; NjP.
10846

---- In Senate of the United
States, Feb. 6, 1822. The Committee of Claims, to whom was
referred the petition of James
Weir, of Kentucky, with the accompanying documents, Report
...[Washington, 1822] (36) 2 p.
DLC; NjP. 10847

---- In Senate of the United
States, Feb. 7, 1822. Mr. Ruggles, from the Committee of
Claims, to whom was referred
the petition of Samuel Walker,
of Indiana, Reported...[Washington, 1822] (44) 1 p. DLC;
NjP. 10848

---- In Senate of the United
States, Feb. 8, 1822. The Committee of Claims, to whom was
referred the memorial of Alfred
Moore, and Sterling Orgain,
praying for the payment of one
hundred and twenty dollars, for
blacksmith work furnished the
Tennessee volunteers, Reports
...[Washington, 1822] (37) 1 p.
DLC; NjP. 10849

---- In Senate of the United
States, February 11, 1822. The
Committee on Claims, to whom
was referred the memorial of
Jacob Barker, of the City of
New York, Report...[Washington, 1822] (4) 2 p. DLC; NjP.
10850

---- In Senate of the United
States, Feb. 11, 1822. The
Committee on the Judiciary, to
which was referred the petition
of Abel Pratt, made the following Report...[Washington, 1822]
(39) 1 p. DLC; NjP. 10851

---- In Senate of the United
States, Feb. 11, 1822. Mr.
Thomas, from the Committee on
Public Lands, to whom was referred the bill to authorize the
state of Illinois to open a canal
through the public lands to con-

nect the Illinois River and Lake Michigan, reported the same with the following amendments... [Washington, 1822] (S. 26) 2 p. DLC.   10852

---- In Senate of the United States, Feb. 12, 1822. The Committee of Finance, to whom was referred the petition of Edmund Kinsey and William Smiley, sureties of Henry Phillips, late a paymaster in the army of the United States,... Report... [Washington, 1822] (41) 1 p. DLC; NjP. 10853

---- In Senate of the United States, Feb. 15, 1822. The Committee of Claims, to whom was referred the petition of Lawrence Muse, of Tappahannock, in the state of Virginia, Report... [Washington, 1822] (42) 1 p. DLC; NjP.   10854

---- In Senate of the United States, Feb. 18, 1822. Mr. Ruggles, from the Committee of Claims, to whom was recommitted the report of the said Committee on the petition of Rebecca Hodgson, for the purpose of laying before the Senate a summary of the evidence upon which the claim is founded, make the following Report... [Washington, 1822] (45) 11 p. DLC; NjP.
                                 10855
---- In Senate of the United States, Feb. 18, 1822. Mr. Thomas, from the Committee on Public Lands, to whom was referred the bill for the relief of the heirs and representatives of Alexander Montgomery, reported the same with the following amendment... [Washington, 1822] 2 p. DLC.   10856

---- In Senate of the United States, Feb. 20, 1822. The Committee of Claims, to whom was referred the petition of An-

toine Bienvenue, of the state of Louisiana, Report... [Washington, 1822] (46) 2 p. DLC; NjP.
                                 10857
---- In Senate of the United States, Feb. 20, 1822. The Committee of Claims, to whom was referred the petition of Jumonville de Villier, of Louisiana, Report... [Washington, 1822] (47) 1 p. DLC; NjP.   10858

---- In Senate of the United States, Feb. 22, 1822. The Committee of Claims, to whom was referred the memorial of Charlotte J. Bullus, widows and administratrix of John Bullus, deceased, late navy agent at New York, Report... [Washington, 1822] (48) 1 p. DLC; NjP.
                                 10859
---- In Senate of the United States, Feb. 25, 1822. The Committee of Claims, to whom was referred the petition of Holden W. Prout, administrator on the estate of Joshua W. Prout, Report... [Washington, 1822] (49) 1 p. DLC; NjP.   10860

---- In Senate of the United States, March 1, 1822. Mr. King, of New York, submitted the following resolution for consideration. Resolved by the Senate and House of Representatives of the United States of America in Congress assembled, That the President of the Senate, and Speaker of the House of Representatives, do adjourn their respective Houses, on the first Monday of April, next. [Washington, 1822] 1 p. DNA. 10861

---- In Senate of the United States, March 1, 1822. Mr. Thomas, from the Committee on Public Lands, to whom was recommitted the bill confirming the title of the Marquis de Maison Rouge, with instructions, reorted the same in pursuance hereof, with the following amendment...[Washington, 1822] (S. 17) 3 p. DNA.   10862

---- In Senate of the United States, March 5, 1822. The Committee of Claims, to whom was referred the petition of Joseph C. Boyd, of Portland, in the state of Maine, late district paymaster of the U. S. Army for said state, Report...[Washington, 1822] (53) 1 p. DLC; NjP.   10863

---- In Senate of the United States, March 5, 1822. The Committee of Claims, to whom was referred the petition of Samuel Monett, Report...[Washington, 1822] (52) 2 p. DLC; NjP.   10864

---- In Senate of the United States, March 6, 1822. The Committee on Foreign Relations to whom was referred the pecion [!] of Francis Henderson and family, Report...[Washington, 1822] (55) 1 p. DLC; NjP.   10865

---- In Senate of the United States, March 6, 1822. The Committee on Foreign Relations, to whom was referred the petion[!] of Reuben Shapley, Report... Washington, 1822] (54) 1 p. DLC; NjP.   10866

---- In Senate of the United States, March 8, 1822. Mr. Holmes, of Maine, submitted the following motions for consideration, which were read, and ordered to be printed. Resolved, Washington, 1822] (6) 1 p. DLC; NjP.   10867

---- In Senate of the United States, March 12, 1822. The Committee of Finance, to whom was referred the petition of J. Remsen, Holmes, and Co. praying relief from the duties on

goods consumed by fire, Report ...[Washington, 1822] (57) 1 p. DLC; NjP.   10868

---- In Senate of the United States, March 12, 1822. The Committee of Finance, to whom was referred the petition of Jesse Hunt, praying relief from the duties on goods consumed by fire, Report...[Washington, 1822] (58) 1 p. DLC; NjP.   10869

---- In Senate of the United States, March 13, 1822. Mr. Lanman, from the Committee on the District of Columbia, to which the subject was referred, made the following Report... [Washington, 1822] (60) 1 p. DLC; NjP.   10870

---- In Senate of the United States, March 15, 1822. Mr. King, of New York, from the Committee on Foreign Relations, to whom were referred the memorial of R. Appleby, and others, of the Colleton District, South Carolina, and the resolutions of the Chamber of Commerce of the city of Baltimore, praying for the repeal of the laws closing the ports of the U. S. against British vessels, employed in the trade between the U. S. and the British colonies in the West Indies, Report... [Washington, 1822] (61) 4 p. DLC; NjP.   10871

---- In Senate of the United States. March 15, 1822. The Committee on Public Lands, to whom was referred the memorial of John Gilder, and others, a committee of superintendence of the East Florida Coffee Land Association, Report...[Washington, 1822] (62) 1 p. DLC; NjP.   10872

---- In Senate of the United States, March 16, 1822. The

Committee of Claims, to whom
was referred the petition of
Richard Woodland, Report...
[Washington, 1822] (65) 1 p.
DLC; NjP.   10873

---- In Senate of the United
States, March 18, 1822. The
Committee on Public Lands, to
whom was referred the memori-
al of the Mayor and Aldermen of
the city of St. Augustine, Report
... [Washington, 1822] (66) 1 p.
DLC; NjP.   10874

---- In Senate of the United
States, March 18, 1822. Mr.
Dickerson, from the Committee
on Commerce and Manufactures,
to whom was referred the bill to
authorize the building a light
house, at Stonington Point, in the
state of Connecticut, reported
the same, with the following
amendments... [Washington,
1822] (S. 45) 2 p. DNA.   10875

---- In Senate of the United
States, March 19, 1822. The
Committee on Pensions, to whom
was referred the petition of
Charles Simpson, Report...
[Washington, 1822] (67) 1 p. DLC;
NjP.   10876

---- In Senate of the United
States, March 19, 1822. Mr.
Benton proposed the following
amendments to the bill to abolish the United States' trading establishment with the Indian
tribes, and to provide for opening the trade to individuals.
Amendments... [Washington, 1822]
(S. 57) 4 p. DNA.   10877

---- In Senate of the United
States, March 19, 1822. Mr.
Noble, from the Committee on
Pensions, to whom was referred
the petition of Joseph Redman,
Report... [Washington, 1822]
(68) 1 p. DLC; NjP.   10878

---- In Senate of the United
States, March 19, 1822. Mr.
Ruggles, from the Committee of
Claims, to whom was referred
the petition of John S. Larrabee
Moses Sheldon, and John Morton
sureties for Walter Sheldon, dis
trict paymaster in the state of
Vermont, Reported... [Washing-
ton, 1822] (69) 6 p. DLC; NjP.
                                 10879

---- In Senate of the United
States, March 21, 1822. The
Committee of Claims, to whom
was referred the petition of Is-
sachar Thorp, Joseph Siddall,
and James Thorp, cotton manufacturers and calico printers, of
Philadelphia, trading under the
firm of Thorp, Siddall & Co.
Report... [Washington, 1822]
(71) 2 p. DLC; NjP.   10880

---- In Senate of the United
States, March 26, 1822. The
Committee of Finance, to whom
was recommitted the petition of
Paul Lanusse and F. Bailey
Blanchard, and the additional
evidence, Report... [Washington,
1822] (72) 1 p. DLC; NjP.
                                 10881

---- In Senate of the United
States, March 28, 1822. The
Committee on Public Lands, to
whom was referred the petition
of William C. Jones, Report...
[Washington, 1822] (73) 1 p.
DLC; NjP.   10882

---- In Senate of the United
States, April 2, 1822. Mr.
Holmes, of Maine, submitted the
following motions for consideration; which were read, and ordered to be printed for the use
of the Senate: Resolved...
[Washington, 1822] (77) 1 p.
DLC; NjP.   10883

---- In Senate of the United
States, April 3, 1822. The Com
mittee on Pensions, to whom wa

referred the bill from the House of Representatives, supplementary to the acts to provide for certain persons engaged in the land and naval service of the U. S. in the Revolutionary war, Report... [Washington, 1822](80) 1 p. DLC; NjP.   10884

---- In Senate of the United States, April 3, 1822. The Committee on Public Lands, to whom was referred the petition of James W. Files, Report... [Washington, 1822] (78) 1 p. DLC; NjP.   10885

---- In Senate of the United States, April 3, 1822. The Committee on the Judiciary, to which was referred the petition of Samuel Buel, Report... [Washington, 1822] (79) 1 p. DLC; NjP.   10886

---- In Senate of the United States, April 9, 1822. The bill from the House of Representatives, entitled "An act granting certain privileges to steam ships and vessels owned by incorporated companies," being under consideration, Mr. Otis proposed to amend the same, by adding thereto the following section... [Washington, 1822] 1 p. DNA.   10887

---- In Senate of the United States, April 10, 1822. Mr. Lowrie proposed the following amendment to the bill to amend an act, entitled "An act to regulate trade and intercourse with the Indian tribes, and to preserve peace on the frontiers," approved thirtieth March, eighteen hundred and two. Amendment... [Washington, 1822] 2 p. DNA.   10888

---- In Senate of the United States, April 10, 1822. Mr. Williams, of Tennessee, from the Committee on Military Affairs, to whom was referred the

bill for the benefit of Thomas Pendergrass, reported the same, with the following amendment... [Washington, 1822] (S. 83) 1 p. DNA.   10889

---- In Senate of the United States, April 15, 1822. The Committee of Claims, to whom was recommitted the bill for the relief of James Morrison, of Lexington, Kentucky, with instructions to make a special report of the facts, submit the following Report... [Washington, 1822] (85) 2 p. DLC; NjP.
                10890

---- In Senate of the United States, April 15, 1822. Mr. Elliott, from the Military Committee, made the following report: The Military Committee, to whom was referred the resolution instructing... Report... [Washington, 1822] (84) 7 p. DLC; NjP.   10891

---- In Senate of the United States, April 24, 1822. The Committee of Commerce and Manufactures, who were instructed to inquire into the expediency of prohibition the importation of foreign spirits... Report... [Washington, 1822] (87) 1 p. DLC; NjP.   10892

---- In Senate of the United States, April 25, 1822. The Committee of Commerce and Manufactures, to whom was referred the act of the legislature of Mississippi, making appropriations for the Natchez Hospital, beg leave to Report... [Washington, 1822] (88) 1 p. DLC; NjP.
                10893

---- In Senate of the United States, April 30, 1822. Ordered, That the injunction of secrecy be removed from the following proceedings and documents, and that they be printed. [Washing-

ton, 1822] (91) 49 p. DLC; NjP.
10894

---- In Senate of the United
States, Dec. 19, 1822. The Com-
mittee of Claims, to whom was
referred the petition of James
Byers, of New York, Report...
[Washington, 1822] (6) 2 p. DLC;
NjP.   10895

---- In Senate of the United
States, December 23, 1822. The
Committee on Military Affairs,
to whom was referred the peti-
tion of Robert Purdy, Report...
[Washington, 1822] (7) 1 p. DLC;
NjP.   10896

---- In Senate of the United
States, December 31, 1822.
Read, and ordered to be printed.
The Committee of Claims, to
whom was referred the petition
of Joseph Forrest, of Washington
City, Report...[Washington,
1822] (9) 4 p. DLC; NjP. 10897

---- In Senate of the United
States, Dec. 31, 1822. Read,
and ordered to be printed for the
use of the Senate. The Committee on Public Lands, to whom
was referred the petition of
Alexander A. White, Report...
[Washington, 1822] (10) 1 p. DLC;
NjP.   10898

---- In Senate of the United
States, Dec. 31, 1822. Read, and
ordered to be printed for the use
of the Senate. The Committee
on Public Lands, to whom was
referred the petition of Joshua
Russell, of Tyler county, Virginia, Report...[Washington,
1822] (11) 2 p. DLC; NjP.
10899

---- In the House of Representatives, April 22, 1822. Read,
and, with the bill, committed to
the Committee of the whole
House, to which is committed
the bill enabling the claimants
to land within the state of Missouri to institute proceedings to
try the validity of their claims.
The following amendments refer
to the engrossed bill from the
Senate... [Washington, 1822] (S.
42) 3 p. DNA.   10900

---- In the House of Representatives, April 26, 1822. Read, and
with the bill committed to the
committee of the whole House to
which is committed the bill of
the House of Representatives providing for the disposal of the
public lands in the state of Mississippi, and for the better organization of the land districts in
the state of Alabama and Mississippi. Amendments...[Washing-
ton, 1822] (S. 62) DLC. 10901

---- In the session of 1821, the
Committee of pensions and revolutionary claims made the following report on the petition of
Sarah Dewees and others...
[Washington, 1822] 1 p. DLC.
10902

---- Indian reserves in Georgia.
The four following resolutions
are appended to the Report made
to the House of Representatives,
on the 7th Jan., 1822, (first session Seventeenth Congress,) by a
select committee, to whom was
referred the subjects growing out
of certain Indian treaties, and
the articles of agreement and
cession entered into between the
U.S. and the state of Georgia,
on the 24th April, 1802. [Wash-
ington, 1822] (1) [!] 2 p. DLC;
NjP.   10903

---- Joint resolution, submitted
by Mr. Walworth, proposing an
amendment to the Constitution of
the United States in relation to
bankruptcies. March 14, 1822.
Committed to a committee of the
whole House on the state of the
Union. [Washington, 1822] (H.R.)

DLC.   10904

---- ---- ---- Dec. 12, 1822.
Ordered to be reprinted. [Wash-
ington, 1822] (H.R.) DLC. 10905

---- Joint resolutions of the
Mayor, Recorder, Aldermen, and
Common Council, of the Borough
of Norfolk, passed the 17th day
of Dec., 1821; and memorial of
sundry citizens of the same place.
Jan. 11, 1822. Read, and referred to the Committee on Commerce. Washington, Pr. by
Gales & Seaton, 1822. (21) 9 p.
2 bdsd. DLC; MiD-B; NNLI;
Nh-Hi; NjP; O; TxU.   10906

---- Journal of the House of
Representatives of the United
States, being the 1st session of
the 17th Congress...Dec. 3, 1821
...Washington, Pr. by Gales &
Seaton, 1821[!] [1822] 736 p.
DLC; NjP.   10907

---- Journal of the Senate of the
United States of America, being
the 1st session of the 17th Congress...Dec. 3, 1821...Wash-
ington, Pr. by Gales & Seaton,
1821[!] [1822] 433 p. DLC; NjP.
                              10908
---- Laws of the United States
of America, from the 4th of
March, 1815, to the 4th of
March, 1821...Corresponding
with, and intended as a continuation of, the edition of Bioren &
co. ...Vol. 6. Washington City,
Davis & Force, 1822. 825 p.
CtY; F-SC; IaU-L; LNL-L;
MdBB; MdBP; MiU; TMeC;
USlC.   10909

---- Letter from John H. Bell,
acting agent for the Indians in
Florida, to the Hon. John Floyd,
of the House of Representatives
of the U.S. relative to Indian
settlements in Florida. Feb. 7,
1822. Referred to the Committee

on Indian Affairs, Washington,
Pr. by Gales & Seaton, 1822.
(55) 5 p. DLC; PU.   10910

---- Letter from Mr. Rodney,
upon the subject of the report of
a select Committee, to examine
the reports of the Secretary of
the Treasury, in relation to the
examination of the land offices.
April 29, 1822. Read, and ordered to lie upon the table.
Washington, Pr. by Gales & Seaton, 1822. (124) 4 p. DLC;
NNLI; NjP.   10911

---- Letter from the Commissioner of the General Land Office, transmitting a report of the
Commissioner at St. Helena.
Jan. 28, 1822. Pr. by order of
the Senate...Washington, Pr. by
Gales & Seaton, 1822. (24) 16 p.
1 bdsd. DLC; NjP.   10912

---- Letter from the Comptroller
of the Treasury, transmitting a
list of balances on the books of
the register, which have remained unsettled, or appear to
have been due, from late collectors of the customs, more than
three years, prior to the 30th of
Sept. last. Feb. 16, 1822.
Read, and ordered to lie upon
the table. Washington, Pr. by
Gales & Seaton, 1822. (68) 3 p.
2 bdsd. DLC; NjP.   10913

---- Letter from the Comptroller
of the Treasury, transmitting a
list of the names of such officers as have not settled their accounts within the year, for moneys advanced prior to 30th Sept.
1821. A list of accounts which
have remained unsettled more
than three years, prior to the
30th Sept., 1821. And an abstract of moneys advanced prior
to 3d March, 1809, on the...
Dec. 31, 1821. Ordered to lie
upon the table. Washington, Pr.

by Gales & Seaton, 1822. (10)
6 p. 95 bdsd. DLC; NjP. 10914

---- Letter from the Comptroller
of the Treasury, transmitting abstracts of balances on the books
of the Fourth Auditor, which
have remained due more than
three years prior to the 30th of
Sept. 1821; abstracts of balances
which have remained due more
than three years, and which have
been certified for suit; ab abstract
of balances which have remained
due more than three years, and
come within the provisions of the
act for the prompt settlement of
public accounts; a list of officers who have failed to settle
their accounts within the year;
and an explanatory letter from
the Fourth Auditor. Feb. 7,
1822. Read, and ordered to lie
on the table. Washington, Pr.
by Gales & Seaton, 1822. (56)
10 p. 24 bdsd. DLC; PU. 10915

---- Letter from the Comptroller
of the Treasury, transmitting
lists of balances standing on the
books of the register, which have
been due more than three years
prior to the 30th Sept., 1821,
Viz. 1. On the... April 25, 1822.
Read, and ordered to lie on the
table. Washington, Pr. by Gales
& Seaton, 1822. (116) 3 p. 23
bdsd. DLC; NjP. 10916

---- Letter from the Paymaster
General, to the Chairman of the
Military Committee, transmitting
a detailed statement of the proposed annual saving in the pay
department of the army, by the
bill now before the House. Feb.
16, 1822. Laid before the House
of Representatives by the Chairman of the Committee of Ways
and Means, and ordered to be
printed. Washington, Pr. by
Gales & Seaton, 1822. (67) 3 p.
1 bdsd. DLC; NjP. 10917

---- Letter from the Postmaster
General, in reply to a resolution
of the House of Representatives,
of the 15th inst. inquiring into
the causes of failures and delays
of the U. S. mail, between Washington City and Wheeling, Va.
&c. March 21, 1822. Read, and
ordered to lie on the table.
Washington, Pr. by Gales & Seaton, 1822. (97) 3 p. DLC; NjP.
10918

---- Letter from the Postmaster
General, to the Chairman of the
Committee on the Post Office
and Post Roads, transmitting a
statement of the actual condition
of the Post Office Department.
May 1, 1822. Laid before the
House by the Chairman of the
Committee on the Post Office and
Post Roads, and ordered to lie
on the table. Washington, Pr.
by Gales & Seaton, 1822. (121)
6 p. DLC; NjP. 10919

---- Letter from the Postmaster
General, transmitting a list of
contracts made in 1821; and of
those made in 1820, not heretofore communicated to Congress.
Feb. 13, 1822. Referred to the
Committee on the Post Office
and Post Roads, Washington, Pr.
by Gales & Seaton, 1822. (64)
8 p. DLC; NjP. 10920

---- Letter from the Postmaster
General transmitting a list of the
names of the clerks in the Post
Office Department, and the compensation allowed to each. Jan.
8, 1822. Read, and ordered to
lie on the table. Washington,
Pr. by Gales & Seaton, 1822.
(17) 4 p. DLC; NjP. 10921

---- Letter from the Postmaster
General, transmitting a list of
unproductive post roads, for the
year 1821. May 2, 1822. Read,
and ordered to lie on the table.
Washington, Pr. by Gales &

Seaton, 1822. (122) 49 p. DLC;
NjP.   10922

---- Letter from the Postmaster
General, transmitting a report
of the number of officers and
messengers retained in the Post
Office Department. In pursuance
of a resolution of the House of
Representatives, of the 16th
April last. Dec. 3, 1822. Read,
and ordered to lie on the table.
Washington, Pr. by Gales &
Seaton, 1822. (7) 6 p. DLC;
NjP.   10923

---- Letter from the Secretary
of State, transmitting a list of
registered seamen in the several
ports of the U.S., for the three
first quarters of the year 1820.
Jan. 10, 1821. Read, and ordered to lie on the table. Washington, Pr. by Gales & Seaton,
1822. (133) 18 p. DLC; NjP.
                              10924
---- Letter from the Secretary
of State, transmitting a list of
the names of persons to whom
patents have been issued for any
new or useful art, or machine,
manufacture, or composition of
matter, or improvement thereon,
for one year, prior to the 1st
January, 1822. Jan. 8, 1822.
Ordered to lie on the table.
Washington, Pr. by Gales & Seaton, 1822. (18) 11 p. DLC; NjP.
                              10925
---- Letter from the Secretary
of State, transmitting a report of
the number of officers and messengers retained in the Department of State. Made in obedience to resolutions of the House
of Representatives, of the 16th of
April, and 7th of May last. Dec.
3, 1822. Read, and ordered to
lie on the table. Washington,
Pr. by Gales & Seaton, 1822. (3)
7 p. DLC; NjP.   10926

---- Letter from the Secretary

of State, transmitting a return of
the Marshal of South Carolina of
the enumeration of the inhabitants of the District of Kershaw,
in that state. Jan. 24, 1822.
Read, and ordered to lie upon
the table. Washington, Pr. by
Gales & Seaton, 1822. (38) 4 p.
1 bdsd. DLC; NjP.   10927

---- Letter from the Secretary
of State, transmitting an abstract
of American seamen, in the several districts of the U.S. Mar.
5, 1822. Referred to the Committee on Commerce. Washington, Pr. by Gales & Seaton,
1822. (19-37) (133) 19 p. DLC;
NjP.   10928

---- Letter from the Secretary
of the Navy, to the Chairman of
the Committee of Ways and
Means, on the subject of the estimates for the naval service,
for the year 1822. Feb. 18,
1822. Laid before the House by
the Chairman of the Committee
of Ways and Means; and ordered to be printed. Washington,
Pr. by Gales & Seaton, 1822.
(70) 8 p. 1 bdsd. DLC; NjP.
                              10929
---- Letter from the Secretary
of the Navy, to the Chairman of
the Committee on Naval Affairs,
in relation to the equipment of
an additional force for the suppression of piracy in the West
Indian Seas, &c. Dec. 12, 1822.
Pr. by order of the Senate of
the U.S. Washington, Pr. by
Gales & Seaton, 1822. (4) 4 p.
1 bdsd. DLC; NjP.   10930

---- Letter from the Secretary
of the Navy, transmitting a list
of the names of the clerks employed in his office, and in the
office of the Board of Navy Commissioners, and the compensation allowed to each. Jan. 7,
1822. Read, and ordered to lie

on the table. Washington, Pr. by Gales & Seaton, 1822. (14) 4 p. DLC; NjP.   10931

---- Letter from the Secretary of the Navy, transmitting a report of the officers & messengers retained in the Navy Department, &c. (Made in pursuance of resolutions of the House of Representatives, of the 16th April, and 7th of May last,) Dec. 3, 1822. Read, and ordered to lie on the table. Washington, Pr. by Gales & Seaton, 1822. (6) 6 p. DLC; NjP.   10932

---- Letter from the Secretary of the Navy, transmitting a statement of the contracts made by the Commissioners of the Navy, during the year 1821. Jan. 23, 1822. Read, and referred to the Committee on Naval Affairs. Washington, Pr. by Gales & Seaton, 1822. (37) 3 p. 21 bdsd. DLC; NjP.   10933

---- Letter from the Secretary of the Navy, transmitting a statement of moneys drawn from the Treasury, by the Secretary of the Navy, during the year ending the 30th Sept., 1821. Feb. 1, 1822. Referred to the Committee of Ways and Means. Washington, Pr. by Gales & Seaton, 1822. (47) 4 p. 2 bdsd. DLC; NjP.   10934

---- Letter from the Secretary of the Navy, transmitting sundry statements in relation to the Navy pension fund. Jan. 9, 1822. Read, and referred to the Committee on Commerce. Washington, Pr. by Gales & Seaton, 1822. (20) 27 p. 3 bdsd. DLC; NjP.   10935

---- Letter from the Secretary of the Navy, transmitting the annual statement of the several sums appropriated for the naval establishment, for the year 1821, and the unexpended balance of each appropriation on the 1st day of Jan., 1822, &c. Feb. 13, 1822. Referred to the Committee of Ways and Means. Washington, Pr. by Gales & Seaton, 1822. (63) 5 p. 3 bdsd. DLC; NjP.   10936

---- Letter from the Secretary of the Treasury, in reply to a resolution of the House of Representatives of the 22d ultimo. accompanied with sundry statements, in relation to the transactions of the Bank of the U. S., for the year 1821. Feb. 2, 1822. Read, and ordered to lie upon the table. Washington, Pr. by Gales & Seaton, 1822. (52) 4 p. 5 bdsd. DLC; DeGE; PU.   10937

---- Letter from the Secretary of the Treasury, in reply to a resolution of the House of Representatives, requiring information in relation to the banks in which the moneys arising from the sales of the public lands since the 1st Jan., 1818, have been deposited, &c. &c. &c. Feb. 15, 1822. Read, and ordered to lie upon the table. Washington, Pr. by Gales & Seaton, 1822. (66) 185 p. 1 bdsd. DLC; NjP.   10938

---- Letter from the Secretary of the Treasury, transmitting a report of the commissioners, appointed to view and inspect the Cumberland Road. Jan. 15, 1822. Read, and referred to the Committee on Roads and Canals. Washington, Pr. by Gales & Seaton, 1822. (27) 7 p. DLC; NjP.   10939

---- Letter from the Secretary of the Treasury, transmitting a report of the Director of the Mint, giving the result of assays of the several foreign coins still current in the U.S. Jan. 4, 1822. Read, and ordered to lie on the table. Washington, Pr. by Gales & Seaton, 1821[!] [1822] (12) 6 p. DLC; DeGE; NjP.   10940

---- Letter from the Secretary of the Treasury, transmitting a report of the progress which has been made in the settlement of the arrears, in the accounts of the Post Office establishment. March 26, 1822. Read, and ordered to lie on the table. Washington, Pr. by Gales & Seaton, 1822. (98) 9 p. 2 bdsd. DLC; NjP.   10941

---- Letter from the Secretary of the Treasury, transmitting a report supplementary to his report of the 2nd March last, in relation to payments made to inspectors, weighers, gaugers, measurers, & markers, employed by the collectors of the customs, during the years 1816, 1817, 1818, and 1819. Feb. 1, 1822. Read, and referred to the Committee of Commerce. Washington, Pr. by Gales & Seaton, 1822. (50) 4 p. 2 bdsd. DLC; PU.   10942

---- Letter from the Secretary of the Treasury, transmitting a statement of drawback on merchandise exported from the U.S., during the years 1818, 1819, and 1820, compared with the duties which accrued on the same respectively. March 19, 1822. Read, and ordered to lie on the table. Washington, Pr. by Gales & Seaton, 1822. (94) 9 p. DLC; NjP.   10943

---- Letter from the Secretary of the Treasury, transmitting a statement of the duties paid and secured to be paid at the custom house at East River, from its establishment, with the vessels employed in foreign trade; also, a statement of the tonnage employed in the Coasting Trade; together with a like statement from the Custom House at York. Feb. 28, 1822. Read, and referred to the Committee on Commerce. Washington, Pr. by Gales & Seaton, 1822. (78) 3 p. 1 bdsd. DLC; NjP.   10944

---- Letter from the Secretary of the Treasury, transmitting a statement op [!] [of] the items of incidental expenses incurred in the land offices in St. Louis, Franklin, Huntsville, and Cahaba, in the year 1820, and the three first quarters of 1821. April 1, 1822. Read, and ordered to lie on the table. April 2, 1822. Referred to the Committee on the Public Lands. Washington, Pr. by Gales & Seaton, 1822. (101) 16 p. DLC; NjP.   10945

---- Letter from the Secretary of the Treasury, transmitting a statement shewing the amount of the nett proceeds from the sale of public lands in Indiana, subsequent to 1st December, 1816; Illinois, subsequent to 1st January, 1819; and Missouri, subsequent to 1st Jan., 1821. Jan. 15, 1822. Read, and ordered to lie upon the table. Washington, Pr. by Gales & Seaton, 1822. (23) 7 p. DLC; NjP.   10946

---- Letter from the Secretary of the Treasury, transmitting additional statements of the amount of duties which have accrued on books imported into the U.S. April 4, 1822. Pr. by order of the Senate of the U.S. Washington, Pr. by Gales & Seaton, 1822. (81) 4 p. DLC; NjP.   10947

---- Letter from the Secretary of the Treasury, transmitting an estimate of appropriations for the service of the year 1822. Jan. 21, 1822. Read, and referred to the Committee of Ways and Means. Washington, Pr. by Gales & Seaton, 1822. (30) 61 p. DLC; NjP.   10948

---- Letter from the Secretary of the Treasury, transmitting extracts from the registers' and receivers' reports of proceedings, under the Act of 2d of March, 1821, for the relief of Purchasers of Public Lands, prior to 1st July, 1820. (Pursuant to a resolution of the House of Representatives, of the 26th ult.) Jan. 9, 1822. Read, and referred to the Committee on the Public Lands. Washington, Pr. by Gales & Seaton, 1822. (19) 5 p. 1 bdsd. DLC; NjP.   10949

---- Letter from the Secretary of the Treasury, transmitting his annual report on the state of the finances. Dec. 27, 1822. Pr. by order of the Senate of the U.S. Washington, Pr. by Gales & Seaton, 1822. (8) 37 p. 2 bdsd. DLC; NjP.   10950

---- Letter from the Secretary of the Treasury, transmitting his annual report on the state of the finances. Dec. 24, 1822. Read, and referred to the Committee of Ways and Means. Washington, Pr. by Gales & Seaton, 1822. (12) 37 p. 2 bdsd. DLC; NjP.   10951

---- Letter from the Secretary of the Treasury, transmitting, (In obedience of a resolution of the House of Representatives,) statements, showing the number of land offices in the different states and territories; the number and location of each; the annual expense of supporting them; and the amount of money received at each during the years 1820 and 1821, &c. March 15, 1822. Read, and referred to the Committee on the Public Lands. Washington, Pr. by Gales & Seaton, 1822. (95) 6 p. 2 bdsd. DLC; NjP.   10952

---- Letter from the Secretary of the Treasury, transmitting, in obedience to a resolution of the Senate, of the 10th of Jan. last, a statement of the duties which have accrued on books imported into the U.S., during the years 1817, 1818, 1819, 1820 and 1821. April 2, 1822. Pr. by order of the Senate...Washington, Pr. by Gales & Seaton, 1822. (75) 7 p. DLC; NjP.   10953

---- Letter from the Secretary of the Treasury, transmitting, in obedience to a Resolution of the Senate of 29th Jan. last, an abstract of all bonds for duties on merchandise imported into the U.S., which shall have become payable and remain unpaid between the 30th of Sept. 1819, and the 30th of Sept. 1821, &c. Feb. 28, 1822. Pr. by order of the Senate... Washington, Pr. by Gales & Seaton, 1822. (83) 264 p. 2 bdsd. DLC; NjP.   10954

---- Letter from the Secretary of the Treasury, transmitting, in obedience to a resolution of the Senate, of the 22d ult. a copy of a patent, which issued under an act of Congress, passed on the 1st day of June, 1796, "conveying to the Society of United Brethren for Propagating the Gospel among the Heathen, three tracts of land of four thousand acres each, to include the towns of Gnadenhutten, Schoenbrun, and Salem, in the state of Ohio, in trust for the sole use of the Christian Indians formerly settled there." March 5, 1822. Pr. by order of the Senate...Washington, Pr. by Gales & Seaton, 1822. (51) 6 p. DLC; NNUT; NjP. 10955

---- Letter from the Secretary of the Treasury, transmitting, (In pursuance of a resolution of the House of Representatives of the 16th April, 1822,) a report of the officers and messengers retained in the Treasury Department &c. &c. Dec. 3, 1822. Read, and ordered to lie on the table. Washington, Pr. by Gales & Seaton, 1822. (4) 13 p. DLC; NjP. 10956

---- Letter from the Secretary of the Treasury, transmitting, (pursuant to a resolution of the House of Representatives,) information of payments made to the person who examined the land offices in Ohio, Indiana, Illinois, and Missouri, in the year 1821; also, the information required respecting the examination of the land offices in Michigan. Feb. 19, 1822. Ordered to lie on the table. Washington, Pr. by Gales & Seaton, 1822. (71) 7 p. DLC; NjP. 10957

---- Letter from the Secretary of the Treasury, transmitting statements in relation to the emoluments and expenditures of the Officers of the Customs. Feb. 28, 1822. Read, and ordered to lie on the table. Washington, Pr. by Gales & Seaton, 1822. (79) 6 p. 7 bdsd. DLC; NjP. 10958

---- Letter from the Secretary of the Treasury, transmitting statements of payments made at the Treasury, during the year 1821, for the discharge of miscellaneous claims not otherwise provided for; of contracts for

oil, light-houses, buoys, &c. of contracts made by the collectors, for the revenue service, for the year 1820; and of expenditures, for the same year, on account of sick and disabled seamen. Feb. 1, 1822. Read, and ordered to lie on the table. Washington, Pr. by Gales & Seaton, 1822. (48) 11 p. 2 bdsd. DLC; PU. 10959

---- Letter from the Secretary of the Treasury, transmitting statements of the several incorporated banks, within the District of Columbia, shewing the state of their affairs at the commencement of the present year. April 5, 1822. Read, and ordered to lie on the table. Washington, Pr. by Gales & Seaton, 1822. (105) 15 p. DLC; NjP. 10960

---- Letter from the Secretary of the Treasury, transmitting statements of the tonnage money received by the Registers of Baltimore, from the year 1800 to 1821, and the expenditure thereof; under acts of the states of Maryland and Georgia, to which the assent of Congress had been given. Feb. 28, 1822. Read, and committed to the committee of the whole House, to which is committed the "Bill to continue in force, 'An act declaring the consent of Congress to certain acts of the states of Maryland and Georgia." Washington, Pr. by Gales & Seaton, 1822. (77) 9 p. 1 bdsd. DLC; NjP. 10961

---- Letter from the Secretary of the Treasury transmitting statements shewing the commerce and navigation of the U. S., for the year ending the 30th Sept., 1821. Jan. 24, 1822. Read, and referred to the Committee on Commerce. Washington, Pr. by

Gales & Seaton, 1822. (39) 169 p.
2 bdsd. DLC; NjP.   10962

---- Letter from the Secretary
of the Treasury, transmitting
statements shewing the names of
the clerks employed in the several offices of that department,
and the compensation of each.
Jan. 15, 1822. Read, and referred to the Committee on Expenditures in the Treasury Department. Washington, Pr. by
Gales & Seaton, 1822. (22) 13 p.
DLC; NjP.   10963

---- Letter from the Secretary
of the Treasury, transmitting
sundry documents in relation to
the defalcation of John Brahan,
late receiver of public moneys at
Huntsville. May 4, 1822. Read,
and ordered to lie on the table.
Washington, Pr. by Gales & Seaton, 1822. (130) 25 p. DLC;
NjP.   10964

---- Letter from the Secretary of
the Treasury, transmitting sundry
documents in relation to uncur-
rent notes received from the
banks of Edwardsville, Tombeck-
be, and Missouri. April 30,
1822. Read, and ordered to lie
upon the table. Washington, Pr.
by Gales & Seaton, 1822. (119)
59 p. DLC; NjP.   10965

---- Letter from the Secretary of
the Treasury, transmitting the
annual statement of the district
tonnage of the U.S. on the thirty-
first Dec., 1820. Together with
the explanatory letter of the register of the Treasury. Jan. 7,
1822. Read, and ordered to lie
upon the table. Washington, Pr.
by Gales & Seaton, 1822. (16) 6
p. 5 bdsd. DLC; NjP.   10966

---- Letter from the Secretary of
War to the Chairman of the Committee of Ways and Means, upon

the subject of the appropriations
for the year 1822. March 5,
1822. Laid before the House by
the Chairman of the Committee
of Ways and Means, and ordered
to be printed. Washington, Pr.
by Gales & Seaton, 1822. (85)
10 p. DLC; NjP.   10967

---- Letter from the Secretary
of War to the Chairman of the
Committee on Military Affairs,
accompanied with a statement of
the expenditures on the fortifica-
tion at the Pea Patch. As, also, the sum originally estimated
for that work, &c. April 20,
1822. Pr. by order of the
House of Representatives. Washington, Pr. by Gales & Seaton,
1822. (115) 8 p. 1 bdsd. DLC;
NjP.   10968

---- Letter from the Secretary
of War to the Chairman of the
Committee on Military Affairs,
in relation to the application of
money appropriated for fortifications. April 19, 1822. Pr. by
order of the House of Representatives. Washington, Pr. by
Gales & Seaton, 1822. (114) 7 p.
DLC; NjP.   10969

---- Letter from the Secretary
of War to the Chairman of the
Committee on Military Affairs,
of the House of Representatives.
Jan. 31, 1822. Pr. by order of
the Senate... Washington, Pr. by
Gales & Seaton, 1822. (27) 7 p.
DLC; NjP.   10970

---- Letter from the Secretary
of War, to the Chairman of the
Committee on Military Affairs,
transmitting a report of the Chief
Engineer, upon the Military Acad-
emy; A list... April 4, 1822.
Read, and ordered to be printed.
Washington, Pr. by Gales & Sea-
ton, 1822. (104) 28 p. DLC;
NjP.   10971

---- Letter from the Secretary of War, to the Chairman of the Committee on Military Affairs upon the subject of fortifications, &c. &c. March 7, 1822. Laid before the House of Representatives, and ordered to be printed. Washington, Pr. by Gales & Seaton, 1822. (87) 8 p. 1 bdsd. DLC; NjP.   10972

---- Letter from the Secretary of War, to the Honorable D. P. Cook, upon the subject of the examination of the land offices of the U. S., in the state of Ohio. April 5, 1822. Pr. by order of the House of Representatives. Washington, Pr. by Gales & Seaton, 1822. (106) 7 p. DLC; NjP.   10973

---- Letter from the Secretary of War, transmitting a list of the names of the clerks employed in the War Department, and the compensation received by each. Jan. 21, 1822. Read, and ordered to lie on the table. Washington, Pr. by Gales & Seaton, 1822. (32) 6 p. DLC; NjP.   10974

---- Letter from the Secretary of War, transmitting a report of the brevet officers in the service of the United States, with the reason for such distinction. March, 14, 1822. Read, and ordered to lie upon the table. Washington, Pr. by Gales & Seaton, 1822. (93) 5 p. 2 bdsd. DLC; NjP.   10975

---- Letter from the Secretary of War, transmitting a report of the number of officers and messengers, retained in the War Department. Made in obedience to a resolution of the House of Representatives, of 16th April, 1822. Dec. 3, 1822. Read, and ordered to lie on the table. Washington, Pr. by Gales & Seaton, 1822. (5) 4 p. DLC; NjP. 10976

---- Letter from the Secretary of War, transmitting a statement shewing the appropriations for the service of the year 1821; the amount expended for each specific object; and the balance remaining unexpended on the 31st of Dec., 1821. Feb. 12, 1822. Read, and referred to the Committee of Ways and Means. Washington, Pr. by Gales & Seaton, 1822. (62) 5 p. 5 bdsd. DLC; NjP.   10977

---- Letter from the Secretary of War, transmitting a statement, shewing the expenditures of the moneys appropriated for the contingent expenses of the military establishment, for the year 1821. Jan. 22, 1822. Read, and referred to the Committee of Ways and Means. Washington, Pr. by Gales & Seaton, 1822. (35) 3 p. 7 bdsd. DLC; NjP.   10978

---- Letter from the Secretary of War, transmitting, (In obedience of a resolution of the House of Representatives of the 18th ult.) information in relation to the superintendency of Indian Affairs, in the Territory of Michigan during the year 1820, and part of the year 1821. Feb. 11, 1822. Referred to the Committee of the Whole House on the bill making a partial appropriation for the military service for the year 1822. Washington, Pr. by Gales & Seaton, 1822. (60) 132 p. DLC; NjP.   10979

---- Letter from the Secretary of War, transmitting (In obedience to a resolution of the Senate of 29th April last) a report of the number of persons placed upon the pension list up to the 4th of September, 1822; by virtue of the Acts of the 18th of March, 1818 and 1st of May, 1820. Dec. 3, 1822. Pr. by

order of the Senate of the U.S.
Washington, Pr. by Gales & Seaton, 1822. (2) 6 p. DLC; NjP.
10980

---- Letter from the Secretary
of War, transmitting statements
exhibiting a comparative view of
the expenses of the army proper
and military academy, for the
years 1818, 1819, 1820, 1821,
and estimates for the year 1822,
&c. &c. March 5, 1822. Read,
and committed to a Committee
of the whole House on the state
of the Union. Washington, Pr.
by Gales & Seaton, 1822. (83) 7
p. DLC; NjP.   10981

---- Letter from the Secretary of
War, transmitting statements of
contracts made by the War Department, during the year 1821.
Jan. 28, 1822. Read, and referred to the Committee on Military Affairs. Washington, Pr.
by Gales & Seaton, 1822. (41)
3 p. 7 bdsd. DLC; NjP. 10982

---- Letter from the Secretary of
War, transmitting statements
shewing the application and expenditure of the sum of thirty
thousand dollars, appropriated by
an act of Congress, passed the
11th April, 1820, for the purpose
of holding treaties with the Creek
and Cherokee tribes of Indians.
Jan. 22, 1822. Read, and ordered to lie upon the table. Washington, Pr. by Gales & Seaton,
1822. (33) 5 p. DLC; NjP.10983

---- Letter from the Secretary
of War, transmitting sundry
statements in relation to the Indian Department.   April 12, 1822.
Read, and referred to the Committee on Indian Affairs. Washington, Pr. by Gales & Seaton,
1822. (110) 20 p. 2 bdsd. DLC;
NjP.   10984

---- Letter from the Secretary

of War, with the opinion of the
Attorney General on the brevet
rank and pay of Generals Gaines
and Scott.   March 7, 1822. Laid
before the House by the Chairman of the Committee on Military Affairs, and ordered to be
printed. Washington, Pr. by
Gales & Seaton, 1822. (88) 9 p.
DLC; NjP.   10985

---- Letter from the Treasurer
of the United States, transmitting
the general account of his office
from 1st July, 1820, to 30th
June, 1821... Feb. 22, 1822. Pr.
by order of the Senate... Washington, Pr. by Gales & Seaton,
1822. (Doc. 95) 210 p. DLC; F;
NNLI; NjP; O; R; TxU. 10986

---- Letter from the vaccine
agent, to the Speaker of the
House of Representatives. Feb.
7, 1822. Read, and referred to
a Select Committee. Washington,
Pr. by Gales & Seaton, 1822.
(57) 3 p. DLC; NjP.   10987

---- Letters from the Secretary
of War to the Chairman of the
Committee of Ways and Means,
in relation to a partial appropriation for the year 1822.   Jan. 4,
1822.   Pr. by order of the House
of Representatives. Washington,
Pr. by Gales & Seaton, 1822.
(7) 5 p. DLC; NNLI; NjP.
10988

---- Letters of the Secretary of
War, and opinions of the Attor-
ney General of the U.S., in re-
lation to the execution of the act
of Congress of 1st of May, 1820.
In addition to the Pension Law
of 1818, &c. &c.   Feb. 22,
1822.   Pr. by order of the
House of Representatives of the
U.S. Washington, Pr. by Gales
& Seaton, 1822. (72) 7 p. DLC;
NjP.   10989

---- A list of reports to be

made to the House of Representatives at the 2d session of the 17th Congress by the Executive Departments: prepared, in obedience to a standing order of the House of Representatives, by Samuel Burch, chief clerk in the office of said house. Dec. 2, 1822. Washington, Pr. by Gales & Seaton, 1822. (1) 15 p. DLC; NNLI; NjP; O; R.   10990

No entry.   10991

---- A list of the members of the House of Representatives at the first session of the 17th Congress, and the delegates from territories, designating the place where each was born, so far as the same has been ascertained. Washington, Pr. by Gales & Sea- DLC; G; MiD-B; NNLI; NjP; NcU; R; TxU.   10992

No entry   10993

---- Memorial and resolutions of the merchants and others, of the town of Portsmouth, N.H. in relation to the acts restricting the West India trade. March 15, 1822. Pr. by order of the Senate of the U.S. Washington, Pr. by Gales & Seaton, 1822. (64) 4 p. DLC; NjP.   10994

---- Memorial of merchants, ship owners, and others, inhabitants of Salem, Mass. March 6, 1822. Read, and referred to the Committee on Commerce. Washington, Pr. by Gales & Seaton, 1822. (86) 4 p. DLC; NjP.   10995

---- Memorial of Richard W. Meade, to the President of the United States, accompanied with sundry documents. Washington, Gales & Seaton, 1822. 35 p. RPB.   10996

---- Memorial of sundry citizens of the City of Troy in the state of New York, (Against a system of bankruptcy.) Feb. 11, 1822. Pr. by order of the House of Representatives. Washington, Pr. by Gales & Seaton, 1822. (61) 4 p. DLC; NjP.   10997

---- Memorial of sundry merchants of Boston, upon the subject of the revenue laws. Dec. 23, 1822. Read, and referred to a Committee of the whole House on the state of the Union. Washington, Pr. by Gales & Seaton, 1822. (11) 9 p. CtY; DLC; NNLI; Nh-Hi; NjP; R.   10998

---- Memorial of the American Philosophical Society of Philadelphia, praying a repeal of the existing duty on books imported, or amendments to the act, as therein suggested. Jan. 15, 1822. Referred to Committee of Ways and Means. Washington, Pr. by Gales & Seaton, 1822. (28) 7 p. DLC; NjP.   10999

---- Memorial of the American Philosophical Society, of Philadelphia, praying a repeal of the existing duty on books imported, or amendments to the Act, as therein suggested. Jan. 15, 1822. Pr. by order of the Senate...Washington, Pr. by Gales & Seaton, 1822. (11) 7 p. DLC;

NNLI; NjP.   11000

---- Memorial of the American
Society for the Encouragement of
Domestic Manufactures.   Jan.
19, 1822.   Pr. by order of the
Senate of the U. S.   Washington,
Pr. by Gales & Seaton, 1822.
(15) 5 p. DLC; NNLI; NjP.
                              11001
---- Memorial of the American
Society for the Encouragement of
Domestic Manufactures. Jan. 21,
1822.   So much thereof as relates to sales of goods at auction, referred to the Committee
of Ways and Means; the residue,
to the committee of the whole
House, to which is referred the
resolutions of Mr. Baldwin, of
the 7th instant, proposing certain alterations in the laws laying and collecting duties on importations, &c. Washington, Pr.
by Gales & Seaton, 1822. (29)
5 p. DLC; NjP.   11002

---- Memorial of the Board of
Manufacturers of the Pennsylvania Society for the Encouragement of American Manufactures.
March 1, 1822.   Referred to
committee of the whole on resolutions of Mr. Baldwin, of Jan.
7, 1822. Washington, Pr. by
Gales & Seaton, 1822. (81) 9 p.
DLC; NjP.   11003

---- Memorial of the citizens of
Charleston, praying the establishment of an uniform system of
bankruptcy.   Feb. 8, 1822. Referred to the Committee of the
whole House to which is committed the bill to establish an uniform system of bankruptcy
throughout the U. S.   Washington,
Pr. by Gales & Seaton, 1822.
(65) 7 p. DLC; NjP.   11004

---- Memorial of the seamen of
New York.   Jan. 28, 1822. Referred to the Committee on Com-

merce.   Washington, Pr. by
Gales & Seaton, 1822. (40) 6 p.
DLC; NjP.   11005

---- Message from the President of the United States, accompanied with sundry documents in relation to the claim
of the representatives of the
late Caron de Beaumarchais.
April 1, 1822. Read, and ordered to lie on the table. April
2, 1822.   Referred to a Select
Committee. Washington, Pr. by
Gales & Seaton, 1822. (102) 7 p.
DLC; NjP.   11006

---- Message from the President of the U. S. , in reply to a
resolution of the House of Representatives, enquiring whether
the Indian Title has been extinguished by the U. S. to any lands,
the right of soil in which has
been, or is, claimed by any particular state; and, if so, the
conditions upon which the same
has been extinguished.   Feb. 25,
1822.   Read, and referred to the
Committee on the Public Lands.
Washington, Pr. by Gales & Seaton, 1822. (74) 12 p. DLC; NjP.
                              11007
---- Message from the President of the U. S. , on the subject
of piracies committed on the
seamen and commerce of the
United States in the West Indies
and Gulf of Mexico.   Dec. 10,
1822.   Read, and referred to the
Committee on Naval Affairs.
Washington, Pr. by Gales & Seaton, 1822. (8) 3 p. DLC; NjP.
                              11008
---- Message from the President
of the United States relative to
such leases or contracts as may
have been agreed upon and entered into between him and the
owners of the new building on
the Capitol Hill, for the use and
accommodation of Congress.
(Pursuant to a resolution of the

Senate, of the 4th inst.) Feb. 15, 1822. Pr. by order of the Senate of the U.S. Washington, Pr. by Gales & Seaton, 1822. (21) 7 p. DLC; NjP.   11009

---- Message from the President of the United States, returning to the House of Representatives, the act, entitled "An Act for the preservation and repair of the Cumberland Road," with his objections thereto. May 4, 1822. Read, and ordered to lie on the table. Washington, Pr. by Gales & Seaton, 1822. (126) 4 p. DLC; NjP.   11010

---- Message from the President of the United States, to both Houses of Congress, at the commencement of the second session of the 17th Congress. Dec. 3, 1822. Pr. by order of the Senate...Washington, Pr. by Gales & Seaton, 1822. (1) 12 p. DLC; NjP.   11011

No entry   11012

---- Message from the President of the United States, to both Houses of Congress, at the commencement of the second session of the 17th Congress...Washington, Pr. by Gales & Seaton, 1822. 91 p. tables (part fold.) 21 cm. ([U.S. 17th Cong., 2d sess., 1822-1823. House. Ex. doc.] 2) 'Dec. 3, 1822. Read, and ordered to lie on the table." 'Documents accompanying the message of the President...:" p. [13]-9]. DLC; DeGE. 11013

---- Message from the President of the United States, transmitting a plan of the naval peace establishment of the Navy of the United States; and also of the Marine Corps. (Made in compliance with a resolution of the House of Representatives, of the 7th of March last.) Dec. 10, 1822. Read, and referred to the Committee on Naval Affairs. Washington, Pr. by Gales & Seaton, 1822. (10) 14 p. 4 bdsds. DLC; NjP.   11014

---- Message from the President of the United States, transmitting a report from the Secretary of the Navy, on the subject of certain detailed information from the Navy Department, in compliance with resolutions of the Senate of the 11th instant. April 2, 1822. Pr. by order of the Senate... Washington, Pr. by Gales & Seaton, 1822. (76) 11 p. DLC; NjP.   11015

---- Message from the President of the U.S., transmitting a report of the Commissioner of the Public Buildings. Made in obedience to a resolution of the Senate, of the 28th of Jan., 1818. Dec. 10, 1822. Read, and ordered to lie on the table. Washington, Pr. by Gales & Seaton, 1822. (9) 6 p. DLC; NjP.   11016

---- Message from the President of the United States, transmitting a report of the Director of the Mint of the U.S., for the year ending Dec. 31, 1821. Jan. 7, 1822. Read, and ordered to lie upon the table. Washington, Pr. by Gales & Seaton, 1822. (15) 6 p. DLC; NjP.   11017

---- Message from the President of the United States, transmitting a report of the Secretary of State, made in pursuance of a

resolution of the House of Representatives, of the 8th inst. in relation to cases of bankruptcy, which occurred under the act of 4th April, 1800. In the districts of Virginia, Maryland, Pennsylvania, New York, and the District of Columbia. Jan. 31, 1822. Read, and committed to the Committee of the whole House, to which is committed the "Bill to establish an uniform system of bankruptcy throughout the U.S., with the exception of the names of the bankrupts. Washington, Pr. by Gales & Seaton, 1822. (49) 22 p. DLC; PU.
                                11018

---- Message from the President of the United States, transmitting a report of the Secretary of State, made in pursuance of a resolution of the House of Representatives, of the 18th inst. requesting to be furnished with a copy of the Judicial proceedings in the District Court of Louisiana, in the case of the French ship La Pensee. April 30, 1822. Read, and ordered to lie on the table. Washington, Pr. by Gales & Seaton, 1822. (118) 5 p. DLC; NjP.   11019

---- Message from the President of the United States, transmitting a report of the Secretary of the Navy, of the number and location of the naval stations; the number and grade of officers at each; what each receives per month as pay and subsistence, &c. &c. March 5, 1822. Read, and referred to the Committee on Naval Affairs. Washington, Pr. by Gales & Seaton, 1822. (82) 21 p. DLC; NjP.   11020

---- Message from the President of the United States, transmitting a report of the Secretary of War, of the expenditures made under the act to provide for the civiliza-

tion of the Indian tribes. Jan. 22, 1822. Read, and ordered to lie upon the table. Washington, Pr. by Gales & Seaton, 1822. (34) 9 p. 1 bdsd. DLC; GU-De; NjP.   11021

---- Message from the President of the United States, transmitting a report of the Secretary of War, of the measures hitherto devised and pursued for the civilization of the several Indian tribes, within the United States. Feb. 11, 1822. Read, and referred to the Committee on Indian Affairs. Washington, Pr. by Gales & Seaton, 1822. (59) 23 p. DLC; NjP.   11022

---- Message from the President of the United States, transmitting a report of the Secretary of War, on the number, value, & position, of the copper mines on the southern shore of Lake Superior. December 11, 1822. Pr. by order of the Senate... Washington, Pr. by Gales & Seaton, 1822. (5) 33 p. DLC; NjP.
                                11023

---- Message from the President of the United States, transmitting a report of the Secretary of War, showing the amount of woollens purchased for the use of the Army, during the years 1820 and 1821, and what proportion thereof was of American manufacture... Washington, Pr. by Gales & Seaton, 1822. 9 p. (incl. tables) (U.S. 17th Cong., 1st sess., 1821-1822. House. Doc.] 84) DLC; DeGE; NjP.   11024

---- Message from the President of the United States, transmitting a report of the Secretary of War, upon the subject of the command of the U.S. Army in Florida with remarks upon the government of the said territory, previous to the cession thereof by Spain to the United States. April 8, 1822. Read, and ordered to lie on the table. Washington, Pr. by Gales & Seaton, 1822. (108) 6 p. DLC; NjP.

11025

---- Message from the President of the United States, transmitting a report of the Secretary of War, with the annual return of the Militia of the United States, and an exhibit of the arms, munitions, &c. of the several states. March 9, 1822. Read, and ordered to lie on the table. Washington, Pr. by Gales & Seaton, 1822. (91) 8 p. 2 bdsd. DLC; NjP. 11026

---- Message from the President of the United States, transmitting a report of William Lambert, on the subject of the longitude of the capitol of the United States. Jan. 9, 1822. Read, and such part thereof as relates to compensation, referred to the Committee of Ways and Means; the residue to lie upon the table. Washington, Pr. by Gales & Seaton, 1822. (51) 81 p. DLC; PU.

11027

---- Message from the President of the United States, transmitting a supplemental report of William Lambert, in relation to the longitude of the Capitol of the United States, from Greenwich, in England. March 19, 1822. Read, and ordered to lie on the table. Washington, Pr. by Gales & Seaton, 1822. (96) 9 p. DLC; NjP.

11028

---- Message from the President of the United States, transmitting copies of a correspondence, concerning the commercial relations of the United States, with the Norwegian Government. May 2, 1822. Read, and referred to the Committee of Commerce. Washington, Pr. by Gales & Seaton,

1822. (123) 8 p. DLC; NjP.

11029

---- Message from the President of the United States, transmitting copies of letters received at the Department of State, on the subject of the duties discriminating between imported rolled and hammered iron. May 3, 1822. Read, and referred to the Committee of Ways and Means. Washington, Pr. by Gales & Seaton, 1822. (125) 12 p. DLC; DeGE; NjP.

11030

---- Message from the President of the United States, transmitting, (In pursuance of a resolution of the House of Representatives,) a report of the ordnance and ordnance stores, now on hand in the several fortifications and arsenals of the United States; also, estimates of the amount required to provide all which are deemed necessary for the public service. Feb. 7, 1822. Referred to the Committee on Military Affairs. Washington, Pr. by Gales & Seaton, 1822. (54) 15 p. 5 bdsd. DLC; PU. 11031

---- Message from the President of the United States, transmitting, (in pursuance of a resolution of the House of Representatives of the 17th ult.) the correspondence which led to the Treaty of Ghent, &c. &c. Feb. 25, 1822. Read, and ordered to lie upon the table. Washington, Pr. by Gales & Seaton, 1822. (75) 53 p. DLC; NjP.

11032

---- Message from the President of the United States, transmitting, in pursuance of a resolution of the House of Representatives, of the 30th Jan. last, communications from the agents of the United States with the governments south of the U.S. which have declared their independence; and the communications from the agents of such governments in the U.S. with the Secretary of State, as tend to shew the political condition of their governments, and the state of the war between them and Spain. March 8, 1822. Read, and referred to the Committee on Foreign Relations. Washington, Pr. by Gales & Seaton, 1822. (90) 74 p. DLC; NjP.   11033

---- Messages from the President of the United States, transmitting, in pursuance of a resolution of the Senate, of 20th April, a report of the Attorney General, relative to the introduction of slaves into the United States, contrary to existing laws. May 6, 1822. Pr. by order of the Senate of the United States. Washington, Pr. by Gales & Seaton, 1822. (93) 53 p. DLC; NjP.
11034

---- Message from the President of the United States, transmitting, (in pursuance of a Resolution of the Senate of the 25th inst.) sundry papers relative to the recognition of the independence of the South American Colonies. April 26, 1822. Pr. by order of the Senate of the U.S. Washington, Pr. by Gales & Seaton, 1821[!] [1822] (89) 13 p. DLC; NNLI; Nh-Hi; Nj; NjP; O; RPB; TxU.
11035

---- Message for the President of the United States, transmitting information respecting the practical operation of the present system of subsistion the Army; pursuant to a resolution of the Senate. ...Washington, Pr. by Gales & Seaton, 1822. (92) 12 p. 1 bdsd. DLC; NjP.   11036

---- Message from the President of the United States, transmitting, pursuant to a resolution of the House of Representatives, a report of the Secretary of State, with the documents relating to a misunderstanding between Andrew Jackson, while acting as Governor of the Floridas, and Elijius Fromentin, Judge of a Court therein; also, the correspondence between the Secretary of State and the Minister of Spain, on certain proceedings in that territory, &c. &c. Jan. 29, 1822 Read, and ordered to lie upon the table. Washington, Pr. by Gales & Seaton, 1822. (42) 326 p. 2 bdsd. DLC; NjP.   11037

---- Message from the President of the United States, transmitting pursuant to a resolution of the House of Representatives, information relating to the amount of public money paid to the Attorney General, over and above his salary fixed by law, &c. April 9, 1822. Read, and ordered to lie on the table. Washington, Pr. by Gales & Seaton, 1822. (109) 11 p. DLC; NjP.   11038

---- Message from the President of the United States, transmitting (pursuant to a resolution of the House of Representatives, of 7th May,) a letter of Jonathan Russell, late one of the Plenipotentiaries of the U.S., at the negotiation of Ghent, with remarks thereon, by the Secretary of State. May 8, 1822. Ordered to lie on the table. Washington, Pr by Gales & Seaton, 1822. (131) 58 p. DLC; NjP.   11039

---- Message from the President of the United States, transmitting (Pursuant to a resolution of the House of Representatives, of the 16th inst.) information in relation to abuses committed upon the persons of the officers and crews of American vessels at the Havana, and other Spanish ports in America; and the conduct of the Spanish authorities in relation thereto. Jan. 31, 1822. Read, and ordered to lie upon the table. Washington, Pr. by Gales & Seaton, 1822. (46) 14 p. DLC; NjP. 11040

---- Message from the President of the United States, transmitting, Pursuant to a resolution of the Senate of the 14th inst. information of the annual disposition which has been made of the sum of fifteen thousand dollars, appropriated by an act of Congress, of the year 1802, to promote civilization among friendly Indian tribes; shewing to what tribes that evidence of the national bounty has been extended; the names of the Agents who have been entrusted with the application of the money; the several amounts by them received; and the manner in which they have severally applied it to accomplish the objects of the act. Feb. 24, 1822. Pr. by order of the Senate of the United States. Washington, Pr. by Gales & Seaton, 1822. (50) 7 p. DLC; NjP. 11041

---- Message from the President of the United States transmitting, pursuant to a resolution of the Senate of the 3d inst. Copies of the Rules and Instructions given to the ministers, consuls, or other agents, of the United States in foreign countries, concerning allowances to or on account of, sick or disabled American seamen; and also, accounts of the money so advanced in the years 1818, 1819, and 1820, and the number of seamen so annually relieved. Jan. 29, 1822. Pr. by order of the Senate of the United States. Washington, Pr. by Gales & Seaton, 1822. (26) 39 p. DLC; NjP. 11042

---- Message from the President of the United States, transmitting pursuant to a resolution of the Senate of the 29th January last, statements, shewing the number of officers and soldiers who served in the Revolutionary War from the state of Virginia on Continental Establishment... March 15, 1822. Pr. by order of the Senate of the United States. Washington, Pr. by Gales & Seaton, 1822. (63) 8 p. DLC; NjP. 11043

---- Message from the President of the United States, transmitting sundry papers relating to transactions in East and West Florida, received at the Department of State since his message of 28th January, last, with copies of two letters from the Secretary of State, upon the same subject. April 19, 1822. Pr. by order of the Senate...Washington, Pr. by Gales & Seaton, 1822. (86) 46 p. DLC; NjP. 11044

---- Message from the President of the United States, transmitting sundry papers relating to transactions in East and West Florida, received at the Department of State since his message of 28th Jan., last, with copies of two letters from the Secretary of State, upon the same subject. April 19, 1822. Read, and ordered to lie on the table. Washington, Pr. by Gales & Seaton, 1822. (113) 46 p. DLC; NjP. 11045

---- Message from the President of the United States, transmitting the annual report of the Commissioner of the Public Buildings. Jan. 17, 1822. Read, and ordered to lie on the table. Washington, Pr. by Gales & Seaton, 1822. (26) 6 p. DLC; NjP. 11046

---- Message from the President of the United States, transmitting the information required by a resolution of the House of Representatives of the 16th of Feb. last, in relation to claims set up by foreign governments to Territory of the U. S. upon the Pacific Ocean, North of the forty-second degree of latitude, &c. &c. April 17, 1822. Read, and ordered to lie on the table. Washington, Pr. by Gales & Seaton, 1822. (112) 38 p. DLC; NjP. 11047

---- Message from the President of the United States, transmitting the information required by a resolution of the House of Representatives, respecting the lead mines of Missouri. May 7, 1822. Pr. by order of the Senate ... Washington, Pr. by Gales & Seaton, 1822. (94) 19 p. DLC; NjP. 11048

---- Message from the President of the United States, transmitting the information required (By a resolution of the House of Representatives of the 22d ult.,) in relation to the progress made by the commissioners under the Fifth Article of the Treaty of Ghent. Feb. 7, 1822. Read, and ordered to lie upon the table. Feb. 8, 1822. Referred to a select committee, and printed by order of the House of Representatives of the U. S. Washington, Pr. by Gales & Seaton, 1822. (58) 8 p. DLC; NjP. 11049

---- Message from the President of the United States, transmitting the information required by resolution of the House of Representatives, respecting the lead mines of Missouri. May 7, 1822. Read, and ordered to lie on the table. Washington, Pr. by Gales & Seaton, 1822. (129) 19 p. DLC; NjP. 11050

---- Message from the President of the United States, transmitting translations of two letters from Don Joaquin d'Anduaga to the Secretary of State, upon the subject of the conduct of Gen. Jackson in Florida, and the independence of Mexico. May 6, 1822. Read, and ordered to lie on the table. Washington, Pr. by Gales & Seaton, 1822. (128) 7 p. DLC; NjP. 11051

---- Message from the President of the United States, upon the subject of fortifications on Dauphine Island and Mobile Point. March 26, 1822. Referred to the Committee on Military Affairs. Washington, Pr. by Gales & Seaton, 1822. (99) 24 p. DLC; NjP. 11052

---- Message from the President of the United States, upon the subject of fortifications on Dauphine Island and Mobile Point. March 27, 1822. Pr. by order of the Senate...Washington, Pr. by Gales & Seaton, 1822. (74) 9 p. DLC; NjP. 11053

---- Message from the President of the United States, upon the subject of Jonathan Carver's claim to a tract of land within the United States, near the Falls of St. Anthony. April 24, 1822. Read, and referred to the Committee on the Public Lands. Washington, Pr. by Gales & Seaton, 1822. (117) 9 p. DLC; NjP. 11054

---- Message from the President of the United States, upon the subject of the extinguishment of the Indian Title to land within the State of Georgia. Feb. 28, 1822. Read, and committed to the committee of the whole House to which is committed the resolution of Mr. Gilmer, of the 7th ult., making appropriations for carrying into effect the articles of agreement and cession between the U.S. and Georgia, on the 24th April, 1802. Washington, Pr. by Gales & Seaton, 1822. (80) 3 p. DLC; GU-De; NjP. 11055

---- Message from the President of the United States, with his objections to the bill for the preservation and repair of the Cumberland Road; also, a paper, containing his views on the subject of internal improvements. May 4, 1822. Pr. by order of the House of Representatives. Washington, Pr. by Gales & Seaton, 1822. (127) 60 p. DLC; NjP. 11056

---- Minutes of proceedings of the court of enquiry into the official conduct of Capt. Isaac Hull, as commandant of the United States Navy yard, at Charlestown, in the state of Massachusetts, convened at the Navy yard, in said Charlestown, on the 12th day of August, A.D. 1822. Pr. by order of the Navy Department, from the official record. Washington City, Pr. and pub. by Davis and Force, (Franklin's Head,) Pennsylvania Avenue, 1822. [ii], 7-244, 64 p. C; CSfLaw; CtHT; CtY; DLC; M; MB; MBS; MH; MdAN; MiU-C; NNC; Nh-Hi; OCHP; OFH; PP; PPB; PPF; ScU; WHi. 11057

---- Minutes of proceedings of the court of enquiry ordered by the Secretary of the Navy on the application of Cpt. James Biddle, begun and held at the Navy Yard, in Charlestown, State of Massachusetts, on Monday, the seventh day of October, 1822...Washington City, Davis and Force (Franklin's Head) Pennsylvania Ave., 1822. 50 p. DLC; MBAt; MBNEH; MdAN. 11058

---- Mr. Dickerson, from the Select Committee, to whom was referred the resolution proposing an amendment to the Constitution of the United States, as it respects the choice of President and Vice President of the United States, and the election of Representatives in Congress of the United States, reported the same with the following amendment... Feb. 18, 1822. [Washington, 1822] DLC. 11059

---- Mr. Francis Johnson, from the Select Committee to which was referred, on the twenty-ninth ultimo, the "Bill to provide for delivering up persons held to labor or service in any of the states or territories, who shall escape into any other state or territory," reported the same, with the following amendments... April 1, 1822. [Washington, 1822] (H.R. 35) DLC. 11060

---- Mr. Smith, of Maryland, moved the following amendments to the bill to authorize the Secretary of the Treasury to exchange a stock, bearing an interest of five per cent, for certain stocks bearing an interest of six and seven per cent. Amendments... March 26, 1822. [Washington, 1822] (H.R. 15) DLC. 11061

---- Official Army Register for 1822. Adjutant General's office, Washington, August 1822. E. De-Krafft, printer. 20 p. MdHi; PPL. 11062

---- Opinion in case Stockton, R.F., vs. Ship Marianna Flora. By John Davis of Boston Judge and J. Story. [Boston] 1822. 27 p. MBAt. 11063

---- Ordenanzas, reglas, e instrucciones, para el servicio de

la marina militar de los Estados
Unidos... Filadelfia, T.H. Palmer, 1822. 127, 36 p. NN. 11064

---- Petition of James Le Ray
de Chaumont. March 1, 1822.
Referred to the Committee on
Agriculture. [Washington, 1822]
(52) 1 p. DLC; PU.   11065

---- Proceedings of a court of
enquiry, held at the Navy Yard,
Brooklyn, New York, upon Capt.
James Barron of tne United
States' Navy, in May, 1821.
Washington City, Pr. by Jacob
Gideon, Junior, 1822. [2], 111 p.
CSmH; Ct; CtY; DLC; DNA;
MH-L; MHi; MWA; MdHi; MiD-
B; NbU; Nh; Nh-Hi; PHi; PP;
PPAmP; PPF.   11066

---- Proceedings of the general
court martial convened for the
trial of Commodore James Bar-
ron, Capt. Charles Gordon, Mr.
William Hook, and Capt. John
Hall, of the United States' ship
Chesapeake, in the month of
January, 1808.   Pub. by order
of the Navy Department. [Wash-
ington] Pr. by J. Gideon, jr.,
1822. 496 p. CSmH; CtHT-W;
DNA; DLC; DeGE; MB; MH-L;
MdBE; MdHi; MiU-C; NBuG;
NIC; NN; NRU; OCLaw; OFH;
PP; PPL; PPiU; RPB; Vi; W;
WHi; BrMus.   11067

---- Proposed amendments to
the Constitution of the United
States (Submitted by Mr. Montgomery.) April 27, 1822. Read,
and ordered to lie upon the table.
Resolved, by the Senate and
House of Representatives of the
United States in Congress assembled, That the following
propositions shall be submitted
to the legislatures of the several
states, as amendments to the national constitution, which, if ratified by three-fourths of the said

legislatures, shall, immediately
... [Washington, 1822] (14) 2 p.
DLC; NjP.   11068

---- A register of officers and
agents, civil, military, and naval, in the service of the United
States, on the 30th of Sept.,
1821, together with the names,
force, and condition of all the
ships and vessels belonging to
the United States, and when and
where built, in pursuance of a
resolution of Congress, of the
27th of April 1816.   Washington,
Pr. by Davis and Force, Pennsylvania Ave., 1822. 141 p.
InU; MiD-B; MsJS; N; R; TKL-
Mc; TNV; USlC; ViRVal.
                           11069
---- Register of the commission and warrant officers of the
Navy of the United States including officers of the Marine Corps
...Washington City, Pr. by
Davis and Force, 1822. 31 p.
DLC; MBNEH; NbU.   11070

---- Register of the commission and warrant officers of the
Navy of the United States [for
1822]; including officers of the
Marine Corps, &c. &c. [Wash-
ington] Pr. by Jacob Gideon, Jr.
1822. 30, [1] p. MBNEH; MiD-
B; NbU.   11071

No entry   11072

---- Report by the Second Auditor of the Treasury, of accounts
which have remained unsettled,
or, on which balances appear to
have been due more than three
years prior to the 30th Sept.,
1821; as appears from the books
of his office.   And, also, of officers who have failed to settle

their accounts within the year terminating on the 30th September, 1821. Jan. 23, 1822. Ordered to lie upon the table. Washington, Pr. by Gales & Seaton, 1822. (36) 4 p. 6 bdsd. DLC; NNLI; NjP.   11073

---- Report in part, of the select committee appointed, on the 18th Feb. last, to inquire into the propriety of a retrenchment of the expenditures of the government, accompanied with a bill altering the compensation of the members of Congress, and delegates of territories; and, also, the salaries of the clerks, and doorkeepers, &c. of each House of Congress. April 20, 1822. Read, and ordered to lie on the table. [Washington, 1822] (95) 2 p. DLC; NjP.   11074

---- Report in the case of John Thomas, and Co. by the Committee of Claims. Feb. 15, 1822. Read, and ordered to lie on the table. Feb. 18, 1822. Committed to a committee of the whole House. Report, and letter of the Third Auditor, pr. by order of the House of Representatives. [Washington, 1822] (39) 4 p. DLC; NjP.   11075

---- Report in the case of John Thomas, and Co. by the Committee of Claims. Feb. 15, 1822. Read, and ordered to lie on the table. Feb. 18, 1822. Report and letter of the Third Auditor pr. by order of the House of Representatives. [Washington, 1822] (41) 4 p. DLC; PU. 11076

---- Report in the case of the heirs of Maria Therese. Jan. 31, 1822. Read, and with a bill for the relief of the legal representatives of Maria Therese, committed to a committee of the whole House to-morrow. [Washington,

1822] (33) 2 p. DLC; PU.   11077

---- Report in the cases of Hoel Lawrence, Frederick White, and of Thaddeus Clark, and others, by the Committee of Claims. Feb. 25, 1822. Read, and ordered to lie on the table. March 11, 1822. Committed to a committee of the whole House to-morrow. Dec. 12, 1822. Reprinted by order of the House of Representatives. [Washington, 1822] (28) 10 p. DLC; NjP.   11078

---- ---- Feb. 25, 1822. Read, and ordered to lie on the table. March 11, 1822. Committed to a committee of the whole House to-morrow. [Washington, 1822] (69) 10 p. DLC; PU.   11079

---- Report of the Committee of Claims in the case of Alvin Bronson. Feb. 15, 1822. Read, and ordered to lie upon the table. Feb. 16, 1822. Committed to a committee of the whole House on Monday next. [Washington, 1822] (40) 22 p. DLC; PU.   11080

---- Report of the Committee of Claims in the case of Alvin Bronson. Feb. 15, 1822. Read, and ordered to lie upon the table. Feb. 16, 1822. Committed to a committee of the whole House on Monday next. Dec. 12, 1822. Reprinted by order of the House of Representatives [Washington, 1822] (12) 20 p. DLC; NjP.   11081

---- Report of the Committee of Claims in the case of Brigadier Gen. T. Glascock. March 29, 1822. Read, and ordered to lie on the table. Dec. 20, 1822. Pr. by order of the House of Representatives. [Washington, 1822] (53) 1 p. DLC; NjP.   11082

---- Report of the Committee

of Claims in the case of Caze
and Richaud. Feb. 22, 1822.
Read, and ordered to lie on the
table. March 6, 1822. Committed to a committee of the whole
House to-morrow. [Washington,
1822] (60) 3 p. DLC; PU. 11083

---- ---- Feb. 22, 1822. Read,
and ordered to lie on the table.
March 6, 1822. Committed to a
committee of the whole House
to-morrow. Dec. 12, 1822. Reprinted by order of the House of
Representatives. [Washington,
1822] (13) 3 p. DLC; NjP.
                                  11084
---- Report of the Committee of
Claims in the case of David Taylor. Dec. 20, 1821. Committed
to a committee of the whole
House to-morrow. Dec. 12,
1822. Pr. by order of the
House of Representatives. [Washington, 1822] (41) 1 p. DLC;
NjP.   11085

---- Report of the Committee of
Claims in the case of Eli Hart.
Jan. 21, 1822. Read, and committed to a committee of the
whole House to-morrow. [Washington, 1822] (19) 11 p. DLC;
PU.   11086

---- ---- Jan. 21, 1822. Read,
and committed to a committee of
the whole House to-morrow. Dec.
12, 1822. Reprinted by order of
the House of Representatives.
[Washington, 1822] (23) 10 p.
DLC; NjP.   11087

---- Report of the Committee of
Claims in the case of Gad Pierce.
Jan. 21, 1822. Committed to a
committee of the whole House to-
morrow. Dec. 12, 1822. Pr.
by order of the House of Representatives. [Washington, 1822]
(32) 2 p. DLC; NjP.   11088

---- Report of the Committee of

Claims in the case of George
Winthrop Fox. Dec. 26, 1821.
Read, and ordered to lie on the
table. Feb. 6, 1822. Committed to a committee of the whole
House to-morrow. Dec. 12,
1822. Pr. by order of the House
of Representatives. [Washington,
1822] (20) 1 p. DLC; NjP.
                                  11089
---- Report of the Committee of
Claims in the case of Heman B.
Potter. Jan. 23, 1822. Read,
and committed to a committee of
the whole House to-morrow.
[Washington, 1822] (23) 4 p.
DLC; PU.   11090

---- ---- Jan. 23, 1822. Read,
and committed to a committee
of the whole House to-morrow.
Dec. 12, 1822. Reprinted by order of the House of Representatives. [Washington, 1822] (4)
4 p. DLC; NjP.   11091

---- Report of the Committee of
Claims in the case of Henry B.
Brevoort. Feb. 7, 1822. Read,
and ordered to lie on the table.
May 28, 1822. Committed to a
committee of the whole House to-
day. Dec. 12, 1822. Pr. by order of the House of Representatives. [Washington, 1822] (9) 2
p. DLC; NjP.   11092

---- Report of the Committee of
Claims in the case of James
May, with a bill for the relief of
James May, and the legal representatives of William Macomb.
Jan. 2, 1822. Read, and, with
the bill, committed to a committee of the whole House to-morrow. [Washington, 1822] (7) 6 p.
DLC; PU.   11093

---- Report of the Committee of
Claims in the case of James P.
Smith, representative of Ambrose
D. Smith. March 4, 1822. Read,
and ordered to lie on the table.

March 26, 1822. Committed to a committee of the whole House tomorrow. Dec. 12, 1822. Pr. by order of the House of Representatives. [Washington, 1822] (35) 1 p. DLC; NjP.   11094

---- Report of the Committee of Claims in the case of John G. Bogert. March 27, 1822. Ordered to lie on the table. Dec. 23, 1822. Committed to a committee of the whole House tomorrow. [Washington, 1822] (56) 6 p. DLC; NjP.   11095

---- Report of the Committee of Claims in the case of Joseph F. White. Jan. 25, 1822. Read, and ordered to lie upon the table. Jan. 28, 1822. Pr. by order of the House of Representatives. [Washington, 1822] (28) 7 p. DLC; PU.   11096

---- Report of the Committee of Claims, in the case of Marinus W. Gilbert. Feb. 14, 1822. Read, and committed to a committee of the whole House tomorrow. [Washington, 1822] (38) 20 p. DLC; PU.   11097

---- Report of the Committee of Claims in the case of Marinus W. Gilbert. Feb. 14, 1822. Read, and committed to a committee of the whole House tomorrow. Dec. 12, 1822. Repr. by order of the House of Representatives. [Washington, 1822] (21) 19 p. DLC; NjP.   11098

---- Report of the Committee of Claims, in the case of Nathaniel Childers. Feb. 1, 1822. Read, and ordered to lie on the table. [Washington, 1822] (35) 2 p. DLC; PU.   11099

---- Report of the Committee of Claims in the case of Samuel Wharton. Dec. 23, 1822. Read,

and ordered to lie upon the table. [Washington, 1822] (54) 3 p. DLC; NjP.   11100

---- Report of the Committee of Claims, in the case of the heirs of William T. Nimmo, with a bill for their relief. Dec. 18, 1822. Read, and, with the bill, committed to a committee of the whole House to-morrow. [Washington, 1822] (49) 2 p. DLC; NjP.   11101

---- Report of the Committee of Claims in the case of the Levy Court of Calvert County. Feb. 6, 1822. Read, and committed to a committee of the whole House to-morrow. [Washington, 1822] (36) 3 p. DLC; PU.
11102

---- Report of the Committee of Claims in the case of the Levy Court of Calvert County. Feb. 6, 1822. Read, and committed to a committee of the whole House to-morrow. Dec. 12, 1822. Repr. by order of the House of Representatives. [Washington, 1822] (3) 3 p. DLC; NjP.
11103

---- Report of the Committee of Claims in the case of William Drakeford. April 27, 1822. Read, and committed to the committee of the whole House on the report of the Committee of Claims in the case of Nathaniel Childers. Dec. 12, 1822. Pr. by order of the House of Representatives. [Washington, 1822] (16) 1 p. DLC; NjP.
11104

---- Report of the Committee of Claims, in the case of William G. and Benjamin Roberts. March 4, 1822. Read, and ordered to lie on the table. March 6, 1822. Committed to a committee of the whole House. Dec. 12, 1822. Pr. by order of the House of Representatives. [Washington, 1822]

(33) 13 p. DLC; NjP.   11105

---- Report of the Committee of
Claims on Senate bill No. 13,
for the relief of Josiah Hook.
Feb. 13, 1822. Ordered to lie
on the table. Feb. 18, 1822. Pr.
by order of the House of Representatives. [Washington, 1822]
(42) 13 p. DLC; PU.   11106

---- Report of the Committee of
Claims on the case of Joseph
Sills. Jan. 23, 1822. Committed
to the committee of the whole to
which is committed the report in
the case of Heman B. Potter.
Dec. 12, 1822. Pr. by order of
the House of Representatives.
[Washington, 1822] (38) 1 p. DLC;
NjP.   11107

---- Report of the Committee of
Claims on the memorial of
Charles Townsend. Jan. 3, 1822.
Read, and committed to a committee of the whole House to-
morrow. Dec. 12, 1822. Pr. by
order of the House of Representatives. [Washington, 1822] (42) 1 p.
DLC; NjP.   11108

---- Report of the Committee of
Claims on the petition of Allen
R. Moore. Jan. 11, 1822. Read,
and committed to a committee of
the whole House to-morrow.
Dec. 12, 1822. Pr. by order of
the House of Representatives.
[Washington, 1822] (31) 6 p.
DLC; NjP.   11109

---- Report of the Committee of
Claims on the petition of Archibald S. Bullock, and others.
Feb. 28, 1822. Read, and ordered to lie on the table. March
11, 1822. Pr. by order of the
House of Representatives. [Wash-
ington, 1822] (63) 4 p. DLC;
PU.   11110

---- ---- Feb. 28, 1822. Read,

and ordered to lie on the table.
March 11, 1822. Pr. by order
of the House of Representatives.
Dec. 12, 1822. Repr. by order
of the House of Representatives.
[Washington, 1822] (10) 4 p.
DLC; NjP.   11111

---- Report of the Committee of
Claims on the petition of Enos
Terry. Feb. 22, 1822. Read,
and ordered to lie on the table.
March 19, 1822. Again referred
to the Committee of Claims.
March 27, 1822. Committee of
Claims again report as follows,
which was committed to a committee of the whole House to-
morrow. Dec. 12, 1822. Pr. by
order of the House of Representatives. [Washington, 1822]
(40) 2 p. DLC; NjP.   11112

---- Report of the Committee of
Claims on the petition of Fred-
erick Halsey. March 4, 1822.
Read, and ordered to lie on the
table. March 6, 1822. Commit-
ted to a committee of the whole
House to-morrow. Dec. 12, 1822.
Pr. by order of the House of
Representatives. [Washington,
1822] (22) 1 p. DLC; NjP.
                             11113
---- Report of the Committee of
Claims on the petition of James
Byers, accompanied with a bill
for his relief. Jan. 9, 1822.
Read, and with this bill commit-
ted to a committee of the whole
House to-morrow. [Washington,
1822] (11) 4 p. DLC; PU.
                             11114
---- Report of the Committee of
Claims on the petition of James
Pierce, with a bill for his re-
lief. Feb. 25, 1822. Read, and,
with the bill, committed to a
committee of the whole House to-
morrow. [Washington, 1822] (50)
2 p. DLC; PU.   11115

---- Report of the Committee of

Claims on the petition of Jean B. Jerome and others.   Jan. 25, 1822. Read, and committed to the committee of the whole House, to which is committed the bill for the relief of James May, and the representatives of Wm. Macomb.   [Washington, 1822] (34) 30 p. DLC; PU.   11116

---- Report of the Committee of Claims on the petition of Jean B. Jerome, and others. Jan. 25, 1822. Read, and committed to the committee of the whole House, to which is committed the bill for the relief of James May, and the representatives of Wm. Macomb. Dec. 12, 1822. Repr. by order of the House of Representatives. [Washington, 1822] (26) 27 p. DLC; NjP.   11117

---- Report of the Committee of Claims on the petition of Joseph Wheaton. Dec. 19, 1821. Read, and ordered to lie on the table. Jan. 3, 1822. Committed to a committee of the whole House to-morrow. Dec. 12, 1822. Pr. by order of the House of Representatives. [Washington, 1822] (43) 2 p. DLC; NjP.   11118

---- Report of the Committee of Claims on the petition of Morgan Brown.   Jan. 30, 1822. Read, and committed to a committee of the whole House to-morrow. [Washington, 1822] (30) 2 p. DLC; PU.   11119

---- ---- Jan. 30, 1822. Read, and committed to a committee of the whole House to-morrow. Dec. 12, 1822. Repr. by order of the House of Representatives. [Washington, 1822] (8) 2 p. DLC; NjP.
                                    11120
---- Report of the Committee of Claims on the petition of Nathan Ford. March 20, 1822. Read, and ordered to lie on the table.

March 25, 1822. Committed to a committee of the whole House to-morrow. The Committee of Claims to which was referred the petition of Nathan Ford, of Ogdensburg, in the state of New York, Report...[Washington, 1822] (77) 12 p. DLC; NjP.
                                    11121

---- ---- March 20, 1822. Read, and ordered to lie on the table. March 25, 1822. Committed to a committee of the whole House to-morrow. Dec. 12, 1822. Reprinted by order of the House of Representatives. [Washington, 1822] (15) 11 p. DLC; NjP.
                                    11122
---- Report of the Committee of Claims on the petition of Septa Fillmore.   March 4, 1822. Read, and ordered to lie on the table. March 6, 1822. Committed to a committee of the whole House to-morrow. Dec. 12, 1822. Pr. by order of the House of Representatives. [Washington, 1822] (19) 1 p. DLC; NjP.
                                    11123
---- Report of the Committee of Claims on the petition of the administrators of Zachariah Schoonmaker. March 29, 1822. Read, and ordered to lie on the table.   May 8, 1822. Committed to a committee of the whole House today. Dec. 12, 1822. Pr. by order of the House of Representatives. [Washington, 1822] (34) 2 p. DLC; NjP.   11124

---- Report of the Committee of Claims, on the petitions of John Anderson, Francis Navarre, and Francis Robert. Jan. 17, 1822. Committed to a committee of the whole House to-morrow. Dec. 12, 1822. Pr. by order of the House of Representatives. [Washington, 1822] (7) 2 p. DLC; NjP.   11125

---- Report of the Committee of

Claims, to which was recommitted the report of the 15th Jan., 1822, in the case of Eli Hart. Feb. 11, 1822. Read, and committed to a committee of the whole House. [Washington, 1822] (37) 7 p. DLC; PU.   11126

---- Report of the Committee of Claims, to which was recommitted the report of the 15th Jan., 1822, in the case of Eli Hart. Feb. 11, 1822. Read, and committed to a committee of the whole House. Dec. 12, 1822. Reprinted by order of the House of Representatives. [Washington, 1822] (24) 6 p. DLC; NjP. 11127

---- Report of the Committee of Claims, to whom was referred the memorial of the Legislature of the state of Tennessee, in relation to payment for horses lost in the Seminole campaign. Jan. 14, 1822. Read, and committed to a committee of the whole House to-morrow. [Washington, 1822] (13) 24 p. 1 bdsd. DLC; PU.   11128

---- Report of the Committee of Claims, upon the subject of a trial in the District Court for the Eastern District of Pennsylvania, between the U.S. and John T. David. April 27, 1822. Read, and ordered to lie upon the table. [Washington, 1822] (101) 11 p. DLC; NjP.   11129

---- Report of the Committee of Elections, in part, on certificates of election. March 11, 1822. To lie on the table. [Washington, 1822] (66) 1 p. DLC; PU.   11130

---- Report of the Committee of Elections on the memorial of Philip Reed, contesting the election of Jeremiah Cosden. March 11, 1822. Read, and committed to a committee of the whole House to-morrow. [Washington, 1822] (64) 14 p. DLC; PU.   11131

---- Report of the Committee of Elections. Jan. 21, 1822. Ordered to lie on the table. [Washington, 1822] (22) 3 p. DLC; PU.   11132

---- Report of the Committee of the District of Columbia, to whom were referred sundry memorials from the inhabitants of Pennsylvania, Maryland, and Virginia, praying the aid of the Federal Government towards the improvement of the navigation of the river Potomac, May 3, 1822. Read, and ordered to lie on the table. [Washington, 1822] (111) 36 p. DLC; NjP.   11133

---- Report of the Committee of Ways and Means in the case of Jonathan S. Smith. March 21, 1822. Read, and ordered to lie on the table. March 25, 1822. Committed to a committee of the whole House to-morrow. The Committee of Ways and Means, to whom was referred the petition of Jonathan S. Smith, Report... [Washington, 1822] (78) 8 p. DLC; NjP.   11134

---- ---- March 21, 1822. Read, and ordered to lie on the table. March 25, 1822. Committed to a committee of the whole House to-morrow. Dec. 12, 1822. Reprinted by order of the House of Representatives. [Washington, 1822] (36) 7 p. DLC; NjP.   11135

---- Report of the Committee of Ways and Means on the bill from the Senate for the relief of Samuel H. Walley and Henry G. Foster. Dec. 27, 1822. Read, and with the bill, committed to a committee of the whole House to-morrow. [Washington, 1822] (55)

2 p. DLC; NjP.   11136

---- Report of the Committee of
Ways and Means, on the petition
of certain distillers of the sixth
collection district of Pennsylvania, with a bill for their relief. Jan. 23, 1822. Read, and,
with the bill, committed to a
committee of the whole House.
[Washington, 1822] (24) 6 p.
DLC; PU.   11137

---- Report of the Committee of
Ways and Means, on the petition
of George B. R. Gove, with a
bill for his relief. Dec. 31,
1822. Read, and, with the bill,
committed to a Committee of the
whole House to-morrow. [Wash-
ington, 1822] (60) 1 p. DLC;
NjP.   11138

---- Report of the Committee of
Ways and Means on the petition
of James Ross, accompanied with
a bill for his relief. Jan. 18,
1822. Read, and, with the bill,
committed to a committee of the
whole House to-morrow. [Wash-
ington, 1822] (16) 1 p. DLC; PU.
                             11139
---- Report of the Committee of
Ways and Means on the petition
of Jonathan Battelle. Jan. 28,
1822. Read, and ordered to lie
on the table. [Washington, 1822]
(25) 1 p. DLC; PU.   11140

---- Report of the Committee of
Ways and Means, relative to an
increase in the appropriation for
arming the militia. Jan. 16,
1822... [Washington, 1822] (70)
5 p., 4 bdsds. DLC; NN. 11141

---- Report of the Committee of
Ways and Means, to which was
referred so much of the President's message, at the commencement of the first session, of the
seventeenth Congress, as relates
to the finances. April 30, 1822.

Read, and ordered to lie upon
the table. [Washington, 1822]
(103) 12 p. DLC; NjP.   11142

---- Report of the Committee of
Ways and Means, to which was
referred the bill from the Senate, entitled "An act for the relief of Samuel H. Walley, and
Henry G. Foster." March 23,
1822. Read, and with the bill,
committed to a committee of the
whole House on Monday next.
[Washington, 1822] (74) 2 p.
DLC; NjP.   11143

---- Report of the Committee on
Agriculture on the petition of
Anthony Dey and James Macdon-
ald. March 12, 1822. Read,
and the resolution therein con-
tained concurred in by the House.
[Washington, 1822] (67) 3 p.
DLC; PU.   11144

---- Report of the Committee on
Commerce, on the petition of
Henry Lee, with a bill for his
relief. April 23, 1822. Read,
and, with the bill, committed to
a committee of the whole House
to-morrow. [Washington, 1822]
(96) 2 p. DLC; NjP.   11145

---- Report of the Committee on
Commerce on the petition of
James Homer. Jan. 18, 1822.
Read, and ordered to lie on the
table. [Washington, 1822] (17)
3 p. DLC; PU.   11146

---- Report of the Committee on
Commerce, on the petition of
John C. and Thomas Vowel, accompanied with "A bill restoring
to the ship Diana the privileges
of a sea-letter vessel." Jan. 15,
1822. Read, and, with the bill,
committed to a committee of the
whole House to-morrow. [Wash-
ington, 1822] (14) 4 p. DLC;
PU.   11147

---- Report of the Committee on Commerce to which was referred so much of the President's message as concerns the commercial intercourse of the U. S. with foreign nations. March 15, 1822. Committed to a committee of the whole House to-morrow. [Washington, 1822] (70) 70 p. 2 bdsd. DLC; NjP.   11148

---- Report of the Committee on Commerce, to which was referred so much of the President's message as concerns the commercial intercourse of the U. S. with foreign nations. March 15, 1822.   Committed to a committee of the whole House to-morrow.   Dec. 12, 1822. Reprinted by order of the House of Representatives. [Washington, 1822] (48) 70 p. 4 bdsd. DLC; NjP.
11149

---- Report of the Committee on Foreign Affairs, on the petition of Alexander Mactier, George W. Dashiell, and Archibald Stewart, of Baltimore. Jan. 31, 1822. Read, and committed to a committee of the whole House to-morrow. [Washington, 1822] (32) 6 p. DLC; PU.   11150

---- ---- Jan. 31, 1822. Read, and committed to a committee of the whole House to-morrow. Dec. 12, 1822. Reprinted by order of the House of Representatives. [Washington, 1822] (29) 6 p. DLC; NjP.   11151

---- Report of the Committee on Foreign Affairs, on the petition of Jacob Schieffelin and Henry Schieffelin.   April 8, 1822. Read, and committed to a committee of the whole House to-morrow. [Washington, 1822] (85) 5 p. DLC; NjP.   11152

---- Report of the Committee on Foreign Affairs on the petition

of Jacob Schieffelin and Henry Schieffelin. April 8, 1822. Read, and committed to a committee of the whole House to-morrow. Dec. 12, 1822. Repr. by order of the House of Representatives. [Washington, 1822] (37) 9 p. DLC; NjP.   11153

---- Report of the Committee on Foreign Relations, to which was referred the President's message concerning the recognition of the late Spanish provinces in America. March 19, 1822. Read, and committed to a Committee of the whole House on the state of the Union. [Washington, 1822] (73) 9 p. DLC; NjP.
11154

---- Report of the Committee on Military Affairs, instructed (by a resolution of the House of Representatives, of the 23d Dec. last) to inquire 'Whether the Army had been reduced according to the provisions of the act, entitled 'An act to reduce and fix the military peace establishment of the U. S. ," passed 2d March, 1821. April 2, 1822. Read, and ordered to lie on the table.   [Washington, 1822] (82) 4 p. DLC; NjP.   11155

---- ---- April 2, 1822. Read, and ordered to lie on the table. Dec. 12, 1822. Reprinted by order of the House of Representatives. [Washington, 1822] (5) 4 p. DLC; NjP.   11156

---- Report of the Committee on Military Affairs on the message of the President of the United States, of the 26th ult., on the subject of fortifications generally, and particularly of those on Mobile Point and Dauphine Island. April 13, 1822. Referred to the committee of the whole House to which is referred the bill making further appropriations for the military service of the U. S. for the year 1822. [Washington, 1822] (94) 5 p. DLC; PU.				11157

---- Report of the Commitee[!] on Military Affairs on the petition of Peter Mills. Feb. 14, 1822. Read, and ordered to lie on the table. May 8, 1822. Committed to a committee of the whole to-day. Dec. 12, 1822. Pr. by order of the House of Representatives. [Washington, 1822] (6) 1 p. DLC; NjP. 11158

---- Report of the Committee on Military Affairs, to which was referred so much of the memorial of the Legislature of the state of Alabama, and of certain citizens thereof, as relates to fortifications. Feb. 28, 1822. Read, and ordered to lie upon the table. [Washington, 1822] (51) 9 p. DLC; PU.				11159

---- Report of the Committee on Military Affairs, to which was referred the report of a select committee of the 7th Feb., 1821, in relation to loans of lead and gunpowder to certain individuals by officers of the government. May 7, 1822. Read, and ordered to lie on the table. [Washington, 1822] (58) 37 p. DLC; NjP.				11160

---- Report of the Committee on Military Affairs upon the subject of the military academy and the corps of cadets, accompanied with "A bill concerning the military academy." March 4, 1822. Read, and with the bill committed to a Committee of the whole House on the state of the Union. [Washington, 1822] (54) 3 p. DLC; PU.				11161

---- Report of the Committee on Military Expenditures. May 1,

1822. Read, and ordered to lie upon the table. [Washington, 1822] (105) 9 p. DLC; PU.				11162

---- Report of the Committee on Naval Affairs in the case of Thomas Kemp. Feb. 19, 1822. Read and committed to a committee of the whole House to-morrow. [Washington, 1822] (44) 2 p. DLC; PU.				11163

---- ---- Feb. 19, 1822. Read, and committed to a committee of the whole House to-morrow. Dec. 12, 1822. Re-printed by order of the House of Representatives. [Washington, 1822] (27) 2 p. DLC; NjP.				11164

---- Report of the Committee on Naval Affairs, on the petition of William Thompson, with a bill for his relief. Feb. 19, 1822. Read, and, with the bill, committed to a committee of the whole House to-morrow. [Washington, 1822] (45) 1 p. DLC; PU.				11165

---- Report of the Committee on Naval Affairs, to which was referred a resolution of the House of Representatives of the 10th inst. instructing said Committee to inquire into the expediency of allowing to the mother of the late Lieutenant William H. Allen, a pension, &c. Dec. 31, 1822. Read, and with a bill for the relief of the mother, &c. of Lieutenant Allen, committed to a committee of the whole House to-morrow. [Washington, 1822] (59) 4 p. DLC; NjP.				11166

---- Report of the Committee on Naval Affairs, upon the subject of affording further protection to the persons and property of citizens of the U. S. in the Gulf of Mexico and West India Seas. March 2, 1822. Read, and or-

dered to lie upon the table.
[Washington, 1822] (53) 4 p.
DLC; PU.   11167

---- Report of the Committee on
Naval Affairs, upon the subject
of modifying the act for the grad-
ual increase of the Navy. March
29, 1822. Read, and ordered to
lie on the table. [Washington,
1822] (80) 3 p. DLC; NjP.
                             11168
---- Report of the Committee on
Naval Affairs, upon the subject
of naval stores and munitions of
war, appertaining to the Naval
Department. March 4, 1822.
Read, and ordered to lie on the
table. [Washington, 1822] (55)
32 p. DLC; PU.   11169

---- Report of the Committee on
Pensions and Revolutionary
Claims in the case of James
Wood. Jan. 25, 1822. Read, and
concurred in; petition rejected.
Jan. 28, 1822. Reconsidered,
and committed to a committee of
the whole House to-morrow.
[Washington, 1822] (29) 33 p.
DLC; PU.   11170

---- Report of the Committee on
Pensions and Revolutionary
Claims in the case of James
Wood. Jan. 25, 1822. Read and
concurred in; petition rejected.
Jan. 28, 1822. Reconsidered,
and committed to a committee of
the whole House to-morrow. Dec.
12, 1822. Reprinted by order of
the House of Representatives.
[Washington, 1822] (46) 33 p.
DLC; NjP.   11171

---- Report of the Committee on
Pensions and Revolutionary
Claims, in the case of Richard
G. Morris. Jan. 29, 1822. Read,
and ordered to lie on the table.
[Washington, 1822] (27) 10 p.
DLC; PU.   11172

---- ---- Jan. 29, 1822. Read,
and ordered to lie on the table.
March 4, 1822. Committed to a
committee of the whole House
to-morrow. Dec. 12, 1822. Reprinted by order of the House of
Representatives. [Washington,
1822] (30) 13 p. DLC; NjP.
                             11173
---- Report of the Committee
on Pensions and Revolutionary
Claims on the case of Ruamah
Williams. Dec. 16, 1821. Read,
and ordered to lie on the table.
Feb. 13, 1822. Again referred
to the Committee on Pensions,
&c. Feb. 19, 1822. Reported
again and committed. Dec. 12,
1822. Pr. by order of the House
of Representatives. [Washington,
1822] (45) 1 p. DLC; NjP.
                             11174
---- Report of the Committee on
Pensions and Revolutionary
Claims on the petition of John
Guthry, accompanied with a bill
for the relief of the legal representatives of John Guthry,
deceased. Jan. 31, 1822. Read,
and, with the bill, committed to
a committee of the whole House
to-morrow. [Washington, 1822]
(31) 1 p. DLC; PU.   11175

---- Report of the Committee on
Pensions and Revolutionary
Claims, on the petition of John
M'Hatton. Jan. 11, 1822. Read,
and ordered to lie upon the
table. [Washington, 1822] (12)
10 p. DLC; PU.   11176

---- Report of the Committee on
Pensions and Revolutionary
Claims on the petition of Roswell Woodworth. March 5, 1822.
Read, and ordered to lie upon
the table. [Washington, 1822]
(57) 1 p. DLC; PU.   11177

---- Report of the Committee
on Pensions and Revolutionary
Claims on the petition of Sarah

Easton and Dorothy Storer. Mar. 19, 1822. Read, and ordered to lie on the table. [Washington, 1822] (75) 17 p. DLC; NjP.
11178

---- ---- March 19, 1822. Read, and ordered to lie on the table. April 12, 1822. Committed to a committee of the whole House. Dec. 12, 1822. Reprinted by order of the House of Representatives. [Washington, 1822] (17) 17 p. DLC; NjP.
11179

---- Report of the Committee on Pensions and Revolutionary Claims, on the petition of William Johnston. Jan. 29, 1822. Read, and ordered to lie on the table. Feb. 16, 1822. Committed to a Committee of the whole House on Bill No. 61, for the relief of Charles A. Swearingen. Dec. 12, 1822. Pr. by order of the House of Representatives. [Washington, 1822] (2) 2 p. DLC; NjP.
11180

---- Report of the Committee on Private Land Claims, in the case of John Girault's heirs, accompanied with a bill for their relief. Jan. 22, 1822. Read, and committed, with the bill, to a committee of the whole House to-morrow. [Washington, 1822] (21) 2 p. DLC; PU.
11181

---- Report of the Committee on Private Land Claims, in the case of John Jenkins. Dec. 17, 1822. Read, and, with a bill, for the relief of John Jenkins, committed to a committee of the whole House to-morrow. [Washington, 1822] (11) 1 p. DLC; NjP.
11182

---- Report of the Committee on Private Land Claims, in the case of S. Henderson. April 10, 1822. Read, and committed to a committee of the whole House to-

morrow. [Washington, 1822] (89) 3 p. DLC; NjP.
11183

---- Report of the Commitee[!] on Private Land Claims in the case of S. Henderson. April 10, 1822. Read, and committed to a committee of the whole House to-morrow. Dec. 12, 1822. Reprinted by order of the House of Representatives. [Washington, 1822] (25) 3 p. DLC; NjP.
11184

---- Report of the Committee on Private Land Claims, in the case of Susan Berzat, &c. with a bill for her relief, &c. Feb. 23, 1822. Read, and committed, with the bill, to a committee of the whole House on Monday next. [Washington, 1822] (49) 1 p. DLC; PU.
11185

----Report of the Committee on Private Land Claims, in the case of Woodson Wren. Dec. 20, 1822. Read, and with an accompanying bill for his relief, committed to a Committee of the whole House to-morrow. [Washington, 1822] (51) 2 p. DLC; NjP.
11186

---- Report of the Committee on Private Land Claims, on the bill from the Senate for the relief of the heirs of Alexander Montgomery. April 4, 1822. Read, and, with the bill, committed to a Committee of the whole House to-morrow. [Washington, 1822] (84) 2 p. DLC; NjP.
11187

---- Report of the Committee on Private Land Claims on the petition of James Brisban, with a bill for his relief. Feb. 15, 1822. Read, and with the bill, committed to a committee of the whole House to-morrow. [Washington, 1822] (39) 1 p. DLC; PU.
11188

---- Report of the Committee on Public Buildings, accompanied with a bill fixing the compensation of the Commissioner of the Public Buildings. April 8, 1822. Read, and, with the bill, committed to a committee of the whole House to-morrow. [Washington, 1822] (87) 2 p. DLC; NjP.   11189

---- Report of the Committee on Roads and Canals, on the subject of internal improvements, accompanied with a bill to procure the necessary surveys, &c. on the subject of roads and canals. Jan. 2, 1822. Read, and, with the bill, committed to a committee of the whole on the third Monday of Jan. instant. [Washington, 1822] (8) 100 p. DLC; DeGE; PU.   11190

---- Report of the Committee on Roads and Canals, to which was referred a report of a select committee, made 12th May, 1820, relative to carrying into effect the treaty of Brownstown, of 25th November, 1808, accompanied with "A bill for laying out and making a road from the Lower Rapids of the Miami of Lake Erie to the Connecticut Western Reserve, in the state of Ohio," &c. March 8, 1822. Read, and, with the bill, committed to a committee of the whole House to-morrow. [Washington, 1822] (61) 13 p. DLC; PU.   11191

---- Report of the Committee on Roads and Canals, upon the subject of internal improvements. April 26, 1822. Read, and ordered to lie on the table. [Washington, 1822] (98) 8 p. DLC; NjP.   11192

---- Report of the Committee on the Expenditures of the Department of State. May 3, 1822.

Read, and ordered to lie on the table. [Washington, 1822] (106) 6 p. DLC; NjP.   11193

---- Report of the Committee on the Expenditures on the Public Buildings. April 8, 1822. Read, and ordered to lie on the table. [Washington, 1822] (86) 5 p. DLC; NjP.   11194

---- ---- March 26, 1822. Read, and ordered to lie upon the table. The Committee on Expenditures on the Public Buildings, Report... [Washington, 1822] (79) 6 p. 2 bdsd. DLC; NjP.   11195

---- Report of the Committee on the Judiciary in the case of Thomas Eames. April 27, 1822. Read, and committed to a Committee of the whole House to-morrow. [Washington, 1822] (99) 2 p. DLC; NjP.   11196

---- ---- April 27, 1822. Read, and committed to a committee of the whole House to-morrow. Dec. 12, 1822. Pr. by order of the House of Representatives. [Washington, 1822] (18) 2 p. DLC; NjP.   11197

---- Report of the Committee on the Judiciary on the memorial of the Legislature of Alabama. Jan. 28, 1822. Read, and ordered to lie upon the table. [Washington, 1822] (26) 1 p. DLC; PU. 11198

---- Report of the Committee on the Judiciary on the petition of Alonzo B. Munoz. May 4, 1822. Read, and ordered to lie upon the table. [Washington, 1822] (107) 4 p. DLC; PU.   11199

---- Report of the Committee on the Judiciary, on the petition of Anthony Dey and James Macdonald, and a remonstrance of David

Melville. April 29, 1822. Read, and ordered to lie on the table. [Washington, 1822] (102) 2 p. DLC; NjP. 11200

---- Report of the Committee on the Judiciary, to which was referred the message of the President of the United States, relating to the amount of the public money paid to the Attorney General, over and above his salary fixed by law. April 12, 1822. Read, and ordered to lie on the table. [Washington, 1822] (90) 3 p. DLC; NjP. 11201

---- Report of the Committee on the Judiciary upon the subject of admitting aliens to the right of citizenship who resided within the United States one year preceding the declaration of the late war with Great Britain. March 13, 1822. Committed to a committee of the whole House on the state of the Union. [Washington, 1822] (68) 1 p. DLC; PU. 11202

---- ---- March 13, 1822. Committed to a committee of the whole House on the state of the Union. Dec. 12, 1822. Repr. by order of the House of Representatives. Washington, 1822. [Washington, 1822] (47) 1 p. DLC; NjP. 11203

---- Report of the Committee on the Post Office affairs. April 29, 1822. Read, and the resolution therein contained, concurred in by the House. [Washington, 1822] (104) 19 p. 6 bdsd. DLC; NjP. 11204

---- Report of the Committee on the Post Office and Post Roads, on the subject of affording greater safety in the transmission of letters, &c. by the public mails, &c. March 18, 1822. Read, and ordered to lie on the table. [Washington, 1822] (72) 2 p. DLC; NjP. 11205

---- Report of the Committee on the Public Buildings, with a bill making appropriations for the public buildings. March 25, 1822. Read, and, with the bill, committed to the committee of the whole House, to which is committed the bill making appropriations for the support of government for the year 1822. The Committee on the Public Buildings Report... [Washington, 1822] (76) 10 p. 1 bdsd. DLC; NjP. 11206

---- Report of the Committee on the Public Expenditures. April 27, 1822. Read, and ordered to lie upon the table. [Washington, 1822] (100) 4 p. DLC; NjP. 11207

---- Report of the Committee on the Public Lands on the petition of Clement B. Penrose, with a bill for his relief. Feb. 20, 1822. Read, and, with the bill, committed to a committee of the whole House to-morrow. [Washington, 1822] (46) 3 p. DLC; PU. 11208

---- Report of the Committee on the Public Lands on the petition of James M'Farland, Hampton Pankey, and William Frizzell, with a bill for the relief of James M'Farland. Jan. 3, 1822. Read, and, with the bill, committed to a committee of the whole House, to which is committed the bill for the relief of Benjamin Freeland. [Washington, 1822] (9) 2 p. DLC; PU. 11209

---- Report of the Committee on the Public Lands on the petition of Peter S. Chazotte and others, in behalf of the American Coffee Land Association. Feb. 20, 1822. Read, and ordered to lie upon

the table. [Washington, 1822]
(47) 35 p. DLC; PU. 11210

---- ---- Feb. 20, 1822. Read,
and ordered to lie on the table.
Dec. 12, 1822. Reprinted by order of the House of Representatives. [Washington, 1822] (14)
35 p. DLC; NjP. 11211

---- Report of the Committee on
the Public Lands, on the petitions of sundry inhabitants of the
Canton District, in the state of
Ohio; of Robert Williams, and of
Abraham Kroft. Feb. 19, 1822.
Read, and ordered to lie upon
the table. [Washington, 1822]
(43) 1 p. DLC; PU. 11212

---- Report of the Committee on
the Public Lands, to which was
referred sundry petitions from
inhabitants of the state of Illinois, praying for a confirmation
of their land claims, accompanied
with a bill confirming certain
claims to land in the state of Illinois. March 5, 1822. Read
twice, and, with the bill, committed to a committee of the
whole House to-morrow. [Wash-
ington, 18221 (58) 2 p. DLC; PU.
11213
---- Report of the Committee on
the Slave Trade, on the petition
of William De la Carrera. April
2, 1822. Read, and ordered to
lie on the table. [Washington,
1822] (83) 1 p. DLC; NjP.
11214
---- Report of the Committee on
the Suppression of the Slave
Trade. April 12, 1822. Read,
and ordered to lie on the table.
[Washington, 1822] (92) 92 p.
DLC; GU-De; ICN; NjP. 11215

---- Report of the committee to
whom was referred the memorial
of the Bank of the United States,
and who were also instructed, by
a resolution of the House, to inquire whether the said Bank has
not, and does not still, in their
discounts, receive more than at
the rate of six per centum per
annum. March 7, 1822. Read
and ordered to lie on the table.
[Washington, 1822] (59) 1 p.
DLC; PU. 11216

---- Report of the Engineer Department, in relation to a required appropriation of $500,000
for fortifications. March 7, 1822.
Laid before the House of Representatives by the Chairman of
the Committee of Ways and
Means, and ordered to be printed.
Washington, Pr. by Gales & Seaton, 1822. (89) 5 p. DLC; NjP.
11217
---- Report of the Joint Committee appointed by the two Houses
of Congress to revise the rules
and orders by which the business
of said Houses shall be regulated. Jan. 21, 1822. Read, and
ordered to lie upon the table.
[Washington, 1822] (20) 1 p. DLC;
PU. 11218

---- Report of the Library Committee, to which was referred a
letter from George W. Erving,
in relation to certain medals
transmitted by him to the House
of Representatives of the United
States, &c. &c. March 9, 1822.
Read, and committed to a committee of the whole House, on
Monday next. [Washington, 1822]
(62) 2 p. DLC; PU. 11219

---- Report of the Military Committee on the Georgia militia
claim. March 26, 1822. Read,
and ordered to lie on the table.
[Washington, 1822] (91) 24 p.
DLC; GU-De; NjP. 11220

---- ---- March 26, 1822. Read,
and ordered to lie on the table.
Dec. 20, 1822. Reprinted by order of the House of Representa-

tives. [Washington, 1822] (52) 23 p. DLC; NjP.   11221

---- Report of the Postmaster General, of the receipts and expenditures of the General Post Office, from the year 1816, to the year 1821, inclusive. Feb. 28, 1822. Read, and referred to the Committee on the Post Office and Post Roads. Washington, Pr. by Gales & Seaton, 1822. (76) 5 p. DLC; NjP.   11222

---- Report of the Secretary of State, of the amount of money paid as salaries, outfits, and contingent expenses, to foreign ministers, since the year 1800, and the amount paid to each: rendered in obedience to a resolution of the House of Representatives of the 8th instant. April 30, 1822. Read, and ordered to lie on the table. Washington, Pr. by Gales & Seaton, 1822. (120) 4 p. 5 bdsd. DLC; NNLI; NjP.
11223

---- Report of the Secretary of State, of the names of the clerks employed in his office, and the compensation allowed to each. Jan. 2, 1822. Read, and ordered to lie on the table. Washington, Pr. by Gales & Seaton, 1822. (11) 3 p. DLC; NjP.   11224

---- Report of the Secretary of State, pursuant to the act to regulate passenger ships and vessels, of the number of persons arriving in the several ports of the United States, from Oct. 1, 1820, to Sept. 30, 1821. April 22, 1822. Read, and ordered to lie on the table. Washington, Pr. by Gales & Seaton, 1822. (134) 4 p. 26 bdsd. DLC; NNLI; NjP.
11225

---- Report of the Secretary of the Navy, of the contingent expenditures of that department, during the year ending on the 30th

September, 1821. Jan. 21, 1822. Read, and referred to the Committee of Ways and Means. Washington, Pr. by Gales & Seaton, 1822. (31) 3 p. 8 bdsd. DLC; NjP.   11226

---- Report of the Secretary of the Treasury, in obedience to a resolution of the Senate of 21st December, 1821, of the names and compensation of deputies and clerks employed in the offices of collectors, naval officers, & surveyors of the customs, during the years 1816, 1817, 1818, 1819, 1820, and 1821. April 8, 1822. Pr. by order of the Senate... Washington, Pr. by Gales & Seaton, 1822. (82) 32 p. DLC; NjP.
11227

---- Report of the Secretary of the Treasury, in relation to fines imposed on the Militia of Pennsylvania, for non-performance of military duty in the late war, &c. &c. Jan. 16, 1822. Read, and ordered to lie upon the table. Washington, Pr. by Gales & Seaton, 1822. (25) 24 p. DLC; NjP.   11228

---- Report of the Secretary of the Treasury, made in pursuance of a resolution of the House of Representatives of the 13th ult. First. ... March 29, 1822. Ordered to lie upon the table. Washington, Pr. by Gales & Seaton, 1822. (100) 23 p. 3 bdsd. DLC; NjP.   11229

---- Report of the Secretary of the Treasury, of the manner in which the several land offices have been examined, by whom examined, the moneys paid for such examinations, &c. Jan. 30, 1822. Ordered to lie upon the table. Washington, Pr. by Gales & Seaton, 1822. (44) 5 p. 2 bdsd. DLC; NjP.   11230

---- Report of the Secretary of
the Treasury, on the petition of
James Green. Jan. 25, 1822.
Read, and ordered to lie on the
table. Washington, Pr. by Gales
& Seaton, 1822. (73) 6 p. DLC;
NjP.   11231

---- Report of the Secretary of
the Treasury, on the petition of
James Morrison. Jan. 30, 1822.
Read, and ordered to lie upon
the table. Washington, Pr. by
Gales & Seaton, 1822. (45) 4 p.
DLC; NjP.   11232

---- Report of the Secretary of
the Treasury, on the Petition of
Lefebvre Desnoettes, and others,
French emigrants in Alabama,
engaged in the cultivation of the
vine and olive, praying a modi-
fication of the condition of their
grant. March 20, 1822. Pr. by
order of the Senate... Washington, Pr. by Gales & Seaton,
1822. (70) 9 p. DLC; NjP.
                              11233

---- Report of the Secretary of
the Treasury on the petition of
William Phillips and Gardner
Greene.   Jan. 15, 1822. Pr. by
order of the Senate of the United
States. Washington, Pr. by
Gales & Seaton, 1822. (12) 1 p.
DLC; NjP.   11234

---- Report of the Secretary of
the Treasury, shewing the application of the fund for the relief
of sick and disabled seamen,
and the description of seamen
relieved thereby. Jan. 4, 1822.
Read, and referred to the Committee on Commerce. Washington, Pr. by Gales & Seaton,
1822. (13) 19 p. 2 bdsd. DLC;
NjP.   11235

---- Report of the Secretary of
the Treasury, shewing the quantity of wool imported into, and
exported from, the U.S., during

the years 1817, 1818, 1819,
1820, and the three first quarters
of 1821; also, the duties which
have been charged thereon. Jan.
30, 1822. Read, and ordered
to lie upon the table. Washington, Pr. by Gales & Seaton,
1822. (43) 8 p. DLC; NjP.
                              11236
---- Report of the Secretary of
War, (In obedience to a resolution of the 29th ult.) of the number of persons placed on the
pension roll, in virtue of the
act, entitled "An act to provide
for certain persons engaged in
the land and naval service of the
United States in the Revolutionary War," passed on the 18th of
March, 1818. Feb. 8, 1822. Pr.
by order of the Senate... Washington, Pr. by Gales & Seaton,
1822. (38) 3 p. DLC; NjP.
                              11237
---- Report of the Secretary of
War, on the subject of rifles
promised Capt. Aikins' Volunteers.   March 22, 1822. Laid
before the House by the Chairman of the Military Committee,
and ordered to be printed.
Washington, Pr. by Gales & Seaton, 1821[!] [1822] (103) 6 p.
DLC; G; NNLI; NjP; O; P.
                              11238
---- Report of the Secretary of
War, relative to disbursements
for the Indian Department, made
in obedience to a resolution of
the House of Representatives of
10th Jan., 1822. Jan. 16, 1822.
Read, and committed to that
Committee of the whole to which
is committed the bill making partial appropriations for the military service for the year 1822.
Washington, Pr. by Gales &
Seaton, 1822. (24) 15 p. 1 bdsd.
DLC; NjP.   11239

---- Report of the Secretary of
War, transmitting, (In obedience to a resolution of the Sen-

ate, of the 16th ult.) a statement of the amount of money furnished to the agent at the Bank of Vincennes, in the state of Indiana, for the purpose of paying pensioners in said state, &c. Feb. 4, 1822. Pr. by order of the Senate of the United States. Washington, Pr. by Gales & Seaton, 1822. (30) 16 p. DLC; NjP. 11240

---- Report of the select committee appointed on the 18th of Feb. last, to inquire whether any part of the public expenditure can be retrenched without detriment to the public service, &c. &c. April 15, 1822. Read, and ordered to lie on the table. [Washington, 1822] (88) 10 p. DLC; NjP. 11241

---- Report of the select committee appointed on the 1st inst, to make inquiry in relation to the publication of a system of field service and police, adopted for the government of the army at the last session of Congress. May 6, 1822. Read, and ordered to lie on the table. [Washington, 1822] (108) 8 p. DLC; NjP. 11242

---- Report of the select committee appointed on the 17th ultimo, to consider of certain treaties with the Creek and Cherokee Indians, and the Articles of Agreement and Cession entered into on the 24th April, 1802, between the United States and the state of Georgia; accompanied with resolutions making appropriations for carrying into effect the Articles of Agreement and Cession entered into between the United States and the state of Georgia, on the 24th of April, 1802, and for other purposes. Jan. 7, 1822. Read, and committed to a committee of the whole House on Thursday next. [Washington, 1822] (10)

12 p. DLC; PU. 11243

---- Report of the select committee appointed on the 17th ultimo, to consider of certain treaties with the Creek and Cherokee Indians, and the Articles of Agreement and Cession entered into on the 24th April, 1802, between the United States and the state of Georgia; accompanied with resolutions making appropriations for carrying into effect the Articles of Agreement and Cession entered into between the United States and the state of Georgia, on the 24th of April, 1802, and for other purposes. Jan. 7, 1822. Read, and committed to a committee of the whole House on Thursday next. Dec. 10, 1822. Taken up in Committee of the whole, progress reported, and ordered to be reprinted. [Washington, 1822] (1) 10 p. DLC; NjP. 11244

---- Report of the select committee appointed on the 6th inst. to inquire whether it be necessary to modify or alter the law to encourage vaccination. Feb. 22, 1822. Read, and the resolution therein contain concurred in by the House. [Washington, 1822] (48) 4 p. DLC; PU. 11245

---- Report of the select committee, appointed on the 10th ultimo, to inquire into the expediency of occupying the Columbia River, and to regulate the intercourse with the Indian tribes; accompanied with a bill to authorize the occupation of the Columbia River. Jan. 18, 1822. Read, and, with the bill, committed to a committee of the whole House to-morrow. [Washington, 1822] (18) 15 p. DLC; PU. 11246

---- Report of the select committee, appointed on the 28th ult. to inquire into the propriety of repealing the act of 1813, to encourage vaccination, accompanied with a bill to repeal the act, entitled "An act to encourage vaccination." April 13, 1822. Read, and, with the bill, ordered to lie on the table. [Washington, 1822] (93) DLC; NjP. 11247

---- Report of the select committee, appointed 24th Jan. last, on the subject of the fines imposed by courts martial on sundry of the militia men of Pennsylvania for delinquencies, during the late war. April 25, 1822. Read, and ordered to lie on the table. [Washington, 1822] (97) 15 p. DLC; NjP. 11248

---- Report of the select committee appointed on the 22d ult. to inquire into the contract between the United States and Elijah Mix, of 18th of July, 1818, and to report to the House whether the same was made according to law. May 7, 1822. Read, and ordered to lie on the table. [Washington, 1822] (109) 50 p. DLC; NjP. 11249

---- Report of the select committee to which was referred, on the 21st ultimo, two reports of the Secretary of the Treasury, upon the subject of the examination of the land offices in Ohio, Indiana, Illinois, Missouri, and Michigan. March 29, 1822. Read, and ordered to lie on the table. [Washington, 1822] (81) 14 p. DLC; NjP. 11250

---- Report of the select committee to which was referred, on the 26th of Dec. last, the report of the Secretary of State upon the subject of weights and measures. March 11, 1822. Read, and committed to a committee of the whole

House to-morrow. [Washington, 1822] (65) 4 p. DLC; PU. 11251

---- Report of the select committee to which was referred, on the 26th of Dec. last, the report of the Secretary of State upon the subject of weights and measures. March 11, 1822. Read, and committed to a committee of the whole House to-morrow. Dec. 12, 1822. Reprinted by order of the House of Representatives. [Washington, 1822] (44) 3 p. DLC; NjP. 11252

---- Report on the petition of Stephen Howard, jun. accompanied with a bill for his relief. March 18, 1822. Read, and, with the bill, committed to a committee of the whole House to-morrow. The Committee on Military Affairs, to whom was referred the petition of Stephen Howard, jun. Report... [Washington, 1822] (71) 1 p. DLC; NjP. 11253

---- Resolution authorizing the delivery of rifles promised to Captain Aikin's volunteers at the siege of Plattsburg. March 22, 1822. Read twice, and committed to a committee of the whole House to-morrow. [Washington, 1822] (H. R.) DLC. 11254

---- Resolution authorizing the purchase of one hundred and thirty-eight copies of the sixth volume of the Laws of the United States. April 12, 1822. Read, and committed to a committee of the whole House to-morrow. Dec. 12, 1822. Reprinted by order of the House of Representatives. [Washington, 1822] (H. R.) DLC. 11255

---- Resolution directing the Secretary of the Treasury to deliver to certain claimants of land their title papers. March 12, 1822.

Read twice, and ordered to lie on the table. [Washington, 1822] (H.R.) DLC.   11256

---- Resolution of Mr. M'Duffie. Feb. 12, 1822. Submitted for consideration, and ordered to lie on the table one day, under the rule. Resolved, That the Secretary of the Treasury be directed to lay before this House a statement of the balances money in the Treasury, and of the amounts of appropriations unexpended, at the end of each year, from the commencement of this government to the 31st December last. [Washington, 1822] (8) 1 p. DLC; NjP.   11257

---- Resolution proposing an Amendment to the Constitution of the United States, as it respects the choice of President and Vice President of the United States, and the election of Representatives in the Congress of the United States. In the House of Representatives, March 12, 1822. Read, and committed to a committee of the whole House on the state of the Union. [Washington, 1822] (S.) 2 p. DNA.   11258

---- Resolution providing for the security, in the transmission of letters, &c. in the public mail. March 30, 1822. Read, and committed to a Committee of the whole House, on Monday next. [Washington, 1822] DLC.   11259

---- Resolution submitted by Mr. Colden. Dec. 11, 1822. Read, and ordered to lie (one day) on the table. Resolved, That the President of the United States be requested to lay before this House such information as he may possess, with regard to any hostile expedition which may have been prepared in the United States and sailed from thence...

[Washington, 1822] (2) 1 p. DLC; NjP.   11260

---- Resolution submitted by Mr. Cook. March 28, 1822. Read, and ordered to lie on the table. Resolved, That the employment of members of Congress by the Executive, or any Executive officer of the United States, in the performance of any public service, during the continuance of their membership, for which they... [Washington, 1822] (10) 1 p. DLC; NjP.   11261

---- Resolution submitted by Mr. Jennings. Dec. 13, 1822. Rejected. Dec. 16, 1822. Vote rejecting re-considered, and Resolution ordered to lie on the table. [Washington, 1822] (3) 1 p. DLC; NjP.   11262

---- Resolution submitted by Mr. Mitchell, of South Carolina. April 10, 1822. Read, and ordered to lie on the table. Whereas an act, passed on the 21st of April, 1808, entitled "An act concerning public contracts," has been so construed as to sanction the appointment of members of Congress to divers public employments, agencies, or trusts, by the authority of Executive officers of the United States: and whereas... [Washington, 1822] (12) 1 p. DLC; NjP.   11263

---- Resolution submitted by Mr. Rich, (To amend the rules.) April 18, 1822. Read, and ordered to lie one day upon the table. Resolved, That the 69th section of the Rules and Orders of the House, be expunged, and the following substituted in lieu thereof, to wit... [Washington, 1822] (13) 1 p. DLC; NjP.
                                                              11264
---- Resolutions and Memorial of sundry merchants, ship-

owners, and other inhabitants of
Boston, relating to the trade of
the United States with foreign
colonies. Feb. 15, 1822. Referred to the Committee on Commerce. Washington, Pr. by
Gales & Seaton, 1822. (69) 8 p.
CtY; DLC; G; MdHi; MiD-B;
NNLI; Nh-Hi; Nj; NjP; O; R.
                                11265
---- Resolutions of Mr. Nelson,
of Maryland. Jan. 15, 1822.
Committed to the committee of
the whole on the state of the
Union. Resolved, That each of
the United States has an equal
right to participate in the benefit of the public lands, the common property of the Union.
[Washington, 1822] (6) 1 p. DLC;
NjP.   11266

---- Resolutions submitted by
Mr. Baldwin, proposing certain
alterations in the existing laws
for laying and collecting duties
on importations. Jan. 7, 1822.
Read, and committed to a Committee of the whole House to-
morrow. Resolved, That it is
expedient to provide by law,
that, from and after the thirtieth
day of June next, the... [Wash-
ington, 1822] (5) 2 p. DLC; NjP.
                                11267
---- Resolutions submitted by
Mr. Bassett. April 9, 1822.
Read, and ordered to lie on the
table. Resolved, That in all future transactions of the government, either where services are
to be rendered, or supplies furnished, no money shall be advanced by the government, of
payment made, but in... [Wash-
ington, 1822] (11) 1 p. DLC;
NjP.   11268

---- Resolutions submitted by
Mr. Cannon. Dec. 10, 1822.
Read, and ordered to lie on the
table. Resolved, That it is expedient to provide for the nation-

al defence, by improving the militia of the United States. [Wash-
ington, 1822] (1) 1 p. DLC;
NjP.   11269

---- Resolutions submitted by
Mr. Cocke. March 18, 1822.
Read, and ordered to lie on the
table. Resolved, That the act of
the 2d of March, 1821, to reduce
and fix the military peace establishment of the United States,
was not intended to authorize the
President of the United States to
dismiss officers then in service,
and introduce others of the same
grade into the army. [Washing-
ton, 1822] (9) 1 p. DLC; NjP.
                                11270
---- Resolutions submitted by
Mr. Reed, of Maryland. April
30, 1822. Read, and ordered to
lie upon the table. Resolved,
That the Secretaries of the State,
Treasury, War, and Navy Departments, and the Postmaster
General, be, and they are hereby, directed to lay before this
House, within ten days after the
commencement of the next session of Congress, a report,
shewing the time when was made
the last statement, upon which a
balance was found to be due, of
the accounts of the officers or
agents, foreign and... [Washing-
ton, 1822] (15) 2 p. DLC; NjP.
                                11271
---- Resolutions submitted by
Mr. Tattnall. Dec. 17, 1822.
Read, and ordered to be printed.
Resolved, by the Senate and
House of Representatives of the
United States of America in Congress assembled, That so much
of the several treaties, made between the United States and the
Creek and Cherokee Indians.
[Washington, 1822] (4) 1 p. DLC;
NjP.   11272

---- Resolutions submitted by
Mr. Trimble. Joint resolutions

acknowledging the independence of Columbia; and declaring that such other Spanish American Provinces as have declared, and are maintaining, their independence, ought also to be acknowledged sovereign and independent governments. Jan. 31, 1822. Read twice, and ordered to lie on the table. Resolved... [Washington, 1822] (7) 1 p. DLC; NjP.
11273

---- Rules and orders for conducting business, in the House of Representatives of the United States. Pr. by order of the House of Representatives. Washington, Pr. by Gales & Seaton, 1822. 23 p. NbU.   11274

---- Rules and orders of the House of Representatives adopted June session, 1822. [Washington, 1822] 8 p. DLC.   11275

---- Rules of practice for the courts of equity of the United States. Columbus, Ohio, pr. by P. H. Olmsted, 1822. 12 p. OCIWHi; PHi.   11276

---- ---- Philadelphia, 1822. 11 p. PHi.   11277

---- ---- Providence, Brown and Danforth, 1822. 12 p. DLC; RHi; RPB.   11278

---- ---- Washington City, Pr. by Davis and Force, 1822. 12 p. DLC.   11279

---- Statement of articles paying ad valorem duties, and of articles paying, or to pay, specific duties. April 12, 1822. Pr. by order of the House of Representatives. Washington, Pr. by Gales & Seaton, 1822. (111) 8 p. DLC; G; NNLI; NjP; P; R; TxU. 11280

---- Table of post offices in the United States, with the names of post-masters, the counties and states in which they are situated; and the distances from the City of Washington, and the capitals of the respective states. By direction of the Post-master General. Washington, 1822. 114 p. ICU; MiU-C; N; NRivHi; PPAmP; TKL-Mc.   11281

---- Trial of Captain John Shaw, by the General Court martial, holden on board the U. S. Ship Independence, at the Navy Yard, Charlestown, Massachusetts, upon charged and specifications preferred against him by Captain Isaac Hull... Washington, Davis and Force, printers, 1822. 88 p. DLC; M; MdAN; NhD; PPL; Vi.   11282

---- ---- Pr. from the Official Record on file in the Navy Department. Washington, Davis and Force, 1822. 104 p. MBAt; MHi.   11283

---- Unfinished business of the first session of the seventeenth Congress. Of the standing rules and orders for conducting the business of the House of Representatives of the United States, the following is... [Washington, 1822] (110) 10 p. DLC; NjP.
11284
The universal preceptor. See Phillips, Sir Richard.

Universalists. New York. Western Association
    Minutes of the proceedings of the Western Association of Universalists in the state of New-York. 1822. Utica, N.Y., 1822. 8 p. MWA.   11285

Upshur, Abel Parker, 1790-1844
    A. P. Upshur, of Richmond, to the citizens of Philadelphia, relative to John Hendree, and his late pamphlet. Richmond

[Pr. by W. Ramsay] 1822. 54 p.
DLC; RPB.   11286

V

Vanbrugh, Sir John, 1664-1726
   ...The provoked husband, or
A journey to London, a comedy.
Boston, Wells and Lilly; and A.
T. Goodrich & co., New York,
1822. 123 p. CSt; CtB; LNMus;
MH; MeB; PPL; RPB.   11287

Van Vechten, Jacob
   The duty of Christians toward
the heathen, taught by the ex-
ample of Christ: a sermon
preached in the city of Schenectady, Jan. 27, 1822. Schenectady,
Cabinet printing-house, Isaac
Riggs, printer, 1822. 20 p.
NCooHi.   11288

Varley, Mrs. Delvalle (Lowry)
   Conversations on mineralogy.
1st Amer. from the last London
ed.   Philadelphia, U. Hunt, 1822.
332 p. CSdNHM; ICU; KU;
MBAt; MH; MS; MSaP; MeBaT;
MiU; NCH; NjR; OClWHi; OO;
P; PPi; RBr; RPB; TBriK;
VtBrt; WHi.   11289

Venn, John
   Sermons by the Rev. John
Venn, M.A. Rector of Clapham.
Three volumes in two. 1st
Amer., from the third London
ed. Boston, R.P. & C. Willi-
ams, S. Etheridge, printer, 1822.
2 v. ArBaA; CBPSR; CtSoP;
ICU; InID; MB; MH; MeBat;
NBuDD; NNUT; NcCJ; NjR; OO;
PLT; PPP; ViR; ViRUT; VtU;
WBeloC.   11290

Vermont (State)
   Acts passed by the Legislature
of the State of Vermont at their
October session, 1822. Poultney,
Pr. by Smith and Shute, 1822.
102 p. CSmH; IaU; In-SC; Ky;
L; Mi; Nb; Nj; NNLI; Nv; R;

TxU; W-L.   11291

---- Journal of the convention of
Vermont, assembled at the State
House, at Montpelier, on the
21st day of February, and dis-
solved on the 23d day of Febru-
ary, 1822. Burlington, Pr. by J.
Spooner [1822] 39 p. Ct; ICJ;
ICLaw; ICN; M; MB; MH; MH-
L; MnU; NhD; NjP; OCLloyd;
Or-SC; W-L.   11292

---- Journals of the General Assembly of the State of Vermont,
at their session begun and held
at Montpelier, in the County of
Washington, on Thursday, 10th
October, A.D. 1822. Montpelier,
Pr. by E.P. Walton [1822] 317,
[1] p. VtU.   11293

Vermont Juvenile Missionary Society
   Proceedings of the Vermont
Juvenile Missionary Society, at
their annual meeting at East Rutland, October 2, 1822; together
with the reports of the directors
and treasurer. Woodstock, Pr.
by David Watson, 1822. 25 p.
Nh; PPPrHi; VtMiM.   11294

Vermont. University.
   Catalogue of the officers and
students of the University of Vermont. In Burlington, May, 1822.
Burlington, E. & T. Mills, 1822.
12 p. DLC; ICJ; VtU; WyHi.
                            11295
---- Catalogue of the officers
and students of the University of
Vermont. September, 1822. [Bur-
lington] E. & T. Mills, printers,
[1822] 14 p. VtU.   11296

---- ---- J. Spooner, printer,
1822. 12 p. DLC.   11297

---- University of Vermont. Exhibition of the Junior Class,
Tuesday evening, August 13th,
1822. [Burlington] E. & T.

Mills, printers [1822] Bdsd. VtU. 11298

The vicar of Iver; a tale...By the author of "The Italian Convert"...Philadelphia, H. C. Carey & I. Lea, 1822. 130 p. PU. 11299

Victoria neo-aureliana... See Ross, James.

Views of the Society for the Prevention of Pauperism in the City of Baltimore. Baltimore, Pr. by Thomas Maund, 1822. 36 p. MdBP; NjR. 11300

Village dialogues. See Hughs, Mrs. Mary (Robson)

Villeneuve, John Baptiste
Administrator's sale. Will be sold at the plantation and dwelling of Joseph Villeneuve, late deceased, at the river, La Natte, in Edwards county, Illinois... March 12th, 1822. [Vincennes? 1822] Bdsd. In. 11301

Vindex, pseud.
Truth advocated: in letters addressed to the Presbyterians. By Vindex... Philadelphia, Joseph Rakestraw, 1822. 158, [1] p. LNH; MH; MdBFr; MdToH; PHC; PPL; PPLT; PPPrHi; PSC-Hi. 11302

A vindication of the character of Alford Richardson against the aspersions of Governor King... Portland, Pr. by Arthur Shirley, 1822. 41 p. DLC; MB; MBAt; MH; MWA; Me; MeBa; MeHi; MeP; MeWC. 11303

Viotti, Giovanni Battista, 1755-1824
Love thee dearest, love thee. A ballad. New York, Dubois & Stodart [1822] [2] p. DLC; NN; RPB. 11304

---- ---- Philadelphia, G. E.

Blake [1822] [2] p. DLC; MWA; NN; PP; PU. 11305

---- ---- Philadelphia, Geo. Willig [1822] [2] p. MB; MWA; NHi; NN; PP; PPL. 11306

Virgilius Maro, Publius
P. Virgilii Maronis Opera, Interpretatione et notis illustravit Cardus Rusaeus, Soc. Jesus. Editio tertia in America... Philadelphia, Impensis H. C. Carey & I. Lea, 1822. 567, 106 p. MAnP; MB; MNS; MeHi; MnSM; NT; PV; TxU-T. 11307

Virginia (State)
Acts passed at a general assembly of the Commonwealth of Virginia, begun and held at the capitol, in the city of Richmond, on Monday, 3d day of December, 1821...Richmond, Pr. by Thomas Ritchie, 1822. 120 p. DLC. 11308

---- A bill concerning the sureties of John Preston. [Richmond, 1822] 2 p. DLC. 11309

---- Report of the Committee of finance. The Committee of Finance have, according to order, prepared an estimate of the probable expenses and receipts of the current year, which they beg leave to report. Expenses of the Commonwealth from 1st of October, 1821, to 30th September, 1822, inclusive. [Richmond, 1822] 3 p. DLC. 11310

---- Sketch of the laws, passed at the session which commenced on Monday, the 3d of December 1821 [1822] 1 p. DLC. 11311

---- To the Honorable the speakers and members of both houses of the General Assembly of Virginia, now in session. The petition of the undersigned sureties of John Preston, late treasurer

of the commonwealth... respectfully represents... [1822] 2 p.
DLC.   11312

The Virginia almanac for 1823.
By Joshua Sharp. Alexandria,
John A. Stewart [1822] DLC.
                              11313
---- ---- Alexandria, Julian A.
Stewart [1822] 20 ll. DLC.
                              11314
---- ---- Richmond, Warner's
Book Store [1822] 24 ll. PHi;
PPi; Vi; ViRVal; ViW.   11315

The Virginia and North-Carolina
pocket almanack and farmers'
companion for 1823. By David
Richardson. Richmond, John
Warrock [1822] 18 ll. DLC;
InU; MWA; N; ViRVal; ViW;
ViWC.   11316

Virtue in a cottage: or, The
history of Sally Bark. ...Hart-
ford, George Goodwin & sons,
1822. 53 p. CtHi.   11317

Der Volksfreund und Hagers-
tauner Calender auf 1823. Hag-
erstaun, Md., J. Gruber und D.
May [1822] 18 ll. CtY; DLC;
MWA; MdBE; NjR; PHi; PPAmP;
PPCS; PPeSchw; PYHi.   11318

Volney, Constantin François
Chasseboeuf, comte de, 1757-
1820
   Las ruinas, escrites en
frances por el señor de Volney,
(hoy conde y par de Francia.)
Tr. conforme a la 5. ed. de
Paris; con tres laminas. Y con
El catecismo de la ley natural.
New York, 1822. vii, [9]-216,
273-301 p. OCMtSM; OU. 11319

---- The ruins: or, A survey of
the revolutions of empires. A
new translation from the French.
Albany, Pr. by S. Shaw, 1822.
320 p. GDC; MB; MH; MMeT;
MWH; MdBJ; Mi; MiD-B; N;

NNFM; NRU; PPL; VtB.
                              11320
Voltaire, François Marie Arouet
de
   The history of Charles XII.
King of Sweden. Published by
Wm. Disturnell, Lansingburgh,
and W. and J. Disturnell, book-
sellers, Troy. E. and E. Hos-
ford, printers, Albany, 1822.
275 p. KHi; KWiU; MB; MBoy;
MStoc; MWHi; N; NGos; NNS;
Bowe.   11321

Vorbericht des John Lechler auf
eine Auflage für die Ermordung
seiner ehefrau Mary Lechler vor
der Court von Oyer und Terminer von Lancaster County gehalten in der Stadt Lancaster am
dritten Montag im August 1822.
Lancaster: Gedruckt und zu hab-
en bey Johann Bär. 1822. 38 p.
(Lancaster County Historical Society.)   11322

W

Waldegrave, James Walde-
grave, 2d earl, 1715-1763
   Memoirs, from 1754 to 1758.
Philadelphia, Abraham Small,
1822. 200 p. CtW; KyLx; MB;
MBC; MMeT; MNBedf; MpiB;
MWH; NRU; Nh; P; PHi; PPA;
PPL; ScCC.   11323

Waldo, Samuel Putnam, 1780-
1826
   The life and character of
Stephen Decatur. Ed. 2. Mid-
dletown (Conn.), Pr. by Clark
& Lyman, for O.D. Cooke,
1822. 378 p. CSf; CoCs; CoU;
Ct; DLC; IC; ICHi; IP; IaMp;
KyLx; M; MB; MBNEH; MH;
MOx; MPiB; MdAN; MdHi;
MeBa; MiD; MiDC; MiU-C;
MnU; NBLiHi; NCH; NE; NSyU;
NT; NcAS; O; P; PHi; PPAmP;
RP; ScU; TBriK; WvU. 11324

Walker, C. E.
  Wallace; a historical tragedy;
in five acts. Philadelphia, T. H.
Palmer, 1822. 64p. ICN; MB;
MH; NjP; PU.   11325

Walker, John, 1732-1807
  Critical pronouncing dictionary, and expositor of the English
language, abridged. Bellows Falls,
Vt., Blake, Cutler & Co., 1822.
507 p. (Private collection of
Mrs. Milton Vaughan, 2201
Broadway, Little Rock, Ark.)
                            11326
---- Walker's critical pronouncing dictionary and expositor of
the English language. Abridged.
(H. & E. Phinney's stereotyped
ed.) Cooperstown, stereotyped
and pr. by H. & E. Phinney,
1822. 400 p. MDeeP; NCooHi;
NNC.   11327

---- A critical pronouncing dictionary, and expositor of the
English language. New-York,
Collins and Hannay. Stereotyped
by B. & J. Collins, 1822. 71,
609, 103 p. MiD; PAtM;
PPeSchw; WBeloC.   11328

---- ---- 11th ed. imp. Phila-
delphia, Thomas and William
Bradford, Johnson and Warner,
Griggs & Dickinson, printers,
1822. 413 p. MB; MStonHi;
NRviHi; PAtM.   11329

---- A rhetorical grammar in
which the common improprieties
in reading and speaking are de-
tected. 2d Amer. ed. Boston,
pub. by Cummings and Hilliard,
Univ. Press, Hilliard & Metcalf,
1822. 383 p. CtHT; CtW; DLC;
GAGT; GDC; GMM; ICLoY;
InGrD; InNd; KAS; MA; MB;
MBBC; MCM; MH; MNe; MS;
MWH; MdBS; MiD; MoSU; NCH;
NGII; NNC; NNF; NNUT; NRU;
NT; NWM; NbHi; NbU; Nj;
OCIW; OO; PHi; PLFM; PU;

RPB; ScC; ScCC; TxU-T; ViL.
                            11330
Walker, Joseph R.
  The believer's confidence; a
sermon, preached in Chester-
town in the month of July 1821;
and subsequently in Beaufort,
South Carolina. Baltimore,
Joseph Robinson, 1822. 36 p.
MdBD.   11331

Walker, Timothy
  ...Two letters addressed to
Gen. William Hull, on his con-
duct as a soldier, in the sur-
render of Fort Detroit to Gen.
Brock, without resistance, in
the commencement of the late
war with Great Britain. Boston,
Timothy Walker, 1822. 11 p.
N; WHi.   11332

Walsh, Michael
  A new system of mercantile
arithmetic adapted to the com-
merce of the United States...4th
ed. Salem, pub. by Cushing &
Appleton, (proprietors), pr. by
J.D. Cushing & brothers, 1822.
iv, 264, [54] p. MB; MH;
MHaHi; MLaw; MSaE; NcAS;
OOxM; PU.   11333

Walton's Vermont register and
farmer's almanack for 1823.
By Zadock Thompson. Montpelier,
E. P. Walton [1822] 72 ll. CLU;
Ct; InU; M; MB; MHi; MWA;
N; NHi; NNC; Nh; OCLloyd;
OO; P; Vt; VtHi; VtWinoS;
VtU.   11334

Ward, John
  A Masonic sermon delivered
at the request of the several
lodges in Lexington, Kentucky,
on Monday, June 24th, 1822; in
honor of the anniversary of St.
John the Baptist. Lexington,
Pr. by William G. Hunt, 1822.
16 p. MBFM.   11335

Ward, William
   Farewell letters to a few
friends in Britain and America,
on returning to Bengal, in 1821.
Lexington, Ky., Thomas T. Skill-
man, 1822. 252 p. ICU; KyBgW;
KyDC; KyHi; KyLoP; MiU-C;
MoSHi; OCHP.   11336

Wardlaw, Ralph
   Lectures on the Book of Ec-
clesiastes... Philadelphia, W.W.
Woodward, 1822. 596 p. CSansS;
CoDI; CtHC; CtW; ICP; IaDL;
KyLoP; MA; MBC; MoSpD;
NBuDD; NSyU; OCIW; OO; OWoC;
PLT; PMA; PPLT; PPPrHi;
PPiW; PWW; RPA; TBriK;
ViAl; ViRU.   11337

Ware, Henry, 1794-1843
   Answer to Dr. Woods' reply,
in a second series of letters ad-
dressed to Trinitarians and Cal-
vinists. Cambridge, pub. by
Hilliard and Metcalf; sold also
by Cummings & Hilliard, Boston,
1822. 163 p. CBPSR; CBPac;
CtHC; CtY-D; DLC; ICMe; ICP;
ICT; ICU; IaGG; M; MA; MAnP;
MB; MBAU; MBC; MCon; MH;
MHi; MNe; MPiB; MeBat; MiU;
N; NNG; NNP; NNS; NNUT;
NjR; OO; PPAmP; PPPrHi; PPL;
RPB; TWcW; WBeloC.   11338

---- A sermon, delivered Dec.
18, 1821, at the ordination of
the Rev. William Ware... 3d ed.
Published at the request of the
Congregation, by the New-York
Unitarian Book Society, 1822.
48 p. CtHT-W; ICMe; ICU; MB;
MH; MDeeP; MH; MHi; MNF;
N; NNS; NjR; OO; PHi; RPB.
                           11339
---- A sermon preached at Am-
herst, N.H., on Lord's day,
August 4, 1822. Amherst, pub.
by Luther Roby. Concord, N.H.,
Pr. by Hill and Moore, 1822.
22 p. ICMe; MH; MPiB; Nh;
Nh-Hi.   11340

---- Three important questions
answered, relating to the Chris-
tian name, character and hopes
... Kennebunk, Pr. by James
K. Remich, 1822. 24 p. MeB.
                           11341
---- Three important questions
answered, relating to the Chris-
tian name, character and hopes.
New York, pub. by the New
York Unitarian Book Society, Pr.
by Van Pelt and Spear, 1822.
24 p. CBPac; ICMe; ICN; MA;
MBAU; MH; MHi; MeB; NCH;
OO.   11342

Warner's almanack for 1823.
By Joshua Sharp. Philadelphia,
Benjamin Warner [1822] 18 ll.
MWA.   11343

---- ---- Philadelphia, Benja-
min Warner's Executors [1822]
18 ll. InU; MWA; NjR; PHi.
                           11344
Warren, John Collins, 1778-
1856
   A comparative view of the
sensorial and nervous systems
in men and animals. Boston,
J.W. Ingraham, 1822. 159 p.
CU-M; CtW; DLC; IU-M;
KyLoJM; KyLxT; MB; MBS;
MBU-M; MH; MHi; MLy; MWA;
MdBJ; MdBM; NN; NNNAM;
NbU; OC; OClM; PPAmP; PPC;
PPL; RPB; ScCM; ViU.   11345

Warren Academy, Warren, Me.
   Catalogue of the officers and
students in the term commencing September, 1822. Brunswick,
Joseph Griffin [1822] Bdsd. MH.
                           11346
Washburn, James, Jr.
   A true and concise narrative
of the voyage and sufferings of
James Washburn, Jr. on board
the Delphos of Boston, John
Knight, Commander. Reduced to
writing from the story as told
by himself. Together with a report of the trial, Washburn vs.

Knight, before the Supreme Judicial Court, holden at Boston, November term, 1821. Extracted from documents filed in the case. Boston, William S. Spear, 1822. 58 p. MA; MHi. 11347

Washington almanack for 1823. By Joshua Sharp. Alexandria, John A. Stewart [1822] 20 ll. DLC; PDoBHi. 11348

The Washington guide. See Elliot, William.

Washington Library Company, Washington, D.C.
Catalogue of books in the Washington Library, July 20, 1822. Washington City, Pr. by Anderson and Meehan, 1822. 43 p. DLC; ICU. 11349

The Watchman's address to his patrons... January 1, 1822. [Boston, Mass., 1822] Bdsd. WHi. 11350

Waterhouse, Benjamin
Cautions to young persons concerning health in a public lecture delivered at the close of the medical course in the chapel at Cambridge, Nov. 20, 1804; containing the general doctrine of chronic diseases; shewing the evil tendency of the use of tobacco upon young persons; more especially the pernicious effects of smoking cigars; with observations on the use of ardent and vinous spirits in general. 5th ed. With additional notes. Cambridge, University press, 1822. 40 p. IEN-M; M; MBC; MH; MdBM; N; NNNAM; RNR; RPB. 11351

---- An essay concerning tussis convulsiva, or, whooping-cough, with observations on the diseases of children. Boston, Munroe and Francis, 1822. 152 p. ICJ; ILM; LNT-M; MB; MBM; MBU-M; MH; MdBM; MoSMed;

NBMS; NNNAM; Nh; NhD; PPHa; PPC; RHi; RNR; TNV. 11352

Watrous, Erastus
An address, delivered before the Council of Select Masters, King Solomon's R.A. Chapter, and Aurora Lodge, No. 9, on laying the cornerstone of the Masonic Hall, Montpelier, Vt. August 9, A.L. 5822. Montpelier, Vt., E.P. Walton, 1822. 12 p. VtU. 11353

Watson, George
Description and use of a diagram of navigation; by which all problems in plane, traverse, parallel, middle latitude and Mercator's sailing may be instantly and accurately resolved. Belfast, Me., Pr. by Fellowes & Simpson, 1822. 64 p. DLC; MH. 11354

Watson, Richard, bp. of Landaff
An address to young persons after confirmation. Philadelphia, Pr. for the Tract and Book Society of the Evangelical Lutheran Church of St. John; J. Rakestraw, printer, 1822. 40 p. KyLoSiU; N; PPLT. 11355

[Watterston, George] 1783-1854
The L... family at Washington; or, A winter in the metropolis. Washington, Davis and Force, 1822. 159 p. CtY; DLC; ICU; MB; MBAt; MH; MWA; NHi; NN; PPL; PU; ViAl; WHi. 11356

Watts, Isaac, 1674-1748
Arrangement of the Psalms, hymns, and spiritual songs; to which is added a supplement... Ed. 6 Boston, Loring, 1822. NB; NRAB. 11357

---- Divine songs. Baltimore, Samuel S. Wood and Company, 1822. 45 p. CtY. (No Balt. imprint) 11358

---- Divine songs for children.
Hartford, G. Goodwin & Sons,
1822. 22 p. CtHi.   11359

---- Hymns and spiritual songs,
in three books... Pittsburgh,
Cramer & Spear, 1822. 332 p.
OCIWHi.   11360

---- ---- Pittsburgh, R. Patterson & Lambdin, 1822. 274 p.
PPLT.   11361

---- The improvement of the
mind, to which are added questions adapted to the work for the
use of schools and academies...
2d ed.   Boston, James Loring,
1822. 220 p. CtSoP; InCW; LNB;
MB; MBBC; MBevHi; MH; MNF;
MShM; NBuG; NCoxHi; NNUT;
OMC; OO; PLT; RNHi; RPB.
                                     11362

---- The improvement of the
mind; or, A supplement to the
art of logic... New-York, pub. by
N. Bangs and T. Mason, for the
Methodist Episcopal Church.
John C. Totten, printer, no. 9
Bowery, 1822. 324 p. CSmH;
CMiC; CtW; LNH; MB; MBNMHi;
MoFayC; NPStA; PHarD;
ScGrwL; TNP; TaAt; TxAuPT.
                                     11363

---- Plain and easy catechism
for children. Hartford, Pr. by
G. Goodwin & Sons, 1822. 23 p.
CtHi; MWo.   11364

---- A short view of the whole
Scripture history: with A continuation of the Jewish affairs
from the Old Testament, till the
time of Christ... 5th Amer.
from the 15th London ed. Philadelphia, pub. by M'Carty & Davis,
Rufus Little... Agent. 1822. 490,
4 p. CSt.   11365

Waverley; or 'Tis sixty years
since.   See Scott, Sir Walter,
bart.

The way of living, in a method,
and by rule; or, A way of employing our time.   Published by
the Protestant Episcopal Tract
Society.   New-York, Pr. by T.
& J. Swords, and sold by them
at the depository of the Society,
no. 99, Pearl-street, for the
benefit of the Society. 1822. 16
p. NNG.   11366

The way to happiness.   Andover,
Pr. by Flagg & Gould, 1822.
16 p. MeB.   11367

Way to wealth and prosperity;
being the substance of two sermons.   By a friend of the human family.   Lexington, Ky.,
Skillman, 1822. 22 p. PPPrHi.
                                     11368
Wayne County, Michigan (terri-
tory)
    Detroit, December 10, 1822.
Sir, the undersigned, a committee on the part of the citizens of
the metropolitan county of the
Territory of Michigan, take the
liberty of inviting your attention
to a memorial, adopted by a
large portion of its inhabitants,
and presented to Congress
through its Delegate, Mr. Sibley.
[Detroit, 1822] Broadside. MiD-
B.   11369

---- Fellow-citizens, a large
proportion of the inhabitants of
Wayne County, desirous of uniting with their brethren of the
other counties of this Territory,
in attempting to effect a change
in that odious form of government, which has too long ex-
cluded them from most of the
privileges of American citizens,
have resolved to use their ut-
most exertions to effect that
change... [Detroit, 1822] Broadside. MiD-B.   11370

Webb, Thomas Smith
    El monitor de los masones

libres; o Ilustraciones sobre la masoneria... Tr. del ingles al espanol. Philadelphia, H.C. Carey and I. Lea, 1822. 292 p. InCW; OCM; PPL; PU; RHi; RP; RPB. 11371

Webster, Noah
The American spelling book ... The revised impression. Stereotyped by E. & J. White, New-York. Albany, Pr. by Websters and Skinners, 1822. 168 p. MPiB; NN; NUtHi; VtMiS. 11372

---- The American spelling book: containing the rudiments of the English language, for the use of schools in the United States. The revised impression with the latest corrections. Stereotyped by G. Bruce, New York. Albany, Pr. by Websters and Skinners, 1822. 168 p. CLSU; NIl; NStc. 11373

---- ---- The rev. impression, with the latest corrections. Boston, Pr. by J.H.A. Frost, 1822. 168 p. MeBa. 11374

---- ---- The revised impression. Stereotyped by E. & J. White, New York. Cincinnati, pub. by J.P. Foote, and Morgan, Lodge and Co., 1822. 168 p. IHi. 11375

---- ---- The revised impression, with the latest corrections. Hartford, Pr. by Hudson & Co., 1822. 168 p. CtHT-W; ICN; MA. 11376

---- Philosophical & practical grammar, of English language. 2d ed. New Haven, Howe & Spalding, S. Converse, printer, 1822. CtSoP; IJI; IaGG; MA; MH; MBL; MWiW; OMC. 11377

[Webster, Redford]
Selections from the Chronicle of Boston and from the book of retrospections, compiled in the last month of the last year of the town, and the first month of city...1822. 132 p. MB; MH; MHi; Me; NNC. 11378

Webster's calendar: or the Albany almanack for 1823. By Andrew Beers. Albany, C.R. & G. Webster; E.W. Skinner and Co. 18 ll. NCooHi; NN; NbO; NSyOHi. 11379

---- ---- 22 ll. CLU; DLC; InU; MB; MWA; N; NHi; NN; NSchU; NRMA; NUtHi; WHi. 11380

Weekes, Refine, b. 1759
The life of William Penn, and other poems, religious, historical, and sentimental. New-York, Pr. by M. Day, for the author, 1822. 192 p. DLC; ICU; IU; InRchE; MH; NBLiHi; Nh-Hi; P; PHC; PHi; PPL; PSC-Hi; PU. 11381

Weeks, William Raymond, 1783-1848
Catechism of scripture doctrine; 4th ed., with the first paragraphs of texts printed at full length, for the use of Sabbath schools. Hartford, S.G. Goodrich, 1822. 106 p. Ct; CtHi; CtSoP; NNUT. 11382

---- The missionary arithmetic; or, Arithmetic made easy, in a new method... Utica [N.Y.] Merrell & Hastings, 1822. 239, [1] p. DLC; ICP; KTW; NSyU; NUt; OClWHi; OO; VtMiM; VtMiS. 11383

---- Part III of the Missionary arithmetic, being a key to part second: containing the answers to the questions in that part. For the use of instructors. Utica, Pr. by William Williams, 1822. 24 p. VtMiM; VtMiS. 11384

Weems, Mason Locke, 1759-1825

Anecdotes of gamblers, extracted from a work on gambling, by M. L. Weems, formerly Rector of Mount Vernon Parish. Philadelphia, To be had of Benjamin & Thomas Kite, Solomon W. Conrad, Kimber & Sharpless, John Richardson, 1822. 8 p. PHC. 11385

[----] ... Effects of drunkenness, illustrated in the History of Peter and John Hay. [Andover, Pr. for the New England Tract Society by Flagg and Gould, 1822] 12 p. MWA. 11386

---- God's revenge against gambling... 4th ed. Philadelphia, Pr. for the author, 1822. 47 p. DLC; MH; MdHi; MiU-C; N; NIC; OC; OClWHi; P; PHi; PPL; PU; TxHuT; WHi; WaSp. 11387

---- The life of Benjamin Franklin; with many choice anecdotes and admirable sayings of this great man... 6th ed. Philadelphia, H. C. Carey & I. Lea, 1822. 264 p. DLC; IU; MB; MHi; MMal; MWHi; MiDSH; NcU; P; PHi; ScCliTO; TNJ; ViU. 11388

---- The life of Gen. Francis Marion, a celebrated partisan officer in the Revolutionary War ... 8th ed. Philadelphia, M. Carey & Son, 1822. 251 p. DLC; PV; WHi. 11389

---- The life of William Penn, the settler of Pennsylvania, the founder of Philadelphia... Philadelphia, H. C. Carey and I. Lea, 1822. 219 p. Ct; CtSoP; DLC; DeGE; ICN; ICT; InRchE; MAm; MH; MHi; MMe; MnM; MdBP; NcH; NcAS; Nh-Hi; NjMD; OClWHi; PHi; PPF; RPB; ScC; ScFl; ViU; WHi. 11390

Welles, Elijah Gardner

The orator's guide; or, Rules for speaking and composing; from the best authorities. Philadelphia, Pr. for the compiler, G. L. Austin, printer, 1822. 104 p. CU; CtHT; CtW; IObB; IU; MB; MH; MLow; MiD; NNC; NbCrD; NjP; P; PLFM; PP; PSC; PU; WvBe. 11391

Wellington, Charles

A sermon preached at Templeton, April 19, 1821, at the interment of late Madam Lucy Rice, relict of the late Rev. Asaph Rice... Boston, Pr. by E.W. Bellamy, 1822. MBAt; MH; MHi; MTemNHi; MiD-B. 11392

Wells, Nathaniel

New Year's sermons, delivered in Deerfield, New-Hampshire, January, 1822. Concord, Pr. by George Hough, 1822. 22 p. MBC; Nh; Nh-Hi. 11393

Welton, A.W.

The beauty and usefulness of sacred music in the worship of God, and the duty of all who can to join it; a sermon, preached at Detroit, March 3, 1822. [Detroit? 1822?] 12 p. OClW. 11394

Wentworth, John

A complete index to Wentworth's System of pleading. New-York, Gould and Banks; Albany, W. Gould and co., 1822. 277 p. C; Ct; DLC; MdBB; NNU; NP-SC; NRAL; NbOC-L; NcD; NhD. 11395

Wesley, John

A collection of hymns for the use of the Methodist Episcopal Church... New York, pub. by N. Bangs and T. Mason, for the Methodist Episcopal Church; Abraham Paul, printer, 1822. 552 p. MBD; MFi; MdBAHi; MiU; OO; PHi; ScSpW; VtMiS;

WM. 11396

West Baton Rouge
Police jury regulations of the parish of West Baton Rouge, state of Louisiana. Baton Rouge: Pr. at the Republican office, 1822. 20 p. LNH; LNT; LU; MiU-C. 11397

Western agricultural almanack for 1823. By Loud & Wilmarth. Rochester, E. Peck & Co. [1822] 18 ll. MWA; NCH; NCanHi; NR; NRU. 11398

The western farmers' almanac for 1823. Louisville, Worsley & Collins. Advertised in the "Louisville Public Advertiser," Nov. 27, 1822. Drake 1813. 11399

Der Westliche Menschenfreund u. Schellsburger Calender auf 1823. Schellsburg, Pa., Friedrich Goeb [1822] 18 ll. MWA; N. 11400

Westminster Assembly of Divines
The Assembly's shorter catechism as used in the Presbyterian Church... Washington, J. Gideon, jr., 1822. 27 p. MiD-B. 11401

Wharton, Thomas Isaac
A digest of cases adjudged in the circuit court of the United States for the third circuit, and in the courts of Pennsylvania... Philadelphia, Philip Nicklin, 1822. 690 p. C; IaDuU; MH-L; MoU; NNC-L; NNU; PPB; PPL; PPFr; PPWa; PU; PU-L. 11402

Wheaton, Josephus
A sermon delivered at Hopkinton, August 25, 1821, at the funeral of the Mr. Benjamin Adams... Boston, Crocker & Brewster, printers, 1822. 20 p. MHolliHi; MWA; MoSpD. 11403

Wheeler, Jacob D.
The criminal recorder... New-York, pub. by Gould and Banks, and W. Gould & Co. Albany, Daniel Fanshaw, printer, 1822. 583 p. MBAt; NNS. 11404

Whelpley, Samuel
A compend of history, from the earliest times... 6th ed., with corrections, by Rev. Joseph Emerson... Boston, pub. by Richardson & Ford; J. H. A. Frost, printer, 1822. 2 v. in 1. MBridT; MFiHi; MH; MPlyA; MTr; MWHi; Nj; PU; RPB; TxU-T; VtNofN. 11405

Whitaker, John, 1776-1847
Oh! say not woman's heart is bought. Boston, G. Grapuner, [1822?] p [1]-2. DLC; MB; MH; MHi; MWA; NN; PP-K; RPB. 11406

---- ---- Boston, S. Wood [1822?] p [1]-2. DLC; MB; MH; MWA; PP-K; RPB. 11407

---- ---- A ballad. New York, E. Riley [1822] 4 p. NBuG. 11408

---- ---- A favorite ballad. Philadelphia, G. Willig [1822] p [1]-2. CSmH; DLC; NBuG; NN; PP. 11409

White, Daniel Appleton
A view of the jurisdiction and proceedings of the Court of Probate in Massachusetts, with particular reference to the County of Essex. Salem, Pr. by J. D. Cushing and Brothers, for Cushing and Appleton, 1822. 158 p. DLC; IaHi; M; MB; MBAt; MH-L; MHa; MHi; MMhHi; MSaE; MWCL; Mi-L; MiD-B; Nh; OCLaw; PPAmP; WU. 11410

White, Henry Kirke, 1785-1806
The remains of Henry Kirke White, of Nottingham late of St. John's College, Cambridge; with an account of his life. Boston, Wells & Lilly, Court St., 1822.

3 v. KyLx; PFal; TWcW.   11411

White, John
A sermon, delivered November 3, 1821 at the interment of the Rev. Stephen Palmer, pastor of the First Church and Society in Needham. Dedham, Pr. by H. & W. H. Mann, 1822. 18 p. CtSoP; DLC; GDC; MBAt; MH; MHi; NBLiHi; Nh-Hi; PHi; RPB.   11412

[Whiting, Henry]
Ontwa, the son of the forest. A poem. New York, Wiley & Halsted, 1822. 136 p. CtHT-W; CtY; DLC; ICN; MB; MBAt; MH; MHi; MdBP; MiD-B; MiPh; MiU-C; NIC; NcD; OClWHi; PHi; RPB; WHi.   11413

Whitmore, Benjamin
A sermon, delivered at Plymouth, on Thanksgiving day, December 5, 1822. Boston, Pr. by Crocker & Brewster, for Ezra Collier, Plymouth, 1822. 20 p. CSt; MHi; MiD-B.   11414

Whittemore, Thomas
False teachers. Some general ideas of a discourse, delivered in Cambridgeport, Sabbath Day, Aug. 4, 1822. [Dedham] Pr. for the Dedham Tract Society, by H. & W. H. Mann, 1822. 11 p. MMal.   11415

---- A sermon delivered before the Universalist Society in West Cambridge on the evening of the last Sabbath in May 1822. Boston, Henry Bowen, 1822. 24 p. MB; MHi.   11416

---- A sermon, pronounced in Milford, Mass. December 6, 1821. Being the day appointed by the Governor of the state, for Thanksgiving praise. Boston, Pr. by True and Green, 1822. 16 p. MMal; MMeT; MHi. 11417

The whole duties of men and women. In two parts with an appendix, containing The polite philosopher and Dr. Franklin's Way to wealth. Georgetown, D. C., J. C. Dunn, printer, 1822. 242 p. DLC; DWP; DGU; MdBL.   11418

Wickliffe, Robert, 1775-1859
To the public. I have this moment seen a scurrilous hand bill, signed George Shannon in answer to me which charges him with having lost at cards the sum of $390, and after giving his note for the amount and renewing his promise to pay, he had availed himself of the gambling act to avoid payment. [Lexington? 1822] Bdsd. DLC. 11419

Wiesenthal, Thomas Van Dyke, 1790-1833
The harper's song. Boston, G. Graupner. Sold by John Ashton. [1822?] p [1]-2. DLC; NN; NRU-Mus.   11420

Wiggins, Richard
The New-York expositor; or, fifth book: ... New York, Samuel Wood and sons and Samuel S. Wood & co., Baltimore, 1822. 324 p. NNC; OFH; PPL.   11421

Wilbur, Josiah
The grammatical key; which, by questions and answers, represents the method of learning the parts of speech, by characters that stand to represent them... 2d ed. Bellows Falls, Pr. by Blake, Cutler & Co., for the author, 1822. 130 p. MH; NNC; OAU; OWervO.   11422

Wilcox, Carlos, 1794-1827
The age of benevolence... New-Haven, Pr. by A. H. Maltby and co., 1822. 72 p. Ct; CtHi; CtSoP; CtY; DLC; IU; MBC; MH; MMal; Nh-Hi; PHi;

PU; RNHi; TxU.   11423

Wilkins, John Hubbard, 1794-
1861
Elements of astronomy, for
the use of schools and academies
... Boston, Cummings & Hilliard,
1822. 116 p. CtHT-W; DLC; ICU;
MB; MBC; MBevHi; MH; MHans;
MPiB; MW; OSW; VtMiS. 11424

Willard, Mrs. Emma (Hart),
1787-1870
Ancient geography, as connected with chronology, and pre-
paratory to the study of ancient
history. Hartford, Oliver D.
Cooke & Sons, 1822. 88 p. MH;
MNS; NNS; PU.   11425

Willetts, Jacob, 1785-1860
Book-keeping, by single entry.
Poughkeepsie, P. Potter, 1822.
18, [10], 21 p. MB.   11426

---- A compendious system of
geography... 2d ed. revised.
Philadelphia, P. Potter & Co.,
1822. 324 p. NFrf; NICLA;
ViSwC; WHi.   11427

---- An easy grammar of geography, for the use of schools...
8th ed. Poughkeepsie, Pr. and
pub. by Paraclete Potter, for
himself, and for S. Potter & co.,
Philadelphia, 1822. 215 p.
CtMMH; NNC; NcWsS; PPL.
                            11428
---- Stereotyped edition. The
scholar's arithmetic. Designed
for the use of schools in the
United States. 4th ed., corr.
and improved. Stereotyped by H.
Wallis, New-York. Poughkeep-
sie, Pr. and pub. by Paraclete
Potter, for himself, and for S.
Potter & co., 1822. 191, [1] p.
MiU; NCH; NNC; NP; NPV;
NjR.   11429

---- The scholar's arithmetic,
designed for the use of schools

in the United States. 4th ed.
corr. and improved. Poughkeep-
sie, Pr. and pub. by Paraclete
Potter, 1822. [5] 6-121 p.
CSmH; CtHT-W; CtY; DLC;
MB; MiU; NN; NNC.   11430

Williams, John
To the people of Montgomery
County. [Lexington? 1822]
Broadside. OCHP.   11431

Williams, Otto H.
Oration, sermon, &c. de-
livered at the ceremony of laying
the foundation stone of the Masonic Hall in Hagers-Town...
Hagerstown, Pr. by William D.
Bell, 1822. 32 p. MdBP. 11432

Williams, Richard L.
Ah did you know enchanting
fair. A much admired song.
New York, N. Thurston [1822?]
3 p. N.   11433

---- Every year impairs life's
treasure. A duet. Composed for
the piano forte. Philadelphia,
Geo. Willig [1822] [2] p. DLC;
MH; NN.   11434

Williams, Samuel Porter
An address delivered and pub-
lished at the request of the
Young Men's Auxiliary Education
Society of Newburyport, Sept.
1822. Newburyport, Pr. by W. &
J. Gilman [1822] 20 p. DLC;
MBC; MH; MWA; MiD-B.
                            11435
---- Plea for the orphan, de-
livered on the anniversary of the
Female Charitable Society, of
Newburyport May 21, 1822. Pub-
lished for the benefit of the asy-
lum. [Newburyport] Pr. by W.
& J. Gilman [1822] 31 p.
CBPac; CtSoP; MB; MBC; MH;
MNe; MPiB; MWA; MeBat;
MiD-B; N.   11436

[Williams, Thomas] 1779-1876
The greatest sermon that ever was preached. By Demons Egomet [pseud.] Published for the benefit of all who did not hear it. [Providence?] New England, 1822. 7 p. DLC; NN. 11437

Williams, Thomas, d. 1854
My country no more. New York, E. Riley, [1822] 4 p. MH; NN. 11438

Willig's pocket companion, containing a selection of songs, airs, waltzes, marches, &c. Arranged for the German flute, violin, or patent flagiolet. Philadelphia, G. Willig [1822?] 26 p. PHi. 11439

Willis, John
Celebrated horse Young Emperor...will stand the ensuing season at my stable in Carlisle, in Sullivan county, and let to mares at the moderate price... of 3 dollars cash the season. Carlisle, Sullivan county, March 1st, 1822. Bdsd. In. 11440

Willis, Richard, d. 1830
The harp of love. Sung in the character of Francis in The spy. New York, pub. for the Author by A. & W. Geib [1822?] 3 p. DLC; MH; N; NN; NRU-Mus; RPB. 11441

Willis, William, of New Bedford
An address, delivered before the New Bedford Auxiliary Society for the Suppression of Intemperance, at their annual meeting, first month 4, 1819. 2d ed. Charleston, Pr. by C. C. Sebring, 1822. 24 p. MiU-C. 11442

Willson, Joseph
The light house. A favorite ballad. New York, E. Riley [1822?] [2] p. NRU-Mus. 11443

Wilmer, William Holland, 1782-1827
The Episcopal manual. Being intended as a summary explanation of the doctrine, discipline, and worship of the Protestant Episcopal Church... Baltimore, Pub. by E. J. Coale & Co. and C. Hall, Norfolk, Va.; B. Edes, printer, 1822. 254 p. DGU. 11444

---- ---- Baltimore, Pub. by E. J. Coale & Co.; B. Edes, printer, 1822. 254 p. CtHW; CtW; ICP; MH; MdBD; MdBE; MdHi; PHi; ViL. 11445

Wilmington, North Carolina
Memorial to the general assembly of North Carolina on the subject of the flats or shoals of the Cape Fear. Raleigh, Henderson, 1822. (No. 3) 4 p. NcU. 11446

Wilson, Amos, b. 1781.
The sweets of solitude: or directions to mankind how they may be happy in a miserable world! By Amos Wilson, who lived 19 years in a cave. Boston, John Wilkey, 1822. Ct; ICN; IHi; MBNEH; MH; MHi; MNBedf; MiD-B; MoSM; NN; Nh; Nh-Hi; PHi; PP; PPL; WHi. 11447

Wilson, James, 1760-1839
A review of the letters of the late Rev. John Bowden, D.D. ...to the Rev. Dr. Miller, one of the pastors of the United Presbyterian Churches in the City of New York, or, Episcopal claims calmly considered. Providence, Brown and Danforth, printers, 1822. 103 p. CtHt; GDC; MH-AH; MHi; MWA; NHi; NN; NNC; PBL; PHi; PPPrHi; RHi; RPB. 11448

Wilson, James Renwick, 1780-1853
An interesting sketch of the

life of Dr. H[enry] T[odd], by
the Rev. J.R.W. Mount-pleasant,
Ohio, reprinted by Elisha Bates,
1822. 22 p. DLC; OCIWHi.
                              11449
Wilson, John
   Map of South Carolina...astro-
nomical observations by Geo.
Blackburn & I.M. Elford. Philadelphia, engraved by H.S. Tanner,
1822. 1 sheet. NcD; PPAmP.
                              11450
[Wilson, John] 1785-1854
   Lights and shadows of Scottish
life. A selection from the papers of the late Arthur Austin,
[pseud.]. Boston, Pub. by
Charles Ewer and Timothy Bedlington, Phelps and Farnham,
printers, 1822. 311 p. MBAt;
MBL; MPiB; MWHi; MiD-B;
OO.   11451

[----] ---- New York, pub. by
E. Bliss and E. White, etc.
1822. 311 p. CStr; PU; ScU.
                              11452
[----] ---- 2d Amer. ed. Philadelphia, E.T. Scott, 1822. 311 p.
NcU; OClStM; OMC.   11453

Wilson, Thomas, bp.
   A short and plain introduction
to the better understanding of the
Lord's Supper...to which is an-
nexed, the office of the Holy
Communion...Boston, Joseph W.
Ingraham, 1822. 152 p. Ct;
CtHT; MBD; MH; MNe; NPV;
ScCMu.   11454

Wilson, Thomas, 1768-1828?
   The biography of the principal
American military and naval
heroes; comprehending details of
their achievements during the
Revolutionary and late wars. 2d
ed., rev. New York, J. Low,
1822. 2 v. DLC; MH; MLex;
MMal; MNt; NN; Nh; NjMD.
                              11455
Wilson's farmers' almanac for
1823. By Joshua Sharp. Trenton,

James J. Wilson [1822] 18 ll.
MWA; PPiHi.   11456

Wilson's Tennessee farmer's almanac for 1823. By Wm. L.
Willeford. Nashville, G. Wilson [1822] 18 ll. MWA; T;
ViW.   11457

Wilt thou be my dearie. A favorite Scotch air. Arranged as a
duett. Baltimore, John Cole
[1822?] [2] p. MWA; NBuG.
                              11458
Winchester, George
   Observations on the Susquehanna River & Maryland Canal,
addressed to the Legislatures of
Pennsylvania & Maryland. Baltimore, F.G. Schaeffer, 1822.
29 p. Md; MdBE; MdBP;
PPAmP.   11459

The winds of the winter are
over. Adapted to a much admired Irish melody. Baltimore,
John Cole [1822?] [2] p. DLC;
MH.   11460

Winslow Blues
   Constitution of the light infantry company of Winslow Blues,
as revised, March 1822. To
which is added a system of drill
exercises. Boston, Pr. by Henry W. Dutton, 1822. 76 p. DLC;
MBMHiM.   11461

Wirt, William
   The question settled. Mr. Way
is eligible for the mayoralty...
[Signed] Wm. Wirt. Washington,
June 3, 1822. 1 p. DLC. 11462

Wiscasset, Maine
   Bye-laws of the town of Wiscasset. Approved by the court
of sessions, April term, 1822.
Wiscasset, Pr. by John Dorr
[1822] 11 p. MeHi.   11463

Wisdom in miniature; or, Choice
lessons for infant minds. Wood-

stock, Pr. by David Watson,
1822. 31 p. DLC.   11464

Wisdom in miniature; or, The
youth's pleasing instructor, being
a collection of sentences, divine,
moral and historical... New York,
M. Day, 1822. 206 p. PU.
                           11465
Witherspoon, John
   Lectures on moral philosophy.
Philadelphia, William W. Wood-
ward, 1822. 298 p. IaGG; InU;
MA; MH; MNS; MdAS; MdBL;
MiU; MoSpD; NNS; NWM; NjP;
NjR; OMC; PPPrHi; PWW.
                           11466
Witherspoon, John, 1722-1794
   Letters on education, also,
Letters on the same subject,
from the Christian Observer.
Salem, N.Y., H. Dodd & co.,
1822. 167 p. NCH; NNUT. 11467

Withington, Leonard
   Puritan morals defended: a
discourse delivered at the dedication of the Crombie Street
Church in Salem (formerly Salem
Theatre) and the installation of
the Rev. William Williams, Nov.
22, 1822. Salem, Palfray, 1822.
36 p. ICN.   11468

Withy, George
   A sermon preached at Friends'
meeting-house, Burlington, New
Jersey, on the 10th of the fifth
month, 1822... Philadelphia,
pub. without the consent of the
speaker, 1822. 24 p. NjP;
OCIWHi; PHC; PHi; PPL; PSC;
PSC-Hi; ScCC; WHi.   11469

The wonders of the world... See
Phillips, Sir Richard.

Wood, Benjamin
   A sermon delivered at Upton,
Nov. 27, 1822, at the funeral of
Mr. Austin Saunders, who died
Nov. 24, aged 27 years. Wor-
cester, William Manning, [1822]

12 p. CBPSR; IaCrM; MH.
                           11470
The wood robin; a collection of
songs, from the most admired
authors,... Philadelphia, pub. by
M'Carty & Davis, John Young,
printer, 1822. 192 p. MiU-C;
PPL.   11471

Woodbridge, John
   A good hope in death: a sermon preached in South Hadley,
April 25, 1822, at the interment
of Mrs. Laura W. Bowdoin,
wife of William Bowdoin, jr.
Springfield, A.G. Tannatt & Co.,
printers, 1822. 18 p. MSHi;
RPB.   11472

Woodbridge, William Channing
   Rudiments of geography, on
a new plan designed to assist the
memory by comparison and classification... 2d ed. Hartford,
Samuel G. Goodrich, 1822. 208
p. OHi; RP; RPB.   11473

---- School atlas to accompany
Woodbridge's Rudiments of Ge-
ography. Hartford, Oliver D.
Cooke and sons [c1822?] 9 maps.
MBC; MH; MiD-B; OCIWHi.
                           11474
The woodman's hut. See Arn-
old, Samuel James.

Woods, Leonard, 1774-1854
   Letters to Unitarians and
reply to Dr. Ware. 2d ed. with
an appendix. Andover, pub. and
for sale by Mark Newman, Flagg
and Gould, printers, 1822. 351 p.
CBPac; CSansS; CtW; GDC;
ICMe; ICP; ICT; IEG; IEW;
IaSlB; InCW; KyLo; MA; MBAU;
MBC; MH; MHi; MW; MeB;
MoFuWc; MoSpD; N; NCH; NN;
NNG; NNUT; NhD; OCIW; OMC;
PPPrHi; RPB; TWcW; WBeaWJC;
WBeloC; ViRUT.   11475

---- Remarks on Dr. Ware's
answer. Andover, pub. and for

sale by Mark Newman. Flagg & Gould, printers, Sept. 1822. 63 p. CBPSR; CBPac; CtY-D; DLC; ICMe; ICN; ICP; MAnP; MB; MBAU; MBC; MH; MHi; MeBat; MiD-B; MiU; MoSpD; N; NNG; NjR; OO; PPPrHi; RPB. 11476

---- A sermon delivered at the ordination of the Rev. Thomas M. Smith as pastor of the Chapel Church and Society in Portland, Me., July 31, 1822. Boston, Lincoln & Edmands, 1822. 26 p. CBPac; ICT; MH-AH; MeHi; RPB. 11477

Wood's almanac for 1823. By Joshua Sharp. Baltimore, Samuel S. Wood & Co. [1822] 18 ll. MdBE. 11478

---- ---- New-York, Samuel Wood & Sons [1822] 16 ll. CtHi; MWA; MeHi; N; NBLiHi; NHi; NNA; PScrHi; RPB. 11479

[Woodville, William]
Reply to a letter, published by James Creighton, esq. [Baltimore, 1822] 6 p. MdBJ-G. 11480

Woodworth, Samuel, 1785-1842
The deed of gift. A comic opera, in three acts. New York, C. N. Baldwin, 1822. 72 p. CSmH; CtY; DLC; ICU; MB; MH; MWA; NN; PU; RPB; WaU. 11481

Woolman, John
Memoir of John Woolman, principally extracted from a journal of his life and travels. Philadelphia, To be had of Benjamin & Thomas Kite, and for sale by Solomon W. Conrad, Kimber & Sharpless and John Richardson, 1822. 28 p. InRchE; NcD. 11482

Worcester, Joseph Emerson
Elements of geography, ancient and modern; with an atlas.

2d ed. Boston, Cummings and Hilliard, 1822. 322 p. CtHT-W; ICN; ICP; KyDC; MA; MAm; MH; MStow; MWHi; MdHi; MSNF; NCanHi; NNC; NjR; OAlM; TNP. 11483

[Worcester, Noah] 1758-1837
...The friend of peace, in a series of numbers: together with A solemn review of the custom of war, as an introduction to said work. By Philo Pacificus [pseud.] Ballston Spa, J. Comstock, 1822. 308 p. CSmH; DLC; MH; MiD; NNUT; NPV; PPL; VtMan; WBeloC; WHi. 11484

---- Friend of youth; or, New selection of lessons, in prose and verse, for schools and families... Boston, Cummings and Hilliard, 1822. 300 p. DLC; LNP; MB; MDeeP; MH; MShi; OClWHi. 11485

---- A sermon on the worship of God, authorized from the Scriptures, divided into several sections. Pr. at Rochester by Levi W. Sibley, for Joseph Badger, August 1822. 30, [1] p. CSmH. 11486

Worcester, Thomas, 1795-1878
Jesus said unto him, follow me. A discourse, delivered before the Boston Society of the New Jerusalem. Cambridge, Pr. Hilliard and Metcalf, 1822. 18 p. CtMMHi; LNH; MB-FA; MBC; MCNC; MH-AH; N; NCH; NjPT; NjR; ViRUT; WHi. 11487

Worcester Co., Mass.
An account of the proposed canal from Worcester to Providence: containing the report of the engineer; together with some remarks upon inland navigation. Published by order of the committee for the county of Worcester. Worcester, Pr. by W.

Manning, 1822. 18 p. DLC;
KHi; M; MB; MCM; MH-BA;
MHi; MWA; MWCL; MWo; MiD;
MiDT; N; NBu; Nh-Hi; NjPT;
PPAmP; RHi; RPB.   11488

Worgan, John Dawes, 1790-1809
   Select poems.   Philadelphia,
Richardson, 1822. 273 p. OO;
PP.   11489

Wright, Richard
   An essay on the nature and
discipline of a Christian church.
Boston, R.M. Peck, printer,
1822. 18 p. MWA; Nh; RPB.
                          11490
The writer.   See Bradford,
Gamaliel.

Wycherley, William, 1640?-1716
   ...The country girl, a comedy;
altered from Wycherley, by David
Garrick.   Boston, Wells and
Lilly; New York, A.T. Goodrich,
& co. [etc., etc.] 1822. 91 p.
CSfCW; CtB; DLC; MH; MeB;
PPL; RPB; ViU.   11491

X, Y, Z

Yale University
   Catalogue of the officers and
students of Yale College, November, 1822.   New Haven, A.H.
Maltby & Company, printers,
1822. 28 p. M; MeB.   11492

---- The laws of Yale College in
New-Haven in Connecticut; enacted by the president and fellows.   New-Haven, Journal office, 1822. 45, 4 p. CtY; N;
NjR; TxU.   11493

---- Order of exercises, at
commencement, Yale College.
Sept. 11, 1822. New-Haven, Pr.
at the Journal office, 1822. 4 p.
DLC.   11494

---- A statement of the course
of instruction, expenses, &c., in

Yale College, New Haven, Conn.
Terms of admission [1822] MH.
                          11495
Yale University. Linonian So-
ciety. Library.
   Catalogue of books belonging
to the Linonian, Brothers' and
Moral libraries. Yale College,
September 1822. New-Haven,
Pr. at the Journal office, 1822.
39, [1] p. CtY; M; MH; TxU.
                          11496
Yankee Doodle.   Arranged with
variations for the piano forte.
Philadelphia, G. Willig [1822?]
[2] p. DLC; MiU-C; MH; NN;
PP; PP-K; PPL; RPB. 11497

Young, E.
   The progress of sin.   A ser-
mon, preached in London, Feb-
ruary 17, 1677. 3d ed., London,
pr. in 1720.   Wiscasset, Pr. by
John Dorr, 1822. 20 p. MeHi.
                          11498
Young, Edward, 1683-1765
   Night thoughts on life, death,
and immortality... Brunswick
(Me.) Pr. by J. Griffin, for T.
Bedlington, Boston, 1822. 270 p.
DLC; ICMBI; KWiU; MB;
MBev; MWA; MeU; NNUT;
OMC; OO; PV; WHi.   11499

---- ---- Providence, Joseph
McIntire, 1822. 270 p. MMAt.
                          11500
---- The revenge; a tragedy, in
five acts.   New York, S. King,
1822. 62 p. MH; PPL.   11501

---- ---- Philadelphia, Thomas
H. Palmer, 1822. 63, [1] p.
ICU; MH; MMal.   11502

Young Men's Bible Society of
Baltimore
   The second report of the
Young Men's Bible Society of
Baltimore, auxiliary to the Amer-
ican Bible Society, including the
first report of the Ladies Branch
of the Young Men's Bible Society:

Presented to the subscribers at
their annual meeting, 27th of December, 1821. Baltimore, Wm.
Ogden Niles, printer, 1822. 28,
9 [1] p. NNG.   11503

Zollickoffer, William, 1793-1853
    A treatise on the use of Prus-
siate of iron, (or, Prussian blue)
in intermitting and remitting
fevers. Frederick, Md. , Pr. by
Samuel Barnes, 1822. 32 p.
MdBM; MeB; N; PPAmP. 11504

Zum 17ten Juny, 1822. [Salis-
bury, N.C. , Bingham & White,
printers, 1822] 4 p. PPL. 11505

Zur Christnacht, den 24sten December, 1822. [Philadelphia,
Gedruckt bey Conrad Zentler,
1822] [4] p. PPL.   11506

Addenda

Associate Church in North America
   Extracts from the minutes of the Associate Synod of North America, at their meeting at Philadelphia, twenty-third day of May,
1822. and continued by adjournment, being their 21st annual meeting.   Carlisle [Pa.] Pr. by Holcomb & Tizzard, 1822. 32 p. MB.
                                                                11507
Dickinson, J. , M.D. , of London (?)
   A syndesmological chart, or, A table of the ligaments of the human skeleton.   1st Amer. from the 1st London edition of 1821.
Philadelphia, Baltimore: J. Webster [1822]   Bdsd. NNNAM. 11508

Gibbons, William
   Truth advocated; in letters addressed to the Presbyterians.
Philadelphia, J. Rakestraw, 1822. 158 p. , 1 l. PSC-Hi.   11509

Grant, Mrs.
   Edwin: a tale.   Portsmouth, T. H. Miller, printer and bookseller... 1822. 23 p. MMhHi (reported lost, 1966)   11510

I won't be a nun.   Baltimore, Cole's music store [1822] 1 l.
MH; MdHi; PU.   11511

---- A second state of the preceding, with pub no "15" added.
MdHi; RPB.   11512

New Brunswick, (N. J.) almanac for 1823. By Joshua Sharp. New
Brunswick, Griggs & Dickson for Joseph C. Griggs [1822] 18 ll.
MWA; NjHi; NjR.   11513

Stearns, John, 1770-1848
   Observations on the secale cornutum, or ergot... 1822. 8 p.
NNNAM.   11514

United States
   A bill authorizing the establishment of a penitentiary within the
District of Columbia.   Dec. 20, 1822. Read twice, and committed
to a committee of the whole House to-morrow. [Washington, 1822]
(H. R. 78) DLC.   11515

---- Report of the Committee on Roads and Canals, to which was
referred a report of a select committee, made 12th May, 1820,
relative to carrying into effect the treaty of Brownstown, of 25th
November, 1808, accompanied with "A bill for laying out, and making, a road from the Lower Rapids of the Miami of Lake Erie to
the Connecticut Western Reserve, in the state of Ohio, " &c. March

8, 1822. Read, and, with the bill, committed to a committee of the whole House to-morrow. Dec. 19, 1822. Ordered to be reprinted. [Washington, 1822] 14 p. (50) DLC; NjP. 11516